MW00835189

ELECTRONICS IN INDUSTRY

FIFTH EDITION

GEORGE M. CHUTE
EMERITUS PROFESSOR OF
ELECTRICAL ENGINEERING
UNIVERSITY OF DETROIT

ROBERT D. CHUTE
LAWRENCE INSTITUTE
OF TECHNOLOGY

INTERNATIONAL STUDENT EDITION

McGRAW-HILL KOGAKUSHA, LTD.
Tokyo Auckland Beirut Bogota Düsseldorf Johannesburg
Lisbon London Lucerne Madrid Mexico New Delhi Panama
Paris San Juan São Paulo Singapore Sydney

Library of Congress Cataloging in Publication Data
Chute, George M.
Electronics in industry.

Includes index.
1. Industrial electronics. I. Chute, Robert D., joint author. II. Title.
TK7881.C48 1979 621.381 78-25939
ISBN 0-07-010934-6

Electronics in Industry, Fifth Edition

INTERNATIONAL STUDENT EDITION

The editors for this book were George J. Horesta and Mark Haas.
The designer was Eileen Thaxton.
The cover designer was Abner Graboff.
The art supervisor was George T. Resch.
The production supervisor was May Konopka.
It was set in Times Roman by A Graphic Method Inc.

TOSHO PRINTING CO., LTD., TOKYO, JAPAN

CONTENTS

PREFACE xi

1 GENERAL USES OF ELECTRONICS 1

1-1 The age of electronics, 1 **1-2** All of electronics is electrical, 1 **1-3** Gradual control versus snap action, 2

2 DIODES, TRANSISTORS, AND TUBES 3

2-1 Why is it called electronic?, 3 **2-2** Electronic advantages, 4 **2-3** Introducing the rectifier diode and tube, 4 **2-4** How a solid-state diode passes current, 6 **2-5** PN diodes in an ac circuit, 6 **2-6** Transistor action, 7 **2-7** How a tube passes current, 8 **2-8** The electronic flow between cathode and anode, 9 **2-9** Can electrons be seen?, 10 **2-10** Types of electron emitter or cathode, 10 **2-11** Electronic flow in a high-vacuum rectifier tube, 11 **2-12** Space charge, 11 **2-13** Control of electron flow within a tube, 11 **2-14** Electron theory, 12 **2-15** Electron emission, 12 **2-16** Head cathode, 13

3 TIME-DELAY ACTION 14

3-1 The *RC* time constant, 14 **3-2** Capacitor discharging time, 15 **3-3** Time for charging a capacitor, 16 **3-4** Combined charging and discharging of a capacitor, 17 **3-5** Inductance may cause time-delay. The *L*/*R* time constant, 19 **3-6** Undesirable effect from inductance, 19 Problems, 20

4 SIMPLE RECTIFIERS AND FILTERS: AC INTO DC 23

4-1 Changing alternating current (ac) into direct current (dc), 23 **4-2** Use of the oscilloscope, 24 **4-3** Full-wave rectification with one tube, 24 **4-4** Single-phase electronic rectifier circuits, 25 **4-5** The single-phase bridge rectifier, 26 **4-6** Solid-state rectifiers and metallic rectifiers, 27 **4-7** Values of current and voltage, 28 **4-8** Rectifier power and efficiency, 31 **4-9** Ripple factor, 31 **4-10** Reverse voltage, 32 **4-11** Disk bridge rectifier, 32 **4-12** Filtering, 33 **4-13** Voltage output from a filter, 35 **4-14** A simple capacitor filter, 36 Problems, 37

5 DIODES AND TRANSISTORS 41

5-1 Semiconductor rectifiers, 41 **5-2** The NPN transistor in common-emitter circuit, 44 **5-3** Transistor performance, 46 **5-4** The PNP transistor, 47 **5-5** The dc load line; the operating point Q, 48 **5-6** Use of the load line to find gain, 49 **5-7** Switching action by a transistor, 49 **5-8** Heat dissipation, 50 **5-9** Common-base circuit, 51 **5-10** Common-collector or emitter-follower circuit, 52 **5-11** Transistor curves, 53 Problems, 53

6 TRANSISTOR AMPLIFIERS 56

6-1 One transistor as an amplifier, 56 **6-2** Class A, B, or C operation, 58 **6-3** Two transistors; push-pull operation, 59 **6-4** Bias without V_{BB} stability, 60 **6-5** Transistor self-bias, 61 **6-6** Coupled amplifiers; direct coupling, 62 **6-7** Darlington circuit, 63 **6-8** Schmitt trigger circuit, 64 **6-9** Drift and temperature effects, 64 **6-10** Differential amplifier, 65 **6-11** Constant-current source, 66 **6-12** Capacitor or *RC* coupling, 66 **6-13** Transformer coupling, 67 **6-14** Dc load line versus ac load line, 68 **6-15** Use of transformer for impedance matching, 69 **6-16** Ac load line for transformer coupling, 71 **6-17** Ac load line for inductive load, 71 Problems, 72

7 SEMICONDUCTOR THEORY 75

7-1 Electrons within atoms, 75 **7-2** Electron arrangement in semiconductor atoms, 77 **7-3** The use of energy levels, 79 **7-4** Changes within atoms caused by doping to form N-type material, 80 **7-5** Doping to form P-type material, 81 **7-6** The PN junction or diode, 82 **7-7** Biasing the PN junction, 84 **7-8** The NPN transistor and energy levels, 86 **7-9** Gain in the common-base circuit, 88 **7-10** Transistor standard currents and voltages, 89 **7-11** The common-emitter circuit and beta, 90 **7-12** Energy levels in PNP transistor, 91 **7-13** Transistor parameters and equivalent circuit, 92 **7-14** Graphical meaning of *h* parameters, 95 **7-15** Change of h^b to h^e parameters, 98 **7-16** Transistor amplifier gain, 98 **7-17** Solid-state devices at high frequencies, 101 **7-18** Special diodes–the Zener diode, 101 **7-19** The tunnel diode, 102 **7-20** Introducing field effect in PN devices, 104 **7-21** The field-effect transistor (FET), 105 **7-22** The PN depletion area, 106 **7-23** The junction FET, 106 **7-24** FET parameters and equivalent circuit, 107 **7-25** Graphical meaning of y parameters, 108 **7-26** The P-channel FET, 109 **7-27** The insulated-gate FET; the MOSFET, 110 **7-28** The induced-channel FET, 111 Problems, 111

8 SENSING OF TIME, VOLTAGE, LIGHT: THE UNIJUNCTION TRANSISTOR 114

8-1 Electronic delay timer (General Electric 3S7504ET560), 114
8-2 A resistance-sensitive relay (3S7511RS570), 116
8-3 A voltage-sensitive relay (3S7511VS580), 117 **8-4** A

reflex photoelectric relay (3S7505PS510), 119 **8-5** A modulated light signal using a light-emitting diode (LED), 120 **8-6** Relay using modulated light (3S7505PS800), 122 **8-7** The unijunction transistor (UJT), 123 **8-8** Delay timer using a UJT (3S7504ET550), 124 **8-9** Register control, 125 **8-10** One-way register control (CR7515CT105), 126 **8-11** Correction-time circuit, 128 Problems, 129

9 THYRISTORS: THE SCR AND TRIAC 130

9-1 The silicon controlled rectifier, 130 **9-2** SCR behavior and rating, 131 **9-3** The SCR in simple ac circuits, 133 **9-4** A transistor may fire an SCR, 134 **9-5** Phase control of the SCR; firing by UJT, 134 **9-6** One UJT fires two SCRs alternately, 135 **9-7** Phase control by pedestal and ramp, 136 **9-8** SCR phase control by temperature or light, 137 **9-9** Turnoff of SCR; Jones Circuit, 138 **9-10** SCRs or thyratrons with resistance load or inductive load, 139 **9-11** SCRs with diodes in ac inductive circuits, 140 **9-12** Voltage change, *dv/dt*, 142 **9-13** Two-SCR rectifier with combined *R* and *L* load, 143 **9-14** Rectifier with back-emf load, 145 **9-15** The triac, 146 **9-16** Triac circuits, 147 **9-17** A triac time-delay relay, 149 **9-18** Thyristors—PNPN devices, 149 **9-19** Zero-voltage switching circuit, 151 **9-20** Optically coupled isolator—solid state relay, 152 Problems, 152

10 SWITCHING AND COUNTING CIRCUITS 155

10-1 Computers and binary counting, 155 **10-2** The flip-flop circuit, 157 **10-3** Each negative pulse flips the circuit; a complementing flip-flop, 158 **10-4** Flip-flops in a counter, 159 **10-5** Counter operation, 161 **10-6** A binary counter of ten pulses, 162 **10-7** Time-selector switches, 163 **10-8** Basic circuits for computers, 163 **10-9** Gate circuits; the AND gate, 164 **10-10** The OR gate, 165 **10-11** Combining AND gates and OR gates, 166 **10-12** Transistor gate circuits; NAND; NOR, 166 **10-13** Inverting the logic, 168 **10-14** Combined transistor gates, 169 **10-15** Binary addition, 169 **10-16** Information storage, 171 **10-17** A basic flip-flop using two NAND gates; RS flip-flop, 171 **10-18** Synchronizing by a clock pulse, 172 **10-19** Other types of flip-flop; JK flip-flop, 173 **10-20** Shift register, 174 **10-21** Serial-to-parallel converter, 174 Problems, 176

11 INTEGRATED CIRCUITS FOR SWITCHING 178

11-1 The need for integrated circuits, 178 **11-2** Inside the IC, 179 **11-3** NAND circuits are used in ICs; DTL, 180 **11-4** High-threshold logic or HTL, 181 **11-5** Transistor-transistor logic or TTL; NAND gate, 182 **11-6** TTL switching speed increased by use of SBDS, 184 **11-7** Combination of gates in one IC, 185 **11-8** Emitter-coupled logic or ECL, 185 **11-9** MOS gates, 186 **11-10** A MOS NOR gate, 187 **11-11** Care and handling of MOSFETs, 188 **11-12** Dynamic MOS gates, 188

11-13 Complementary MOS or CMOS, 189 **11-14** CMOS voltage transfer characteristics and noise margin, 190 Problems, 192

12 INTEGRATED CIRCUITS FOR LINEAR APPLICATIONS 193

12-1 The manufacture of the IC, 193 **12-2** Formation of transistors in the IC, 194 **12-3** Arrangement patterns in an IC, 197 **12-4** The linear IC, 197 **12-5** The operational amplifier or "opamp", 199 **12-6** Operational amplifiers perform mathematics, 202 **12-7** The Bailey go/line recorder, 204 **12-8** An IC phase control, 205 **12-9** Pedestal and negative-going ramp, 208 **12-10** Digital-to-analog converter (DAC), 209 **12-11** Analog-to-digital converter (ADC), 211 **12-12** Sample-and-hold, 213 Problems, 214

13 INFORMATION CONVERSION 216

13-1 Input-output equipment, 216 **13-2** Sending signals over long lines, 217 **13-3** Three-state logic, 219 **13-4** Parallel-to-serial converter, 220 **13-5** Multiplexers (MUX), 221 **13-6** Addressing, 223 **13-7** Buffering, 225 **13-8** Monostable multivibrator rebuilds a pulse, 225 **13-9** BCD and octal binary codes, 226 **13-10** Numeric display or lighted number indicators, 228 Problems, 230

14 MEMORY SYSTEMS 231

14-1 Shift register memory, 231 **14-2** Random-access memory (RAM), 232 **14-3** Read-only memory (ROM), 235 **14-4** Programmable read-only memory (PROM), 236 **14-5** Electrically alterable read-only memory (EAROM), 236

15 MICROPROCESSORS 239

15-1 The program, 239 **15-2** Inside the central processing unit (CPU), 241 **15-3** How the CPU processes an instruction, 242 **15-4** Timing in the CPU, 244 **15-5** Hexadecimal code, 246 **15-6** The CPU used in a system, 247

16 PROGRAMMABLE CONTROLLERS 250

16-1 Elementary or ladder diagram, 250 **16-2** Logic circuits replace relays and contracts, 252 **16-3** A programmable controller, 254 **16-4** Time-delay relays help to detect malfunctions, 257 **16-5** How the programmable controller operates, 257

17 GAS TUBES FOR LARGE CURRENTS 259

17-1 The phanotron rectifier, 259 **17-2** Greater electron flow in a phanotron, 260 **17-3** Arc-drop; constant voltage across a vapor filled tube, 260 **17-4** Glow and arc-discharge tubes, 261 **17-5** The voltage-regulator tube, 262 **17-6** A Zener diode or VR tube example, 264 **17-7** Electron tubes or SCRS as an ac switch, 264 **17-8** The ignitron, 266 **17-9** The ignitor, 267 **17-10** Simple ignitron control, 268 Problems, 268

18 RESISTANCE-WELDING CONTROL: IGNITRON CONTACTOR 271

18-1 Resistance welding, 271 **18-2** The ignitron contactor, 272
18-3 Operating the ignitron contactor, 274
18-4 Oscilloscope pictures of circuit operation, 275
18-5 Operation with welder load, 276 **18-6** Ignitron rating, 278
18-7 Ratings of ignitron contactors for welders, 279
18-8 Percent duty, 279 **18-9** Averaging time, 280
18-10 Complete calculations of percent duty, 281
18-11 Formula for percent duty, 281 **18-12** Overloaded ignitrons, 282
18-13 Correct tube averaging time, 283
18-14 Ignitron controls for larger loads, 283
18-15 Complete controls for resistance welding: sequence timer, 284
18-16 Synchronous timing, 284 **18-17** Slope control, 286
18-18 Resistance welding with direct current, 286
18-19 Circuits that control the ignitron sequence, 288
Problems, 290

19 RESISTANCE WELDING WITH SOLID-STATE CIRCUITS 294

19-1 Weltronic binary solid-state control, 294 **19-2** Overall sequence of operation, 298 **19-3** Coincidence control of *Q*25, 300
19-4 The program of squeeze, weld, hold, off, 300
19-5 Checking the ac circuits during weld time, 302
19-6 Firing the SCRs to make the weld, 303 **19-7** Ring counter using PUTs, 304 **19-8** Weltronic PUT welder control, 305
19-9 Circuits at the start, 308 **19-10** The ring counters, 308
19-11 Solenoid valve energized through a triac, 309
19-12 Clock pulse; coincidence; reset, 309 **19-13** Off time and repeat welding, 310 Problems, 311

20 THYRATRON TUBES AND PHRASE CONTROL 312

20-1 Thyratron action, 312 **20-2** Action on ac supply, 313
20-3 Deionization time, 313 **20-4** Critical grid voltage, 314
20-5 Effect of thyratron temperature, 315 **20-6** Grid construction, 315 **20-7** The shield-grid thyratron, 316
20-8 Gradual control of a thyratron, 317 **20-9** Shifting the thyratron-grid phrase, 318 **20-10** Grid-voltage waves that lag, 319
Problems, 320

21 REGULATORS OF VOLTAGE AND MOTOR SPEED 322

21-1 A voltage compensator, 322 **21-2** A solid-state dc voltage regulator, 323 **21-3** The dc shunt motor, 325 **21-4** Armature control and field control of motor speed, 327 **21-5** Electronic control of a dc motor, 328 **21-6** Control of small motors, 329
21-7 Speed-regulator action, 330 **21-8** Full-wave motor-speed regulation by one SCR, 331 **21-9** The dc or ac generator, 332 **21-10** Basic generator-voltage regulator, 332
21-11 Transistor response to generator voltage, 333

21-12 A speed regulator, 335 **21-13** Car-alternator voltage regulator, 335
21-14 A transistor may control large field current, 337 Problems, 337

22 LARGE-CURRENT POLYPHASE RECTIFIERS 339

22-1 Polyphase rectifiers, 339 **22-2** A three-diode (three-phase, half-wave) rectifier, 340 **22-3** A four-diode (four-phase, half-wave) rectifier, 342 **22-4** A six-diode (six-phase, half-wave) rectifier, 342
22-5 A six-diode (three-phase, full-wave) rectifier, 344
22-6 Rectifier performance, 346 **22-7** Diode load and current rating, 349 **22-8** Effect of inductance, 350 **22-9** PRV in polyphase rectifiers, 351 **22-10** Phase-shifting a polyphase rectifier, 351
22-11 Phase control of SCRs in a three-phase bridge, 353
22-12 Six-tube rectifier with interphase transformer, 354
Problems, 356

23 HIGH FREQUENCIES AND SHORTER WAVELENGTHS 359

23-1 The frequency spectrum, 360 **23-2** Figures on the spectrum chart, 362 **23-3** Frequency and wavelength, 363 **23-4** Sound, 363
23-5 Ultrasonics, 364 **23-6** Radio, television, radar, 365
23-7 Industrial electric heating of materials, 366
23-8 Induction heating of conducting materials, 367 **23-9** Dielectric heating of nonconducting materials, 368 **23-10** Light and color, 369
23-11 Infrared, or heat, rays, 371 **23-12** Ultraviolet rays, 372
23-13 The laser and its coherent light, 373
23-14 Color response of phototubes, 375 **23-15** Solar cell and solid-state lamp or LED, 376 **23-16** X-rays and gamma rays, 376 Problems, 377

24 OSCILLATORS AND INVERTERS 379

24-1 Oscillators, 379 **24-2** From an amplifier to an oscillator, 380
24-3 A simple oscillator, 380 **24-4** Main oscillator features, 381
24-5 Standard oscillator types, 382 **24-6** Inverters to supply large ac power, 384 **24-7** A UJT relaxation oscillator to trigger an inverter, 385 **24-8** A transistor multivibrator, 385
24-9 A two-SCR inverter, 387 **24-10** Adjustable frequency inverter for ac motor drive (General Electric ST100), 388
24-11 SUS oscillator causes inverter frequency, 390
24-12 A feedback oscillator fires each SCR, 390
24-13 Firing the inverter SCRs in sequence, 392
24-14 Turnoff or commutation of inverter SCRs, 393 Problems, 394

25 TEMPERATURE RECORDERS 395

25-1 A change of 0.0001 volt turns a motor, 395 **25-2** The Honeywell continuous balance palentiometer, 397
25-3 Capacitor-coupled amplifiers, 399 **25-4** Running the balancing motor, 400 **25-5** Ac bridge signal for the amplifier, 401

26 MAGNETIC AMPLIFIERS 403

26-1 The saturable reactor, 403 **26-2** Inductance of a steel core, 404
26-3 Direct current increases reactor saturation, 405

26-4 Rectifiers are added to cause self-saturation, 407
26-5 Dc control of the self-saturated reactor, 409 26-6 The bias winding, 410 26-7 Magnetic amplifier with dc load, 411
26-8 The feedback winding, 412
26-9 Effects of feedback, 412 26-10 Output waneshape of magnetic amplifier, 414 26-11 Reset control, 415
26-12 Speed of response, 416 26-13 A push-pull magnetic amplifier, 417 26-14 Positive feedback to cause switching action, 419 Problems, 421

27 AUTOMATIC CONTROL OF DC MOTORS 422

27-1 Motor control by one SCR, 422 27-2 Speed variation by SCR control, 423 27-3 Half-wave statotrol drive (3SRA71), 425
27-4 Three-phase 20-hp SCR speed variator, 427
27-5 Gate-pulse generator, 429

28 CLOSED-LOOP SYSTEMS SERVOMECHANISMS 432

28-1 Open-loop and closed-loop systems, 432 28-2 Regulators and servomechanisms, 433 28-3 Basic parts of a servo, 434
28-4 Amplifiers and error correctors, 435
28-5 Error detectors and transducers, 435
28-6 Complete servo diagram, loop gain, 436
28-7 An oil-furnace temperature regulator, 437
28-8 Standstill or static accuracy, 438 28-9 Speed-regulating system, 438
28-10 Open-loop action, 439 28-11 Closed-loop action, 440
28-12 Motor performance, 441 28-13 Loop gain and speed change, 442 28-14 Dynamic response, 444
28-15 Transient response, 445 28-16 Response to constant-velocity signal, 449 28-17 Use of error-rate control, 450
28-18 Dimensionless form, 451 28-19 Simple servos only, 452
Problems, 452

29 FREQUENCY RESPONSE OF SERVO SYSTEMS 455

29-1 Time constant of an inductive winding, 455 29-2 Fast response, 456 29-3 Cause of unstable operation, 457 29-4 The transfer function, 459 29-5 Equation for a regulator loop, 460
29-6 Analysis of a servo; the Nyquist approach, 461
29-7 *M* circles, 464 29-8 Corrective or antihunt networks, 465
29-9 Servo types 0, 1, 2, 477 29-10 Transfer function of a mechanical system, 468 29-11 The Bode attenuation diagram, 470
29-12 The Bode diagram for one element, 471 29-13 Combining the system elements, 472 29-14 Study of the Bode diagram, 474
29-15 The phase-lag network, 474 29-16 Stabilizing with a lag network, 476 29-17 The phase-lead network, 477
29-18 Bode diagram of a type 1 servo, 478
29-19 The notch, or lag-lead, network, 480 29-20 Stabilizing with a notch network, 481 29-21 Summary of Bode plots, 482
Problems, 484

30 SERVO ANALYSIS BY THE ROOT-LOCUS METHOD 489
30-1 Outline of procedure, 489 **30-2** System example 1, 490
30-3 Step 3. Closing the loop, 492 **30-4** Portions of loci in the real axis, 493
30-5 Loci leaving the real axis, 493 **30-6** Step 4. Calibrating the locus, 495
30-7 Step 5. Overshoot limits K_0, 496
30-8 System example 2, a type-2 Servo, 496 **30-9** Rules for locating loci, 497
30-10 Breakaway point from real axis, 499
30-11 Results of example 2, 500 Problems, 502

31 ELECTRONIC SERVICE INSTRUMENTS 505
31-1 The need for an electronic voltmeter, 505 **31-2** An electronic voltmeter (RCA solid-state voltohmyst, type WV-500 A), 507
31-3 Measuring dc volts, 507 **31-4** Measuring ac volts, 509
31-5 Measuring ohms, 510 **31-6** A digital voltmeter (Hewlett-Packard 3440A), 511 **31-7** Forming Ramp *R* of Fig. 31-3, 512
31-8 Sample rate in Fig. 31-4, 514 **31-9** The downward ramp starts and stops the pulse count, 514 **31-10** The oscillator and counters prepare the number display, 515 **31-11** The cathode-ray tube, 516
31-12 A basic oscillograph circuit, 518 **31-13** Ac signals at *X* and *Y* inputs, 518 **31-14** A cathode-ray oscillograph (Dumont type 292), 520
31-15 Amplifiers in the oscillograph, 522 **31-16** The sweep circuit, 523
31-17 Synchronizing the wave, 524 **31-18** A stroboscope (General Radio Company Strobotac 1531-A), 525
31-19 Timing the stroboscope flashes, 527 Problems, 529

32 NONELECTRONIC DEVICES 531
32-1 The amplidyne, 531 **32-2** Amplidyne fields, 532
32-3 Antihunt methods, 534 **32-4** Constant-voltage transformer, or stabilizer, 535 **32-5** The selsyn—electric gearing, 536
32-6 The differential selsyn or phase shifter, 536
32-7 Thyrite, 537 **32-8** Strain gages, 538
32-9 Vibrator or convertor, 541 Problems, 542

ANSWERS TO ODD-NUMBERED PROBLEMS 543

INDEX 551

PREFACE

The purpose of this book is to give a broad introduction to the use of industrial electronic circuits and equipment. It is intended for use as a text in electronic technology and survey courses offered by technical institutes, junior and community colleges, and universities, and for training programs in industry.

This edition continues the trend toward the use of more solid-state circuits and few electron tubes. Solid-state devices and integrated circuits dominate twelve chapters and are included in four more.

While we often refer to sections or figures that appear in preceding chapters for the convenience of the reader, the text does not necessarily have to be followed sequentially.

New chapters 13 to 16 include the conversion of information and the use of memory systems, microprocessors, and programmable controllers. We do not survey many variations of a certain circuit by other makers, but try to give students the intuitive "feel" of that circuit before they advance to systems in Chapters 15 and 16. Rather than favor one logic family over another, we select the family that most effectively demonstrates the principles of the circuit, and also is prevalent in the industry. We describe those memory systems that are needed to understand their use in the succeeding chapters.

This text is not a programming manual but tries to give enough background to whet the student's curiosity to consult many sources on programming and microprocessors.

Chapters 28, 29, and 30 permit an understanding of closed-loop systems and servo analysis at a level that does not require an advanced mathematical background. While arithmetic is sufficient for solution of most problems in the book, Chapter 28 and a few sections elsewhere require some additional advanced mathematics.

George M. Chute
Robert D. Chute

1

GENERAL USES OF ELECTRONICS

Electronics is the science or practice of using electricity in devices similar to transistors and radio tubes so as to get results not possible with ordinary electrical equipment.

1-1 THE AGE OF ELECTRONICS

Without electronics there might be no radio, television, sound pictures, fluorescent lighting, public-address systems, or long-distance telephone calls. Recall that most of these familiar equipments serve to carry or give information; so communication early was a main purpose of electronics and still holds the interest of many workers and students in this field.

Meanwhile industry, seeking faster and more accurate methods of production, has adapted electronic equipment to its own needs. Gradually during the past fifty years, industrial plants have installed electronic equipment to give better operation of motors, better spot or seam welding, and more useful heating of metal, along with the better-known "electric-eye" control of varied operations. Recent decades have seen the introduction and application of the transistor; such "solid-state" devices replace most small electron tubes.

1-2 ALL OF ELECTRONICS IS ELECTRICAL

No matter what result is desired or what kinds of tube or electronic device are used, this equipment is electrical. Understanding electronics includes the understanding of ordinary electrical devices and circuits, some of which are reviewed here.

Some people believe that electronic devices can hear, see, feel, smell, or even think; this is true only when the sound, image, feeling, or thought can be changed into an electrical signal, to which the transistor or tube-operated device can then respond. Much of the success of electronics depends on the cleverness of the methods used to obtain an electric signal that can be used to stimulate the electronic device into action. This signal may be so small or so fleeting that it was ignored by ordinary electrical devices; the electronic circuit can be made to detect such a signal, increase its strength, and put it to useful work.

Ordinary electrical equipment enters the electronic class whenever its circuit includes an electron tube or solid-state device. The special behavior of electricity within such a tube or transistor changes the performance of the entire circuit, especially its high-speed operation.

1-3 GRADUAL CONTROL VERSUS SNAP ACTION

A newcomer to electronics sees numerous types, styles, shapes, and ratings of transistor or tube. The performance of such units may be divided into two classes; the first class permits gradual control of a load, often called linear control. The second class provides sudden or snap action so that the load either is all on or is all off; this often is called digital control or switching action. Most transistors and many tubes provide gradual control; a high-vacuum tube has had all air pumped from inside it and has then been sealed to keep high vacuum inside. Into the second class of tube, after it has been similarly pumped free of air, an amount of a certain gas or vapor is inserted before the tube is sealed. Thus tubes are correctly divided into high-vacuum types and vapor-filled types. The circuit containing either a transistor or a tube may be designed to give sudden on-off switching action. The vapor-filled tube often may be replaced by a semiconductor controlled rectifier, called the SCR.

Later chapters show why transistors and high-vacuum tubes have speedy and gradual control of their circuits, unmatched by any vapor-filled tube; the SCR and the vapor-filled tube can handle much greater amounts of current but usually cannot decrease or interrupt this current flow. The transistor is able to respond to very small signals and will follow them, although these signals may change a million times per second; it is ideal for most circuit operations but often lacks the ability to pass reasonably large amounts of current (such as 1 to 30 amperes). In comparison, the SCR or the vapor-filled tube has current-carrying ability to 1000 A; it responds to a starting signal, but usually it cannot stop its own current flow or be used where signals change many thousands of times per second. Both classes of device will rectify (pass current in only one direction).

Until recent years the transistor was found mainly in communication equipment, where the SCR was almost unknown. It is natural that many electronic textbooks stress the transistor and its use in communication circuits. Today, SCRs or vapor-filled tubes are included in communications; the modern industrial electronic equipment (that controls high-current circuits to large motors, welders, or furnaces by the SCR or by vapor-filled tubes) is supervised by groups of transistors or high-vacuum tubes.

2

DIODES, TRANSISTORS, AND TUBES

Most persons know how electric current flows in motors, incandescent lamps, electric furnaces, and transformers; here the electricity always flows in the copper wire or other metal parts. But consider a stroke of lightning, where electricity jumps through space. The great electric pressure of lightning forces the electric current to pass through the air. In the same way, inside any radio tube, tiny electric currents are made to pass through the space separating certain parts in the tube. Such action—where electricity flows through space instead of being confined to metal conductors or circuits—is electronic.

2-1 WHY IS IT CALLED ELECTRONIC?

Early scientists who were trying to explain how electricity passed through space thought that such an electric current was a steady stream of tiny electrical particles. They called these particles *electrons*. Thus any electric current is made of countless numbers of electrons. When electricity passes through space, as occurs within a tube, such action is called *electronic*. More recently, when layers of semiconductor metals are joined together so that current flows through the junction in one direction only, as in a solid-state diode or a transistor, such action also is called electronic, as is explained in Sec. 2-4. If a device passes its stream of electrons through internal space, or through the junction where certain different metals meet, that device is called electronic.

In ordinary air, electrons can be made to jump through space only by the pressure of high voltage. But if they are enclosed in a tube from which the air has been removed, the electrons flow across the space more easily. All electronic tubes are carefully sealed to maintain the desired conditions inside the tube.

Some electric lights are electronic. The common incandescent light bulb is not considered electronic, even though it is enclosed like a radio tube, for the electricity flows entirely within the metal filament. In contrast, the fluorescent lamp is electronic, for its light is produced by the action of electricity that flows through the internal space between the two ends of the lamp.

2-2 ELECTRONIC ADVANTAGES

Five important ways are listed in which a transistor or an electron tube gives operation unequaled by other electrical equipment:

1. Either electronic device can respond to very small control signals and produce a corresponding but larger signal. In this way, transistors or tubes increase, or amplify, the input signal.
2. Transistors or tubes can respond at speeds far beyond those reached by the most sensitive moving devices.
3. Acting at high speeds or high voltages, electronic devices can produce radiations such as radio or x-rays.
4. Some kinds of transistor or tube respond to light, serving as electric eyes.
5. With alternating voltage applied, either device can carry electricity in one direction, while refusing to carry it in the opposite direction. In this way, such diodes change or rectify alternating current into direct current.

This last type of action exists in most solid-state devices or electron tubes, whether or not they are used as rectifiers. The action of such a device in an electric circuit is described next.

2-3 INTRODUCING THE RECTIFIER DIODE AND TUBE

In Fig. 2-1 is an ordinary transformer winding *TR*, whose output voltage can force current through a relay coil *C* whenever switch *S* is closed. We know that the alternating current flows in both directions through *S* and through *C*, and the curve in Fig. 2-1 shows that both halves of the ac voltage wave are applied to the terminals of the coil. [This wave picture, in Fig. 2-1, represents one complete cycle of the ac voltage, which changes from positive (above the line) to negative (below the line) and back to positive at the rate or frequency of, say, 60 hertz or cycles per second (Hz).] However, in Fig. 2-2 a solid-state diode *D* or a vacuum tube *T* replaces switch *S*, to see what happens.

Figure 2-3 shows that the solid-state diode contains a junction of P-type material and N-type material (as is explained in Sec. 2-4); electrons can flow easily from the N cathode to the P anode, but not from P to N This junction

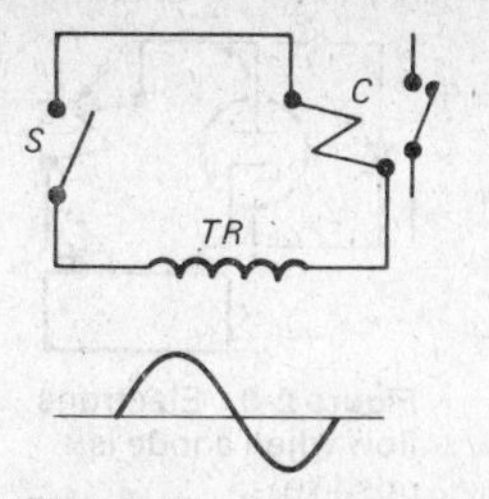

Figure 2-1 The complete ac wave passes through *S* to pick up *C*.

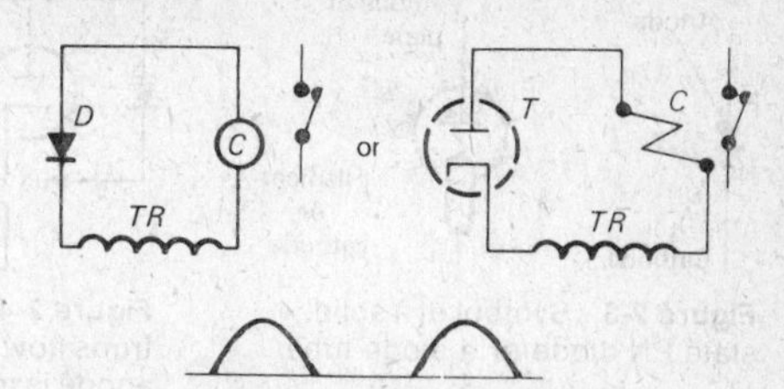

Figure 2-2 Only half of the wave passes through diode *D* or tube *T*.

requires no heat to make it work. Also, the complete tube symbol in Fig. 2-3 shows that this simple tube has an anode, or plate, entering the top of the tube circle, while at the bottom there is a cathode. Having two elements (anode and cathode), either device is called a diode. The tube cathode is heated by the output of a small transformer winding and is usually red-hot before electricity can flow through the tube. This electricity passes through the space between the cathode and the anode, even though there is no piece of metal connecting these two parts of the tube. So, in Fig. 2-2, we must realize that the electric circuit may be continuous, or closed, between cathode and anode of the tube, even though the circuit line is not shown as connecting these two points within the tube. To permit this electricity to flow through the tube, the cathode produces or emits electrons from its heated surface, which may be made of material such as tungsten. In simple diagrams such as Figs. 2-2 and 2-4, the tube filament is not shown; a horizontal line is used within the circle to represent the heated part of the tube that produces the electrons.

In the following discussion, the name *rectifier* is used to mean either the solid-state diode *D* or the tube *T*, since either one will cause the same rectifying action.

With connections as in Fig. 2-2, it is found that current flows through the rectifier and the relay coil but the relay chatters. Only a half wave of the ac power supply is able to pass through the rectifier. We need to know which half wave can flow through the rectifier (or to distinguish whether the right-hand side of the transformer is positive or negative when current flows through the rectifier). So, in Fig. 2-4 a battery is used in place of the transformer; the negative side of the battery is connected to the relay coil. This means that the anode or top of the rectifier has a more negative potential than the cathode or bottom of the rectifier. With this connection the rectifier refuses to pass current. However, in Fig. 2-5 the battery connection is reversed, so that the positive terminal is now connected to the relay coil and the anode has a more positive potential than the cathode. Current flows, energizing the relay coil. This confirms the previous observation that current

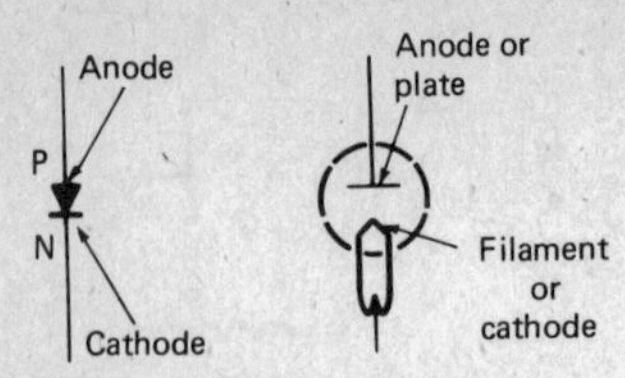

Figure 2-3 Symbol of a solid-state PN diode or a diode tube.

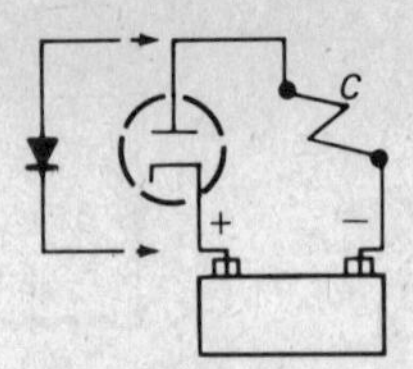

Figure 2-4 No electrons flow while anode is more negative.

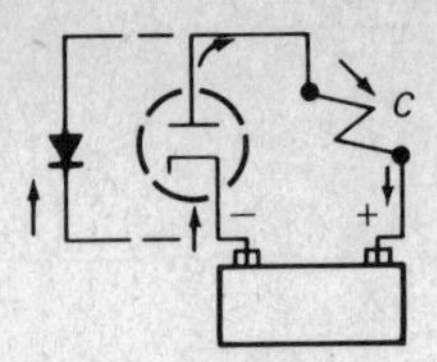

Figure 2-5 Electrons flow when anode is positive.

can flow in only one direction through a solid-state diode or through an ordinary vacuum tube and that these electrons flow only when the anode has a more positive potential than the cathode. The stream of electrons,[2-1*] produced at the heated cathode, flows through the tube from cathode to anode. Electrons flow through the solid-state diode in the direction opposite to the arrow of the symbol.

2-4 HOW A SOLID-STATE DIODE PASSES CURRENT

As is explained later, in Sec. 5-1, pure silicon may be converted into P-type or N-type material. When a layer of P type is formed next to an N-type layer, this forms a PN junction. Electrons flow easily from the N layer to the P layer when the P is more positive; this is shown as a large forward current in Fig. 2-6. But very few electrons can flow from P to N when the N layer is more positive; only a tiny reverse current is shown for a (−) or reverse diode voltage (if its rated voltage is not exceeded). Thus a PN junction is used as a rectifier. Conventional current *I* flows easily in the direction of the symbol arrow whenever the top of the arrow is more positive than its point; the electrons flow opposite to conventional current *I*, or from the point to the top of the symbol arrow. Resistor *R* is needed to limit the amount of forward current.

2-5 PN DIODES IN AN AC CIRCUIT

To show how such diodes can be used in an ac circuit, Fig. 2-7 has a transformer winding *TR* that applies alternating voltage across center resistor *R*. During the half cycle when point 2 is more positive than point 1, electrons flow through *R* and also through R_1 and diode *A*, so that most of the *TR* voltage appears across R_1. Capacitor C_1 becomes charged by this voltage across R_1, (+) at the top. During this same half cycle, diode *B* acts as an open circuit so that the *TR* voltage does not reach R_2 or C_2. During the following ac

*Small superior numbers used throughout this book refer to other sections where further pertinent information will be found. Here, for instance, we suggest that you see Sec. 2-1 of Chap. 2.

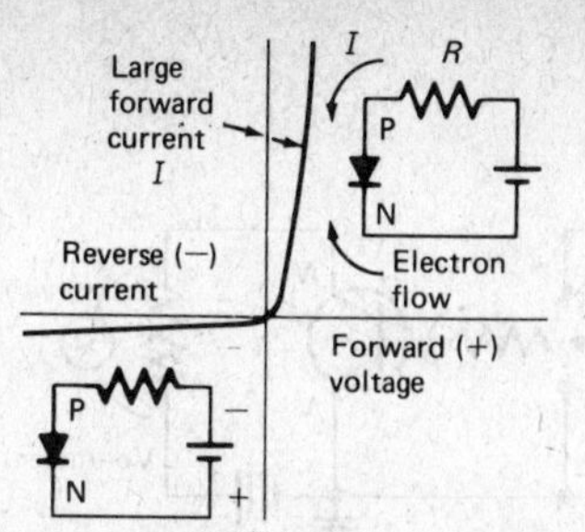

Figure 2-6 Current flow in PN diode depends on voltage.

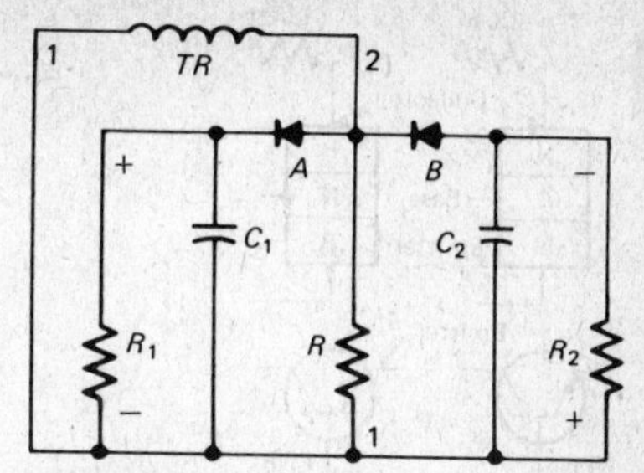

Figure 2-7 Action of PN diodes with ac applied.

half cycle, when *TR* terminal 2 becomes more negative than terminal 1, electrons now flow through diode *B* and R_2; capacitor C_2 becomes charged by the voltage across R_2, which is (−) at the top. Meanwhile, diode *A* disconnects R_1 and C_1 from terminal 2 during this negative half cycle. Capacitor C_1 gradually loses its voltage by discharging through R_1; this time-delay action is discussed in Chap. 3.

2-6 TRANSISTOR ACTION

If two of the above diodes are made at one time by forming three P and N layers together as shown in Fig. 2-8, this makes a transistor, as is explained in Secs. 5-2 and 5-4. If the P layer is formed between two N layers, making an NPN transistor, electrons can flow from the negative emitter to the positive collector if the positive potential applied to the base causes current to flow in the base. Making the base more positive increases the electron flow through the NPN transistor and the load in its collector circuit. The symbol for the NPN transistor uses an arrow or triangle that points out of the circle and away from the base.

However, a PNP transistor has an N-type base between two P layers. Electrons can flow from a negative collector to a positive emitter; this flow increases as the base is made more negative. The symbol for the PNP transistor has an arrow or triangle that points toward the base. In either transistor, a small change in base current can cause a larger change in collector or load current; this shows that the transistor may be used as an amplifier, as is explained further in Chap. 5.

To illustrate transistor action, Fig. 2-9 shows an NPN transistor (similar to Fig. 5-6, discussed later, in Sec. 5-2). The emitter is at ground potential; a 20-volt (or 20-V) battery applies (+) potential through *R* to the collector. Voltmeter *V* reads the *IR* drop across *R*. A potentiometer ("pot") *T* can be turned clockwise gradually to increase the small voltage applied between base and emitter. Starting with the *T* slider at the bottom, the base is at ground and no electrons flow in the base; as a result, almost no current flows

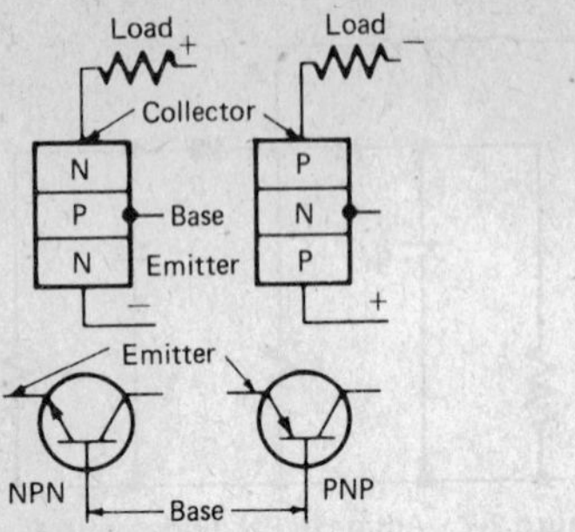

Figure 2-8 The transistor—NPN or PNP.

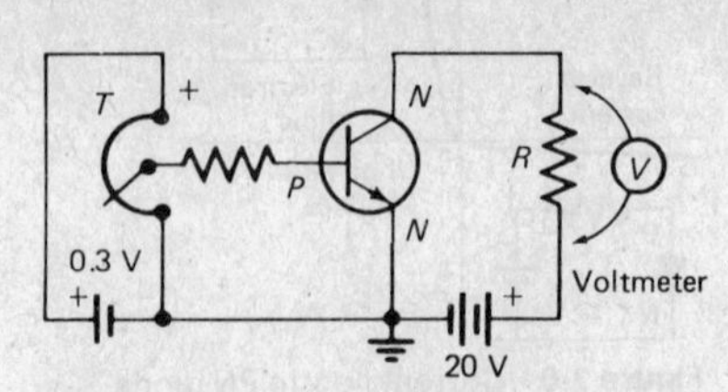

Figure 2-9 Raising the P base increases collector current in *R*.

in the collector or through load resistor *R*; so the voltmeter reads near zero. Now as *T* is turned clockwise, the base is made perhaps $^1/_{10}$ volt more positive, so that electrons flow into the emitter and out of the base. This causes a much larger flow of electrons in the emitter and collector and through resistor *R*, so that voltmeter *V* may read about 5 volts. Further turning of *T* may apply $^3/_{10}$ volt to the transistor base circuit; *V* now may read 15 volts, showing that only a $^3/_{10}$-volt change in input at the base can cause 15-volts change in output at the collector.

But the vacuum tube needs to be discussed further, and will be the subject of the rest of this chapter.

2-7 HOW A TUBE PASSES CURRENT

The process is as follows (1) Heat is required at the cathode before the usual vacuum tube can work; (2) current or electrons pass through space within the tube, requiring no metal conductor; (3) the electrons pass in one direction only, flowing from cathode to anode (or from heater to plate).

Further study shows why a tube works this way. If there were merely two wires connected to a source of voltage and the ends of the two wires were slightly separated, in open air, we know that rather high voltage would be needed before this gap would break down and permit current to flow across the gap. Connected to a high-voltage ac supply, the current would jump across the gap in both directions. The current jumping such a gap may be quite large, in amperes; this current flow also consists of billions of electrons.

If now the ends of two wires are enclosed as in a bottle from which all the air is pumped, we find that rather high voltage is required to force even a small amount of current across the space between the ends of these wires. However, if some way is provided for heating the end of one of these wires, inside the enclosure, a small amount of current will easily flow across the space, with very low voltage applied. This was discovered over ninety years ago, when Edison was experimenting with his early electric-light bulb. In such a lamp, we see that he had an air-free enclosure, with a heated wire, the filament. One day, to study an unusual action of the lamp, he inserted the end of another wire and found that he could measure a tiny flow of current through this second wire, connected outside to a battery, even though the wire did not touch any other object inside the lamp bulb. This observed "Edison effect" was a basic discovery upon which much of the subject of electronics depends; it also is the basis for conventional current.

2-8 THE ELECTRON FLOW BETWEEN CATHODE AND ANODE

In such a tube, the heated part is called the *cathode*. If electricity can flow through the tube when the cathode is hot but refuses to flow when the cathode is cold, the heated cathode must be responsible for producing this current flow through the space. Today, this current flow is regarded as merely a stream of electrons forced out of the cathode by the heat; they are attracted to the anode only when the anode is positive (as when it is connected to the positive battery terminal). To explain this, we say that electrons are negatively charged particles of electricity. Since such negative charges are attracted by an opposite, or positive, potential, the electrons rush toward the positive anode; when the anode becomes negative, the flow of electrons stops.

If the positive anode voltage of a typical vacuum tube is increased, the flow of electrons through the tube and its external circuit is also increased. This holds true up to the point where all the electrons produced at the cathode are being attracted to the anode, as at *A* in Fig. 2-10. However, at higher anode voltages, the electron flow (anode current) will increase further if cathode temperature is raised to produce more electrons within the tube. As the temperature of the filament increases, more electrons are forced to leave the cathode surface and enter the open space, where they can be attracted to the anode. However, a constant anode voltage attracts only a certain amount of electrons to produce anode current, shown at *B* in Fig. 2-11.

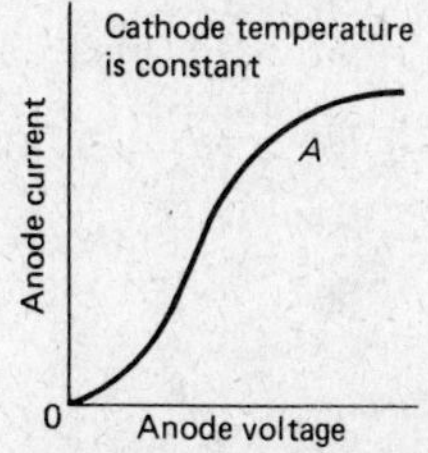

Figure 2-10 How tube current increases as anode voltage is increased.

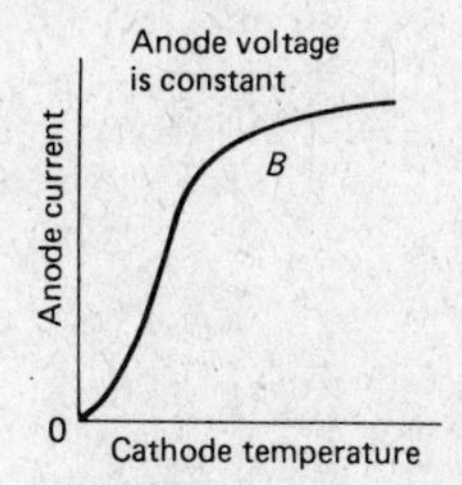

Figure 2-11 How tube current increases with cathode temperature.

If the filament temperature is raised further, producing excess electrons, the anode current increases very little.

2-9 CAN ELECTRONS BE SEEN?

This question of causing electrons to be emitted or forced out of the cathode is of special interest here, because it explains why the subject of electronics is so frequently illustrated by pictures of particles whirling in colored orbits, etc. Such pictures are merely the physicist's mental idea of how electrons behave while they gain sufficient energy (from added heat) to break loose finally from the bonds that hold them within the atom and thereby jump into space. For students of engineering, this electron theory is described further in Sec. 2-14 and Chap. 7. For now, it is enough to know that large quantities of these electrons are driven into the open space inside an electron tube, where they may be controlled more easily and more rapidly than when these same electrons are still flowing in an ordinary metal circuit.

When a glass high-vacuum tube is operated, properly connected in its socket, usually the red-hot filament can be seen, but no other evidence of its operation. The amount of current through such vacuum tubes is usually a few milliamperes, or thousandths of an ampere. The other class of tube (vapor-filled, see Sec. 17-1), which can carry more current, shows not only the red-hot filament but also a blue or purple glow when electrons are flowing between cathode and anode.

A solid-state diode or a transistor has no visible flow of electrons, since they flow within metal.

2-10 TYPES OF ELECTRON EMITTER OR CATHODE

In many tubes, the cathodes are merely the filaments; the electron stream comes directly from the surface of the hot filament as indicated in the tube in Fig. 2-3. (The metal filament may be coated with an oxide, thereby greatly increasing the electron emission or permitting operation of the filament at lower temperature.[2-16])

Other tubes, usually larger or industrial types, need cathodes that can produce much greater quantities of electrons; these tubes are built with indi-

Figure 2-12 A diode with indirectly heated cathode.

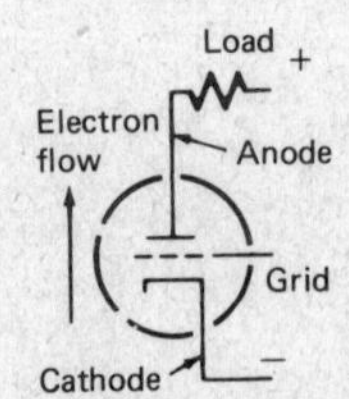

Figure 2-13 Diagram of a triode vacuum tube.

rectly heated cathodes, as is indicated in the tube symbol in Fig. 2-12. In such a tube the heat is produced in a filament, which heats a separate cathode structure, whose surface is better suited to emitting large quantities of electrons. A tube consisting of an anode, a filament, and an indirectly heated cathode is classed as a diode; it has two separate elements, not three.

2-11 ELECTRIC FLOW IN A HIGH-VACUUM RECTIFIER TUBE

Electric current flows through the space within a tube because great quantities of electrons are emitted or "boiled out" of the hot filament of the tube, or cathode; many of these electrons pass across to the anode. This flow of electrons is prevented if the anode is at a considerably more negative potential than the cathode (or here we say that the anode is negative). If the anode of this tube is made, say, 75 volts (V) more positive than its cathode, enough electrons may pass across to the anode so that a meter shows a current flow of 6 milliamperes (mA). If the anode voltage is now raised to 150 V, the more positive anode attracts so many electrons that the current flow increases to about 15 mA. In the usual operation of such a tube, many more electrons are available at the hot cathode; only part of them pass across to the anode. We may ask why the rest of the electrons do not likewise pass across to the anode and further increase the current; something seems to be limiting the amount of electron flow.

2-12 SPACE CHARGE

When the electrons come out of the hot cathode, they fill the space near the cathode like a tiny cloud. Since these electrons are negatively charged particles, the clouded space near the cathode quickly acquires a negative potential or charge; this *space charge* repels those additional electrons just coming out of the cathode, so that they return back into the cathode. Meanwhile, the anode (if it is positive) attracts electrons from this cloud near the cathode; for each electron that flows from the cloud to the anode, a replacing electron from the cathode is permitted to join the cloud. In this way, the amount of electron flow within the tube increases as the anode is made more positive. (A similar action does not occur in a PN solid-state diode.)

2-13 CONTROL OF ELECTRON FLOW WITHIN A TUBE

Much as the base current of a transistor can vary its collector or load current, the plate or anode current of a vacuum tube can be varied by adding a third part, called the grid, located between cathode and anode. As is shown in Fig. 2-13, electrons flow from the heated cathode toward the more positive anode, unless repelled by a negative potential applied to the grid. When the grid is kept much more negative than the cathode, no electrons or anode current flows. As the grid is made less negative, the decreased electric field lets the electron flow increase through the anode and the external load. Having three elements, this is a vacuum *triode*; similarly, a transistor is a solid-state triode whose collector current may be controlled by varying the current in its base.

2-14 ELECTRON THEORY

This tries to explain the action of electricity, including even the basic flow of electric current in a metal wire. Earlier science courses show how any substance or material consists of billions of atoms and molecules; each atom includes a central nucleus surrounded by a number of electrons that whirl around the nucleus. The nucleus includes positively charged protons; the electrons are negatively charged. In a normal neutral atom the negative charges of the electrons just balance the positive charges of the protons. The electrons are attracted by the positive nucleus; the electron farthest from the nucleus is attracted least and, in some substances, may become detached from the atom.

In a metal or other conductor of electricity, the outer electron of each atom is held so loosely that it may be made to transfer or move from one atom to the next if an electric pressure or voltage is applied that attracts such loose or "free" electrons toward the positive end of the conductor or wire. An electric current is the combined movement of such electrons; a huge quantity of these electrons (6.24×10^{18} electrons per second) must flow to become just one ampere. In other materials that we consider to be insulators or nonconductors of electricity, even the outer electron of each atom is attracted to its nucleus so strongly that there is negligible drift or movement of electrons between atoms, and so there is no flow of electricity. This is discussed further in Sec. 7-1.

2-15 ELECTRON EMISSION

Even though the "free" or most distant electrons may move within a metallic conductor and thereby may become a flow of electricity within the conductor, these same free electrons normally do not escape through the metal surface into the air or space surrounding the metal. But if these free electrons are given additional energy, they may escape. For example, if the metal conductor is brought to much higher temperature, the heat may give enough additional energy to the whirling outer electron of each atom so that such electrons may pass through the surface boundary of the metal. We say that such electrons are emitted from the surface; any such liberation of electrons from the metals is called *electron emission*. Several methods of causing electron emission are described later; this present example, using heat to give the added energy to the electrons, is called *thermionic emission*. (See third paragraph in Sec. 17-9.)

Considering the heated metallic filament or cathode of a vacuum tube (mentioned in Secs. 2-3 and 2-5), a stream of electrons passes out of the hot metal into the evacuated space within the tube; when many of these electrons are attracted so that they move toward the anode or plate of the tube, an electric current flows through the space inside the tube and continues beyond the anode in the metallic part of the complete electric circuit.

2-16 HEATED CATHODES

The emission of large quantities of electrons from heated surfaces has been mentioned in Sec. 2-10. The amount of energy that must be added to the electron to enable it to pass into space and out from the cathode depends upon the material used for the emitting surface of the cathode. For each material, this required energy may be stated as a "work function," expressed in volts. (The energy gained by an electron as it passes through a 1-volt difference of potential is called an *electronvolt*; it equals 1.6×10^{-19} joule. Since this energy has a direct ratio to the voltage difference through which the electron passes, this energy may be expressed in volts. This cannot be taken to mean that this amount of voltage, placed just outside the surface, can extract electrons.) Tube cathodes generally are made of tungsten, thoriated tungsten, barium nickelate, or oxide-coated materials. As is shown in Table 2-1, tungsten has a high work function; therefore, to emit electrons, it must operate at a high temperature; thus its efficiency (milliamperes of output per watt of input to the heater) is low. By adding to tungsten about 1 percent of thorium, the resulting thoriated-tungsten cathode has a lower work function so that it may operate at lower temperature and higher efficiency. For most tube cathodes, a base of nickel is coated with an oxide of barium and strontium or calcium; the lowered work function permits these tubes to produce high currents (milliamperes per watt) at much lower temperatures. Overheating such tubes greatly reduces their ability to emit electrons.

TABLE 2-1

Material	Work function, volts	Operating temperature, °C	Milliamperes per watt	General use
Oxide-coated	1 to 2	750	250	To 100 W, 750 V
Thoriated tungsten	2.6	1650	100	To 1 kW, 5000 V
Tungsten	4.5	2300	4 to 8	Above 1 kW, 5000 V

3

TIME-DELAY ACTION

Most electronic circuits include time delays, so that the action in one circuit can cause a second circuit to operate at a desired later time.

Many common electric circuits in industry use time-delay devices, which operate a contact at a definite time after a signal is given; there are motor-operated timers and time delays produced while air escapes from a bellows. Industrial electronics includes great numbers of time-controlling circuits that use transistors and electron tubes.

3-1 THE *RC* TIME CONSTANT

The time delay usually is obtained while a capacitor (or static condenser) changes its charge through a resistor. The rate of capacitor discharge may be fast at first, but it always becomes slower as the capacitor charge or voltage decreases. As shown in Fig. 3-1, the capacitor voltage may decrease to about one-third of its full pressure in 5 sec, yet 10 sec later there is still some voltage left. If the size of the capacitor is known (in microfarads) and also the resistance (in megohms, which equals ohms × 1,000,000), then the

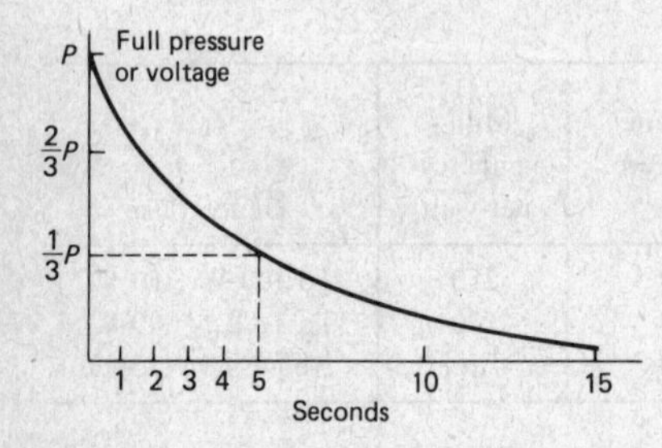

Figure 3-1 Capacitor discharges rapidly at first, more slowly later.

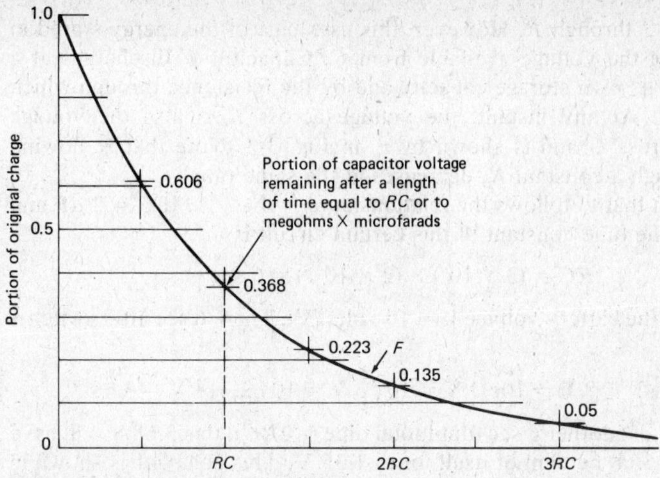

Figure 3-2 Rate of capacitor discharge.

length of time required for the capacitor voltage to decrease to approximately one-third of its starting value is shown by this relation:

Time (seconds) = resistor (megohms) × capacitor (microfarads)

For example, a 1-μF capacitor, discharging through 5,000,000 ohms (Ω) (5 MΩ), requires about 5 sec to discharge to one-third of the voltage it had at the start. Similarly, a 20-μF capacitor with a 250,000-Ω resistor has this same rate of discharge.

This length of time, obtained by multiplying together R (resistance) and C (capacitance), is called the *RC constant* or the *time constant* of this resistor-capacitor combination. (This time constant, equal to RC, must not be confused with the length of actual time delay of the circuit. Some circuits are designed to prevent a desired action until after a time delay equal to three times RC or even five times RC.) This time constant shows how long the capacitor voltage remains above one-third its starting value. As shown in Fig. 3-2, the remaining capacitor voltage is exactly 0.368 times the original voltage after the passage of time equal to RC sec; here the capacitor has lost 63.2 percent of its charge. When time equal to $3RC$ has passed, the remaining voltage is 5 percent, or 0.05 of its starting value.

3-2 CAPACITOR DISCHARGING TIME

The time-delay actions above are demonstrated by the circuit of Fig. 3-3. As long as switch S remains closed, capacitor C is charged to the voltage of the battery, so the current $I = V / R$ amperes (A), flowing steadily in R. (With this steady voltage applied, no current flows into or out of the capacitor.) For an instant after S is opened, C retains this voltage V, which continues to force current I through R. However, this uses part of the energy stored in C, decreasing the voltage available from C. Capacitor C discharges at a rate fixed by its own storage capacity and by the resistance through which it discharges. At any instant, the voltage across R is also the voltage remaining across C and is shown by v_c in Fig. 3-3. Note that i_c, flowing from C through a constant R, decreases at the same rate.

It is known that v_c follows the relationship $v_c = V\epsilon^{-t/RC}$. If $C = 2\ \mu F$ and $R = 3\ M\Omega$, the time constant of this certain circuit is

$$RC = (3 \times 10^{6}) \times (2 \times 10^{-6}) = 6 \text{ sec}$$

Assume that the battery voltage $V = 10$ volts (V). Then, 6 sec after switch S is opened,

$$v_c = 10e^{-6/(2\times3)}\ V = 10e^{-1}\ V = 10/e\ V = 10/2.718\ V = 3.68\ V$$

After a delay of another 6 sec (until total time $= 2RC$), this 3.68 V will have decreased to 36.8 percent of itself, or to 1.35 V. This behavior is shown in detail in Fig. 3-2.

The above relationship may be transposed to $e^{+t/RC} = V/v_c$, from which $t/RC = \ln V/v_c$, and so $t = RC \ln V/v_c$. (Note that ln is the natural logarithm, to the base e, or 2.718. The $\ln = 2.3 \times \log_{10}$.)

3-3 TIME FOR CHARGING A CAPACITOR

The reverse of the above action is shown in Fig. 3-4. Before switch S is closed, it is assumed that C holds no electrical charge, so that voltage v_c is zero. The instant after S is closed, battery voltage V forces a large current ($i_c = V/R$) to flow through R and into C; most of V is consumed in the IR voltage drop across R. As time passes and the charge in C increases, v_c increases also, thereby reducing the difference between V and v_c, thus causing i_c to decrease. While i_c in Fig. 3-4 decreases as fast as it did in Fig. 3-3, it is seen that v_c in Fig. 3-4 is equal to (V − the previous curve), or $v_c = V - (Ve^{-t/RC})$. So, the voltage across the capacitor is $v_c = V(1 - e^{-t/RC})$. When $t = RC$ sec, v_c has risen to 63.2 percent of its final value V. When time t becomes very large, $e^{-t/RC}$ becomes negligible

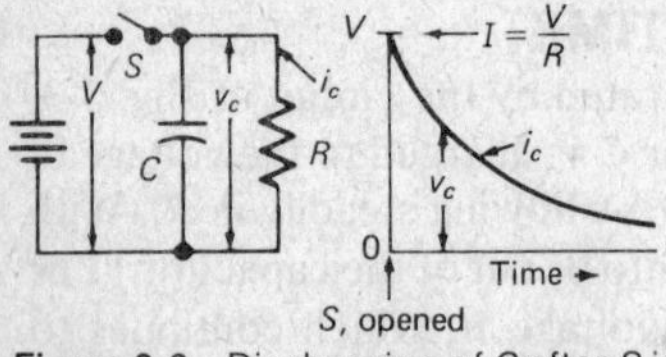

Figure 3-3 Discharging of C after S is opened.

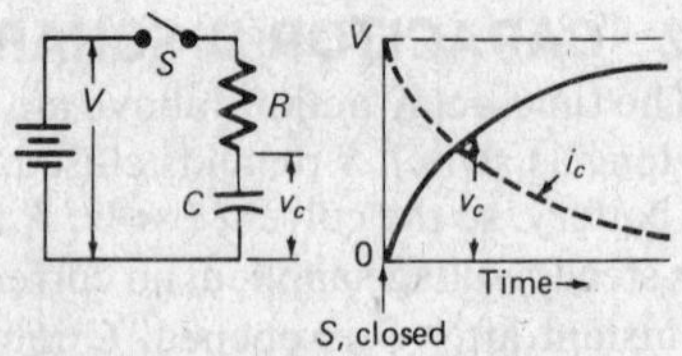

Figure 3-4 Charging of C after S is closed.

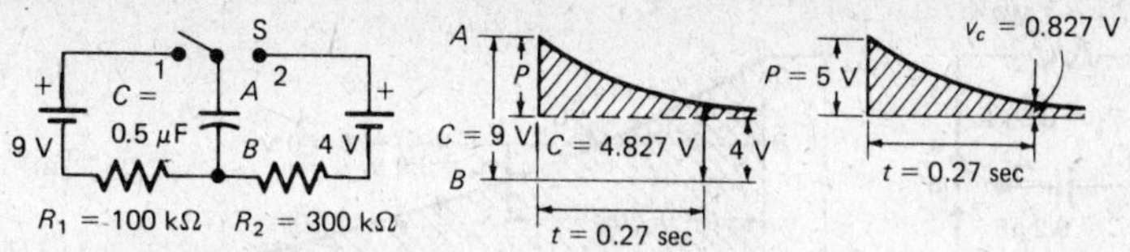

Figure 3-5 Capacitor C discharges toward a lower voltage.

and v_c becomes equal to the entire battery voltage V. So

$$t = RC \ln \frac{V}{V - v_c}$$

3-4 COMBINED CHARGING AND DISCHARGING OF A CAPACITOR

To help the student apply the above formulas, the following examples are given. In Fig. 3-5, if switch S has touched at 1 for a long time, capacitor C has charged through R_1 until the C voltage equals the 9 V of the battery, so that the upper terminal A of the capacitor is 9 V more positive than its lower terminal B. If S now is thrown quickly to 2, the voltage across C changes so as to reach a final value of 4 V; C discharges or loses energy as the voltage across C decreases in size. The shaded portion in Fig. 3-5 shows that the changing voltage across C has the same shape and size as though C had discharged from a value P toward a value of zero volts. The final possible change in voltage (9 V − 4 V = 5 V) is used for P.

To find the voltage across C, at 0.27 sec after S is moved from 1 to 2, it first is necessary to find v_c of the shaded area. Since a 0.5-μF capacitor is discharging through a 300-kΩ resistor, the value of $RC = 0.3\ \text{M}\Omega \times 0.5\ \mu\text{F} = 0.15$ sec. As shown in Sec. 3-2, $v_c = Ve^{-t/RC} = 5\ \text{V}\ (e^{-0.27/0.15}) = 5\ \text{V}/e^{1.8} = 5\ \text{V}/6.05 = 0.827$ V. The corresponding voltage across C is $0.827 + 4 = 4.827$ V.

If the 4-V battery in the above example is replaced by a 12-V battery, Fig. 3-6 shows that C gains more charge as the voltage across C increases from 9 V toward the new value of 12 V. This is a change of 3 V, shown at P, to be

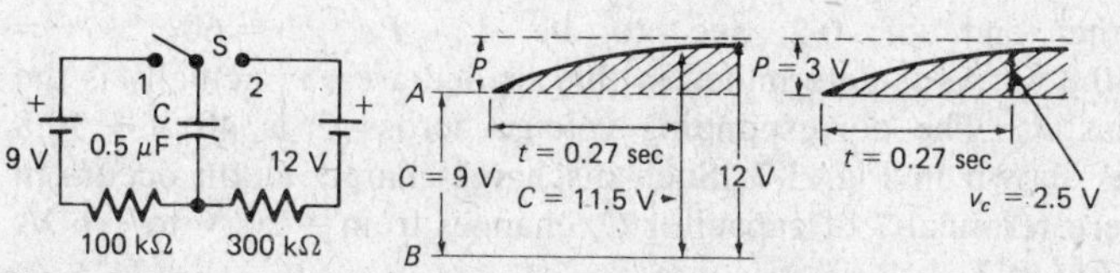

Figure 3-6 Capacitor C charges toward a higher voltage.

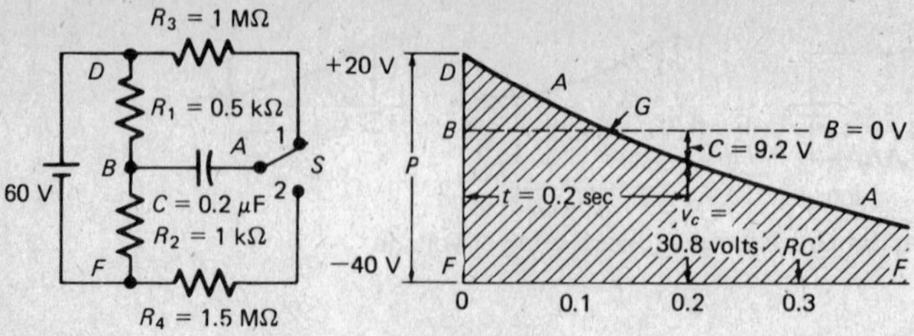

Figure 3-7 Polarity of C voltage reverses.

used as V in the equation of Sec. 3-3 for the charging of C. Using the shaded area in Fig. 3-6, $v_c = P\ (1 - e^{-t/RC}) = 3\ \text{V}\ (1 - e^{-0.27/0.15}) = 3\ \text{V}\ (1 - 1/6.05) = 3\ \text{V}\ (0.835) = 2.5$ V. The corresponding voltage across C is 2.5 V + 9 V = 11.5 V.

At this instant (when C has 11.5 V), if S is moved back to terminal 1, C now discharges from 11.5 V toward 9 V, or a change of 2.5 V = P. To find the time t until the C voltage = 10 V, $t = RC \ln P / v_c$, where v_c = 10 V − 9 V = 1V. So t = 0.1 MΩ × 0.5 μF × ln 2.5 / 1 = 0.05 × 0.916 = 0.0458 sec.

In Fig. 3-7, the problem is to find the voltage across capacitor C at a time 0.2 sec after S is moved from 1 to 2.

Terminal B of the capacitor is connected to a voltage divider (R_1 and R_2) so that B is 40 V above F but B is 20 V below or more negative than D. While S touches at 1, C has charged through $R_2 + R_3$ until its terminal A is at +20 V as compared with B. When S is moved quickly to 2, the charge in C changes until A finally reaches the potential at F, which is −40 V with respect to B. As shown by the curve in Fig. 3-7, C at first discharges through R_2 and R_4 until the voltage across C reaches zero, at G; then C recharges through R_1 and R_4 but to the opposite polarity, as terminal A now moves to a potential below B.

Here again the changing voltage across C depends on the total difference of potential through which A must pass, which is shown by P; here P = 20 V + 40 V = 60 V. Since 0.2 μF is charging through 1.5 MΩ and 0.5 kΩ, the time constant RC = 1.50005 MΩ × 0.2 μF. Here the ohm values of the divider R_1 and R_2 purposely are chosen so small (as compared with R_3 or R_4) that the effect of R_1 may be neglected when finding RC, which therefore is 1.5 × 0.2 = 0.3 sec. Using the shaded area in Fig. 3-7, the value of v_c is found at the end of 0.2 sec to be $V_C / Pe^{-t/RC} = 60e^{-0.2/0.3} = 60 / 1.95 = 30.8$ V. As is determined in this shaded area, v_c actually is the voltage across R_4. The corresponding voltage across C is 40 V − 30.8 V = 9.2 V as shown in Fig. 3-7. Such discharge-charge action occurs in Fig. 8-1, where terminal 7 of capacitor C_4 changes from + 20 V to − 6 V, as shown in Fig. 8-2.

3-5 INDUCTANCE MAY CAUSE TIME DELAY. THE *L/R* TIME CONSTANT

When wire is wound into a coil (as in a relay or transformer winding) this forms an inductance, whose effect is stated in henrys; this inductance L stores energy that tries to maintain steady *current through* the coil wire. (Similarly, in Sec. 3-1, a capacitance C tries to maintain steady *voltage across* or between its terminals.

As switch S closes in Fig. 3-8, a current i_L flows through inductor L in series with resistor R, increasing to a final steady ampere value equal to V / R. (The waveshape of i_L is like the rise of v_c in Fig. 3-4.) The seconds of time needed for i_L to rise to 63.2 percent of its final value is obtained by dividing L (the inductance, henrys) by R (the resistance, ohms) and is called the *inductive time constant.*

More generally we may state that the current flowing at time t is $i_L = I_{\text{final}} + (I_{\text{inital}} - I_{\text{final}})\ e^{-t/T_L}$ (where $T_L = L / R$).

In Fig. 3-8, $I_{\text{initial}} = 0$ and $I_{\text{final}} = V / R$.

In Fig. 3-9, $I_{\text{inital}} = V / R$. Here when S opens, battery current stops but i_L continues, flowing through L, R and up through diode D. But i_L decreases, as shown by the curve at the right in Fig. 3-9, so that $I_{\text{final}} = 0$.

We may use a similar equation in Sec. 3-3 for the voltage in a capacitor circuit

$$v_c = V_{\text{final}} + (V_{\text{initial}} - V_{\text{final}})\ e^{-t/T_C} \text{ (where } T_C = RC)$$

This form of equation is useful when neither V_{final} nor V_{initial} is zero. Notice that Figs. 3-8 and 3-9 (which plot values of current) have waveshapes like Figs. 3-3 and 3-4 (which plot values of voltage).

3-6 UNDESIRABLE EFFECT FROM INDUCTANCE

Since an inductance L tries to maintain constant current through itself, the opening of switch S in Fig. 3-8 causes L to generate a high voltage called its

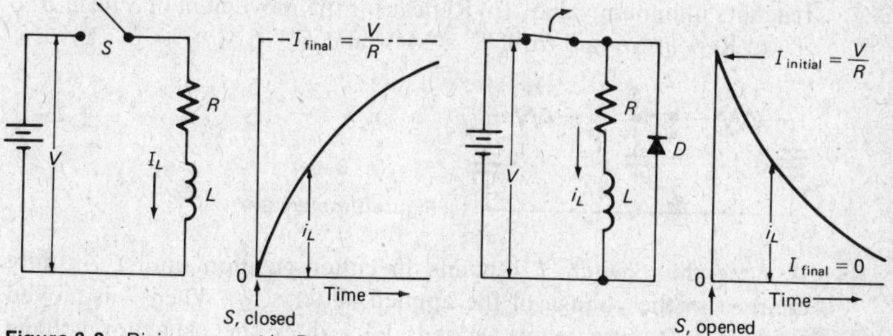

Figure 3-8 Rising current in R and L after S is closed.

Figure 3-9 Decreasing current in R and L and D after S is opened.

"inductive kick." This voltage rises to whatever value is needed to make i_L continue to flow; thus this voltage may spark between the S contacts.

If a transistor Q is used in place of S to open such an inductive circuit, then Q may be damaged by this high voltage generated by L as it stops the flow of i_L. To prevent such damage, a diode is added across L as is shown at D in Fig. 3-9. A similar protector or suppression diode is used in Fig. 6-22, and used as D_3 across the CR coil in Fig. 8-1; or D_1 across CR in Fig. 8-3.

Problems

3-1 True or false? Explain why.

(a) The rate of discharge of a capacitor increases with time.

(b) Discharging through a constant resistance, the voltage of a capacitor becomes zero after a time equal to about $5 \times RC$.

(c) Megohms × microfarads is equal to ohms × farads.

(d) In Fig. 3-2, the shape of the curve changes if the capacitor has been charged to double voltage.

(e) A discharged 0.2-μF capacitor C is placed in series with R across a 10-volt (V) battery; 1 sec later, if C has a charge of 8 V, $R = 3.1$ MΩ.

(f) During a continuous discharging and charging operation, the voltage polarity across a capacitor does not reverse.

(g) The value of $\ln 1.105 = 0.1$; $\ln 1.35 = 0.3$; $\ln 1.65 = 0.5$; $\ln 2.0 = 0.693$; $\ln 2.72 = 1.0$; $\ln 30 = 1.1$; $\ln 3.7 = 1.31$; $\ln 5 = 1.61$; $\ln 10 = 2.3$; $\ln 20 = 3.0$.

3-2 When a voltmeter suddenly is connected across a 0.5-μF capacitor that has been charged to 90 V, this voltage decreases to 30 V in 1.1 sec. Find the internal resistance of the voltmeter.

3-3 If a discharged 2-μF capacitor and a 250-kΩ resistor in series suddenly are connected across 80 V dc, how many seconds later will the capacitor voltage become (*a*) 64 V, (*b*) 76 V?

3-4 Note the polarities of batteries E and F. (*a*) If $E = F = 12$ V, how long after switch S is moved from A to B does the capacitor voltage reach its minimum value? (*b*) Repeat for the movement of S from B to A. (*c*) Repeat (*a*) and (*b*) if $E = 24$ V and $F = 6$ V.

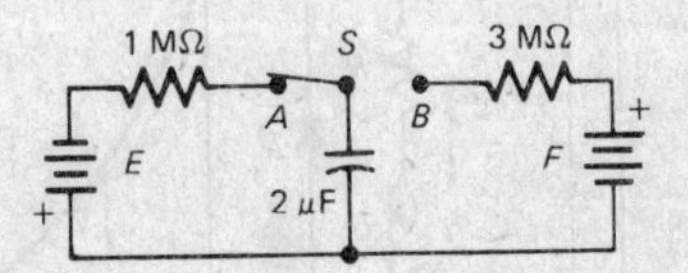

Figure Problem 3-4

3-5 Assume that switch T remains in either position until C is fully charged to the voltage of the applied battery. (*a*) When T is moved from 1 to 2, how many seconds later does the capacitor voltage become either one-third or three times its original value? (*b*) Repeat for the movement of *T* from 2 to 1.

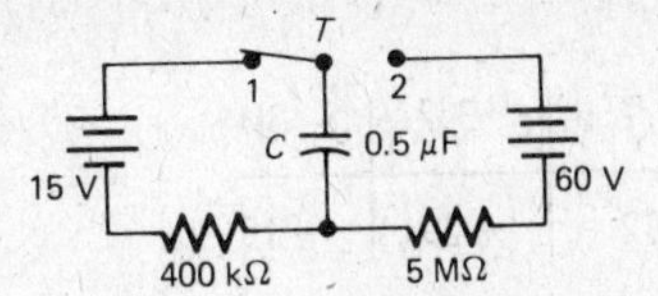

Figure Problem 3-5

3-6 Starting while C_3 is charged to 60 V, switch *S* then is moved to *B* for 1.6 sec, then instantly is returned to *A*. (*a*) Find the minimum voltage across C_3. (*b*) Find the voltage across C_3 0.5 sec after *S* is returned to *A*.

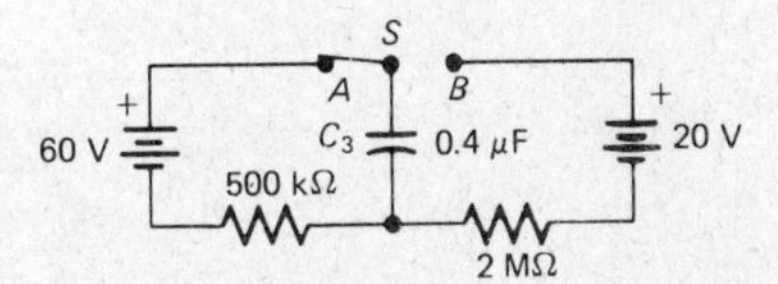

Figure Problem 3-6

3-7 Switch *W* has been at 2 for a minute. At time = 0, *W* is raised to 1. Just as capacitor v_c reaches 25 V, *W* is returned to 2. Find the *total* time until v_c has decreased to 12 V.

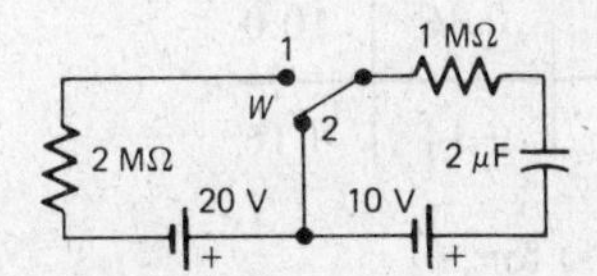

Figure Problem 3-7

3-8 At zero time, switch *T* is closed to let capacitor C_4 charge through 2 megohms (MΩ) from 0 volts (V) toward a final voltage *V*. After 2 sec, v_c across C_4 is 80 V; at this same instant *T* is moved to another position which lets C_4 discharge through 5MΩ toward 0 V. After a *total* time of 6 sec, $v_c = 20$ V. Find C_4 and *V*.

3-9 When a switch is closed, battery voltage *V* charges a capacitor through a resistance of 1.2 MΩ. One second after closing the switch, the capacitor voltage has risen to 150 V; at this same instant the switch is moved to another position, which discharges the capacitor through a 6-MΩ resistor. Two seconds later only 100 V remains across the capacitor. Find the size of the capacitor and the voltage *V* of the battery.

3-10 A dc supply of 50 V is available at *P*; also a single-pole double-throw switch *S*. (*a*) By adding only resistors and a capacitor, show a simple circuit that will cause the voltage at *AB* to have the following values at the times stated, after switch S is operated at time = 0. Make a voltage sketch showing also the value of RC. State value of each R and C used.

Seconds	0	0.58	1.7	3.7	30
Volts	+10	+15	+22	+29	+35

(*b*) Repeat the above for:

Seconds	0	0.3	0.6	1.5	10
Volts	+25	+10	0	−14	−20

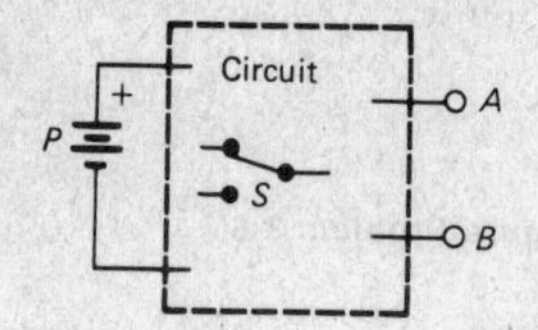

Figure Problem 3-10

3-11 Repeat Prob. 3-10, changing P to 40 volts, (*a*) for:

Seconds	0	0.11	0.18	0.36	10.0
Volts	−24	0	+7	+14	+16

(*b*) Repeat the above (P = 40 volts) for:

Seconds	0	0.3	1.0	1.5	20.0
Volts	+30	+21	+12.7	+11	+10

4

SIMPLE RECTIFIERS AND FILTERS: AC INTO DC

In electronic circuits, some direct current usually is needed, although the whole equipment may operate on ac supply. Several diodes or small tubes may be included for this purpose alone, acting as rectifiers.

4-1 CHANGING ALTERNATING CURRENT (AC) INTO DIRECT CURRENT (DC)

Similar to Fig. 2-2, a single diode[2-3] may be used, which permits only one-half of each cycle of ac to reach the load or dc circuit; this pulsating output must be smoothed or filtered[4-13] before it becomes a useful dc supply. This half-wave rectifier is most useful in communication circuits, computers, and electronic instruments, which require small amounts of direct current, perhaps at high voltage.

To produce a somewhat larger amount of direct current, two such diodes may be combined into one circuit so as to rectify and use both halves of the ac supply voltage wave. The output waveshape of such a two-diode rectifier is like the solid lines in Fig. 4-1 and often must be smoothed into more useful form. Basic circuits of this rectifier appear in Fig. 4-2; here a transformer is shown whose secondary winding is connected through fuses to the anodes of the two tubes (or to the P side of each PN junction). The two tube cathodes (or the N side of the junction) are connected together and form the positive connection to the load. The negative load terminal connects to a midpoint of the secondary or output winding of the anode transformer. The ac power supply causes point *A* to be more positive than *B* during one-half of each cycle. During this half cycle (shown as *X* in Fig. 4-1), the voltage of the right half of the transformer secondary winding forces electrons to flow from the

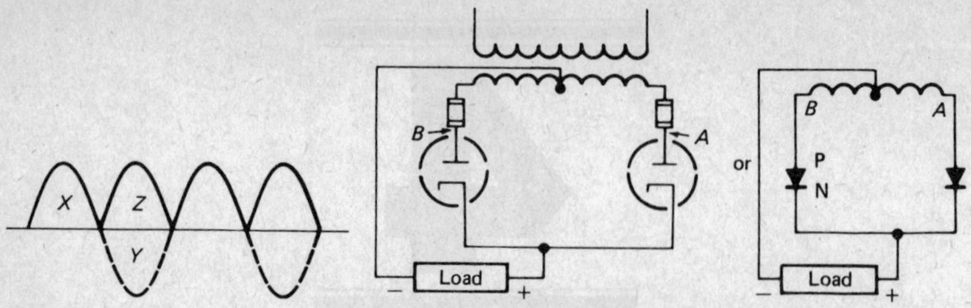

Figure 4-1 Output waveshape of two-diode rectifier.

Figure 4-2 Two-diode rectifier, passing both halfwaves to the load.

transformer center tap to the load and through the right-hand diode to point *A*. At the same instant, point *B* is at a more negative potential than the transformer center tap, and it is impossible for current to flow through the left-hand diode. One half cycle later (as during *Y* in Fig. 4-1), point *B* is more positive, and the left-hand half of the transformer forces electrons to flow from the transformer center tap through the load and left-hand diode to point *B*. Notice that the flow of electrons through the load is always in the same direction, regardless of which diode carries the current; therefore, during half cycle *Y* of Fig. 4-1, the voltage across the load is also above the horizontal line, as at *Z*.

4-2 USE OF OSCILLOSCOPE

To demonstrate the operation of this rectifier and show these waveshape patterns (such as Figs. 2-2 and 4-1), an oscillograph or oscilloscope is used. The cathode-ray oscillograph[31-11] is itself an electronic device. This "scope" or "CRO" contains a high-voltage electron tube, which is able to focus its stream of electrons so that they strike the end of the tube, causing a green spot where they strike the fluorescent material at the end of the tube. When the scope (like a voltmeter) is connected across the load circuit of this rectifier in Fig. 4-2, the green spot on the scope screen is made to trace a pattern or picture that shows the changes in voltage across the load during each cycle. With the scope adjusted so that it shows two complete cycles on its screen, a pattern is obtained as shown by the solid wave in Fig. 4-1. If the anode circuit of one of the diodes is opened, the scope picture resembles Fig. 2-2, since with one diode disconnected, the other diode acts as a half-wave rectifier.

4-3 FULL-WAVE RECTIFICATION WITH ONE TUBE

Where small amounts of direct current are needed, such as could be furnished by a pair of high-vacuum rectifier tubes, it is customary to combine

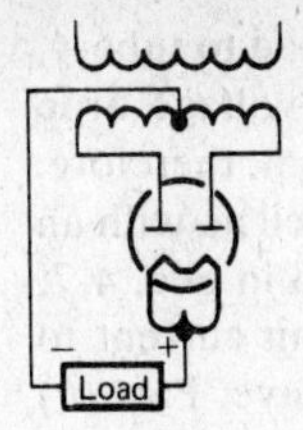

Figure 4-3 Two anodes in a single rectifier tube.

the parts of two such diode tubes into one envelope or enclosure, forming a duplex tube. This is shown in Fig. 4-3, using a small full-wave rectifier tube, such as the well-known type 5Y3. This circuit operates the same as the two-tube circuit of Sec. 4-1. The cathodes are connected together inside the tube. The electron flow between the cathode and the left-hand anode has no effect on the corresponding stream of electrons between the cathode and the right-hand anode. There is no electron flow from one anode to the other anode; neither anode is heated or emits electrons to produce such a flow.

4-4 SINGLE-PHASE ELECTRONIC RECTIFIER CIRCUITS

Tube circuits similar to Figs. 2-2 and 4-3 are shown in Fig. 4-4; the same circuits using PN diodes are shown in Fig. 4-5. Note here that the tube filaments are omitted, along with transformer windings to supply heater voltage. Omitted also is any device or circuit that would smooth or filter this output or load voltage; such filtering is discussed in Sec. 4-12.

The following description applies also to the PN diodes in Fig. 4-5.

Figure 4-4*a* shows the most simple form of rectifier, but this circuit applies voltage to the load during only half of each wave of ac supply voltage. Voltage V_{ac} is supplied by the transformer during both halves of the ac voltage wave, but current can flow through the transformer winding, the load, and tube *A* during only that half wave when point *X* is more positive

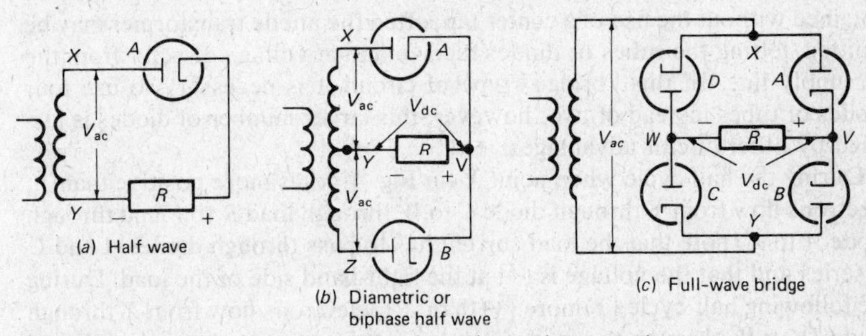

Figure 4-4 Rectifier circuits operating from single-phase supply.

than *Y*. Since electrons always must flow from *Y* through the load to tube *A*, the load current flows in one direction only. The resulting voltage drop across the load always is positive on the right-hand side as shown; therefore, such load voltage or current may be read with a dc meter as well as with an ac meter. The comparison of such meter readings is discussed in Sec. 4-7.

Figures 4-4*b* and *c* and 4-5*b* and *c* show circuits that permit current to flow through the load during both halves of the ac voltage wave. Part (*b*) shows the same two-tube circuit previously described in Sec. 4-1. Tube *B* is a duplicate of tube *A*, but the supply transformer (often called the anode or plate transformer) is different from that used in (*a*). The output winding of the transformer now must supply V_{ac} between *X* and center tap *Y*, as it did in (*a*), and also must apply V_{ac} between *Z* and *Y*. Here V_{ac} is called the *leg-to-neutral voltage*, or the *voltage per leg*. During the half cycle when *X* is more positive than *Z* or center tap *Y*, electrons flow from *Y* through the load to *V* and through tube *A* to *X;* this flow applies only one half wave of voltage across the load. During the following half wave, when *Z* is more positive than *X* or center tap *Y*, electrons flow from *Y* through the load to *V* and through tube *B* to *Z;* this flow applies the other half wave of voltage across the load. At any instant, note that current flows in just one tube and in only one-half of the transformer output winding. Using PN diodes as in Fig. 4-5, nearly all of V_{ac} is applied to the load. If tubes are used, each tube may have an internal voltage drop or loss of, say, 12 volts (*V*) while conducting, and the load receives 12 V less than the voltage V_{ac} supplied at that instant by the transformer. (Whereas the two-tube circuit of Fig. 4-4*b* often is called a single-phase full-wave rectifier, the center-tapped anode transformer actually supplies two phases of voltage. That is, voltage *XY* lags 180° behind voltage *ZY;* each of these voltages causes anode current to flow during only one half-wave. This circuit more properly is called a biphase half-wave rectifier or a diametric rectifier.)

4-5 THE SINGLE-PHASE BRIDGE RECTIFIER

Whereas Fig. 4-4*b* requires a transformer with a secondary center tap, Fig 4-4*c* shows how almost the same full-wave rectified output voltage may be obtained without the use of a center tap; often the anode transformer may be omitted, letting the tubes or diodes receive anode voltage directly from the ac supply line. In this "bridge" type of circuit it is necessary to use four diodes or tubes instead of two; however, this larger number of diodes is justified by other circuit advantages.

During the half cycle when point *X* (in Fig. 4-4*c*) is more positive than *Y*, electrons flow from *Y* through diode *C* to *W* through load *R* to *V* and through diode *A* to *X;* note that the load current has to pass through diodes *A* and *C* in series and that the voltage is (+) at the right-hand side of the load. During the following half cycle [*Y* more (+) than *X*], electrons flow from *X* through diode *D* to *W* through the load (in the same direction as before) to *V* and through diode B to Y; thus the load current must pass through diodes B and D in series, and the resulting voltage across the load is again (+) at the right-hand side. If each rectifier tube has 12-V internal loss or drop, the voltage across the load now is 24 V less than the voltage V_{ac} supplied at that instant by the transformer.

4-6 SOLID-STATE RECTIFIERS AND METALLIC RECTIFIERS

In place of the diode tubes mentioned above, rectifier circuits long have used metallic-disk units that are not tubes; two types of such disks are the copper oxide and the selenium rectifier cell. Today silicon PN or germanium diodes often are used, as is discussed in Chap. 5. Such disks or solid-state diodes may be used in any of the circuits shown in Fig. 4-4. This substitution is shown in Fig. 4-5, where the symbol ⇥ represents a single PN diode or a rectifying unit that may include many metallic disks assembled in series and in parallel. The arrow in this symbol points in the direction of conventional current flow, or opposite to the direction of electron flow.

In each disk or cell of such a metallic rectifier, two layers of different metals are joined to form a "sandwich." A thin layer of copper oxide (CuO) thus is joined to a heavier layer of copper, or a layer of selenium (deposited on a steel plate) is sprayed with a metal alloy, called the counterelectrode. Where these layers join, there is a blocking action which permits a large flow of electrons in one direction (from copper to copper oxide or from counterelectrode to selenium) but offers much higher resistance to electron flow in the reverse direction. In the forward direction each disk alone may pass about one ampere or less, requiring about one volt between the two faces of the disk. However, when the voltage is reversed, 5 to 30 volts (V) forces only a few milliamperes to flow; since this small reverse current may flow, the metallic rectifier does not have such complete or perfect rectifying ability as a tube possesses.

The above values for metallic rectifiers are shown in detail in Fig. 4-6. Note that the scales used for the right-hand side differ from the scales at the left. For example, for a selenium rectifier Fig. 4-6 shows that 1 ampere (A)

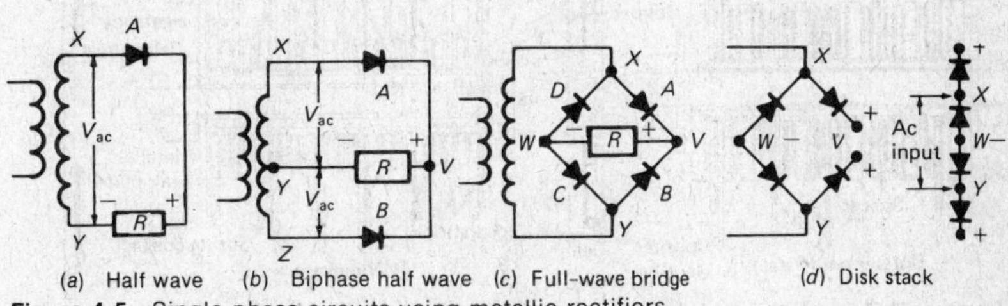

Figure 4-5 Single-phase circuits using metallic rectifiers.

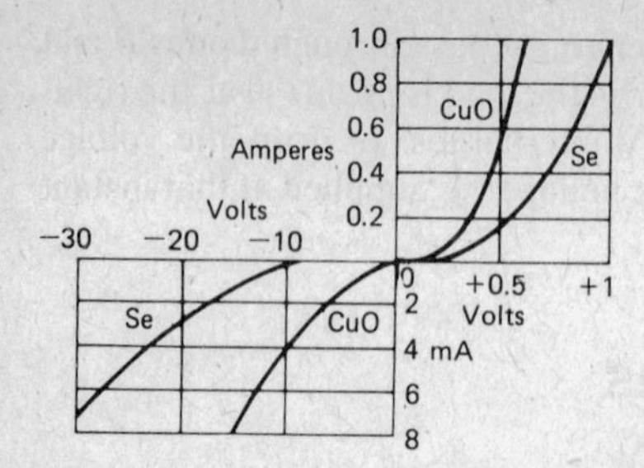

Figure 4-6 Curves of voltage versus current for metallic rectifiers.

may flow through a certain cell when 1 V is applied across that cell in the forward direction, but that only 7 milliamperes (mA) may flow through that same cell although 30 V appears across it in the reverse direction. In this case the cell has an internal voltage drop or loss of 1 V when passing 1 A to the load. Figure 4-6 shows also that since only 150 mA flows through this cell when 0.5 V is applied across it, the internal resistance of the cell is not constant but rises rapidly as the voltage across it decreases.

The permissible current that a given metallic rectifier may supply to a load depends on the cross-sectional area of the cell. Selenium and copper oxide cells may be connected in parallel to supply larger loads.

The disks of a small full-wave bridge rectifier usually are mounted on a single rod (as is shown in Fig. 4-7). If the bridge rectifier of Fig. 4-5*c* is opened or separated at *V*, the result is shown in Fig. 4-5*d*. When these four legs are straightened into a single line, it is seen that this entire bridge rectifier may be mounted so that the dc output may be taken from the center (−) and from the two ends (+) joined together.

4-7 VALUES OF CURRENT AND VOLTAGE

A wave of ac voltage has values as shown in Fig. 4-8. A voltage wave (of what is called 120 V ac) rises to maximum values equal to $\sqrt{2} \times 120$ V, or

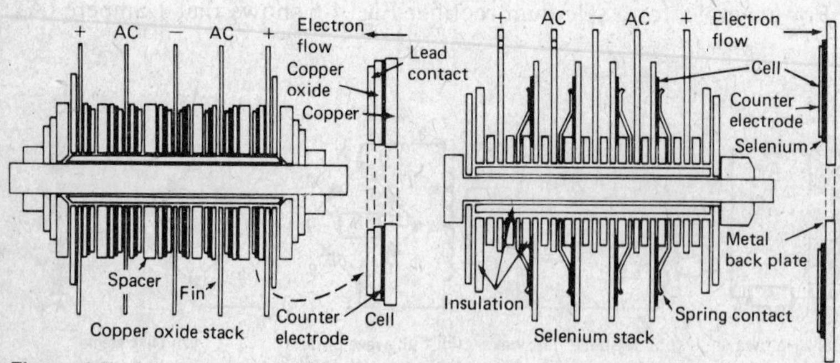

Figure 4-7 Arrangement of disks in metallic rectifiers (full-wave bridge).

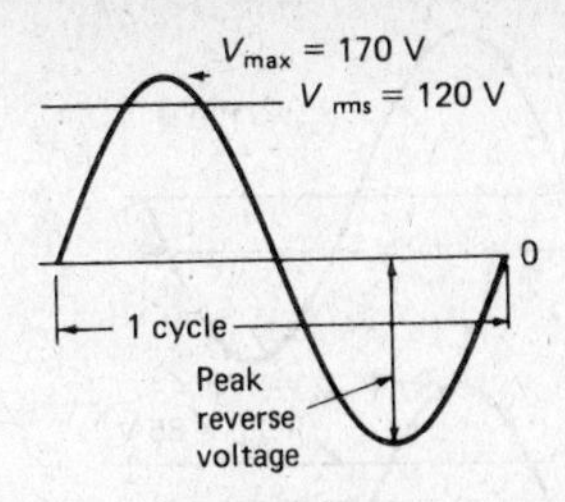

Figure 4-8 Voltage values in a sine wave.

1.414 × 120 V = 170 V, called V_{max}. The value $V_{rms} = 120\ \text{V} = 0.707\ V_{max+}$ V_{rms} is called the *root-mean-square* or *effective value* of the voltage wave and is the amount read on the usual ac voltmeter. A dc voltmeter, if connected across this same ac voltage, will read zero; its pointer will not move up-scale. This is because the usual dc instrument is constructed so that it responds to the average height of the voltage applied to it. In Fig. 4-8, it is seen that the ac wave (during one complete cycle) has equal areas above and below the 0 line; therefore, its average height is zero.

A two- or four-diode rectifier circuit [either (*b*) or (*c*) of Fig. 4-4 or 4-5, having no filter circuit] causes a voltage like that of Fig. 4-9 to appear across the load. (Here it is assumed that the rectifier diodes have no internal voltage drop resulting from any current flowing through them.) Then, if $V_{ac} = 120$ V (in Fig. 4-4, as read by an ac voltmeter), the corresponding $V_{max} = 170$ V; this also is the maximum height of each half wave of voltage shown in Fig. 4-9. An ac voltmeter, if connected across this load, still reads 120 V = $V_{rms.}$ But a dc voltmeter, connected across the same load, reads the average voltage, which is

$$0.636 \times 170\ \text{V} = 108\ \text{V} = V_{dc}$$

If the output load on the full-wave rectifier is a resistance R of 240 ohms (Ω), the resulting current through the load is

$$\frac{120\ \text{V rms}}{240\ \Omega} = 0.5\ \text{A rms}$$

as read on an ac ammeter in series with the load. This current reaches peak values where $I_{max} = \sqrt{2} \times 0.5\ \text{A} = 0.707$ A. However, a dc ammeter in this same load circuit reads the average value of current, or 0.636 × 0.707 A = 0.45 A. So, for this full-wave rectifier circuit, we also see that $I_{dc} = 0.9 I_{rms}$; $V_{dc} = 0.9 V_{rms.}$

Now consider the half-wave rectifier circuit (Fig. 4-4*a*) which, although it has the same supply voltage V_{ac}, causes only one half wave of each cycle of voltage to appear across the load, as shown in Fig. 4-10. This half wave rises to the same $V_{max} = 170$ volts (V). However, throughout one complete cycle, the average height of this voltage is only half as large as before, since the

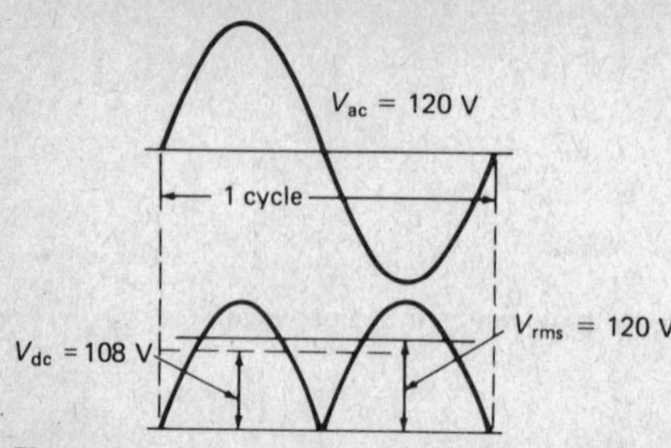

Figure 4-9 Voltage values in full-wave rectification.

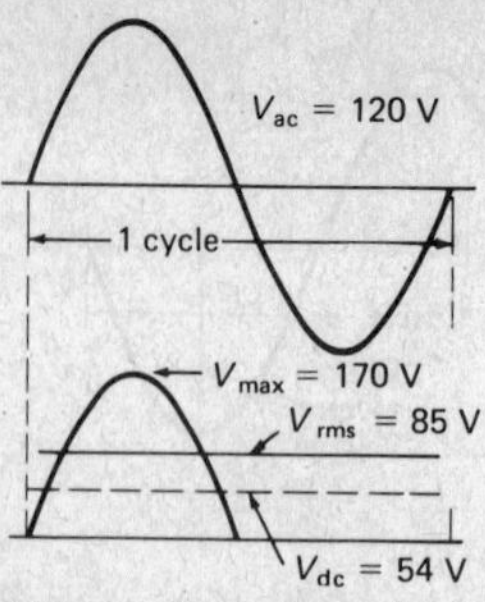

Figure 4-10 Voltage values in half-wave rectification.

total area under the curve, per cycle, is seen to be the area under only one half wave instead of the area under both half waves. So here

$$V_{avg} = \frac{0.636}{2} V_{max} = 0.318 V_{max} = 0.318 \times 170 \text{ V} = 54 \text{ V} = V_{dc}$$

An ac voltmeter connected across this same load (in Fig. 4-4*a*) also will respond to this single half wave, but it will read the rms value. Since V_{rms} of each half wave by itself is $V_{max} / \sqrt{2}$, the mean square of voltage during this half cycle is $V_{max}^2 / 2$. When averaged over a complete cycle, the mean square of this half-wave voltage is a half of $V_{max}^2 / 2$, or $V_{max}^2 / 4$. So the root mean square is $V_{max} / 2 = 0.5\ V_{max}$. The ac voltmeter, connected across the rectified half wave of load voltage in Fig. 4-10, reads

$$0.5 \times 170 \text{ V} = 85 \text{ V} = V_{rms}$$

If the load R is 240 Ω, the rectified half wave of voltage will force a maximum current to flow, equal to $V_{max} / R = 170 \text{ V} / 240\ \Omega = 0.707$ A; a dc ammeter reads $I_{avg} = 0.318 I_{max} = 0.318 \times 0.707 \text{ A} = 0.225$ A, but an ac ammeter in this load circuit reads

$$I_{rms} = \frac{V_{rms}}{R} = \frac{85 \text{ V}}{240\ \Omega} = 0.354 \text{ A}$$

Since the ac input to the rectifier is changed into a dc output, the above discussion may be summarized as follows (assuming internal $R = 0$):

	Full-wave output	Half-wave output
Input side	$V_{ac} = V_{rms} = 0.707 V_{max}$	$V_{ac} = V_{rms} = 0.707 V_{max}$*
	$I_{ac} = I_{rms} = 0.707 I_{max}$	$I_{ac} = I_{rms} = 0.5 I_{max}$
Output side	$V_{dc} = V_{avg} = 0.636 V_{max}$	$V_{dc} = V_{avg} = 0.318 V_{max}$
	$I_{dc} = I_{avg} = 0.636 I_{max}$	$I_{dc} = I_{avg} = 0.318 I_{max}$

*At the input, both half waves of voltage are present although only half-wave current flows.

In the output of a single-phase half-wave rectifier, the effective value ($I_{rms} = I_{max} / 2$) is useful only in determining the heat produced in a load having constant resistance R; here heat $= (I_{rms})^2 R$. But in an inductive load or when the rectifier output is filtered (as is described in Sec. 4-12), the output current has very little variation or ripple; therefore, the average or I_{dc} value commonly is used, so that heat may be $(I_{dc})^2 R$.

4-8 RECTIFIER POWER AND EFFICIENCY

The useful power output of a rectifier is considered to be $V_{dc} I_{dc}$, which is also $I_{dc}^2 R_L$. At the same time, the power input is measured by ac instruments and is $V_{ac} I_{ac}$ (for a resistive load), which is also $I_{ac}^2 (r_p + R_L)$. Here r_p is the internal or plate resistance of the rectifier and R_L is the resistance of the load. Since the efficiency of the rectifier equals P_{out} / P_{in}, then

$$\text{Efficiency} = \frac{I_{dc}^2 R_L}{I_{ac}^2 (r_p + R_L)} = \frac{I_{dc}^2}{I_{ac}^2 (1 + r_p / R_L)}$$

But Sec. 4-7 shows, in a half-wave one-tube rectifier, that $I_{dc} = I_{avg} = 0.318 I_{max}$ while $I_{ac} = I_{rms} = 0.5 I_{max}$. The efficiency becomes

$$\frac{(0.318 I_{max})^2}{(0.5 I_{max})^2 (1 + r_p / R_L)} = \frac{0.406}{1 + r_p / R_L)}$$

The theoretical maximum efficiency, occurring when internal resistance r_p becomes very small, approaches 0.406, or 40.6 percent.

Similarly, for a rectifier that supplies both half waves of voltage to the load, $I_{dc} = 0.636 I_{max}$ and $I_{ac} = 0.707 I_{max}$; so the efficiency becomes

$$\frac{(0.636 I_{max})^2}{(0.707 I_{max})^2 (1 + r_p / R_L)}$$

As r_p becomes very small, the efficiency approaches 0.812, or 81.2 percent.

4-9 RIPPLE FACTOR

Although the purpose of the rectifier is to change ac into dc, a considerable variation or ripple may remain in the rectified output voltage or current. To help to evaluate or compare various rectifier circuits, we use a term called *ripple factor*, which equals (effective value of the alternating portion of the output wave)/(average value of the output wave). In Fig. 4-11 the area under the straight line V_{avg} shows the average output (as measured by a dc meter), while the shaded areas show the alternating portion. This shaded portion may be measured separately by using an ac meter together with a 1-to-1 transformer as shown in Fig. 4-11; the dc portion cannot cause any voltage to appear beyond the transformer at the meter. By dividing the reading of the ac meter by the dc meter reading, it is found that the ripple factor

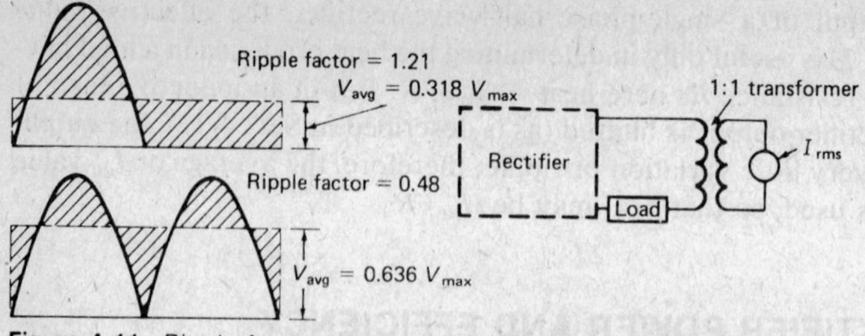

Figure 4-11 Ripple-factor curves and circuit to measure the ac portion.

of the single-phase full-wave circuit is 0.48; for the half-wave circuit it is 1.21, showing that the ac portion of its output wave is larger than the average dc output.

4-10 REVERSE VOLTAGE

The permissible voltage that may be applied to a rectifier tube, disk, or PN diode is limited by the *peak reverse voltage*, or PRV (also called *peak inverse voltage*, PIV), which is the maximum instantaneous voltage that appears across the rectifier during the negative half cycle, when the rectifier tries not to pass current. The value of V_{max}, as shown in Fig. 4-8, is the peak reverse voltage applied to each ⯈|, for either circuit (*a*) or (*c*) of Fig. 4-5. However, for the two-leg circuit of (*b*), each ⯈| must resist twice as great reverse voltage. While transformer terminal Z is at its most positive potential, current flows through rectifier B so that point V is held very close to Z. But V connects also to one side of rectifier A, whose other side is at X. So rectifier A must resist the entire voltage X to Z, or $2 \times V_{ac}$. The peak reverse voltage or PRV $= 2V_{max} = 2\sqrt{2}\ V$ (leg to neutral). (The rated value of PRV of rectifier A is determined as though the voltage drop is zero across B.)

To prevent excessive reverse current, most copper oxide rectifiers are limited to a peak voltage V_{max} of about 12 V per disk or cell. Since 12 V max = 8.5 V rms, it is seen that 14 of such disks are required in series for each ⯈| shown in (*a*) or (*c*) of Fig. 4-5 if $V_{ac} = 120$ V.

In comparison, most selenium rectifiers are limited to a peak voltage of about 25 V per cell, so that seven such cells in series are required for each ⯈| in (*a*) or (*c*) of Fig. 4-5 if $V_{ac} = 120$ V. (Today some selenium cells are supplied, rated at 45V peak reverse. The silicon PN diodes described in Sec. 5-1 are available, have PRV ratings from 25 V to more than 1000 V.)

4-11 DISK BRIDGE RECTIFIER

For the bridge rectifier of (*c*) in Fig. 4-5, we see that current flows through the load by passing through two legs (such as A and C) of the bridge, in series. If each leg ⧐ consists of seven disks in series and each disk has 0.6-V internal drop when the given rms current passes through it, the rms voltage across the load $= V_{ac} - 2 \times 7$ disks $\times 0.6\text{V} = V_{ac} - 8.4$ V.

Although the A and B disks conduct load current in series, we must not consider that these two legs are yet in series when resisting the reverse voltage. During the half cycle when reverse voltage appears across legs A and C, the other legs B and D are conducting current to the load; so there is a voltage drop or difference of only a few volts across leg B or leg D. Therefore, point V is at nearly the same potential as point Y; so the reverse voltage applied across leg A alone (X-to-V) is nearly as large as the voltage X-to-Y, which is V_{ac}. So the number of disks in *each* leg ⧐ of the bridge must withstand the peak value of V_{ax}.

4-12 FILTERING

A filter is a device or circuit used to remove unwanted ripple or variation in the output voltage of a rectifier like those previously described. Figure 4-12 includes a filter in a circuit that converts an ac supply into a smooth dc supply. Here is a pair of PN diodes or the rectifier tube (previously met in Sec. 4-3) and its center-tapped anode transformer, which converts alternating voltage into a pulsating dc voltage. Lower in Fig. 4-12, the output voltage (without filter) consists of half cycles, all above the 0 line; it is no longer alternating current, but neither is it a smooth direct current. It is a pulsating current, which can be used for some dc purposes but is not suitable for most electronic circuits; it must be filtered to take out the unwanted ripple, or curve, that remains of the ac waveshape. Just as the rough "washboard" surface of a country gravel road makes an automobile vibrate, so the ripples in this pulsating current can shake or disturb an electronic circuit. Also, just as the rough road is made smooth by scraping the ridge tops down into the

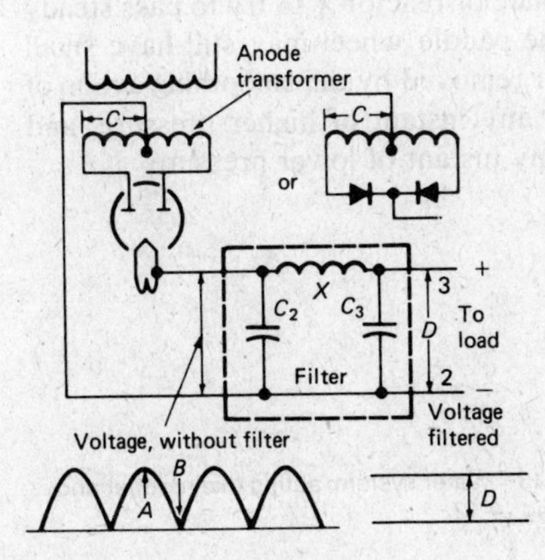

Figure 4-12 Dc power supply—rectifier with pi filter.

grooves, or hollows, so this pulsating current is smoothed by electrical devices that take energy from the high spots and discharge or lay this energy into the low spots of the pulsating wave. As shown in Fig. 4-12, this smoothing of the voltage or current is done by making the diode or tube current pass through a reactor X and by connecting capacitors C_2 and C_3 from X to the other (negative) side of the load. This combination is called a *pi* filter, because the parts are arranged on the diagram so as to resemble the Greek letter pi (π). (Sometimes a resistor is used in place of X.)

This reactor X is made of wire, wound on an iron core, so that X has a large amount of inductance. This inductance tries to maintain a steady current through its winding, by storing energy during moments when current increases and then discharging this energy to help a decreasing current. So X helps to smooth the current wave by reducing the high spots and filling the low spots.

Similarly, capacitors C_2 and C_3 help to smooth the voltage across the load by charging or storing energy during the high-voltage parts of the wave (such as A in Fig. 4-12) and then discharging this energy into X or into the load, during the low-voltage periods such as B.

The operation of a full-wave rectifier with its filter circuit is like that of a two-cylinder water pump, equipped with surge tanks and a heavy paddle wheel, as shown in Fig. 4-13. In each cylinder, the piston forces water into the pipe during its forward stroke. Just at the time when the pistons change direction, there is no force. The result is a pulsating water pressure, which is smoothed by the surge tanks and the paddle wheel. While one piston is in the middle of its forward stroke, its force turns the paddle wheel and also pumps water into tank A. Although at the end of the stroke there is no force from the pump, the heavy paddle wheel still tries to turn at the same speed and pass the same amount of water between its vanes. This water is supplied from tank A, and this lowers the water level there until the pump can again force water into the pipe and restore the water level in A. It is natural for the heavy paddle wheel to try to turn at constant speed and pass steady water flow, just as it is natural for an inductance or reactor X to try to pass steady flow of current. The water leaving the paddle wheel may still have small pressure changes, and these are further removed by the smoothing action of tank B, which receives water during any instant of higher pressure, and discharges the water into the line at any instant of lower pressure.

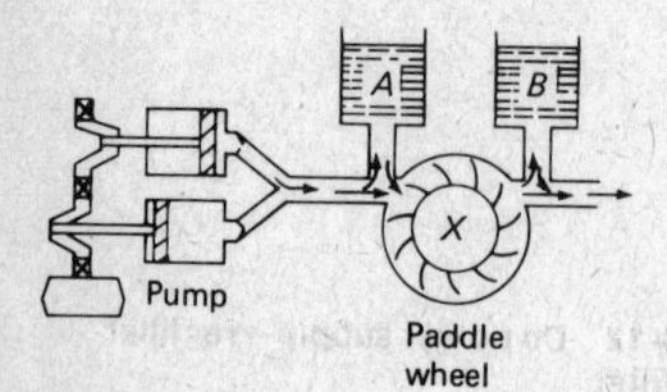

Figure 4-13 Water system, acting like rectifier and filter of Fig. 4-12.

4-13 VOLTAGE OUTPUT FROM A FILTER

The dc voltage output from a filter depends on the ac voltage supplied to the rectifier anodes; the filter arrangement and the amount of dc load also will change this output voltage. As a rough figure, a dc voltmeter across the load (at *D* in Fig. 4-12) reads about the same number of volts as an ac voltmeter connected at *C* (across one-half of the anode transformer). This is also shown by the upper curve in Fig. 4-16; at an output current of 75 to 100 milliamperes (mA), the output voltage from this pi filter is about 300 volts(V) dc, whereas the ac voltage (at *C* in Fig. 4-12) is 300 V rms (as read by the usual ac voltmeter). Notice that, as the dc current load decreases, the filter-output voltage *D* rises toward 425 V, which is the peak[4-7] value of the voltage applied at *C*.

To make clear why the filter-output voltage (*D* in Fig. 4-12) rises as the load current decreases, the solid upper curve in Fig. 4-14 shows how the voltage changes across capacitor C_2 while the dc load is 100 mA. When this load is almost zero, Fig. 4-15 shows the result. In both diagrams capacitor C_2 is charged to the 425-V peak value of the ac wave. At point *K* this ac wave decreases faster than capacitor C_2 can discharge, so current through the diode stops; C_2 continues to supply all the current needed by the load, until the other tube or diode passes current, at *L*. When supplying a dc load current of 100 mA, the capacitor C_2 loses its voltage quickly, decreasing to *L* in Fig. 4-14. As a result, the average height of the voltage across C_2 is much lower than the peak voltage. The corresponding output voltage of the filter, after being smoothed by *X* and C_3, is slightly below this average voltage in Fig. 4-14. In contrast, when there is very little dc load current, capacitor C_2 does not need to give up much of its charge or lose its voltage. Figure 4-15 shows that the voltage across C_2 remains very close to the peak of the ac voltage wave, so that the average voltage of C_2 is also high; the filter output is nearly the same as the 425-V peak input.

The shaded portions in Figs. 4-14 and 4-15 show that the diode or tube passes current in spurts, or during only part of each cycle. This is satisfactory for low-current dc supplies, using high-vacuum rectifier tubes. When a

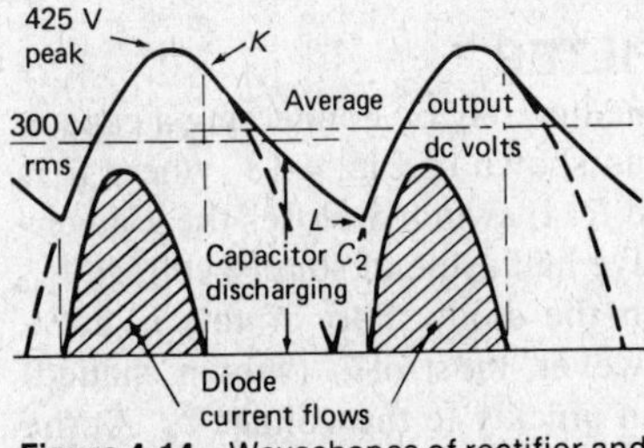

Figure 4-14 Waveshapes of rectifier and filter at heavy load (100 mA).

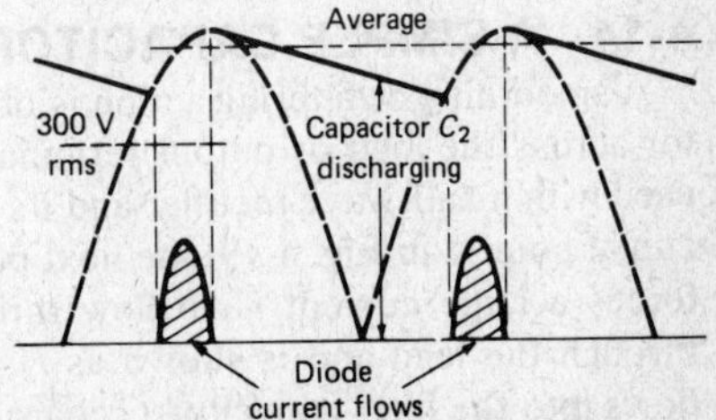

Figure 4-15 Waveshapes of rectifier and filter at light load.

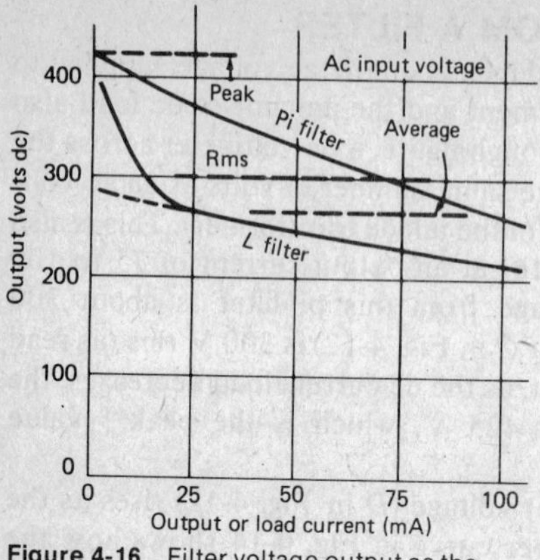

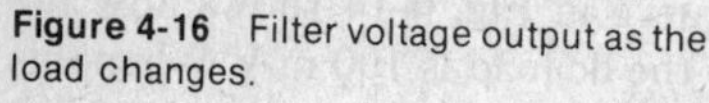

Figure 4-16 Filter voltage output as the load changes.

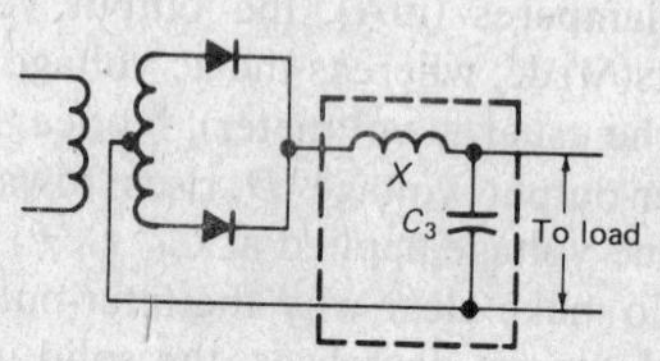

Figure 4-17 Rectifier circuit with L filter.

vapor-filled rectifier tube is used with a filter to supply a larger amount of direct current, the high momentary currents needed for charging capacitor C_2 may be prevented if C_2 is omitted, as next described.

When only reactor X and capacitor C_3 are used, as shown in Fig. 4-17, this arrangement is called an L filter. Here the current flowing in X flows also in a diode at the same instant. Since it is natural for reactor X to keep current flowing quite steadily through its own winding, this action also keeps current flowing more continuously through the diode. Moreover, as long as there is considerable load current to cause voltage drop across X, the peaks of the ac voltage wave do not reach capacitor C_3; instead, the output voltage of this L filter is close to the average value of the ac supply wave, as shown in Fig. 4-16. However, if the direct load current becomes small, reactor X loses its ability to smooth the voltage wave; the peak of the ac wave then reaches C_3 (as though X were not in the circuit), and the load voltage rises sharply toward the 425-V point. In practice, the L filter is kept loaded and gives less variation of output voltage than the pi filter.

4-14 A SIMPLE CAPACITOR FILTER

A smoothing or filtering action is obtained merely by connecting a capacitor across the load or output terminals, as shown in Fig. 4-18, where C is used with a half-wave rectifier and its load R. If switch S closes the load circuit at point S in Fig. 4-19, the next positive half cycle of supply voltage V_{ac} forces a large current i_P to flow through the diode. Part of this i_P flows through the load and is shown as i_R; however, most of i_P (shown shaded) flows into the filter capacitor C charging it quickly to the voltage v_R. At the instant F, the sine wave V_{ac} starts to decrease; here this ac supply becomes

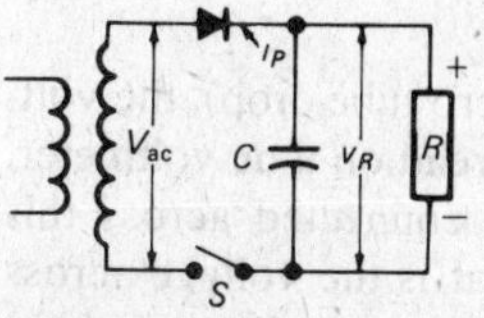

Figure 4-18 Simple capacitor filter.

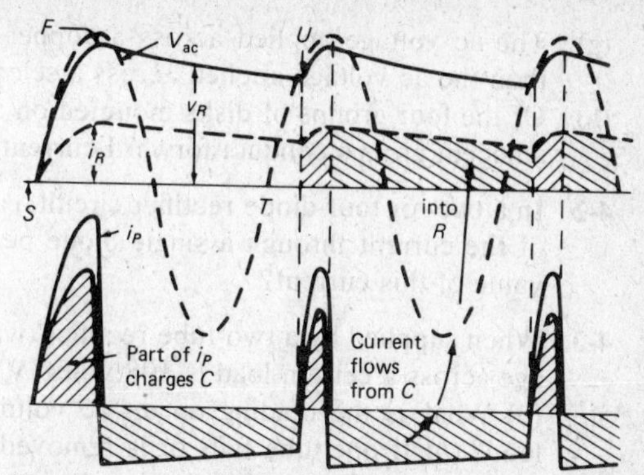

Figure 4-19 Waveshapes of voltage and current in Fig. 4-18.

less than the voltage of the capacitor. Diode current i_P stops; the capacitor cannot discharge back into the ac system because of the one-way action of the diode. Instead, current now flows out of C to furnish the current i_R through the load. While giving up this energy, the capacitor voltage also decreases, at a rate depending on the amount of current required by the load. When the supply V_{ac} enters its next positive half cycle, note that diode current does not restart at T but waits until U, where the wave of V_{ac} rises higher than the voltage v_R remaining across C. This second pulse of i_P is of shorter duration than the initial charging surge, for it serves mainly to restore into C the energy that C meanwhile had supplied to the load. Thus, while each pulse of diode current lasts much less than a half cycle, the load receives current more continuously from C.

Problems

4-1 True or false? Explain why.

(a) There may be several separate streams of electrons within a single tube enclosure.

(b) In a full-wave rectifier circuit, no tube or diode conducts the full wave.

(c) In a bridge rectifier, current flows in only one tube or diode at any instant.

(d) A biphase half-wave rectifier uses one duplex tube or two diodes.

(e) In a selenium rectifier, there is zero current flow in the reverse direction.

(f) A metallic rectifier has a total of ten disks per leg if each leg has two disks in parallel and five disks in series.

(g) The ac voltage applied across a copper oxide disk may be greater than the ac voltage applied across a selenium disk.

(h) Of the four groups of disks mounted on a single rod in Fig. 4-7, two adjacent groups conduct forward current at the same time.

4-2 In a two- or four-diode rectifier circuit, can the effective or rms value of the current through a single diode be equal to 0.707 of the peak value of this current?

4-3 When supplied by a two-tube rectifier (with zero tube drop), the voltage across a certain load is 108 volts (V), as read on a dc voltmeter. (*a*) What is the reading on an ac voltmeter connected across this load? (*b*) If one tube fails or is removed, what is the voltage across this same load as read on each voltmeter?

4-4 A transformer that delivers 100 V rms on each side of the center tap furnishes voltage to a two-leg rectifier which contains a total of 60 semiconductor disks. Each disk is rated 0.3 A rms and 30 V peak reverse and has no internal voltage drop. (*a*) In each leg, find the least number of disks in series and the number of parallel paths. (*b*) Find the largest current in the resistor load as read by a dc ammeter, without exceeding the rectifier rating.

4-5 A voltage of 22 V rms is applied at V_{ac} through a metallic rectifier to a resistor R as shown. The rectifier consists of a total of 24 CuO disks, each rated 0.5 A rms and 11 V peak reverse. Assume zero internal voltage drop in disks. (*a*) Find the least number of disks in series in each stack and the number of parallel stacks. (*b*) Find the largest current through R as read by a dc meter, without exceeding the rectifier rating.

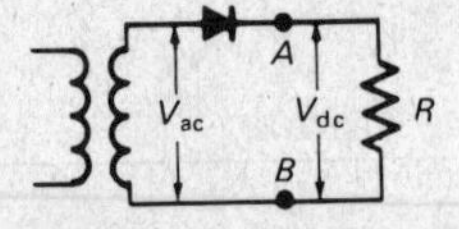

Figure Problem 4-5

4-6 Work Prob. 4-5 if $V_{ac} = 46$ V rms and each disk is rated 0.8 A rms and PRV = 11 V. (*c*) For the current in part (*b*), find the heat loss in R.

4-7 A silicon diode is rated 12 A average and 200 V peak reverse, with negligible internal drop. When used at its maximum rating in the circuit shown in Fig. Prob. 4-5, (*a*) find V_{ac}, V_{dc}, and R; (*b*) find the heat loss in R; and (*c*) find the dc power available between A and B, without exceeding the diode rating, if R is disconnected.

4-8 If a dc meter reads 135 V between A and B above, what does an ac voltmeter read at V_{ac}? Assume a metallic rectifier having negligible voltage drop. If each disk is rated 30 V peak reverse, what is the minimum number of disks in the rectifier?

4-9 Meters read 65 V and 1.2 A ac input to a single-phase CuO bridge rectifier. Each disk can withstand only 12 V peak reverse. When conducting its maximum permissible instantaneous current of 0.61 A, each disk has 0.4-V internal drop. (*a*) In each leg, how many disks must be used in series and how many in parallel? (*b*) What output voltage and load current would be read by dc meters?

4-10 Four disk-rectifier assemblies are available. Each assembly has 3 ohms (Ω) internal resistance. When used alone as a half-wave rectifier, each assembly is designed for an output of 5 A dc at 150 V dc; under this condition the circuit is operating at its *PRV*. Find the largest permissible applied rms ac voltage and the greatest dc load kilowatts (kW), (*a*), for one assembly, (*b*) for two assemblies connected biphase half wave, and (*c*) for a single-phase bridge rectifier.

4-11 A single-phase bridge rectifier has a total of 20 disks. Each disk may safely resist a maximum of 25 V reverse; each has a 1-V drop at that instant when it is conducting 4.1 amperes. A current of 4.1 A peak value passes through load resistor *R*. (*a*) What maximum ac supply voltage may be applied? (*b*) What is the corresponding value of *R* that permits the 4.1 A to flow?

4-12 Specify the copper oxide rectifier to operate on single-phase alternating current and to give the dc outputs tabulated below if each disk is rated at 11 V peak reverse and 0.4 A rms. Neglect internal *IR* drop.

Type	Dc output	Disks per leg		Total disks in rectifier
		In series	In parallel	
Half wave	17 V, 0.75 A			
Full-wave center tap	40 V, 1.5 A			
Full-wave bridge	60 V, 0.9 A			

4-13 Work Prob. 4-12, using these values of dc output:

Half wave	6 V, 1 A
Full-wave center tap	28 V, 1/3 A
Full-wave bridge	115 V, 1 A

4-14 The ac voltmeter *V* reads 140 V. Each of two dc ammeters *I* reads 175 mA. For this condition, the internal resistance r_p of each tube is

$0.25\ R_L$. (*a*) Find R_L. (*b*) Find reading of an ac voltmeter at X. (*c*) Find efficiency of rectification.

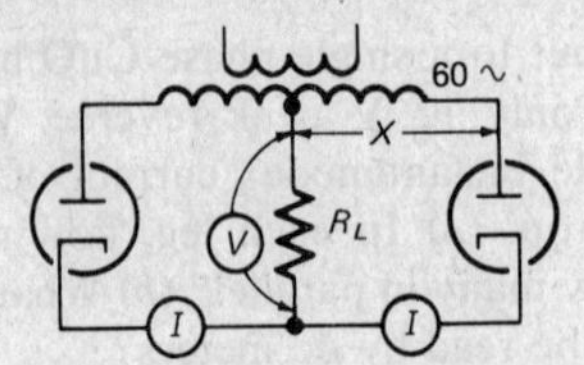

Figure Problem 4-14

4-15 If the ac meter in Fig. 4-11 reads 1.9 A and the dc load is 2 kW at 500 V, which types of rectifier circuit (of Fig. 4-5) will satisfy this ripple factor?

4-16 Neglect voltage drop in disks. When switch *S* is closed, a current of 3.5 A flows in *R*, as measured by dc ammeter D. With *S* closed (*a*) find readings of ac ammeter *A*, ac voltmeter *V*, and dc voltmeter *B*, and (*b*) find watts loss in *R*. (*c*) Now open *S* and repeat (*a*) and(*b*) above. (*d*) For each position of *S*, find PRV applied to each rectifier unit.

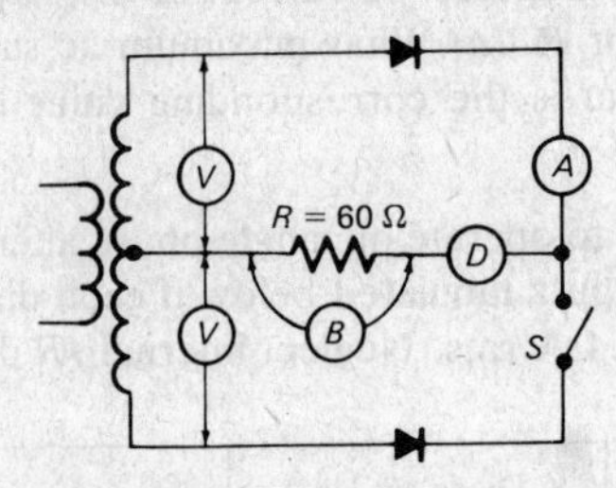

Figure Problem 4-16

4-17 Neglect voltage drop in disks. When switch *T* is open, a current of 1.5 A flows in *R*, as measured by dc ammeter *D*. With *T* open (*a*) find readings of ac ammeter *A*, ac voltmeter *V*, and dc voltmeter *B*, and (*b*) find watts loss in *R*. (*c*) Now close *T* and repeat (*a*) and (*B*) above. (*d*) For each position of *T*, find PRV applied to the lower rectifier.

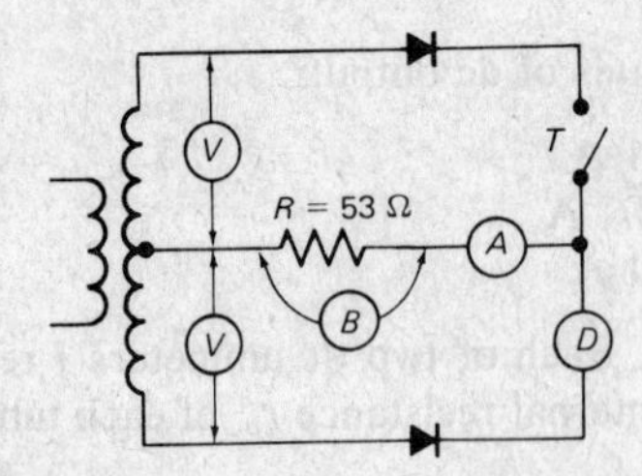

Figure Problem 4-17

5

DIODES AND TRANSISTORS

This chapter describes solid-state diodes and transistors in simple terms and shows how they are used. Chapter 6 shows transistors in amplifier and control circuits. Then Chap. 7 explains how and why transistors work, in terms of electrons, holes, and energy-level diagrams such as are discussed in most texts or manuals.

As described in Sec. 2-6, a transistor consists of two diodes or rectifying junctions combined within a single small unit, which can perform as an amplifier better than can many vacuum tubes. Each diode or transistor requires two kinds of material which are joined together at high temperatures by special manufacturing processes developed in recent years. In fact, the materials as used in transistors do not exist in nature but are produced artificially; the transistor would not exist except for the original discovery of how to produce these special materials.

In all transistors, the necessary materials are made from a group of special metals called *semiconductors*, next described. Since these materials are solid and include no moving parts, these also are called *solid-state* devices. Before discussing the transistor further, we must learn how each diode or junction behaves; then two of these will be joined properly to form the transistor.

5-1 SEMICONDUCTOR RECTIFIERS

Among the various metals there are a few that act in an unusual way when electricity passes through them; at very low temperatures they seem to be insulators, but as they become warmer, a small current may pass through them. Such materials are called semiconductors; they include germanium, silicon, selenium, and certain oxides. [Since the current through them increases at higher temperature, semiconductors have negative temperature coefficients; certain types (silver sulfide, uranium oxide, nickel-manganese

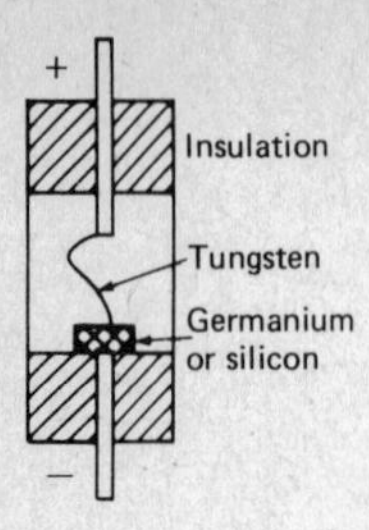

Figure 5-1 Point-contact semiconductor rectifier.

oxide) are made into temperature-sensitive units called thermistors (see Sec. 9-8).]

When a layer of a semiconductor is joined tightly against a layer of certain metals, a blocking action appears at the junction of these layers and is caused by the difference in work function[2-16] of the two different materials; this means that electrons flow more easily out of one of the materials than they can flow out of the other. If alternating potential is applied across this pair of layers, electrons may flow easily from metal to semiconductor, but the blocking action prevents nearly all electron flow in the reverse direction. This one-way action is used in the metallic rectifiers of Sec. 4-6.

Since 1950, larger rectifier units have been made of germanium or silicon; today the silicon diode is available in sizes that can handle up to 1500 amperes. (Although silicon is to be considered in further discussion, germanium can be used just as well, in many cases.) Earlier types of diode use a pointed tungsten wire pressed firmly against a tiny crystal of silicon, as shown at twice actual size in Fig. 5-1; this is called a *point-contact* rectifier. (Early radio crystal sets used similar action.)

Most recent diodes and transistors are made with junctions of large area formed between two different types of silicon. Before the diode is made, the silicon first must be produced in pure form. Then, by carefully adding a very small amount of another metal (considered as a controlled "impurity"), the current-carrying ability of the silicon may be changed greatly. If the added impurity is phosphorus, arsenic, or antimony, the silicon is given an excess of electrons, so that it has N-type conductivity; the main electrical flow through it takes the direction of electrons, negative charges. In contrast, if the added impurity is boron, aluminum, gallium, or indium, the silicon is made to lack electrons, so that it acquires P-type conductivity; the main electrical flow is opposite to that of electrons and is in the direction of positive charges. (These actions are explained in Secs. 7-4 and 7-5.)

Thus the kind of added impurity can make silicon behave like either of two different materials. Moreover, a rectifier unit can be formed in a single piece of silicon if one end is changed into P-type material while its other end is changed into N-type material. In this way, a barrier layer or junction appears between the two kinds of material, as shown in Fig. 5-2; this is called a *junction* rectifier or diode, and it contains a PN junction. Current passes easily

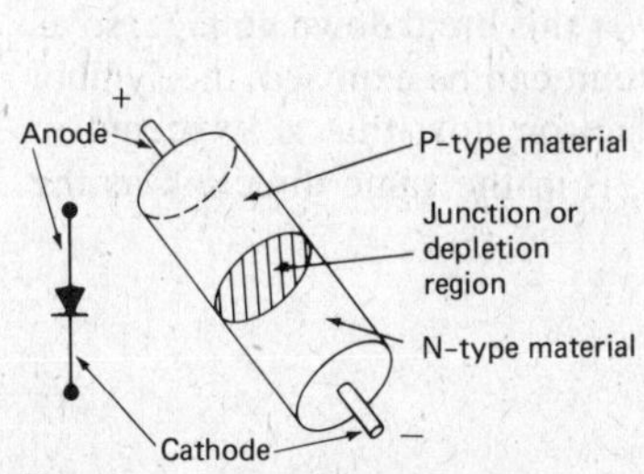

Figure 5-2 PN junction rectifier or diode.

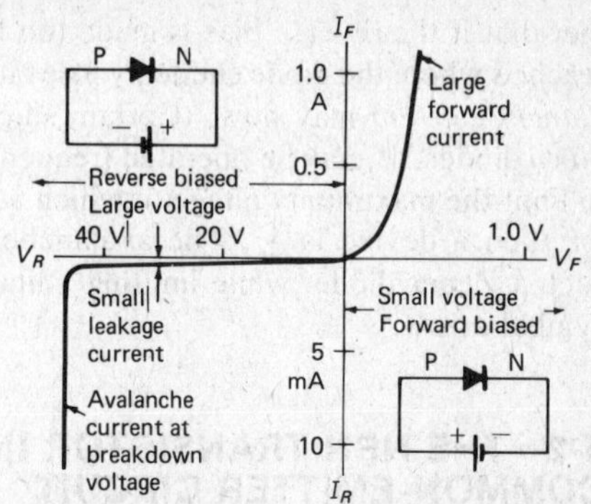

Figure 5-3 Diode current versus applied voltage.

through this diode if the P terminal is made more positive than the N terminal; here the diode is said to be *forward-biased*, as shown at the lower right in Fig. 5-3. Only a fraction of a volt may cause an ampere of forward current to flow. With this forward bias, (*a*) of Fig. 5-4 shows that the (+) battery terminal attracts the electrons of the N-type material so that they flow through the barrier layer.

However, if the applied voltage is reversed, so that the P-type material is made more negative than the N-type material, the diode is *reverse-biased*. Now (*b*) of Fig. 5-4 shows that the (+) battery terminal attracts the electrons of the N-type material away from the junction, while the (−) battery terminal attracts the positive charges of the P-type material away from the junction. Since this removes all charges from the junction or causes depletion of charges, the junction also is called the *depletion region*. This depletion or barrier region prevents all flow except the small *leakage current* shown at the left in Fig. 5-3. Here 20 reverse volts causes a flow of less than 1 milliampere; this reverse or leakage current increases if the diode temperature rises.

The performance curves of Fig. 5-3 (quite like those of Fig. 4-6) show fur-

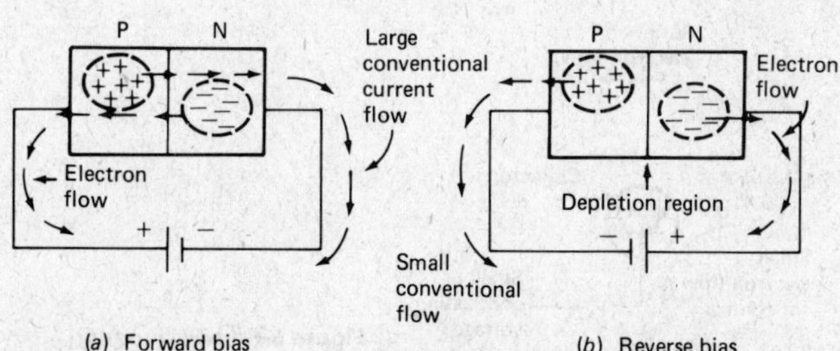

Figure 5-4 Movement of electrons and positive charges.

ther that if the reverse bias is made too large, a *breakdown voltage* may be reached where the diode suddenly loses its blocking ability so that a large *avalanche current* may flow. (Certain silicon diodes, called *Zener* or *breakdown* diodes,[7-18] may be operated frequently at this breakdown voltage, so as to limit the maximum voltage to which a circuit can be exposed; the symbol for such a device is ⊕. The avalanche electron flow that is expected in such a Zener diode, while limiting voltage, is in the same direction as the symbol arrow.)

5-2 THE NPN TRANSISTOR IN COMMON-EMITTER CIRCUIT

Much like the rectifier or diode described above, a piece of silicon or other semiconductor can be made to act as a triode if a third section is included, so as to form two diodes. A *junction transistor* may be produced by carefully adding impurities to a single piece of silicon (as described above) so that a thin central section has characteristics different from those at either end. If, as shown in Fig. 5-5, the end sections are changed into N-type material while the thin center section is made into P-type material, this arrangement is called an *NPN junction transistor*. Connections to the two end sections are called the *emitter* and the *collector;* connection to the center section is called the *base*. Although both may be of N-type material, the emitter and collector are not interchangeable, since the emitter is made with different dimensions and with heavier doping (greater percentage of impurity) than the collector. The actual physical arrangement within the transistor varies, and depends on its method of manufacture and its desired characteristics.

In such a transistor there is a controlled flow of electrons within the metal (into the emitter and out of the collector), depending on a small voltage applied between emitter and base. The resulting action is much like that of an electronic vacuum triode, so that transistors have replaced tubes in most applications. The transistor requires no filament power or heat and is ready instantly for operation when power is applied. Because of its ruggedness, small size, and long life, the transistor is ideal for portable radios and minia-

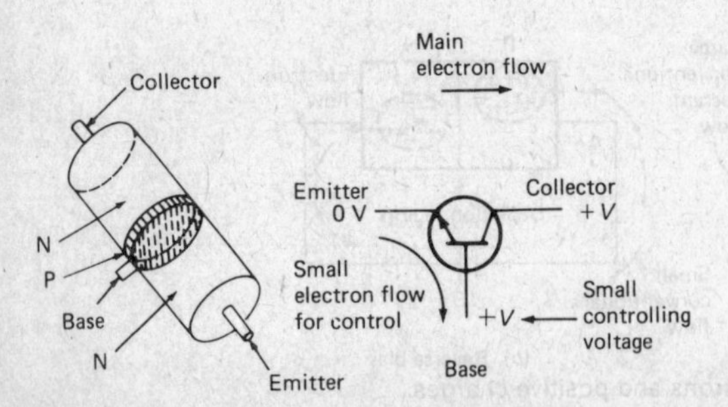

Figure 5-5 NPN junction transistor.

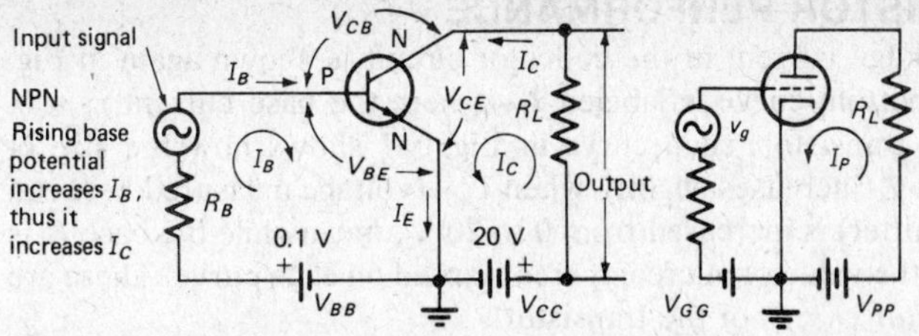

Figure 5-6 Common-emitter NPN circuit compared with common-cathode tube circuit.

turized equipment; it makes more practical the use of thousands of triodes within a single computer. [Each transistor type is given a JEDEC number (such as 2N1304) by the Joint Electron Devices Engineering Council.]

The symbol for the NPN transistor is shown in Fig. 5-5; often the circle is omitted. Here the arrow points in the direction in which conventional current flows in the emitter circuit; electrons flow opposite to the arrow. Connections suitable for this transistor are shown in Fig. 5-6 (similar to Fig. 2-9), for the popular common-emitter circuit or configuration. (This is called the *common-emitter* circuit since the emitter connects to or is common to both the input and the output circuit.) Here also is shown the comparable common-cathode circuit for a vacuum triode. In this comparison, the emitter acts like a cathode, as a source of electrons; the collector serves as an anode or plate, so the base receives the input signal, as does the tube grid. In Fig. 5-6, the transistor output I_C increases when I_B is increased, as occurs when a more positive potential is applied to the P-type base.

It was stated in Sec. 2-6 that a transistor consists of two diodes. One diode is the junction between base and emitter, which usually is forward-biased; the other diode is the junction between base and collector, which must be reverse-biased. In Fig. 5-6 the emitter is forward-biased (with respect to the base), since battery V_{BB} makes the N-type emitter more negative than the base (which is the same as making the P-type base more positive than the emitter). This small voltage V_{BB} has correct polarity to force a tiny current [I_B of perhaps 0.06 milliampere (mA)] in the forward or low-resistance direction through the base-to-emitter junction.

If no base current I_B is permitted to flow, then very little current I_C can flow in the collector circuit. The collector in Fig. 5-6 is reverse-biased, since the positive side of battery V_{CC} makes the N-type collector perhaps 20 volts (V) more positive than the connection at the base. Because of the reverse bias on this diode, only the tiny leakage current can flow, as shown by the curve in Fig. 5-3; this is also the collector current I_C, whose electrons flow in this diode in the reverse direction, or from P-type base to the N-type collector. Since I_B is zero, these electrons come into the base region from the emitter.

5-3 TRANSISTOR PERFORMANCE

The small leakage current in the collector circuit is shown again in Fig. 5-7, where the bottom curve is labeled I_{CEO}; here the base current $I_B = 0$. For this certain transistor, each curve in Fig. 5-7 shows how the size of collector current I_C increases slightly when V_{CE} (voltage measured between collector and emitter) is increased from 0 to 20 V; meanwhile the base I_B is held constant at the value of microamperes marked on each curve. These are called the *collector curves* of the transistor.

If base current I_B is increased from zero to 0.1 mA (as is shown by the higher curve marked $I_B = 100\ \mu A$), this may increase the collector current to more than 4 mA, as marked at *A* in Fig. 5-7. Since a small change in I_B causes about 40 times as much change in I_C, the current amplification or current gain in this circuit is said to be 40 and corresponds to β, or the beta of the transistor. (With present use of *h* parameters, as discussed in Sec. 7-13, this β also is the transistor value or parameter called h_{fe}.) The way by which the small I_B can control the larger I_C is discussed in Sec. 7-11.

When two variable quantities like I_C and V_{CE} are plotted as in Fig. 5-7, the third quantity, I_B, is called a *parameter*; the values marked on its lines are selected in certain increments (or jumps of 50 μA between curves in Fig. 5-7). Transistor performance may be stated in terms of ratios or parameters such as α or β.

This larger I_C consists of a greater quantity of electrons that flow from the N-type emitter into the base and then continue into the collector by flowing in the reverse direction through the PN base-to-collector junction. These electrons flow upward through the transistor in Fig. 5-6, attracted toward the +20 V of V_{CC}; they give the effect of a conventional current that flows downward from collector to base and out of the emitter, in the direction shown by the arrow in the emitter of the transistor symbol. The tiny conventional base current I_B also flows out of the emitter, so that $I_E = I_B + I_C$.

The transistor works at lower voltages than are used with most tubes. The transistor in the common-emitter circuit of Fig. 5-6 may be described by collector current I_C, collector-to-emitter voltage V_{CE}, and base signal current I_B in the same manner as vacuum-tube operation is described in terms of plate current, plate-to-cathode voltage, and grid-to-cathode signal voltage. In contrast to a tube, whose output is controlled by a change of grid *voltage*,

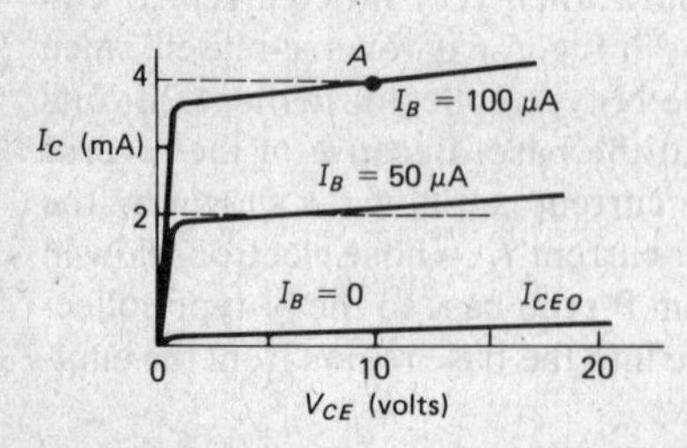

Figure 5-7 Collector curves for NPN common-emitter operation.

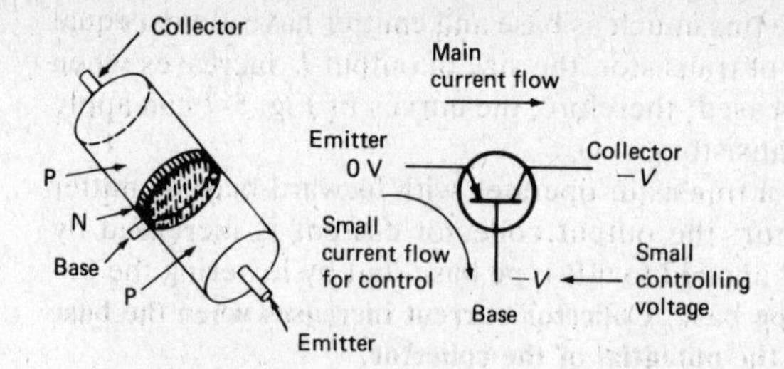

Figure 5-8 PNP junction transistor.

the output of this transistor is controlled by a change of base *current*. Whereas the input or grid circuit of a tube has high impedance and requires negligible current, the transistor input circuit has low impedance and may require considerable current.

5-4 THE PNP TRANSISTOR

In contrast to the NPN transistor described in Sec. 5-2, a PNP transistor is produced when both end sections (emitter and collector) of a piece of pure silicon are changed into P-type material while the thin center base section is made into N-type material, as shown in Fig. 5-8. Here the symbol shows, in the emitter, an arrow that points toward the base. Whereas the NPN transistor has an emitter made of N-type material which emits electrons into the base, the emitter of the PNP unit is made of P-type material which appears to emit positive charges (also called holes[7-2]); since these positive charges flow in the same direction as does conventional current, the main current of the PNP transistor flows from outside the transistor into the emitter, upward through the base region, then out of the collector, as shown in the circuit of Fig. 5-9; the size of this main I_C is controlled by a much smaller amount of conventional current I_B flowing out of the base. Therefore, the PNP transistor is turned on (so that its output I_C is increased) when the potential at its base is lowered so that greater current I_B can flow out of the base.

In the common-emitter circuit of Fig. 5-9, the polarities of batteries V_{BB} and V_{CC} are reversed, as compared with those in Fig. 5-6. Therefore, V_{BB} in Fig. 5-9 applies forward bias between base and emitter, since the positive battery terminal is connected to the P-type emitter; V_{CC} applies reverse bias

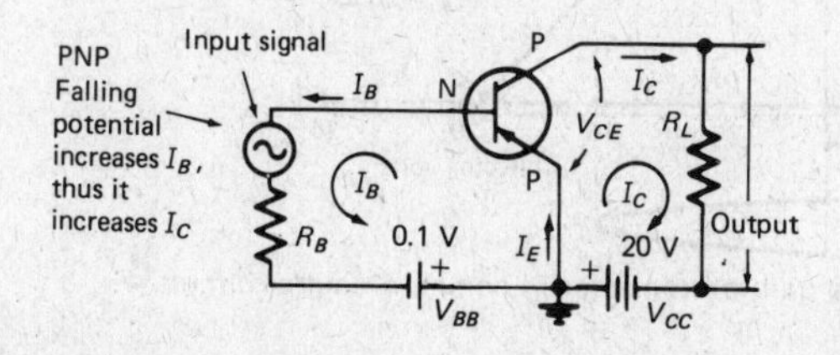

Figure 5-9 Common-emitter PNP circuit.

between collector and base (inasmuch as base and emitter have almost equal potential). For either type of transistor, the size of output I_C increases when the size of signal I_B is increased; therefore, the curves of Fig. 5-7 can apply to either NPN or PNP transistors.

As a general statement, a transistor operates with forward-biased emitter and reverse-biased collector; the output collector current is increased by raising the signal potential applied to a P-type base, but by lowering the potential applied to an N-type base. **Collector current increases when the base potential is moved toward the potential of the collector.**

5-5 THE DC LOAD LINE; THE OPERATING POINT Q

Whereas the curves in Fig. 5-7 show how a certain transistor acts by itself, a load line can be added to show how the external load resistance affects the amount of transistor current in a circuit such as Fig. 5-6 or 5-9. The load line is a plot of the collector-to-emitter voltage V_{CE} of the transistor as the amount of its collector current I_C is varied; a certain amount of load resistance must be specified. An example of such a load line is added to the transistor curves in Fig. 5-10, using a supply voltage $V_{CC} = 20$ volts (V) and a load resistance $R_L = 4$ kilohms (k Ω). The bottom of the load line, on the x axis of Fig. 5-10, must occur at the value of V_{CE} when $I_C = 0$. With no flow of collector current, the voltage across R_L also is 0, so V_{CE} = supply voltage

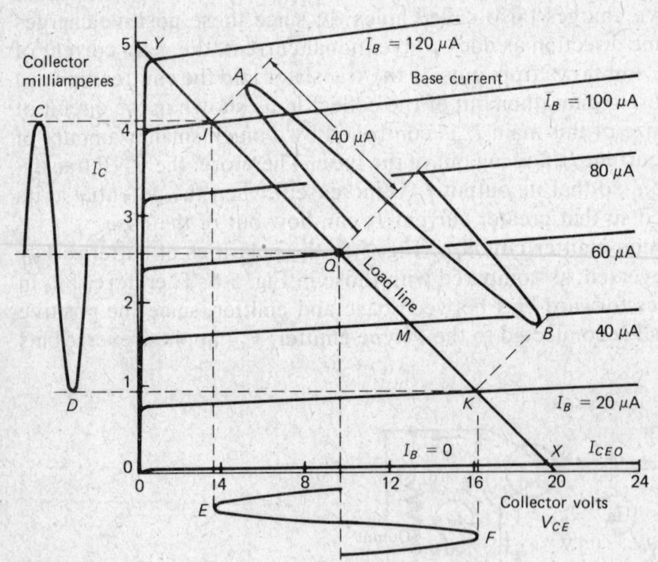

Figure 5-10 Use of load line to find gain of transistor in common-emitter circuit.

$V_{CC} = 20$ V. Furthermore, the load line crosses the y axis when $V_{CE} = 0$, so that the entire supply voltage is consumed in forcing collector current to flow through R_L; therefore, $I_C = 20\ \text{V} / 4000\ \Omega = 0.005$ A, or 5 mA (at point Y in Fig. 5-10). Since R_L is a constant resistance, the values of I_C lie on a straight line. Draw this load line from X to Y, and find where it crosses the sloping lines of base current I_B. For the load resistance of 4 kΩ, this added line shows that when $I_B = 100\ \mu\text{A}$, $I_C = 4.1$ mA (at J); when $I_B = 40\ \mu\text{A}$, $I_C = 1.7$ mA at M.

To obtain low distortion when used as an amplifier (as is discussed in Sec. 6-2), the operating or quiescent point Q may be selected near the middle of the load line; this Q point lies at that spot on the load line where it intersects the I_B line marked for the desired amount of steady current that flows in the transistor base during "quiet" conditions when no signal is applied. To make the transistor operate at Q shown in Fig. 5-10, R_B in Fig. 5-9 is adjusted so that base current $I_B = 60\ \mu\text{A}$, or 0.06 mA. If $V_{BB} = 0.1$ V, then $R_B = 0.1\ \text{V} / 0.06\ \text{mA} = 1.67\ \text{k}\Omega$ (since the emitter-to-base voltage is assumed to be negligible, for this example). As a result of I_B, a steady current I_C of 2.5 mA flows in the collector, and about 10 V dc (V_{CE}) exists between collector and emitter.

5-6 USE OF THE LOAD LINE TO FIND GAIN

Having adjusted the transistor circuit to the Q point selected above, suppose that an ac input signal (whose maximum or peak value is 40 μA) is applied to the base, as shown between A and B in Fig. 5-10. Now the total base current varies between peak values of 100 μA at J and 20 μA at K. The resulting collector current varies from 4.1 mA at C to 0.9 mA at D, which is a change of 3.2 mA. Since a change in I_B of only 80 μA (0.08 mA) causes a change in I_C of 3.2 mA, the current amplification or gain in this complete circuit is $3.2 / 0.08 = 40$. Similarly, the collector-to-emitter or output voltage V_{CE} changes from 3.5 V at E to 16 V at F. The input voltage, which is the voltage needed to force I_B through R_B, varies from a minimum of $20\ \mu\text{A} \times 1.67\ \text{k}\Omega = 0.033$ V up to $100\ \mu\text{A} \times 1.67\ \text{k}\Omega = 0.167$ V. This change of 0.134 V at the input causes a change of 12.5 V at the output; so the voltage amplification or gain in this transistor circuit is $12.5 / 0.134 = 93.3$. Power gain or amplification $= 40 \times 93.3 = 3730$.

5-7 SWITCHING ACTION BY A TRANSISTOR

In the circuit action described above, the variation or swing of base current I_B is kept small enough so that the transistor operates between J and K on the load line in Fig. 5-10; this provides linear or class A operation, fairly free of distortion.[6-2] However, many recent computer circuits use a transistor mainly as an on-off device, so that it acts like a circuit contact that is either closed or open. If base current I_B is increased above 120 μA, Fig. 5-10 shows that the transistor operates near point Y, where the collector current I_C is nearly 5 mA; here the voltage V_{CE} across the transistor is only a fraction of a volt, so small that the transistor seems to act like a closed contact. Any further increase of I_B above 120 μA cannot raise I_C above 5 mA, nor can it decrease V_{CE} further. This condition is called *saturation*; a large signal I_B thus is used to drive the transistor into saturation, where it acts like a short circuit or a contact that is closed, joining the collector and emitter circuits. We say that the transistor is ON.

In contrast, if all base current is removed, this transistor operates at point X in Fig. 5-10. The tiny collector current I_{CEO} usually is so near to zero that the transistor now acts like a nearly open circuit; the transistor is OFF.

A small reverse bias, which drives the P-type base about 0.2 V more negative than the emitter, may be used to reduce further the collector current to obtain *cutoff*. As a completely open circuit, V_{CE} now equals battery V_{CC}.

5-8 HEAT DISSIPATION

A transistor is so small and its material is so sensitive to temperature that it is very important to operate the transistor within its rating, which often is stated in milliwatts, when operating in 25°C air or ambient temperature. [To make sure that a transistor (or solid-state diode) can dissipate or get rid of the heat produced within it, the transistor often is made with such shape that it can be mounted solidly onto a plate of metal, to which the heat of the transistor is conducted directly. This metal plate acts as a "heat sink" to drain away the heat and lower the transistor temperature. The minimum size of required heat sink often is specified as a part of the transistor rating.] The power input to the transistor closely equals the product of I_C and V_{CE}; this product must not exceed the rated power dissipation. When no input signal exists, no power comes out of the transistor (except by a dc flow that heats the collector resistor). Thus most of the power input is changed into internal heat which must be removed or dissipated.

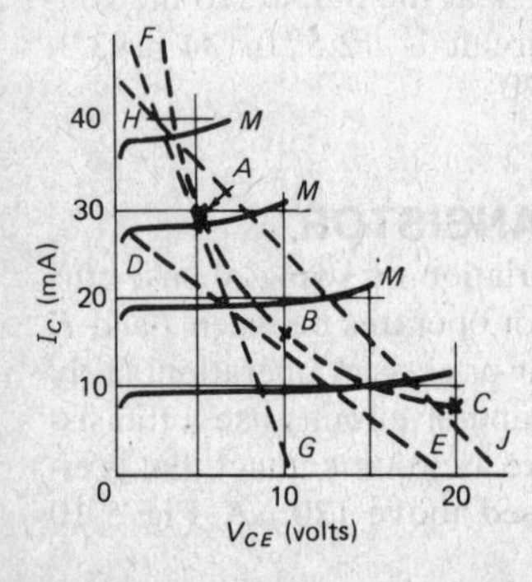

Figure 5-11 Selection of load line within power-dissipation limit.

For the transistor whose collector curves appear in Fig. 5-11, the rated power dissipation is 150 milliwatts (mW). When $V_{CE} = 5$ volts (V), I_C must not exceed 150 mW / 5 V = 30 mA, as shown at *A*. When $V_{CE} = 10$ V, I_C can be 150 mW / 10 V = 15 mA, at $B_{CE.}$ At $V_{CE} = 20$ V, I_c can be 150 mW / 20 V = 7.5 mA, at *C*. Drawn through such points, the curve *ABC* shows the limits of safe operation, and is called the *power-dissipation line*. Load lines such as *DE* or *FG* may be used. Switching circuits may use a higher line such as *HJ* since the portion of the load line above *ABC* is used only during quick passage from one end to the other.

Figure 5-11 shows, at *M*, how the collector current tends to increase as the transistor becomes overheated, causing the increase in I_{CEO} mentioned in Sec. 6-4.

5-9 COMMON-BASE CIRCUIT

Preceding circuits show the transistor as used in the common-emitter configuration. The same transistor may be used in the common-base circuit shown in Fig. 5-12; here the input is applied between emitter and base while the output is obtained between collector and base. For this NPN transistor, battery V_{EE} furnishes forward bias to the N emitter, while V_{CC} supplies reverse bias to the N collector. (A vacuum triode also is shown in Fig. 5-12, as connected in a similar common-grid circuit; this tube circuit rarely is used.)

Figure 5-13 shows the collector curves for a transistor used in the common-base circuit; but R_L is short-circuited while these performance curves are obtained. After R_E is adjusted so that emitter current I_E remains at 1mA, Fig. 5-13 shows that the collector current is nearly constant from *A* to *B*, although V_{CB} is varied between 0 and 20 V by changing V_{CC}. If R_E is decreased so that I_E becomes steady at 5 mA, the curve *CD* shows that I_C has reached a higher level but is slightly less than 5 mA. Both I_C and I_B flow in this transistor and combine to form I_E; thus the output or change in I_C always is smaller than the input or change in I_E, so that the current amplification is less than 1. This common-base circuit is not used in two-stage amplifiers.

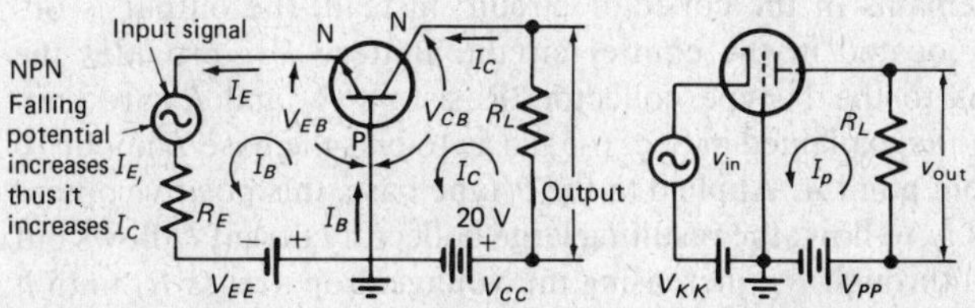

Figure 5-12 Common-base NPN circuit compared with common-grid tube circuit.

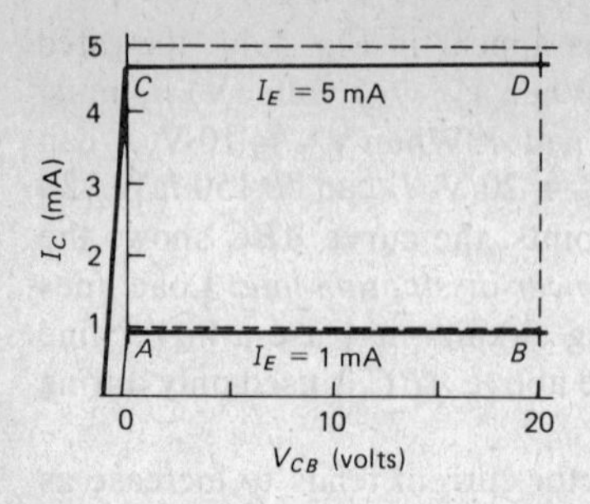

Figure 5-13 Collector curves in common-base circuit.

A transistor often is described or selected by its value of α. This alpha or forward current ratio is obtained by measuring the change of I_C that is caused by a change of I_E; meanwhile, the value of V_{CB} is held constant. If points B and D are used (having a constant value of $V_{CB} = 20$ V), Fig. 5-13 shows that I_C changes from 4.7 to 0.9 mA when I_E is changed from 5 to 1 mA. Thus

$$\alpha = \frac{\text{change in } I_C}{\text{change in } I_E} = \frac{3.8 \text{ mA}}{4.0 \text{ mA}} = 0.95$$

[Section 7-10 shows that α is used as a (−) quantity.]

We may select a transistor that has a higher value of α, such as 0.98, since this can be used to provide larger voltage amplification and power gain, even without amplification of current. [When this same transistor is used in the common-emitter circuit of Fig. 5-6, it provides higher current gain, inasmuch as β (the common-emitter beta of Sec. 5-3) is equal to $\alpha / (1 - \alpha) = 0.98 / 0.02 = 49$.]

Although this common-base circuit provides high voltage gain, its current gain always is less than 1, and therefore only medium power gain can be obtained.

5-10 COMMON-COLLECTOR OR EMITTER-FOLLOWER CIRCUIT

This third basic transistor circuit is shown in Fig. 5-14, together with the vacuum-tube cathode-follower circuit that is similar in action and use. No load resistance remains in the collector circuit; instead, the output is obtained across R_L located in the emitter circuit. Battery V_{CC} provides the usual reverse bias to the N-type collector. Resistors R_2 and R_3 are connected across V_{CC} (as explained in Sec. 6-5) so as to bias the base B about 10 V above the bottom point A. Applied to the P-type base, this positive potential causes a small I_B to flow; the resulting large collector current I_C flows out of the emitter and through R_L, increasing the voltage drop across R_L until it nearly equals the voltage V_B across R_2. As the top of R_L approaches the

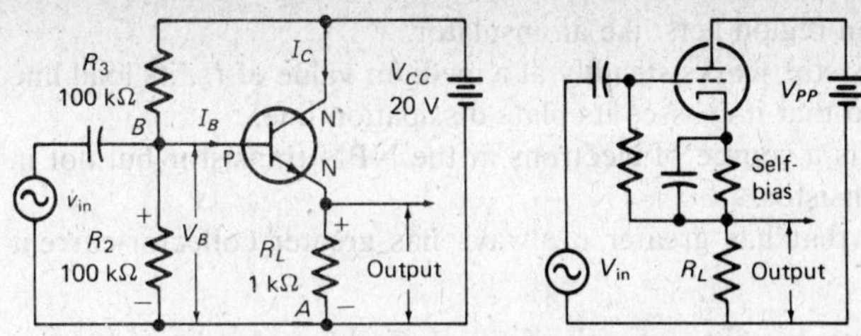

Figure 5-14 Common-collector NPN circuit compared with tube cathode follower.

same potential as base B, the forward bias on the emitter is decreased so that the emitter current remains just large enough to keep $(I_E + I_C) \times R_L = V_B$.

If the ac input signal v_{in} raises base B and V_B by 8 V, a slight increase in I_B causes I_E to increase by about 8 mA so that the voltage across R_L also is increased by 8 V. (Since the emitter potential rises or follows the change in input, this also is called an emitter-follower circuit.) Thus the change in output voltage is seen to equal exactly the change in input signal voltage; the voltage amplification of this circuit = 1.0, and the power gain is quite small. However, this common-collector circuit is useful for controlling a low-impedance output circuit by means of a high-impedance input circuit; thus it serves as a device for impedance matching.[6-15]

5-11 TRANSISTOR CURVES

For use in certain problems that follow, Fig. 5-15 shows output or collector characteristics for a type 2N1308 NPN transistor when used in a common-emitter circuit (the load line and points S, T, U, V are used in Sec. 6-1). Curves for a 2N1413 PNP transistor appear in Fig. 5-16.

Problems

5-1 True or false? Explain why.

(a) The arrow within the transistor symbol points in the same direction as conventional current flows.

(b) The symbol arrow reverses if one reverses the voltage between collector and base.

(c) One can make a transistor by pressing together pieces of P- and N-type material.

(d) In a working transistor, I_C usually is much larger than I_B.

(e) In a given transistor, the value of α usually is greater than β.

(f) A higher value of α means that I_C becomes larger as compared with I_B.

(g) If load current I_C enters a transistor, I_B also enters it.

(h) The depletion region acts like an insulator.

(i) When a transistor works steadily at a medium value of I_C, its load line is selected so that it crosses its plate-dissipation line.

(j) The emitter is a source of electrons in the NPN transistor but not in the PNP transistor.

(k) A transistor that has greater α always has greater collector-current rating.

5-2 Use the common-emitter circuit of Fig. 5-6 with a transistor that has the characteristics shown in Fig. 5-10. Let $V_{CC} = 24$ V, $V_{BB} = 0.2$ V, $R_L = 8$ kΩ. The Q point lies at $V_{CE} = 7.2$ V. Find (*a*) I_C, (*b*) I_B, and (*c*) R_B.

5-3 Again use Figs. 5-6 and 5-10, letting the collector battery be 20 V and the load resistance be 5 kΩ. At the quiescent point, the base current is 40 μA. Find (*a*) V_{CE} and (*b*) I_C. If the signal at the base is 40 μA p-p, find (*c*) the maximum and minimum values of collector voltage and current.

5-4 Repeat Prob. 5-3 for common-base operation, using Figs. 5-12 and 7-14. At Q, the emitter current is −2 mA. Find (*a*) V_{CB} and (*b*) I_C. In (*c*) use an input signal of 3 mA p-p.

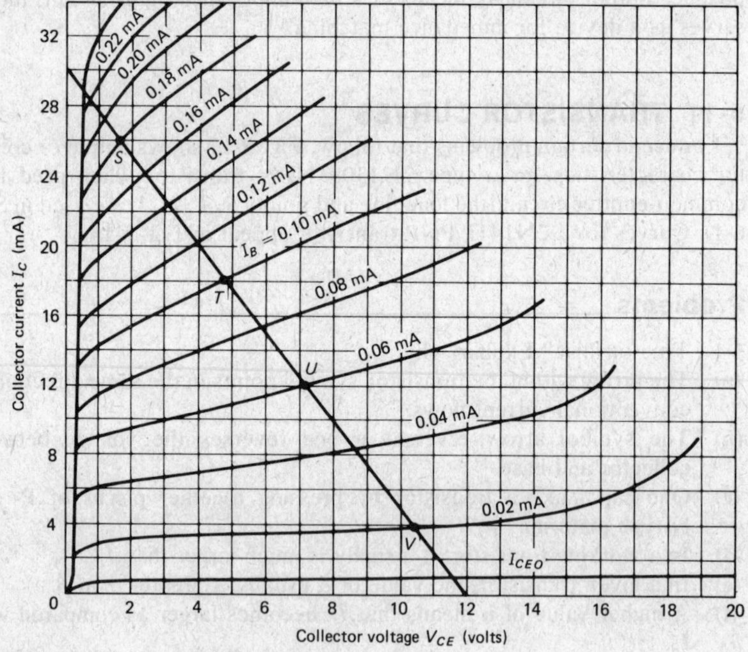

Figure 5-15 Type 2N1308 NPN transistor.

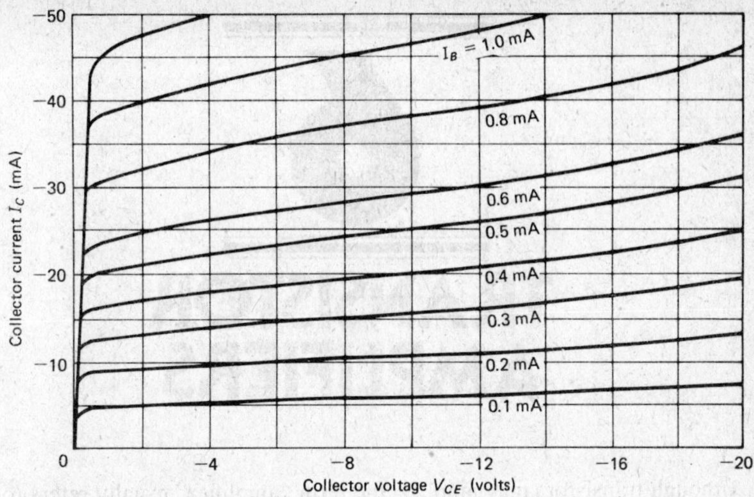

Figure 5-16 Type 2N1413 PNP transistor.

5-5 If the transistor of Fig. 5-15 is rated at 150 milliwatts (mW) dissipation in free air, plot its power-dissipation line. At this rating, find the lowest permissible resistance of R_L when V_{CC} is (*a*) 10 V, (*b*) 15 V, and (*c*) 20 V. (*d*) Determine what effect the characteristic curves have upon these results.

5-6 Repeat Prob. 5-5 for the transistor of Fig. 5-16 if rated at 200-mW dissipation.

5-7 A transistor having the characteristics shown in Fig. 5-15 is used in Fig. 5-6, letting $R_L = 0.6$ kΩ, $V_{CC} = 12$ V, $R_B = 1.5$ kΩ, $V_{BB} = 0.12$ V. The input signal is 0.18 V p-p. At Q, find (*a*) I_B, (*b*) I_C, and (*c*) V_{CE}. Find (*d*) current gain, (*e*) voltage gain, and (*f*) power gain.

5-8 Repeat Prob. 5-7 if V_{CC} is 18 V and R_B is 1.0 kΩ.

6

TRANSISTOR AMPLIFIERS

Although transistors may amplify, the term "amplifier" usually refers to the complete circuit in which the transistor serves or to the conditions under which it operates. The same transistor may be used in many different kinds of amplifiers, or it may be used as an oscillator, as described in Chap. 24.

No amplifier produces greater power or energy; it merely controls some outside source of energy so that this source supplies greater power in response to the small base or input signal. The transistor in Fig. 6-1 controls the power supplied from the 12-volt battery V_{CC}.

6-1 ONE TRANSISTOR AS AN AMPLIFIER

A single transistor appears in Fig. 5-6 (and earlier in Fig. 2-9), used in the popular common-emitter circuit. Section 5-6 explains how, by the use of a load line added in Fig. 5-10, this certain transistor acts as an amplifier to produce a current gain of 40 and a voltage gain of 93.3. Also, since the sine-wave input signal (varying between A and B in Fig. 5-10) causes collector current I_C to flow during the entire cycle, this is a class A amplifier (or here the transistor has class A operation, as will be explained in Sec. 6-2). The output wave of I_C collector current (C to D) has the same shape as the I_B input wave; so this amplifier causes little distortion (except that it inverts the wave). Another example may help.

Figure 6-1 shows again the common-emitter circuit; but let the NPN transistor have the collector characteristic curves shown in Fig. 5-15. On those curves draw the load line for the circuit of Fig. 6-1; starting from $V_{CE} = V_{CC} = 12$ volts (V) when $I_C = 0$, the line crosses the vertical axis when V_{CE} is zero and all of V_{CC} is used in forcing I_C through R_L; thus $I_C = 12\ \text{V} / 400\ \Omega = 0.03\ \text{A} = 30\ \text{mA}$. At points where this load line crosses the slanting lines of I_B base current, the resulting collector current can be read.

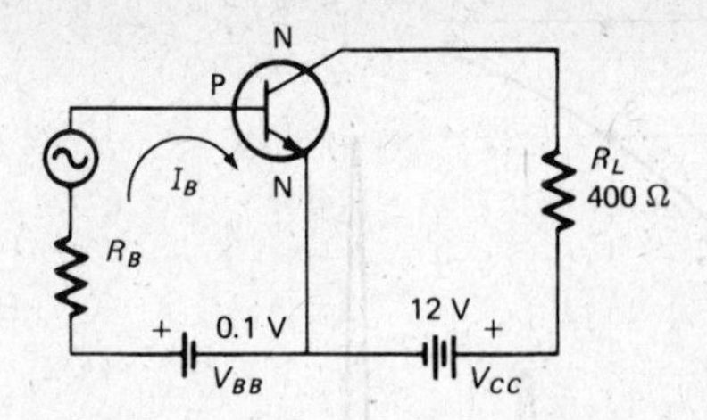

Figure 6-1 Amplifier with one transistor.

At the point marked S in Fig. 5-15, an I_B of 0.18 milliampere (mA) causes an I_C of 26 mA; at point V, an I_B of 0.02 mA causes an I_C of 4 mA. Thus a *change* in signal I_B from 0.18 to 0.02 mA (a difference of 0.16 mA) causes a *change* in output from 26 to 4 mA (which is 22 mA). The current amplification or gain of this circuit is equal to 22 mA / 0.16 mA = 137.5.

Other factors must be considered, such as distortion. As a graphical aid to reveal distortion, a dynamic collector curve may be plotted, as in Fig. 6-2. Here the same vertical values of collector current I_C are plotted against horizontal values of signal or base current I_B. Points S, T, U, and V in Fig. 5-15 are relocated in Fig. 6-2; the resulting curve has considerable bend. We now may apply the input signal (or change in I_B) to the horizontal scale, and read the resulting output waveshape on the vertical scale. (The change in signal I_B has nearly the same waveshape as the change in V_{BE} that causes it.)

First an operating or Q point is chosen. For example, if point U is to be the operating point, a bias current $I_B = 0.06$ mA must flow when there is no input signal; so R_B in Fig. 6-1 is adjusted to 1667 ohms (Ω), so that 0.1 V / 1667 Ω = 0.00006 A = 0.06 mA = I_B. If a small current signal is applied so that I_B varies 0.02 mA above and 0.02 mA below the 0.06-mA steady value, the resulting wave of I_C appears between E and F, reflected off the dynamic collector curve. Here I_C varies between values of 8.5 and 15.5 mA, caused by a change of I_B from 0.04 to 0.08 mA. Current gain is 7 mA / 0.04 mA = 175. Moreover, there is little distortion.

Now a larger signal may be tried in Fig. 6-2, varying between 0.18 and 0.02 mA, as was used three paragraphs earlier. (Note that the operating point now is changed to point T with a bias current of 0.10 mA, so that the signal does not swing down below V.) A larger change in collector current appears (G to H), reflected from the dynamic collector curve between V and S; the half wave above axis T is smaller than the half wave below T, showing distortion.

This example shows why circ ts are designed using small signals that can decrease distortion, by letting e transistor operate over only a small portion of its collector curve. The Q point is chosen in a part of the load line where the intersecting I_B lines are more equally spaced and are more nearly parallel.

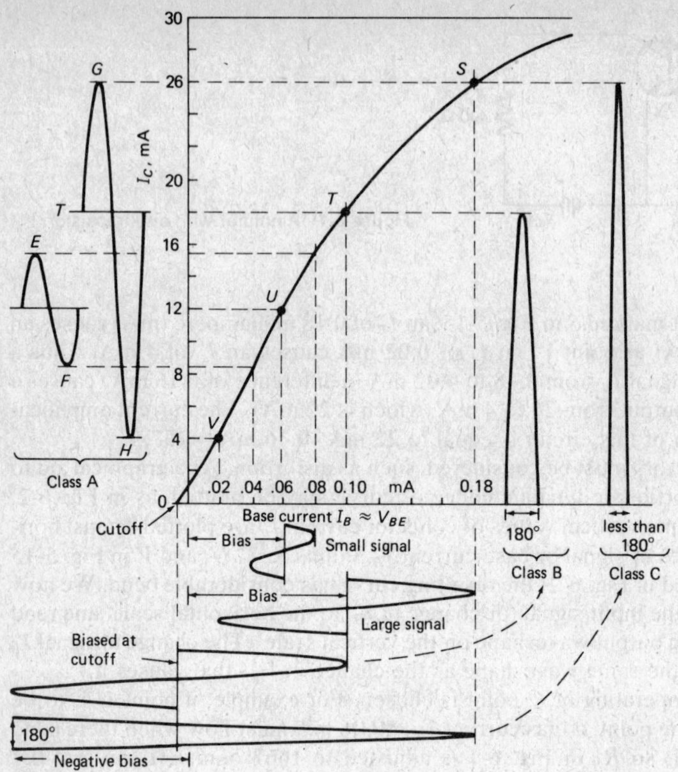

Figure 6-2 Bias current determines class A, B, or C operation (by use of dynamic transfer curve).

6-2 CLASS A, B, OR C OPERATION

In each example above, the current signal in the base of the transistor lets current flow in the collector during all parts of the signal cycle. This is class A operation, as is indicated at the upper left in Fig. 6-2. A bias current is chosen so that the transistor operates always in the active (or transition) region between saturation and cutoff.

If the V_{BB} battery and R_B resistor are short-circuited from the base circuit in Fig. 6-1, no base current flows until the input signal is applied; as a result, only the tiny leakage current I_{CEO} flows in the collector. (A small reverse bias may be applied to reduce the collector current to zero;[5-7] thus the transistor is "biased at cutoff.") Since an applied input signal may swing equally above and below the cutoff value, collector current flows for only half of each cycle (or 180°); this is class B operation. Having only a half-time collector current, the transistor now has greater current rating than in class A operation. Transistors may operate class B when connected in push-pull in Sec. 6-3. (Class

AB allows class A operation with small signals, but class B operation with large signals.)

Often the same transistor may be used in class A, class B, or class C operation; the transistor does not change; only its method of use changes, depending on its bias current.

For class C the transistor is biased below cutoff; here a voltage is used to oppose the input signal so that base current flows during only the central portion of its upper half wave. Class C often is more efficient, but it causes greater distortion.

6-3 TWO TRANSISTORS; PUSH-PULL OPERATION

Several transistors may operate in parallel as shown in Fig. 6-3; each receives the same signal at its base. Resistors R_E (less than 0.5 Ω) help the R_L current to divide more equally between the two collectors. Bias current flows through each R_B to the base, as explained in Sec. 6-4.

Two transistors may be connected in push-pull, as shown in Fig. 6-4. In Fig. 6-4*a* the alternating input signal passes through transformer T_1 to drive the Q_A base more positive at the same time that it drives the Q_B base more negative; the duplicate transistors conduct in turn. As T_1 raises the Q_A base to let base current flow, load electrons flow from the dc supply terminal 1, emitter to collector of Q_A, down through the upper half of the output transformer T_2 to terminal 2; this is the "push" in T_2. When the T_1 signal reverses so as to permit current in the Q_B base instead, load electrons flow from 1 through Q_B and up through the lower half of T_2; this is the "pull," for it reverses the current flow in the T_2 output.

In push-pull operation, Q_A or Q_B may pass collector current during only half of the cycle, yet the combined output (through T_2) may have nearly the same waveshape as the input signal in T_1. Operating class B, two transistors cause nearly as little distortion as a single transistor operating class A. No bias battery is used in Fig. 6-4 and no bias current flows. A small positive bias may be added to decrease crossover distortion at low currents.

In Fig. 6-4*b*, a PNP transistor Q_D has replaced one NPN transistor, Q_B, to

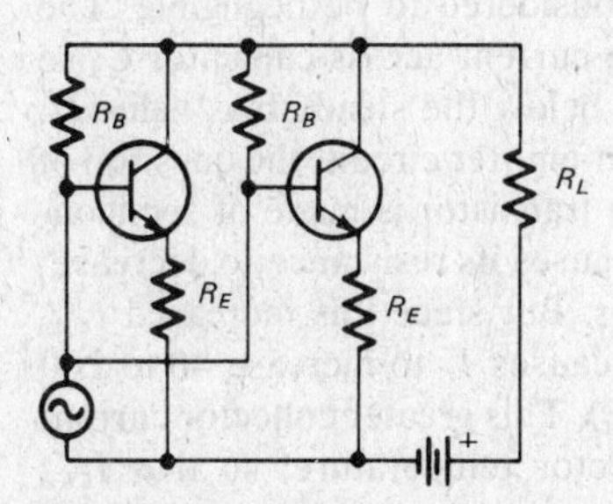

Figure 6-3 Transistors operating in parallel.

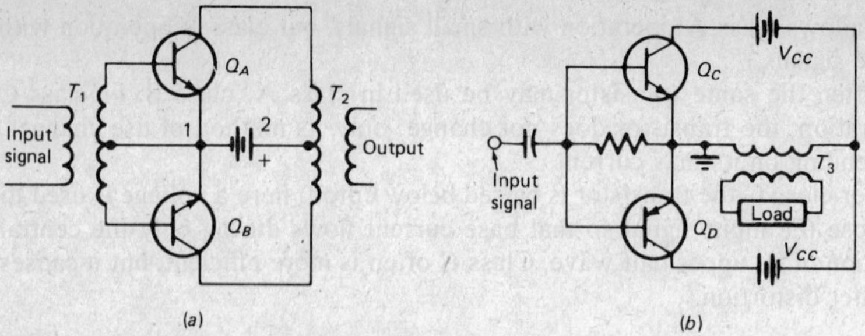

Figure 6-4 Transistors operating in push-pull.

form a *complementary* push-pull circuit; the center-tap transformers T_1 and T_2 are removed, but two separate V_{cc} power supplies are needed. The one input signal is applied to both transistor bases; becoming more positive, it turns on the NPN Q_C as it turns off the PNP Q_D. Thus the upper battery supplies electrons that flow clockwise in the loop through the output transformer T_3 and Q_C. As the input signal becomes negative at both transistor bases, Q_D conducts and lets the lower battery supply electrons clockwise through Q_D and T_3; this reverses the flow in T_3. The load receives alternating output; T_3 also may serve as an impedance-matching transformer, as described in Sec. 6-15.

Since Q_C conducts during one half cycle (class B) and Q_D conducts during the other half cycle, the combined output waveshape from T_3 closely matches the input signal, with little distortion.

6-4 BIAS WITHOUT V_{BB}; STABILITY

In Fig. 6-1 (and earlier, in Figs. 5-6 and 5-9) a battery V_{BB} causes a constant value of I_B to flow, adjusted by R_B so as to bias the transistor at the desired operating point. It is common practice to omit V_{BB} and obtain the bias current directly from the collector battery V_{CC}, as shown in Fig. 6-5. To cause 0.06 mA, the same value of bias current as is used in Sec. 5-5, resistor R_B now must be 20 V / 0.06 mA = 333 kΩ. Here the emitter-to-base resistance (within the transistor) and V_{EB} are considered to be negligible. The varying input signal v_{in} forces an alternating current across capacitor C_1 so that the total base current varies above and below the steady bias value I_B.

For the transistor operated in this common-emitter circuit, the question of stability now must be considered. Since the transistor is made of semiconductor material, any rise in its temperature causes its resistance to decrease; therefore, the I_{CEO} leakage current increases. But since this increased I_{CEO} flows also in the base, the transistor action causes I_C to increase 40 to 200 times as much (depending on the value of $\beta^{5\text{-}3}$). This greater collector current produces heat that raises further the collector temperature, so that I_{CEO}

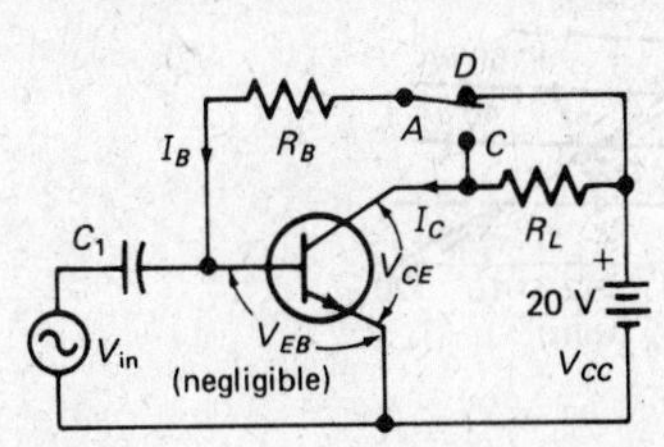

Figure 6-5 Bias obtained from V_{CC}.

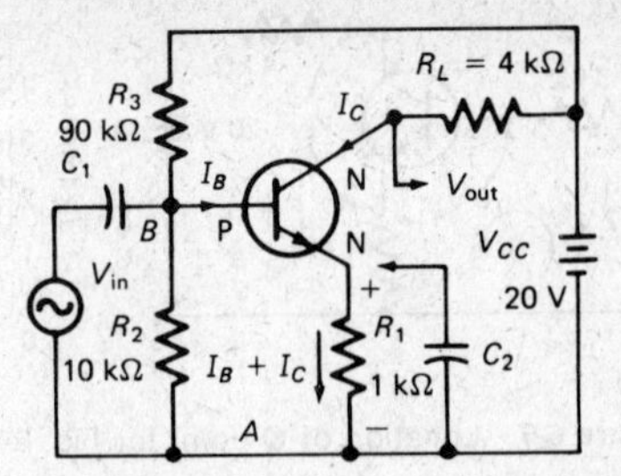

Figure 6-6 Self-bias in common-emitter circuit. Bias by voltage divider.

increases further. This unstable action produces "thermal runaway" that can damage the transistor; such action is to be expected in the simple circuit of Fig. 6-5, so long as the R_B terminal A is connected to D as shown.

To help to stabilize this circuit, A may be connected instead to collector C in Fig. 6-5. Now, when I_C increases, the resulting additional voltage drop across R_L lowers the potential at C and thereby decreases the base current I_B. Since this decreased I_B tends to limit the rise in I_C, the possibility of runaway or instability is decreased by this collector-to-base bias.

6-5 TRANSISTOR SELF-BIAS

To make the common-emitter circuit less sensitive to load and temperature variations, self-bias often is used as shown in Fig. 6-6. Here resistor R_1 is added in the emitter circuit; both I_B and I_C flow in R_1, but I_B is very small compared with I_C. These conventional currents flow downward so that the top of R_1 is made more positive; this positive potential at the N-type emitter forms a reverse bias that turns off the transistor. Therefore, resistors R_2 and R_3 are added; since these are connected in series across V_{CC}, they act as a voltage divider so that the drop across R_2 is one-tenth of V_{CC}. In this way base B is held 2 volts (V) above bottom terminal A, so that when I_C is small and causes little drop across R_1, the emitter is more negative than B and thus has the necessary forward bias. Now, if I_C increases because of rising temperature, a larger voltage drop appears across R_1; this opposes or decreases the amount of forward bias so that I_B is decreased. In turn, I_C is decreased so as to offset its rise caused by higher temperature.

This self-bias across R_1 decreases the useful circuit gain unless capacitor C_2 is added in Fig. 6-6. For dc operation (without input signal v_{in}), C_2 has no effect; the dc load line for this circuit is drawn in Fig. 6-7 from 20 V at 0 mA to 0 V at 4 mA = 20 V / $(R_L + R_1)$. But at the high frequency of the ac input signal, C_2 acts as a short circuit, so that R_1 has no effect. So the ac load line (explained further in Sec. 6-16) is drawn through the Q point and parallel to a line drawn from 20 V at 0 mA to 0 V at 5 mA = 20 V / R_L.

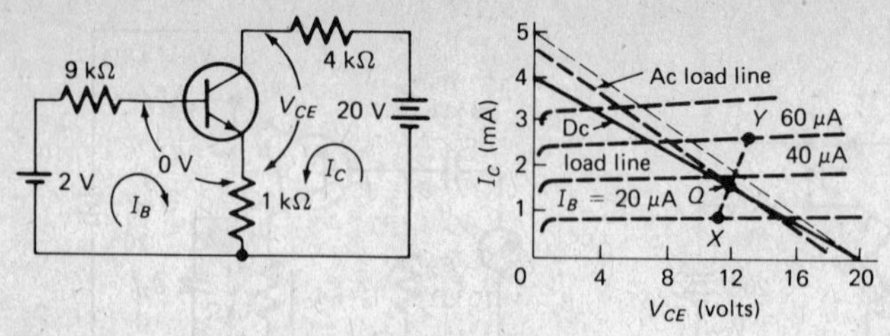

Figure 6-7 Location of Q point for Fig. 6-6.

An engineer finds the Q point after simplifying Fig. 6-6 by Thévenin's theorem, obtaining Fig. 6-7. Writing the voltage equation around each loop (in values of volts, kilohms, and milliamperes) gives $-20 + 5I_C + I_B + V_{CE} = 0$ and $-2 + I_C + 10I_B = 0$. The solution is $V_{CE} = 49I_B + 10$. By this equation, when $I_B = 20\ \mu A$, $V_{CE} = 10.98$ V; when $I_B = 60\ \mu A$, $V_{CE} = 12.94$ V. These values are plotted at X and Y in Fig. 6-7. The Q point lies where the line XY crosses the dc load line.

6-6 COUPLED AMPLIFIERS; DIRECT COUPLING

To obtain greater amplification than is available from a single transistor, we may connect several transistors Q_1 and Q_2 in cascade, so that the output of Q_1 (or first stage) becomes the input to Q_2 (or second stage). These stages may be connected or coupled together through capacitors or transformers[6-12] to amplify rapidly changing signals.

If the input signal is a slowly changing dc voltage, or if the amplifier must be able to respond to low-frequency alternating signals, a direct connection is made from the collector of Q_1 to the base of Q_2, as shown in Fig. 6-8; this combination is a two-stage *direct-coupled* amplifier. If a small increase in signal raises the base of Q_1, this increases the electron flow from emitter to collector through Q_1 and R_1, causing a larger voltage to appear across R_1. This lowers the potential at point 2, decreasing the base current of Q_2; this decreases the amount of electrons flowing from emitter to collector through Q_2 and R_2 to point 4, and decreases the output voltage across R_2. Each transistor is an amplifier; Q_1 is coupled to Q_2 by the voltage across R_1.

In such a direct-coupled amplifier circuit note that, for each amount of steady base current applied to Q_1, there is a different but fixed amount of base current at Q_2. Also, when collector current increases in Q_1, the collector current decreases in Q_2; this relation exists if both transistors are NPN (or if both are PNP).

However, if the NPN Q_2 is replaced by a PNP transistor, shown as Q_3 in Fig. 6-9, the increase of Q_1 collector current still drives point 2 more nega-

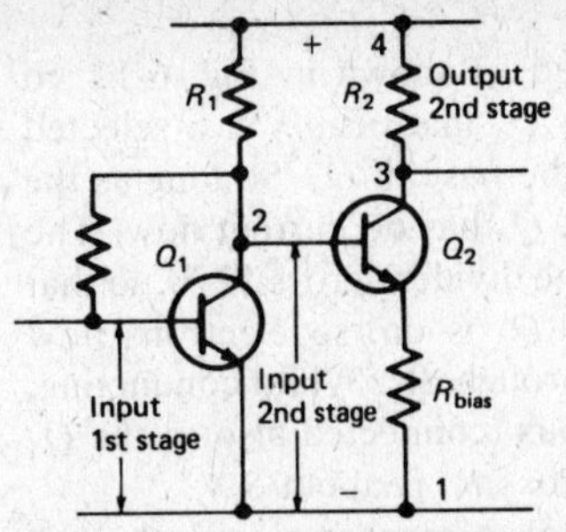

Figure 6-8 Two NPN transistors in a two-stage direct-coupled amplifier.

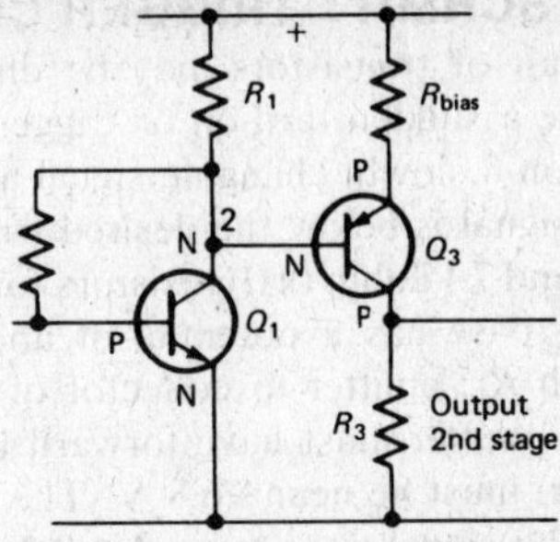

Figure 6-9 NPN and PNP direct-coupled amplifier.

tive. Applied to the N-type base of Q_3, this *increases* the flow of electrons through R_3 and from collector to emitter of Q_3. Note that the Q_3 collector and its output load have been moved to the lower or negative side of the circuit in Fig. 6-9; negative potential at the P-type collector provides the needed reverse bias. Near the top, positive for the P-type emitter gives the needed forward bias.

6-7 DARLINGTON CIRCUIT

Two transistors of the same type may be direct-coupled as shown in Fig. 6-10; the emitter current of Q_1 is also the base current of Q_2. This combination has a total of three external connections (B, C, and E); together Q_1 and Q_2 act like a single transistor whose gain equals the Q_1 gain × the Q_2 gain.

To handle greater load current, a similar circuit in Fig. 6-11 lets Q_1 control both Q_2 and Q_3, connected in parallel. The R_E resistors help to equalize load current, as shown also in Fig. 6-3. A single Darlington unit may contain all parts of either circuit, having only three terminals.

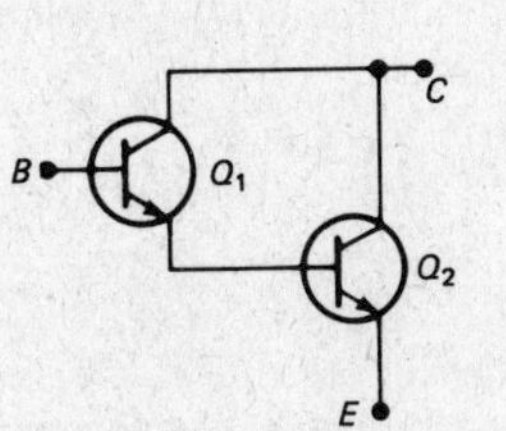

Figure 6-10 Darlington circuit.

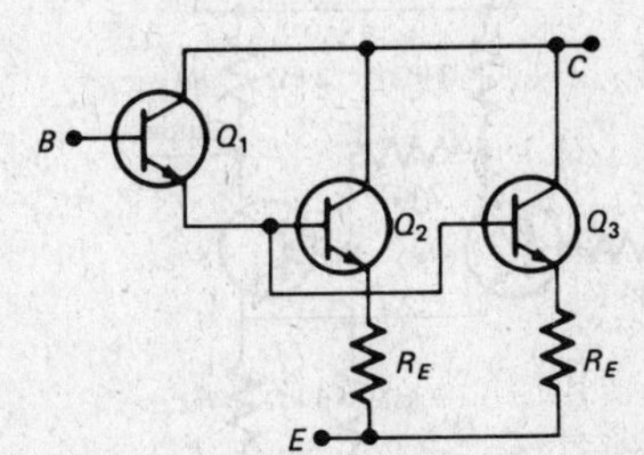

Figure 6-11 High-current Darlington circuit.

6-8 SCHMITT TRIGGER CIRCUIT

A pair of transistors may be direct-coupled as shown in Fig. 6-12, to provide a sudden turn-on or trigger action by Q_5 that occurs at a selected value on a slowly changing signal applied to the base of Q_4. So long as the input signal is below the desired trigger point, Q_4 has no current flow. The 3-, 2- and 7-kilohm (kΩ) resistors form a voltage divider across 12 V, so that the Q_5 base has a potential of about +7 V; Q_5 is on, so electrons flow through R_6, emitter to collector of Q_5 and through R_4. While conducting, the Q_5 emitter must have forward bias and thus (connected also to the Q_4 emitter) must be near +6.8 V. The output across R_4 is about 5 V.

As the signal rises toward 6.8 V (at Q_4base), it reaches a critical point where some base current begins to flow in Q_4, letting collector current flow through Q_4 and the 3-kΩ resistor. The increased voltage drop across 3 kΩ quickly lowers the potential at the Q_5 base so that current decreases in the Q_5 collector and through R_6. The lower potential at the top of R_6 is applied also to lower the Q_4 emitter; this turns on Q_4 further, thus completely turning off Q_5 and removing the output from across R_4. A further rise in input signal causes no further change in this circuit; the potential at the Q_4 and Q_5 emitters becomes steady at a new value, say +6.2 V.

When the input signal to Q_4 decreases to 6.5 V, the Q_4 current through 3 kΩ decreases, raising the potential at the Q_5 base so that the Q_5 collector current increases through R_6; this raises the potential at the Q_4 emitter. As Q_4 turns off suddenly, Q_5 is turned on completely. The amount or level of the input signal that causes the sudden trigger action may be selected by the choice of resistance values in the circuit. Such a trigger is formed by Q_1 and Q_2 in Fig. 8-3.

When a sine-wave voltage is applied at the input, this trigger action produces a square-wave output.

6-9 DRIFT AND TEMPERATURE EFFECTS

In simple dc solid-state amplifiers (as in Fig. 6-8 or 6-9), a variation in transistor temperature can change the circuit performance; as the transistor

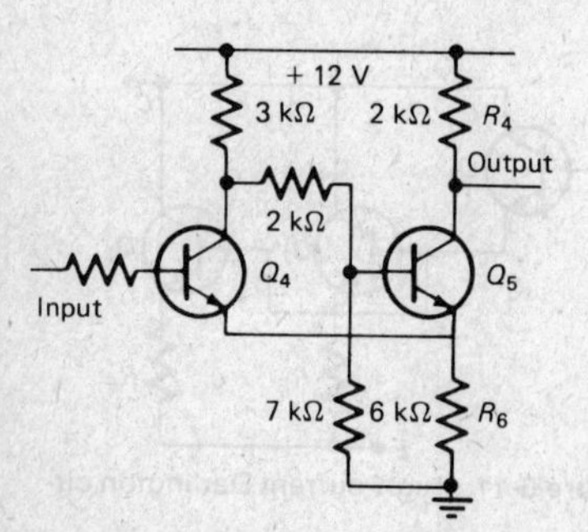

Figure 6-12 Schmitt trigger circuit.

ages, a further drift in transistor characteristics can be expected. To reduce these effects of temperature and age, various compensating and stabilizing networks may be included in the circuit design.

Complete multistage solid-state amplifiers now are marketed in tiny modules or capsules that contain also the compensating networks as needed. Looking ahead to integrated-circuit (IC) design in Chap. 18, complex circuits now are developed as "building blocks" to be especially useful in small solid-state packages used as parts of computers or industrial control. A popular basic direct-coupled amplifier circuit is known as the differential amplifier.

6-10 DIFFERENTIAL AMPLIFIER

In Fig. 6-13 two duplicate transistors have equal collector resistors R_1 and R_2; they are direct-coupled through the emitter resistor R_3. With steady conditions and no input signal at either base, the Q_1 current through R_1 equals the Q_2 current through R_2; the output voltage is zero, measured between collectors 3 and 5. The sum of the Q_1 and Q_2 currents flows through R_3 so that the emitters are at about +4V; therefore, the Q_1 base and Q_2 base must be biased slightly above +4 V so that equal collector currents flow in Q_1 and Q_2.

First apply a signal to the base of Q_2 but hold the Q_1 base steady (so that input 1 = 0). As the signal at input 2 becomes more positive, increasing the base current of Q_2, the current through R_2 increases so that the collector-5 potential drops. But the Q_2 current increases through R_3 also; therefore, point 4 rises and drives the Q_1 emitter more positive, so that the base-to-emitter voltage is less. This decreases the Q_1 current through R_1, so that the collector-3 potential rises. The output voltage increases, with 3 more positive than 5.

This circuit, also called a comparison amplifier, may be used in a voltage regulator; here the load voltage to be regulated is compared with a standard or reference voltage; any difference between these two voltages becomes the *error voltage*, which causes a corrective action that makes the regulated voltage return to more nearly equal the reference. In Fig. 6-13, the reference voltage (perhaps supplied from across a Zener diode [7-18]) is connected between input 1 and ground, while the to-be-regulated load voltage is applied between input 2 and ground. The output 3 to 5 becomes the error voltage; if 5 becomes more positive than 3, this error makes the regulator increase the load voltage. If 5 drops below 3, this error lowers the load voltage, so that the Q_2 base receives less current.

Now apply instead, between the two inputs in Fig. 6-13, a signal voltage that drives input 1 negative at the same time as it drives input 2 positive. This further decreases the Q_1 current so that collector 3 rises higher than before, to provide greater output between 3 and 5. The increase of Q_2 cur-

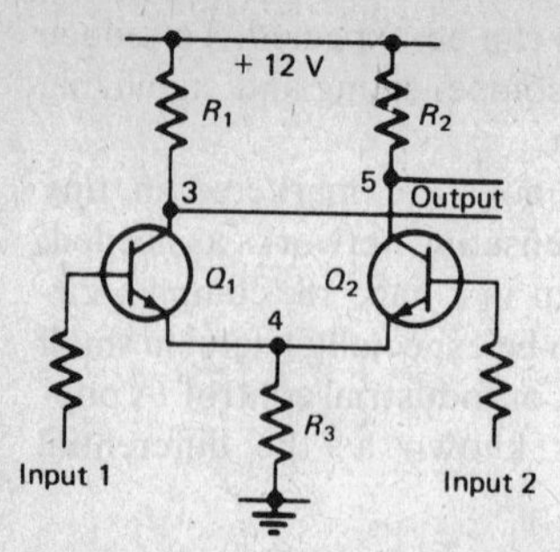

Figure 6-13 Differential amplifier using transistors.

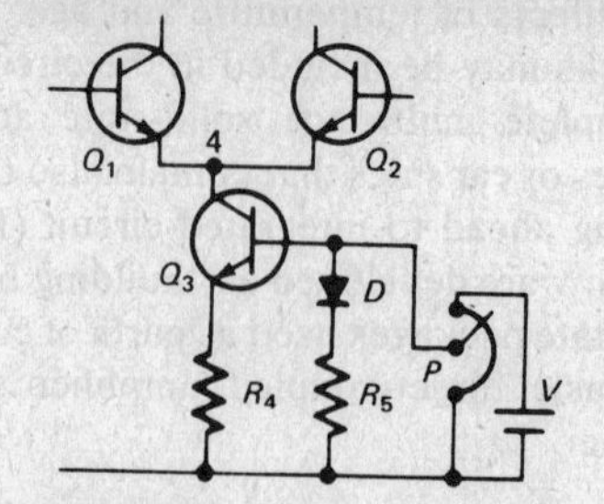

Figure 6-14 Constant-current source for Fig. 6-13.

rent offsets the decrease in Q_1 current; thus the total current through R_3 remains nearly constant.

To improve the operation of the differential amplifier of Fig. 6-13, the resistance value of R_3 must be increased. Greater improvement is obtained if R_3 replaced by a transistor Q_3, as next described.

6-11 CONSTANT-CURRENT SOURCE

In Fig. 6-14, transistor Q_3 acts as a regulator so as to supply constant collector current to a load circuit; the load here consists of Q_1 and Q_2, whose combined currents we wish to hold constant, as in Sec. 6-10.

The base of Q_3 is held at a constant potential (such as is supplied by a battery V and adjusted by P), so that Q_3 passes the desired amount of collector current; this produces a voltage drop across R_4. If this Q_3 current starts to decrease, it causes less drop across R_4; thus the Q_3 emitter is lowered (in effect, raising the Q_3 base), so that Q_3 is turned on further. But if the Q_3 current increases above the value set by P, the greater drop across R_4 turns off Q_3 toward the desired value. If P is turned clockwise to less voltage, Q_3 holds a lower value of constant current. (A similar action is given by Q_{17} and R_{54} near the center of Fig. 31-4). To offset a change if the Q_3 current varies with temperature, a diode D is selected that has opposite change with temperature.

This differential amplifier (Fig. 6-14) is well suited to provide the long-life close accuracy needed in the integrated circuits (ICs) described in Chap. 12.

6-12 CAPACITOR OR RC COUPLING

For use in circuits at higher frequencies [60 hertz (Hz or cps) or radio, TV, etc.], amplifiers need to respond only to the rapid changes of the input signal; any slow change or dc portion of the signal purposely is excluded from the next stage. Figure 6-15 is seen to consist of two circuits like that of

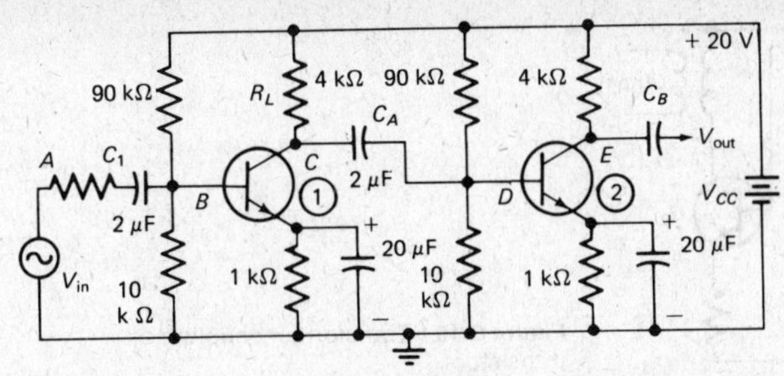

Figure 6-15 Two-stage common-emitter amplifier, capacitor-coupled.

Fig. 6-6; each transistor has self-bias and is stabilized as explained in Sec. 6-5. Near the center of Fig. 6-15, capacitor C_A serves to connect the varying output from the collector of transistor 1 to the base of transistor 2; this forms a resistance-capacitance-coupled two-stage amplifier.

Both transistors in Fig. 6-15 receive dc operating power from the single battery V_{CC}. When no alternating or changing signal is received at A, the base current at B is constant; therefore, the potential at collector C does not vary; no signal passes across C_A to change the base current of transistor 2, at D.

However, when a signal is received at A of sufficient frequency to pass across C_1, this causes a small variation of the base current of transistor 1; by transistor action in this common-emitter circuit, a much larger change in current appears at collector C. This varying output from transistor 1 passes across the coupling capacitor C_A and becomes a strong current signal into base D of transistor 2; again by transistor action, a very large change in current at collector E now can pass across capacitor C_B and become an alternating output that is many thousand times greater than the original signal at A.

A two-stage capacitor-coupled amplifier in a temperature recorder is shown in Fig. 25-3.

6-13 TRANSFORMER COUPLING

In the same way that capacitor C_A in Fig. 6-15 lets the base at D receive only the fast-changing part of the output from collector C, a transformer T is used in Fig. 6-16 to supply base current to Q_2 only when Q_1 changes the amount of its collector current flowing in the primary winding of T. Transistor Q_2 is *transformer-coupled* to Q_1. A transformer produces no voltage in its secondary or output winding so long as its primary current is not changing. However, when the ac signal at the base of Q_1 causes its collector current to change, the resulting change of magnetic flux in transformer T makes its secondary winding produce a voltage at the base of Q_2. The size of this swing of Q_2 base current may be much larger than the signal input to Q_1. In Fig. 6-16 an increasing Q_1 current may turn off Q_2, or the connections to T may be chosen so that the turn-on of Q_1 also turns on Q_2.

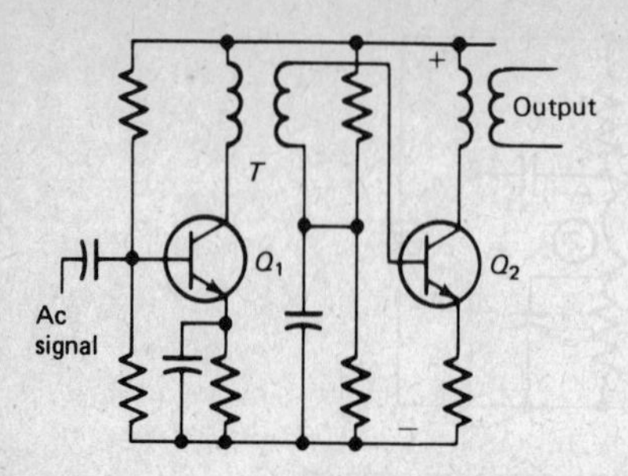

Figure 6-16 Transformer coupling of transistors.

6-14 DC LOAD LINE VS. AC LOAD LINE

So long as the collector circuit contains only resistance, the load line (discussed in Sec. 5-5) is the same for either dc or ac operation, whether or not an ac signal is applied. But when two stages of an amplifier are coupled by a capacitor or by a transformer (as shown in Figs. 6-15 and 6-16), the dc load line no longer shows the conditions that exist when the ac signal is applied.

To present this point simply, Fig. 6-17 shows the circuit used in Sec. 5-5, with the addition of capacitor C that couples load R_B to R_A. The curves for transistor G are shown in Fig. 6-18, together with the load line of Fig. 5-10, using the same operating point Q. The slope of this load line is 5 mA / 20 V = l/R_A. Capacitor C has no effect during the steady conditions that exist while the ac signal is zero, since C has charged through R_B to the voltage across R_A; no current remains in C, so that the capacitor acts as an open circuit to dc voltage. Thus R_B has no effect on the dc load line.

However, an ac signal in Fig. 6-17 causes the collector voltage across R_A to vary. The voltage across R_B is the same as only the *changing* portion of the voltage across R_A. For such coupling purposes, C must have large enough microfarad rating so that its X_c (reactance $1/2\pi fC$) or its opposition to

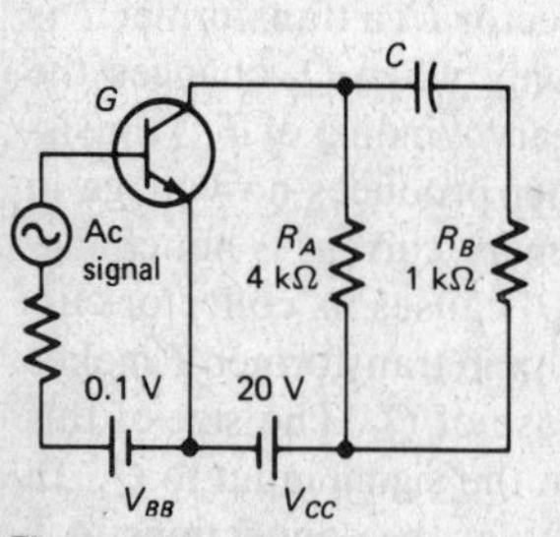

Figure 6-17 Transistor with capacitor-coupled load.

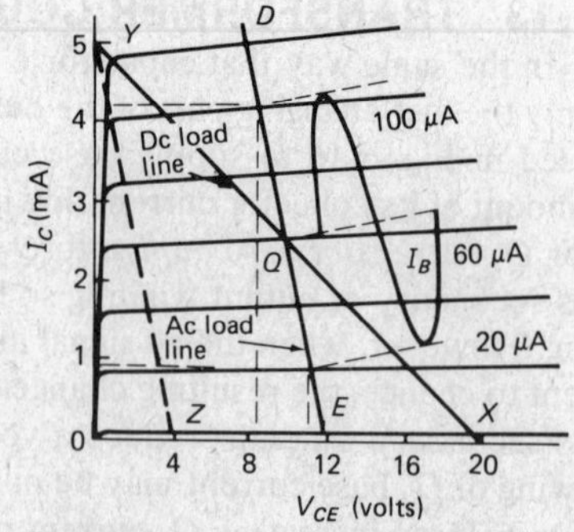

Figure 6-18 Use of dc and ac load lines for Fig. 6-17.

ac voltage must be very small; thus chosen, C acts like a short circuit so as to connect R_B directly to the ac portion of the voltage across R_A, while yet preventing the dc voltage V_{CC} from reaching R_B. This means that, for the "working" or ac conditions, R_B is connected in parallel with R_A, as though both C and V_{CC} were short-circuited; so a battery is considered as being short-circuited whenever just the ac voltages are studied in an amplifier circuit.

When the ac signal is applied in Fig. 6-17, the total base current moves above and below its steady value at Q; therefore, the resulting collector current I_c and voltage V_{CE} also vary about Q as a center. But a new load line now must be drawn through Q in Fig. 6-18, since the load resistance in the transistor-G collector circuit is no longer merely the 4 kilohms (kΩ) of R_A, but consists instead of 4 kΩ and 1 kΩ (R_B) in parallel, which is 0.8 kΩ. The new load line must be drawn at a slope $= {}^{1}/_{0.8}$ k Ω. To find this slope, use any convenient voltage such as 4 V; then $I_C = 4$ V / 0.8 kΩ $= 5$ mA. A line drawn through these points (Y to Z in Fig. 6-18) has the desired slope; therefore, the final ac load line is drawn parallel to line YZ, but it must pass through Q, shown by the line DE. This ac line no longer crosses the bottom edge at $V_{CC} = 20$ V.

So, for the capacitor-coupled circuit of Fig. 6-17, its dc load line XY is used for locating Q. But when the ac base signal is applied, the circuit operates along the steeper ac load line DE. On this ac line a base-current signal of 80 μA p-p causes a collector-current variation of 3.4 mA p-p and an output voltage of 2.5 V p-p across R_A and also across R_B.

Just as a coupling capacitor like C causes the ac load line to have a steeper slope than the dc load line, Sec. 6-16 shows that the presence of a coupling transformer may produce an ac load line having lesser slope.

6-15 USE OF TRANSFORMER FOR IMPEDANCE MATCHING

A problem exists when a transistor or vacuum tube is used to furnish power to a load that has low resistance. To transfer maximum power from a generator or source S into a power user or load L as shown in Fig. 6-19*a* the resistance R_L of the load must be made equal to the resistance R_S of the source. (Here it is assumed that the capacitance or inductance of the load is negligible when compared with the load resistance. However, if the source is inductive, the X_L ohms of the source may be matched by placing an equal amount of capacitive X_C ohms in the load.)

In circuit analysis a transistor may be represented by an ac current generator in parallel with an internal resistance.[7-13] (Similarly, a vacuum tube may be represented as an ac voltage generator in series with the r_p within the tube.) To make a transistor transfer greater power into its output or load, the R_L in its output circuit must have about the same number of ohms

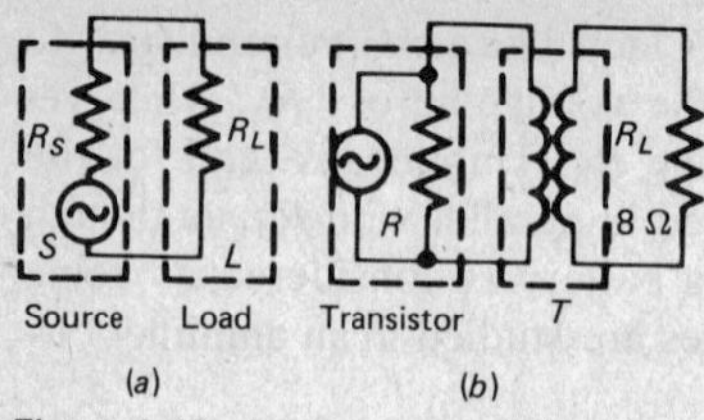

Figure 6-19 Impedance matching by transformer *T*.

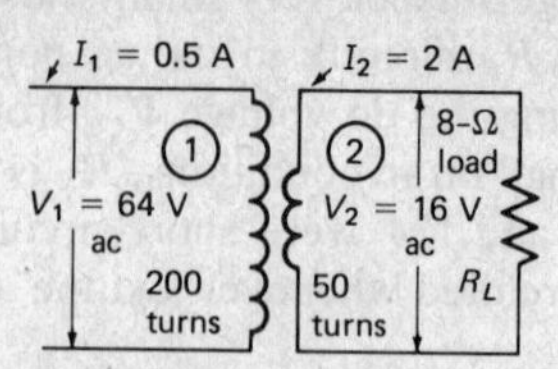

Figure 6-20 Transformer voltages and currents.

as the internal *R* of the transistor. Generally stated, the load impedance must be matched to the source impedance.

For this example the internal *R* of the transistor is about 125 ohms (Ω). So, in Fig. 6-19*b*, the 8-Ω coil R_L should not be placed directly in the transistor collector circuit, since 8 Ω is a poor match for the 125 Ω inside the transistor. However, a transformer *T* may be used to produce the desired match if *T* has 4:1 turns ratio, as is next explained.

A transformer usually has two separate windings, shown as 1 and 2 in Fig. 6-20. When alternating voltage is applied to winding 1, a voltage is produced by winding 2. If winding 2 has only one-fourth as many coil turns as winding 1, the voltage produced by 2 is only one-fourth as large as the voltage applied to 1; this transformer has a turns ratio of 4:1. So if 64 V at 1000 Hz (or cps) is applied across a winding 1 that has 200 turns, then 16 V at 1000 Hz is produced across winding 2 that has 50 turns. In Fig. 6-20, this 16-V winding is connected across the 8-Ω load coil; therefore, in this coil, $I_2 = 16\text{ V} / 8\ \Omega = 2\text{ A}$.

In such a transformer (which is assumed to have very little internal power loss) the product of output volts × amperes must equal the product of input volts × amperes, or $V_2 I_2 = V_1 I_1$. Therefore, if the 8-Ω coil lets 2 A flow in winding 2, then only one-fourth of 2 A flows in winding 1 at the same instant, so $I_1 = 0.5$ A. Since only 0.5 A flows into the transformer although 64 V is applied to it, this circuit acts the same as a resistance of 64 V / 0.5 A = 128 Ω. Because of this transformer, the 8-Ω load has the same effect as a 128-Ω resistor connected directly into the 64-V circuit. Thus the resistance as felt in the 64-V circuit equals the 8 Ω of the load multiplied by the square of the turns ratio, or $128\ \Omega = (4)^2 \times 8\ \Omega$.

However, if a dc or steady voltage is applied to winding 1 of the transformer, no voltage is produced by winding 2; the 8-Ω load now has no effect in the circuit of winding 1. But winding 1 alone still is connected across the dc input voltage. Winding 1 has only the low resistance caused by the wire of which it is wound; since this usually is only a few ohms, the current input to winding 1 will be quite large if a dc voltage is applied to it.

For the ac conditions shown in Fig. 6-19*b*, the transformer *T* can make the 8-Ω coil act like a 128-Ω load in the collector circuit; since this

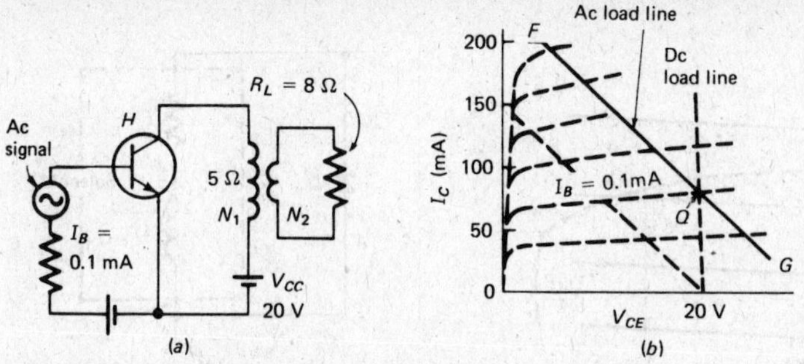

Figure 6-21 Load line and Q point for transformer coupling.

load nearly matches the 125-Ω value of internal R, the transistor now can deliver maximum power into the transformer, and thus into the 8-Ω coil.

6-16 AC LOAD LINE FOR TRANSFORMER COUPLING

In Fig. 6-21, R_L may represent the 8-Ω coil of a loudspeaker. If $N_1 / N_2 = 4$, then R_L affects the collector circuit like a resistance of 128 Ω, but only during the working condition with ac signal.

To find the Q point for this circuit, only dc conditions can be used, as when the transformer receives only the steady voltage of the 20-V battery. Only the low resistance of the N_1 turns can limit the flow of current; if this is 5 Ω, the dc load line in Fig. 6-21*b* crosses the bottom edge at $V_{CC} = 20$ V and would cross the vertical edge at $I_C = 4$ A, which is far off scale; this dc load line is nearly vertical. Selecting a bias current $I_B = 0.1$ mA, the Q point is located as marked in Fig. 6-21.

When the ac signal is applied, the changing collector current is limited by the 128-Ω effect of R_L, added to the 5-Ω dc resistance of the transformer winding. The ac load line will have the same slope as a line drawn from $V_{CE} = 20$ V to $I_C = 20\text{ V} / 133\ \Omega = 150$ mA. The final ac load line is drawn through Q as shown at F to G.

Since the ac load line reaches to larger values of V_{CE} (as at G) than are available from the 20-V battery, we must recall that this larger voltage is produced by the inductive effect of the transformer winding as the current decreases within it during each ac cycle.

6-17 AC LOAD LINE FOR INDUCTIVE LOAD

Often we use a transistor to energize a solenoid or relay. If this action occurs slowly or there is little load inductance, this transistor follows a straight load line as is shown in Fig. 5-10. But if our circuit has large inductance and we need fast switching action, the ac load line becomes like loop

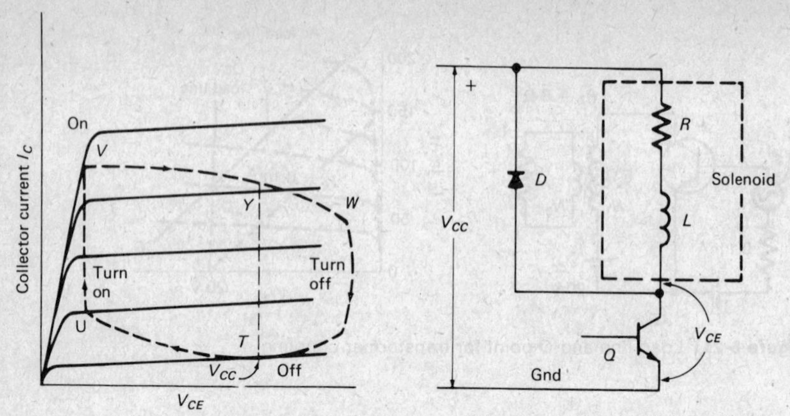

Figure 6-22 Ac load line for inductive load *L*.

TUVW shown in Fig. 6-22; here we use NPN transistor *Q* to energize a solenoid that has inductance *L* and internal resistance *R*.

First let the circuit of Fig. 6-22 be OFF so that *Q* has no collector current except the leakage current I_{CEO}[5-3]; nearly all of supply voltage V_{CC} now appears across *Q*. When we apply positive V_{BE} so that *Q* turns ON, the voltage V_{CE} is nearly zero, so that the voltage across the solenoid is nearly all of V_{CC}. Current I_C starts to flow and it increases slowly to points *U* and *V*; at point *V* the current reaches the value V_{CC} / R (after a time delay L / R as mentioned in Sec. 3-5).

When the base voltage becomes zero and tries to turn *Q* OFF, the load line now follows path *VWT*. While decreasing the current I_c below its full value of V_{cc} / R, the inductance *L* causes voltage V_{CE} to increase (considerably exceeding the supply voltage V_{CC}) until *Q* reaches its breakdown voltage, at point *W*. The energy stored in inductance *L* now is converted to heat within *Q* while I_C decreases to the turnoff point *T*. This *W*-to-*T* turnoff procedure often damages the transistor junction inside *Q* unless a protector diode is added as is shown at *D* in Fig. 6-22. Diode *D*, connected across the solenoid, provides a path for the solenoid current after *Q* has turned OFF.

While *Q* is turning ON, the load line follows path *TUV* as before; but while *Q* is turning OFF, the current I_C decreases slightly and the voltage at *Q* collector is limited to V_{CC} plus the forward bias voltage of diode *D* while it conducts the inductive current I_L: this is shown in Fig. 6-22, from point *Y* back to *T*.

Problems

6-1 True or false? Explain why.

(a) To decrease distortion in the output, a transistor is operated class C.

(b) Using identical transistors Q_1 and Q_2 in a two-stage direct-coupled amplifier, the collector current of Q_2 decreases only when the base signal to Q_1 increases.

(c) With capacitor coupling, the steady collector current of Q_1 does not affect the Q_2 current.

(d) The output of a pair of transistors operating class B never has the same waveshape as the input signal.

(e) When a transistor is operating class B, its bias current may be doubled to obtain class C operation.

(f) In Fig. 6-13, the emitter potential at 4 rises as fast as does either input signal .

(g) Transistors may be chosen in a two-stage direct-coupled amplifier so that the turn-on of Q_1 also turns on Q_2.

(h) A Darlington circuit is used so as to provide faster circuit operation.

(i) A sine-wave input to Q_4 in Fig. 6-12 can produce a nearly square wave across R_4.

(j) If A is capacitor-coupled to B, the ac load line of A has less slope than the dc load line.

(k) For the same size of V_{CC}, a capacitor-coupled amplifier usually has a different Q point than has a transformer-coupled amplifier.

(l) A transformer that has 80 turns in one winding and 16 turns in the other can match a 500-ohm (Ω) load to 12.5 kilohms (kΩ) or to 20 Ω.

6-2 In Fig. 6-1, use the transistor characteristics of Fig. 5-15. Let $V_{CC} = 16$ V, $I_B = 60$ μA, $R_L = 1$ kΩ. (*a*) Find operating point Q. (*b*) Apply a signal of 80 μA p-p and find current gain.

6-3 Use values given in Prob. 6-2, but increase the bias I_B to 80 μA. (*a*) Find point Q; (*b*) find current gain. (*c*) Comment on distortion, compared with the use of $I_B = 60$ μA.

6-4 The transistor of Fig. 5-16 is used in the circuit of Fig. 6-5; $R_L = 500$ Ω. While the switch connects A to D, $R_B = 40$ kΩ. At this operating point find (*a*) I_B and (*b*) I_C. If the switch is moved to connect A to C, find (*c*) the new value of R_B that holds the transistor at the same operating point. (*d*) If higher temperature now causes a 6-mA increase in I_C, describe the effect on I_B and the final value of I_C.

6-5 Repeat Prob. 6-4 using the transistor of Fig. 5-15; $R_L = 667$ Ω. While the switch connects A to D, $R_B = 250$ kΩ.

6-6 Let transistor G in Fig. 6-17 have characteristics as shown in Fig. 5-16. Capacitor C is large; $V_{CC} = 20$ volts (V). The Q point is at -20 mA, -10 V. The ac load line crosses the horizontal axis at -14 V. Find (*a*) bias I_B, (*b*) R_A, (*c*) R_B. If an ac signal causes I_B to vary between limits of 0.2 and 0.6 mA, find the p-p values of (*d*) I_C and (*e*) V_{CE}.

6-7 The transistor of Fig. 5-15 is used in the circuit shown. At the signal frequency, each C acts as a short circuit. (*a*) Find I_B, I_C, and V_{CE} at the operating point. If the output voltage is 4 V p-p, find (*b*4) the p-p value of I_C and (*C*) the rms value of the sine-wave input signal.

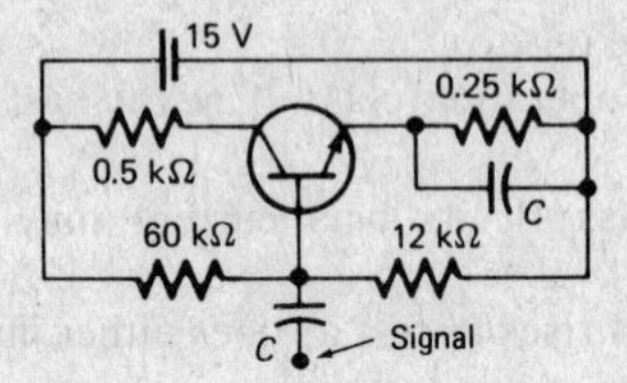

Figure Problem 6-7

7

SEMICONDUCTOR THEORY

While studying the behavior of P-type and N-type materials made from silicon or germanium, as described in Sec. 5-1, we should ask why such semiconductor materials behave so queerly that they (and they alone) can be used in transistors.

7-1 ELECTRONS WITHIN ATOMS

The unusual behavior of crystals of silicon and germanium often is explained by study of the arrangement of electrons within each atom of these materials.[2-14] By similar study it is shown below why copper is a good electrical conductor or why neon is an inert gas that will not affect other materials.

Present scientific knowledge shows that there are 92 elements which, singly or in combination, form all the materials found on earth. (This does not include the "transuranium" elements recently discovered.) Each tiny atom of any element contains a nucleus around which rotate a certain number of electrons. This total number of electrons is different for each element, and is called the *atomic number* of the element; this number ranges from one electron in each atom of hydrogen to 92 electrons per atom of uranium. The atomic numbers for many familiar elements are listed in Table 7-1, along with the symbol or abbreviation used for each element.

A physicist shows that, within each atom, these electrons are grouped or arranged in "shells," as though the electrons can move only on the surfaces of hollow balls of increasing size, so that a larger shell surrounds the smaller ones. Moreover, the behavior of any element material depends almost entirely upon the number of electrons that are located in its largest or outermost shell.

Only two electrons can lie or move in the inner shell, where the shell

TABLE 7-1 Arrangement of Electrons in Selected Elements

Atomic number	Element	Symbol	Electrons in shell numbered $n = 1$	$n = 2$	$n = 3$	$n = 4$	$n = 5$
5	Boron	B	2	3			
6	Carbon	C	2	4			
8	Oxygen	O	2	6			
10	Neon	Ne	2	8			
11	Sodium	Na	2	8	1		
13	Aluminum	Al	2	8	3		
14	Silicon	Si	2	8	4		
15	Phosphorus	P	2	8	5		
17	Chlorine	Cl	2	8	7		
18	Argon	A	2	8	8		
26	Iron	Fe	2	8	14	2	
28	Nickel	Ni	2	8	16	2	
29	Copper	Cu	2	8	18	1	
30	Zinc	Zn	2	8	18	2	
31	Gallium	Ga	2	8	18	3	
32	Germanium	Ge	2	8	18	4	
33	Arsenic	As	2	8	18	5	
47	Silver	Ag	2	8	18	18	1
49	Indium	In	2	8	18	18	3
50	Tin	Sn	2	8	18	18	4
51	Antimony	Sb	2	8	18	18	5

number $n = 1$; from 1 to 8 electrons can be in the next larger shell, $n = 2$. Similarly, 1 to 18 electrons can exist in the third shell, $n = 3$; from 1 to 32 electrons belong in $n = 4$. For each element shown, Table 7-1 lists the number of electrons in each shell.

Each shell is completely filled when the number of electrons contained in that shell is equal to $2n^2$; thus, for the third shell, $n = 3$, and $2 \times 3^2 = 18$. Each larger shell may be said to include several subshells having 2, 6, 10, or 18 electrons. Thus, when shell 4 has a total of 18 electrons, three of its subshells (2, 6, 10) are filled; since its largest subshell is empty, this atom may behave as though the entire shell 4 is filled.

An atom tends to be stable or inert when each of its shells is complete or filled. Reference to Table 7-1 shows that neon (10, Ne) has two shells entirely filled with 2 and 8 electrons; this gas is "satisfied" and shows no tendency to interact with other materials so as to lose or gain an electron; thus it is inert. Similarly, argon (18,A) has two filled shells, also two filled subshells in the third shell; this also is an inert gas. In contrast, an atom of sodium (11, Na) has just one electron in its third shell; such single electrons are held loosely to the rest of the atom, and so may be captured easily. But chlorine gas (17, Cl) lacks one electron from the eight needed to complete two subshells; therefore, it chemically attacks other materials in its search to obtain that needed electron. When chlorine is added to sodium, these elements combine to form sodium chloride (NaCl) or common table salt. Here the excess or loose electron of each Na atom is captured by a Cl atom so as to complete its outer subshell; this results in a stable compound that, when dry, is a poor conductor of electricity.

Copper (29), in Table 7-1, has three filled shells and a single electron in its fourth shell. Countless atoms are pressed tightly together in a piece of copper; their single outer electrons are held so loosely that they are free to move along from one atom to another, drifting toward any positive electric potential that may be applied. These electrons move or drift so easily through copper that this metal is a good conductor of electricity. Similarly, silver (47) has a single electron in its fifth shell, while shells 1, 2, and 3 are complete, and exactly three of the four subshells in its shell 4 are filled; therefore, silver is a fine conductor of electricity and is used wherever its higher cost is justified.

7-2 ELECTRON ARRANGEMENT IN SEMICONDUCTOR ATOMS

Consider now those elements that have four electrons in the outer shell of the atom. Table 7-1 shows that silicon (14), germanium (32), and tin (50) possess these four outer electrons; therefore, they have similar qualities and may be used in the manufacture of solid-state diodes or transistors, as described below. [Also, when gallium (31, three outer electrons) is combined with arsenic (33, five outer electrons), the resulting gallium arsenide (GaAs) has an average of four outer electrons; thus GaAs also may serve in solid-state diodes.] First these materials are studied in their pure or intrinsic form; then other elements are added by a controlled process called *doping*.

Figure 7-1*a* illustrates the arrangement of electrons within each single atom of silicon. Since only the four electrons in the outer shell influence the behavior of this material, it is customary to combine the nucleus and all the electrons of inner shells into the larger circle, called the *core*. The four black dots outside of the core represent the electrons in the outer shell; these are called *valence electrons*, and we say that this atom has a valence or combining power of 4.

Since many such atoms lie close together in a piece of pure semiconductor material, Fig. 7-1*b* shows how each of the four electrons is close to an electron of a neighbor atom. As a result, one electron of atom *A* and one of *B* are shared by both *A* and *B*; similarly, atoms *B* and *C* share the two electrons lying between them. This sharing produces a double bond between every two atoms, as shown in Fig. 7-1*c*. Thus all four of the valence electrons are held tightly in these bonds; since none are free to move, this material acts as a good insulator.

The above description is true only when the material is so cold (at

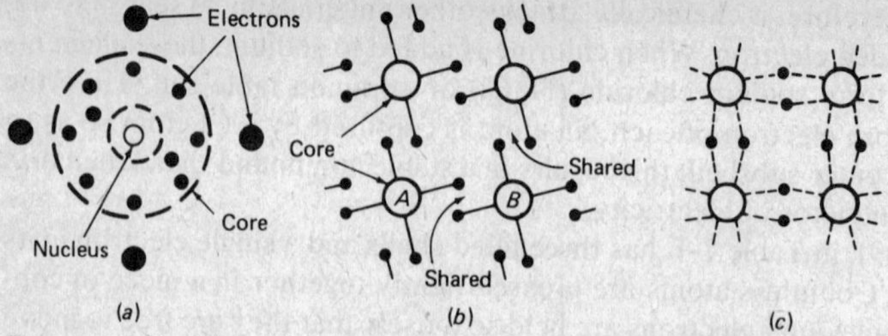

Figure 7-1 Arrangement of electrons in a pure semiconductor.

absolute zero) that it receives no heat energy. However, at room temperature the pure silicon or germanium receives enough heat energy to make one of these outer electrons break loose from this bond; these loosened electrons, though few in number, can move through the material toward any positive potential that may be applied. In Fig. 7-2, the heat energy has broken a bond between atoms *A* and *B* so that electron 1 is free to move to the left. In the broken bond, the space that now lacks an electron is shown as a hollow circle, and is called a *hole*. Since this hole represents a positive charge, it can attract electron 2, which moves to the left; now the hole at 1 is filled, but a new hole is formed at 2. Electron 3 is attracted and moves to the left to fill this hole at 2; but now a new hole appears at 3. As this action continues, we see that the electrons flow to the left but that the resulting holes appear to move toward the right. So, at room temperature, a pure or intrinsic semiconductor permits a small electric flow within it; this flow consists of the movement of electrons (negative charges) toward whichever end is (+), and also the movement of holes (positive charges) toward whichever end is (–). So, while electron flow is opposite to the direction of conventional current flow, the flow of holes is in the same direction as conventional current. Both electron flow and hole flow contribute to the total current. This type of current conduction (composed of both holes and electrons) gives rise to the term *bipolar* as applied to transistor action.

In contrast, a pure conductor such as copper does not have holes as described above, since copper has a loosely held single electron in the valence shell. The pure semiconductor material does not rectify; although it is a poor conductor, its electrons or holes can flow with equal ease in either direction.

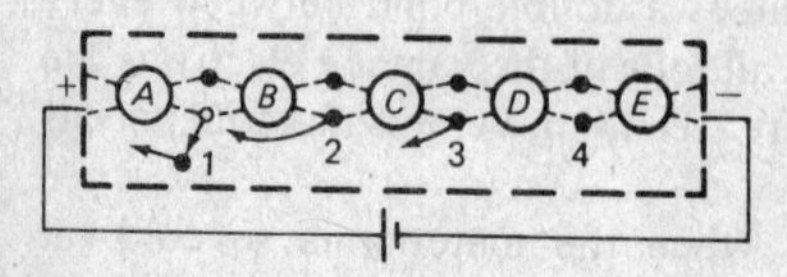

Figure 7-2 Movement of electrons freed by heat energy, causing movement of holes.

If the temperature of this material rises, this added heat energy causes the breaking of a larger number of bonds; this is described also as the formation of additional electron-hole pairs. Since more electrons thus are freed to flow to (+) and more holes are formed to move to (−), the material has greater conductivity at the increased temperature. Since the resistance of the semiconductor decreases as temperature rises, this behavior is seen to be opposite to that of usual copper or aluminum conductors.

7-3 THE USE OF ENERGY LEVELS

While Fig. 7-2 shows that the addition of energy to a single atom can free an electron, a physicist uses an energy-level diagram like Fig. 7-3 to explain the behavior of countless atoms close together within a semiconductor. Each electron in the inner shell ($n = 1$) of any atom is strongly attracted to its positively charged nucleus; so it has great potential energy. Less attraction to the nucleus is felt by electrons in more distant shells ($n = 2$, $n = 3$); so their potential energy is less. An electron can be removed from an atom if enough energy can be added to move this electron from the outer shell up to a point called the *ionization* or *conduction level;* here the electron no longer is attracted to the nucleus; so it is free to assist in the conduction of current. Since only the valence electrons (those in the outer shell) can thus be freed by added energy, the inner shells are omitted in Fig. 7-3*b* and in later energy-level diagrams. Here all outer-shell electrons are considered as having energy values that lie within the valence band.

To become free, a valence electron must be given enough extra energy to overcome the potential attraction of its nucleus, and thus to move the electron from the valence band into the conduction band. To do this, a definite or discrete amount of energy must be added, as is indicated by the width of the forbidden gap. In every material some electrons have energies that lie in the valence band; materials differ in the size of forbidden gap or the amount of energy needed to free the valence electrons and to permit the material to conduct electricity. Figure 7-4 shows that an insulator has so large a gap that its electrons cannot be given enough added energy to cause conduction, ex-

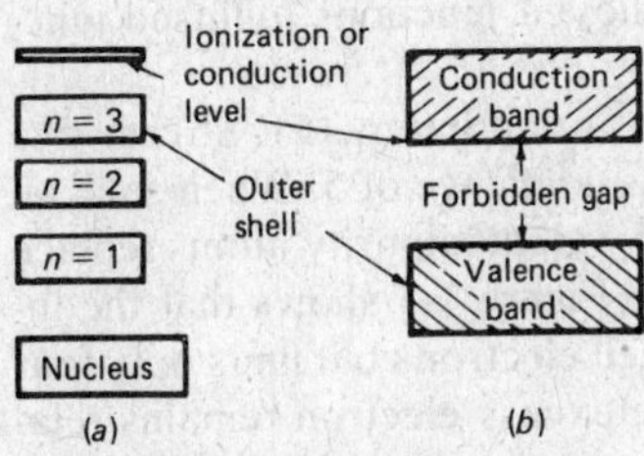

Figure 7-3 Energy levels of shells within the atom.

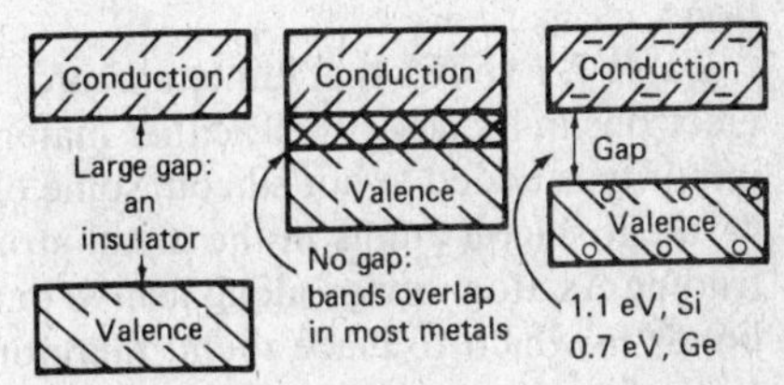

Figure 7-4 Energy levels in an insulator, a conductor, and a semiconductor.

cept at excessive temperatures or voltages. In contrast, in a good conductor the valence band overlaps the conduction band so that, at ordinary temperatures, plenty of free electrons permit large conduction.

In a semiconductor at absolute zero, no electrons have enough energy to leave the valence band. At room temperature the heat energy breaks a few bonds to form electron-hole pairs; the added energy raises these electrons into the conduction band as is shown in Fig. 7-4, while the holes remain in the valence band and are free to act as carriers of current in this band. The minimum energy needed to move an electron into the conduction band is known to be 0.7 eV for pure germanium and 1.1 eV for pure silicon (where eV, an electronvolt, is the energy given to an electron when it is accelerated through a potential difference of one volt). Electrons in pure semiconductor materials cannot have energy levels lying between those of the valence band and those of the conduction band—they must gain enough energy to jump the whole gap or not jump at all; therefore, the separating distance is called the *forbidden gap*.

Since the apparent motion of holes, as described above, really is accomplished by the exchanging of electrons from atom to atom, this hole flow must occur entirely within the valence band. Thus the exchanging of electrons between atoms does not require ionization energy, but does require the existence of holes. On the other hand, free electron flow requires that these electrons have enough energy to be within the conduction band.

7-4 CHANGES WITHIN ATOMS CAUSED BY DOPING TO FORM N-TYPE MATERIAL

Pure semiconductor material is not used in a transistor, but the silicon (Si) or germanium (Ge) must be produced in this pure or intrinsic form before certain other elements are added, to form what are called N-type or P-type materials.

While the pure Si (or Ge) is at high temperature in a special furnace, a very small quantity of arsenic or antimony is added; this is considered as a carefully controlled impurity, for it is added in quantities far less than one part in ten million parts of silicon. (Various handbooks or manuals explain these manufacturing details, whereby N-type and P-type materials are produced in the form of grown junctions, alloyed junctions, diffused junctions, etc.)

Table 7-1 shows that either arsenic (33, As) or antimony (51, Sb) has five electrons in its outer shell; either material has a valence of 5. When such an impurity is added to hot silicon, some of the 5-valent impurity atoms replace 4-valent silicon atoms in the metal structure. Figure 7-5 shows that the intruding As atom brings along its five outer-shell electrons but finds only four bonds in which to place them; therefore, the excess electron remains relatively free to move, since it is not held in a bond shared with another atom. Each 5-valent intruder is called a *donor atom*, since it donates an extra elec-

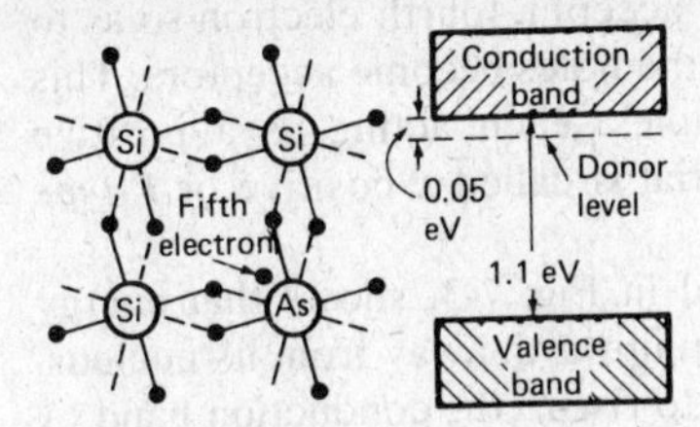

Figure 7-5 Donor electrons form N-type material.

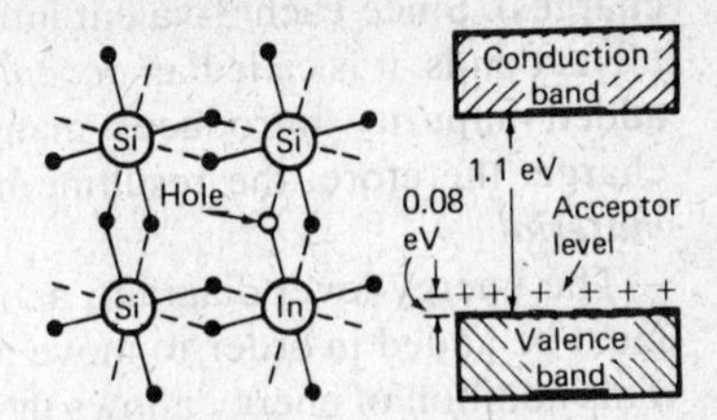

Figure 7-6 Acceptor holes form P-type material.

tron into the silicon; the extra electrons are called donor impurities or donor electrons. Since the impurity adds many such electrons, each having a negative charge, the resulting new material is called a negative or N-*type material*.

At absolute zero these donor electrons are held so weakly to their atoms that only 0.05 eV of extra energy needs to be supplied by heat in order to move these electrons into the conduction band. Therefore, Fig. 7-5 shows that the energy level of the donor electrons is very near the conduction band; this level is within the gap that is forbidden when the silicon is pure.

At room temperature the heat energy breaks bonds and produces a few electron-hole pairs as it did in the original pure material; in addition, this heat energy easily raises the donor electrons into the conduction band, without producing additional holes. Thus the conductivity of N-type material may be ten to twenty times greater than that of the pure material. The free electrons so outnumber the few holes that the electric flow is carried almost entirely by electron movement; thus, in N-type material, electrons are thought of as *majority carriers*, while the holes in the valence band are *minority carriers* of electricity.

7-5 DOPING TO FORM P-TYPE MATERIAL

While the pure silicon (or germanium) is at high temperature, a tiny amount of 3-valent material may be added as a controlled impurity, instead of the arsenic or antimony used above. Table 7-1 shows that such 3-valent materials include aluminum (13, Al), gallium (31, Ga), or indium (49, In); each has three electrons in its outer shell. When one of these impurities is carefully added to hot silicon, some of the 3-valent impurity atoms replace 4-valent silicon atoms in the metal structure. Figure 7-6 shows that this intruding atom cannot supply four electrons like those of the silicon atom it displaces; the three valence electrons of the indium atom fill three of the four bonds, but a hole remains where the fourth electron is missing. As seen in Fig. 7-2, this hole easily can attract an electron from a nearby atom; in this way the location of the hole can move, thus acting as a motion of positive charges (in the same way that free electrons can act in a motion of negative charges). Since each 3-valent intruder will accept a fourth electron so as to fill its bonds, it is called an *acceptor atom*; the holes become acceptors. This added impurity introduces many such holes, each acting as a positive charge; therefore, the resulting new material is called a positive or *P-type material.*

The energy-level diagram, as introduced in Fig. 7-3, shows that energy must be added in order to move an electron upward, away from its nucleus. This addition of energy allows the electron to rise to the conduction band. A hole, the space left by an electron, represents a positive charge and also requires the addition of energy to create it. As stated before, the hole remains in the valence band; so, instead of going upward in the energy-level diagram, the hole is said to move downward with the addition of energy. In the following energy-level diagrams this convention is used: that the addition of energy lets electrons go upward but makes holes go downward.

At absolute zero these holes cannot move; but only 0.08 eV of additional energy is needed to push these holes down into the valence band where they can act as a flow of (+) charges. Therefore, Fig. 7-6 shows the energy level of the acceptors just above the valence band and lying within the gap that is forbidden when the silicon is pure.

At room temperature electron-hole pairs are formed, so that a few electrons move in the conduction band, the same as in pure silicon. But the acceptor atoms also provide a much larger number of holes, without increasing the number of electrons; the holes move in the valence band at room temperature and thus can increase greatly the conductivity of this P-type material. Holes are the majority carriers in P-type material, moving in the valence band; the few electrons in the conduction band are minority carriers.

7-6 THE PN JUNCTION OR DIODE

Having shown above how a piece of pure or intrinsic silicon or germanium can be converted into either N-type or P-type material, next we show that a useful rectifying junction or diode is obtained when such P- and N-type materials are formed side by side. Many different methods are used to produce this junction between P- and N-type materials, but high temperatures always are needed while the two materials are being formed together; a suitable junction cannot be formed by squeezing together the cold pieces of previously formed P- and N-type materials.

To indicate the behavior of electrons and holes near this PN junction, most scientists include a reference line within the energy-level diagram of each material, and this is called the *Fermi level.* Located with respect to the conduction and valence bands, the Fermi level shows the average amount of energy possessed by the free electrons and holes within the material. In a pure or intrinsic semiconductor, the number of free electrons must equal the number of holes, since the only free electrons are those produced by thermal breaking of bonds to form electron-hole pairs. The level of energy of each free electron lies in the conduction band, but the energy level of each hole is in the valence band; therefore, it is logical that the average level of these energies lies halfway between these bands, as shown in Fig. 7-7*a*. {The Fermi level also indicates the greatest energy that any electron can have while the material is at the temperature of absolute zero. Therefore, to free any electron from this material, it must be given enough additional energy to raise it from the Fermi level into the conduction band. The amount of this needed energy [expressed in electronvolts (eV) and known as the *work function*] is shown by this distance in Fig. 7-7*a*. Since P- and N-type materials have different Fermi levels, they also have different work functions.} So it can be stated, as a rule of thumb, that electrons are always above the Fermi level but holes remain below it. Both electrons and holes tend to drift toward the Fermi level unless some energy such as heat tends to move them away.

But N-type material has a greater amount of free electrons (without any increase in the number of holes), as is shown by energies at higher than the donor level, in Fig. 7-7*c*; therefore, the average energy or Fermi level lies near this donor level. In contrast, since the 3-valent doping produces P-type material that has a greater amount of holes (without increase in the number of electrons), the average of the energies of all holes and electrons places the Fermi level near the acceptor level, as is shown in Fig. 7-7*b*.

When P-type material is formed very close to N-type material, this PN junction undergoes a shifting of energy bands until the Fermi levels of the two materials are at the same height. This action resembles the behavior of water in two tanks, as shown in Fig. 7-8. While the tanks are separated, the water levels can be different; when the tanks are joined through a pipe, water (like electrons) flows from the N tank to raise the level in the P tank. Similarly, during formation of the PN junction, free electrons flow from the N side into the P material, thus forcing the P side to a more negative potential, while the N side rises to a more positive potential because of this loss of electrons. This forms a potential gradient or barrier, shown in Fig. 7-9*a*,

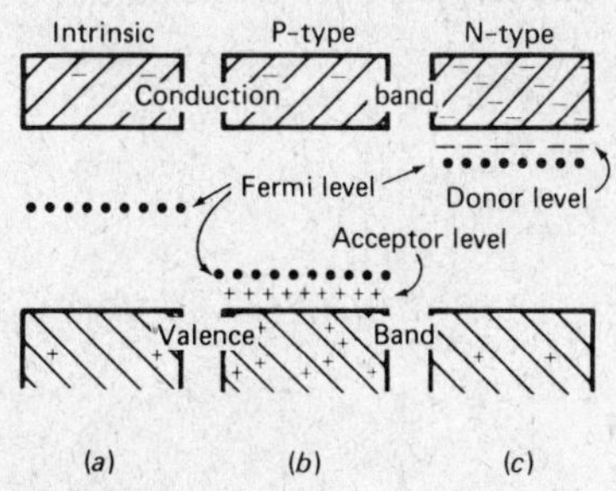

Figure 7-7 Change in Fermi level caused by impurities.

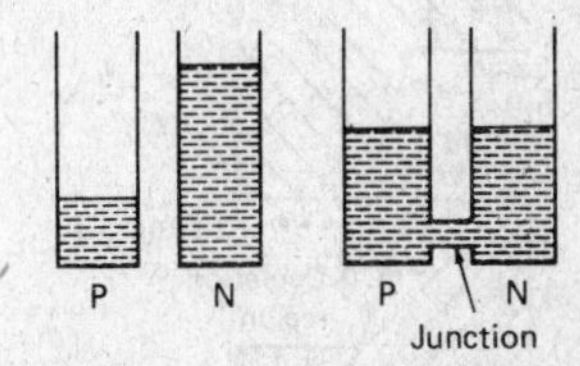

Figure 7-8 Fermi levels at PN junction, compared with water levels.

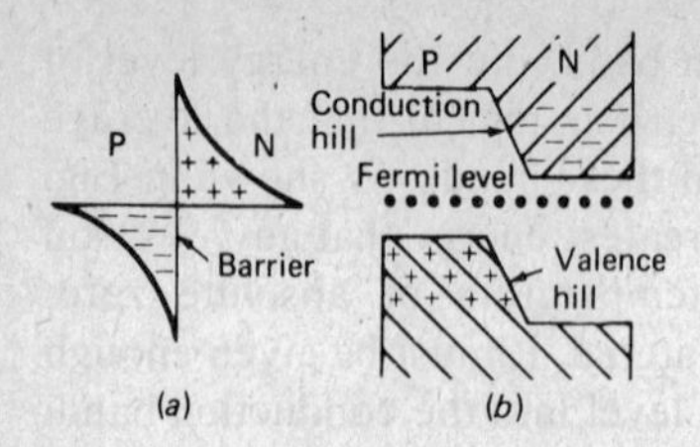

Figure 7-9 Potential barrier or "hill" at PN junction.

which exists at the PN junction when it is completely disconnected from any external voltage.

Within each material, the Fermi level has a definite location with respect to the conduction and valence bands. Therefore, Fig. 7-9*b* shows that these bands have been shifted upward in P-type material when the Fermi levels have reached equal heights in P and N. Thus, in the final or equilibrium state, a "conduction hill" is formed that opposes further flow of electrons from the N side to the higher P side. Similarly, a "valence hill" prevents further flow of holes, since these positive charges cannot move downward in the energy-level diagram (as is mentioned in Sec. 7-5) unless energy is added to them.

7-7 BIASING THE PN JUNCTION

When an external voltage is applied between the two terminals of a PN junction, the bands and energy levels of the P side are shifted with respect to those of the N side; the Fermi levels also become separated. Figure 7-10 shows that battery *A* applies its negative potential to the P side, which already has an excess of electrons, obtained across the junction from the N-type material. But *A* drives more positive the N side, which already has an excess of holes; this connection gives reverse bias to the PN junction. Connection of the $+A$ terminal to the N side reduces the energy of the free electrons so that they move downward in the energy-level diagram; the $-A$ terminal, connected at the P side, reduces the energy applied to the holes, so

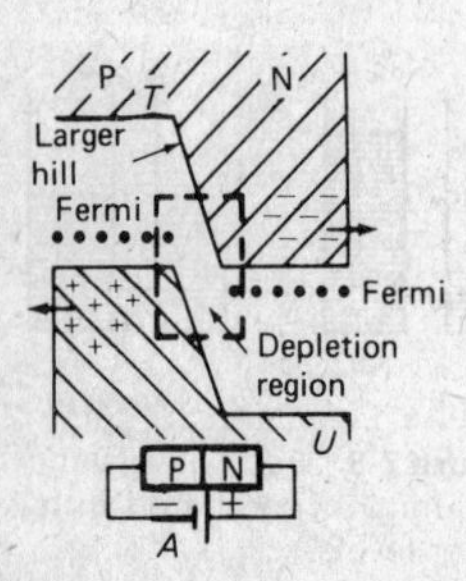

Figure 7-10 Energy levels at reverse-biased junction.

that they move upward. Since the "hills" are made higher, no majority carriers (electrons of N or holes of P) can flow across the junction. (Reference to Fig. 5-4*b* shows that the free electrons of N in Fig. 7-10 are attracted to the right, away from the junction; the holes of P are attracted to the left, away from the junction, thus forming an area depleted of charges, called the *depletion region.*)

But the minority carriers must be considered; in both N- and P-type materials a few electron-hole pairs are formed at room temperature. Thus a few free electrons appear at T in Fig. 7-10 and can fall down the hill of the conduction band; similarly, holes appear at U and can lose energy by falling up the valence-band hill. This movement of minority carriers forms the tiny leakage current that is shown at the left in Fig. 5-3; this current is nearly constant in size even when the reverse voltage is increased. In Fig. 7-10, an increase of reverse-bias voltage A increases the height of the hills; this has little effect on the minority carriers since they are falling to regions of less energy. This small current, flowing while the junction is reverse-biased, is called I_{co}, the cutoff or leakage current; it is an important factor in the later use of this junction as part of a transistor.

Here we show that this leakage current I_{co} is not affected by the size of the reverse voltage. However, I_{co} is greatly affected by the temperature at the junction. A rising temperature supplies more energy to break bonds and to form more electron-hole pairs. Any electrons produced in the P-type material can fall down the hill of the reverse-biased PN junction; any holes in the N-type material likewise can fall (uphill) to lower energy levels. (In Sec. 7-8, the emitter current adds controlled amounts of these minority carriers, thus increasing the current through this reverse-biased junction, which is the collector circuit of a transistor.)

If now the battery connections are interchanged so as to give forward bias, Fig. 7-11 shows that the negative terminal of battery B supplies energy to the free electrons of the N side, raising the positions of all energy levels; meanwhile, $+B$ supplies energy to the holes, lowering the band positions of the P side. (This forward bias also may be regarded as a means for lowering the barrier shown in Fig. 7-9*a*; the connection of + battery potential to P

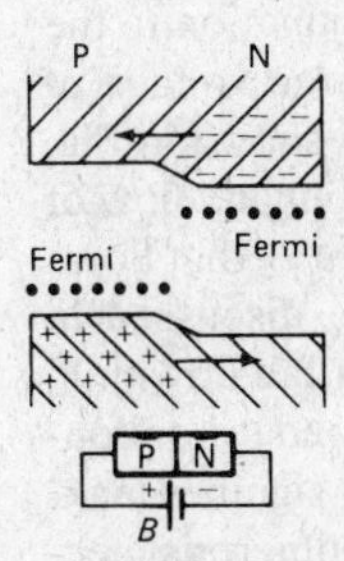

Figure 7-11 Energy levels at forward-biased junction.

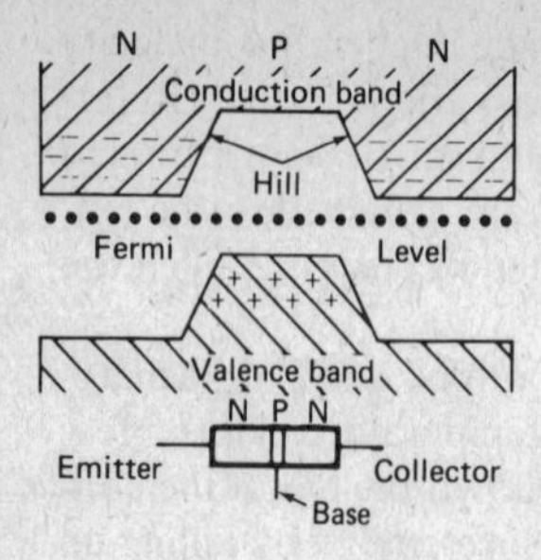

Figure 7-12 Energy levels in NPN transistor before voltages are applied.

serves to offset or decrease the negative charge shown at the P side of the junction.) The hills seen in Fig. 7-9 have become lower in Fig. 7-11, so that many more donor electrons of N can fall across the junction into the P side and more holes from P can cross into N. The size of this forward flow is much greater than the reverse current I_{co}. Moreover, as the size of the forward bias B is increased, the forward current increases very rapidly; Fig. 5-3 shows that less than one volt of forward bias may cause one ampere to flow across the junction.

7-8 THE NPN TRANSISTOR AND ENERGY LEVELS

The NPN transistor is made by forming another layer of N-type material onto the PN junction described above. As shown in Fig. 5-5 and again in Fig. 7-12, a very thin layer of P-type material lies between two sections of N-type material, thus forming two PN junctions. A connection made to the center or P material is called the *base*. One of the N sections is more heavily doped and is called the *emitter;* the other N section is the *collector*.

Until external voltages are applied, this transistor has an energy-level diagram as shown in Fig. 7-12; this is the same as Fig. 7-9, except that another N section is added at the left side. The Fermi levels are equal in all three sections, thus raising the conduction and valence bands of the P section so as to form the hills, as is described in Sec. 7-6.

In Fig. 7-13 external voltages are applied to this NPN transistor. (This is the common-base connection described in Sec. 5-9.) The PN junction to the right, between collector and base, is reverse-biased by the large voltage of battery V_{CC}, thus increasing the hill at K, in the same way as is shown in Fig. 7-10. So long as there is no signal and switch S is open to prevent any flow of current I_E through the emitter-to-base junction, the only current I_C that flows through the collector-to-base junction is the tiny leakage I_{co} discussed in Sec. 7-7; this consists of minority carriers (electrons in P that fall downhill, or holes in N that fall uphill to a level of less energy. In the standard or convention used for transistors, this properly is called I_{CBO}, which signifies leakage current from *Collector to Base with emitter Open*.) The numerous electrons shown in the conduction band of the N-type collector in Fig. 7-13 cannot flow uphill; therefore, majority carriers are not a part of the collector current I_C.

Figure 7-14 shows this I_{CBO} as the bottom curve when collector current I_C is plotted against V_{CB}, the voltage between collector and base. (This curve is the same as that shown in Fig. 5-3, except that it has been given a half turn, or has been rotated through 180°.) So long as emitter current I_E is zero, the tiny I_{CBO} (as conventional current) flows from the positive side of V_{CC} into the collector, then across the PN junction and out of the base, thus becoming the base current I_B. Note that all the free electrons that appear in the P-type base easily fall downhill, thus producing I_{CBO}.

When switch S is closed in Fig. 7-13, applying a slightly more negative potential to the N-type emitter, this raises the energy level of the numerous electrons in the emitter conduction band, as shown in Fig. 7-13*b*. Even a small change in potential at the emitter lowers the hill at J and now lets many electrons flow through the left-hand PN junction and into the P-base conduction band. Thus an emitter current I_E flows; more than 98 percent of these added electrons continue across the very narrow base and fall downhill into the collector, thus increasing the collector current I_C. [As these free

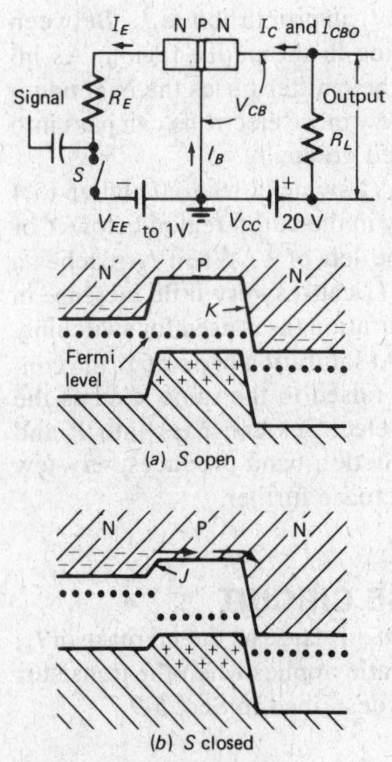

Figure 7-13 Energy levels in common-base connection.

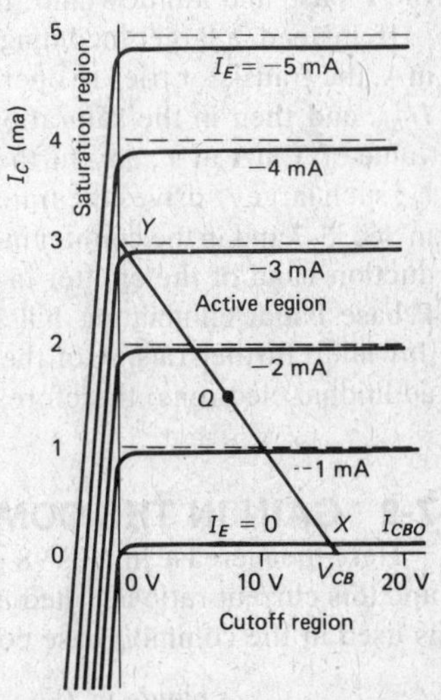

Figure 7-14 Collector curves to show α for common-base operation.

electrons flow through the base they become minority carriers in the P-type material; therefore, all of I_C consists of minority carriers flowing out of the base into the collector. (This is an essential point in bipolar transistor operation that is different from unipolar or "field-effect" transistor operation as described in Sec. 7-21.) The collector-to-base junction is reverse-biased, thus attracting majority carriers away from both sides of this junction. Only minority carriers pass through a reverse-biased junction; in the NPN transistor these minority carriers always are electrons.] If this I_E amounts to 1 milliampere (mA), Fig. 7-14 shows that I_C has increased to about 1 mA; if V_{EE} is changed so that I_E becomes 4 mA, I_C rises to nearly 4 mA. Thus, by increasing slightly the forward bias across the emitter-to-base junction, the size of I_E is increased. Perhaps 98 percent of this increase in I_E becomes a corresponding increase in I_C; the other 2 percent flows through the base connection, opposing and reversing the tiny base current that previously furnished I_{CBO}.

In Fig. 7-14 a load line XY is added (for $R_L = 5\ \text{k}\Omega$, at $V_{CC} = 15$ V) and V_{EE} is adjusted until $I_E = 1.5$ mA, so that the transistor operates at the quiescent point Q; this procedure is similar to that shown in Fig. 5-10 and discussed in Sec. 5-5. If an incoming signal now makes I_E swing down to 0.5 mA and up to 2.5 mA, this 2-mA p-p input I_E causes about 1.96-mA p-p output I_C; the transistor is operating along the straight line between X and Y, thereby gradually varying the output current I_C in proportion to I_E. Between X and Y the transistor is said to be operating in the *active* region. As indicated in Fig. 7-13*b*, each slight change at the emitter raises the N conduction band and lowers hill J slightly so that a few more electrons can pass into the P base and fall downhill; thus I_C is varied gradually.

If, instead, a larger incoming signal makes I_E swing down to 0 and up to 4 mA, the transistor tries to operate alternately in the cutoff region below X or I_{CBO}, and then in the saturation region to the left of Y. When I_E reaches a value of 3 mA at Y, any further increase in I_E causes very little increase in I_C; such large I_E drives the transistor into saturation (as is used for switching, in Sec. 5-7 and in the counter in Sec. 10-14). At saturation or point Y, the conduction band of the emitter in Fig. 7-13*b* is raised to the same level as the P-base band, eliminating hill J so that all electrons can pass into P and downhill; further raising of the emitter conduction band produces very few additional electrons; therefore, I_C cannot increase further.

7-9 GAIN IN THE COMMON-BASE CIRCUIT

Here the increase in I_C is 98 percent, or 0.98, as large as the increase in I_E, and this current ratio is called α, where this ratio applies when the transistor is used in the common-base connection. As described in Sec. 5-9,

$$\alpha = \frac{\text{change in } I_C}{\text{change in } I_E} = -\frac{\Delta I_C}{\Delta I_E} \qquad \text{(while } V_{CB} \text{ is constant)}$$

The minus sign for α is explained in Sec. 7-10. (Δ = delta.) Since a change in I_E applies a varying input signal to this transistor, this signal moves forward through the circuit so as to cause a change in the output signal I_C. Since α is less than 1.0 this common-base circuit cannot provide current amplification. Moreover, the entire change in emitter current must be supplied by the input signal; this is not true in the common-emitter circuit of Sec. 7-11.

With forward bias, the emitter-to-base junction contains little resistance; therefore, I_E is limited by a small external resistor R_E of less than 50 ohms (Ω) or by resistance within the source. Here, if an input signal changes I_E by 2 milliamperes (mA), the voltage variation in the emitter circuit is only 0.1 volt (V). But I_C is nearly equal to I_E, so this 2 mA flows also through R_L in the collector circuit; since R_L easily can be 10,000 Ω, or 10 kΩ, the variation in output across R_L is about 20 V. Here the voltage gain is 20 V/0.1 V, or 200; a power gain of 20 to 1 easily is available. [Since the transistor makes it possible to transfer a small signal (applied across a small input resistor) into a large signal across a large output resistor, it acts as a "transfer resistor," thus suggesting the name "transistor."]

7-10 TRANSISTOR STANDARD CURRENTS AND VOLTAGES

For the NPN transistor, conventional current I_C flows into the collector and combines with I_B flowing into the base, to form I_E flowing out of the emitter (as is shown by the arrow direction in its symbol). However, adopted standards state that all currents *entering* a transistor are considered to be positive, as shown in Fig. 7-15; positive values of V_{EB} and V_{CB} also are established. On this basis, the outgoing I_E of the NPN transistor is treated as a negative quantity; this explains why a (−) appears before the values of I_E in Fig. 7-14. Also, since the N-type emitter is biased by a voltage whose polarity is opposite to that of V_{EB} shown in Fig. 7-15, the V_{EB} of the NPN transistor is considered to be a negative quantity.

For a PNP transistor, conventional current I_E flows into its emitter, as is shown by the arrow direction in its symbol in Fig. 7-15. Therefore, both I_B and I_C flow out of this transistor and are said to be negative quantities. Likewise, since the P-type collector is biased by a voltage whose polarity is opposite to that of the standard V_{CB}, the collector-to-base voltage of the PNP

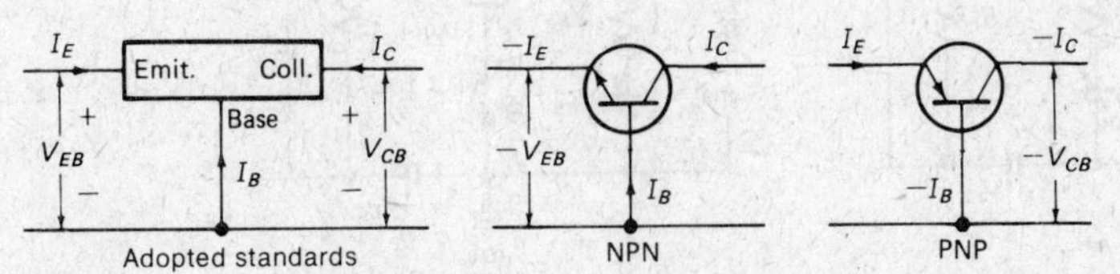

Figure 7-15 Polarities and current directions considered as standard.

transistor is negative. Using these standards, the collector curves (similar to Fig. 7-14 but giving data for a PNP transistor) show values of $-I_C$ versus $-V_{CB}$, for selected amounts of $+I_E$.

Notice that α is the ratio of the changes in the current I_C and I_E. Using the standard directions shown in Fig. 7-15, I_E leaves the NPN transistor as I_C enters it, or I_E enters the PNP transistor as I_C leaves it; therefore, one of these two currents must be negative. Thus α is used as a negative quantity merely to conform to these standard directions; α never is less than zero. In the common-emitter circuit below, β is the ratio of the changes in the currents I_C and I_B. Since both I_C and I_B enter the NPN transistor, and both leave the PNP transistor, β is a positive quantity. (In Secs. 7-13 and 7-15, h_{fb} is negative but h_{fe} is positive.)

7-11 THE COMMON-EMITTER CIRCUIT AND BETA

The NPN transistor (used above in the common-base circuit) next is connected into the more frequently used common-emitter circuit, as shown in Fig. 7-16; two arrangements in Fig. 7-16*a* and *b* show the same circuit. This circuit differs from Fig. 7-13 in that the transistor now is to be controlled by its base current I_B instead of by I_E; the emitter remains steady at ground potential. Since the negative side of V_{BB} is applied to the N-type emitter, the emitter-to-base junction is forward-biased; the collector-to-base junction is reverse-biased by V_{CC}, which is a much larger voltage than V_{BB}.

For Fig. 7-16, while no signal is applied and while S is open to prevent emitter current, the transistor energy levels are like those in Fig. 7-13*a* and are shown again by the solid lines in Fig. 7-17. Whereas in the common-base circuit of Fig. 7-13, the bias V_{EE} made the emitter more negative so as to raise the band levels and to lower hill J, in Fig. 7-17 the bias V_{BB} makes the base more positive. Since this added energy moves the P-type base downward to levels of greater energy, this also lowers the hill at J; this increases the flow of electrons from the N emitter into the P base and

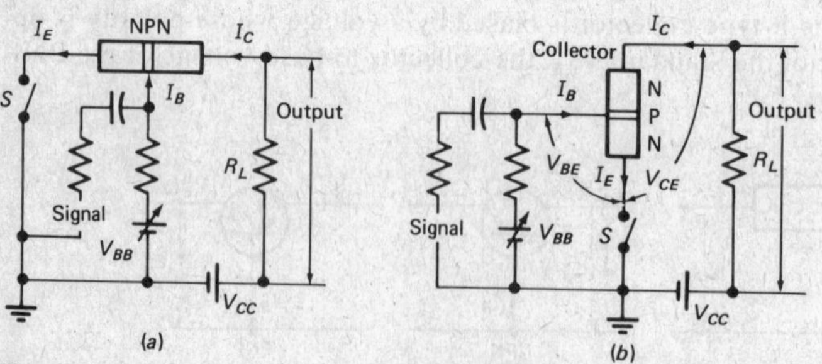

Figure 7-16 NPN transistor in common-emitter circuit.

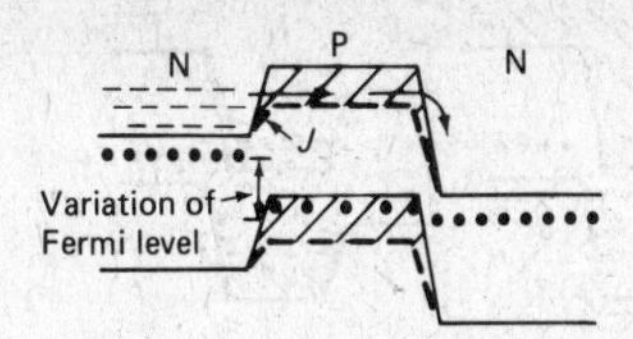

Figure 7-17 Shift of energy level of base can control the common-emitter circuit.

downhill so as to increase the collector current. When a rapidly changing signal changes the base current, the energy level of this P-type material alternately is raised and lowered within the region shown shaded in Fig. 7-17.

In Sec. 7-8 an input signal change of 2 mA in I_E is needed to cause a 1.96-mA change in output current I_C; since $I_E = I_C + I_B$ this shows also a 0.04 mA variation in I_B. In contrast, in the common-emitter circuit of Fig. 7-16, the input signal can be merely this small 0.04 mA change in I_B, yet this can cause a 2-mA variation in I_E; therefore, I_C undergoes the same 1.96-mA change in output as before. Note that the current-amplification factor now is

$$\beta = \frac{\text{change in } I_C}{\text{change in } I_B} = \frac{\Delta I_C}{\Delta I_B} \qquad \text{(while } V_{CE} \text{ is constant)}$$

Therefore, this "common-emitter beta" $\beta = 1.96 \text{ mA} / 0.04 \text{ mA} = 49$. Since the transistor $\alpha = 0.98$ in this example, it is seen that $\beta = \alpha / (1 - \alpha) = 0.98 / 0.02 = 49$. This common-emitter circuit has a high current amplification as well as good voltage gain; therefore, it provides much better power gain than does the common-base circuit.

7-12 ENERGY LEVELS IN PNP TRANSISTOR

When a PNP transistor is used in a common-base circuit, Fig. 7-18*a* shows that the battery polarities are reversed as compared with those shown in Fig. 5-12; all current directions are reversed, as is shown also by the arrow of the emitter within the transistor symbol. Before connection into the circuit, the energy levels of the PNP unit are shown in Fig. 7-18*b* (for comparison with the NPN unit in Fig. 7-12). The holes cannot move downhill, since extra energy is needed to push these (+) charges downward, nearer to the positive nucleus of the atom.

A reverse bias, applied across the collector-to-base junction, raises the position of the P-type collector (to a level of lower energy for P material), at the right-hand side in Fig. 7-18*c;* the few holes originally present in the N base at room temperature (minority carriers) easily move up the hill *F* and become the flow of I_{CBO}. When forward bias is added across the emitter-to-base junction, this added positive potential lowers the position of the P-type emitter, thus increasing its energy level so that the holes move more easily down the smaller hill at *G*, then pass quickly across the thin N-type base (as minority carriers) and continue up the hill *F*, thus increasing the collector current.

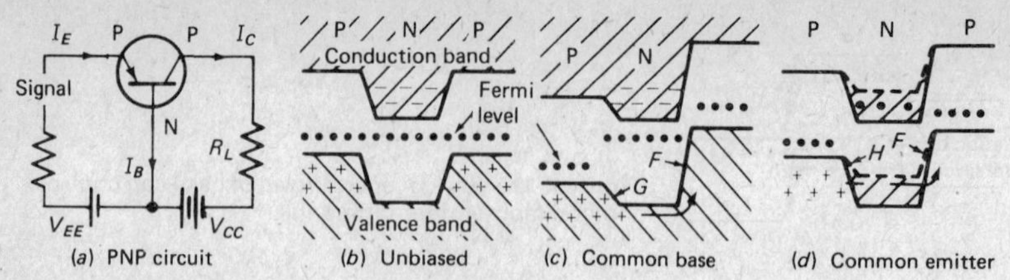

Figure 7-18 Energy levels in PNP transistor.

When the PNP transistor is used instead in a common-emitter circuit, Fig. 7-18*d* shows that the energy level of the P-type emitter now remains constant. When the incoming signal drives the base more negative, the energy level of this N-type base is raised so as to decrease the hill at *H*, thus increasing the flow of holes from the emitter through the base and up the hill *F*. Comparison with Fig. 7-17 shows that the movement of electrons (as minority carriers) is the main controlled electric flow within the NPN transistor but that the movement of holes (as minority carriers) is the main controlled conventional current in the PNP transistor.

7-13 TRANSISTOR PARAMETERS AND EQUIVALENT CIRCUIT

How well a transistor can perform usually is stated by giving the values of its parameters; such numerical values are published by each manufacturer of transistors. A transistor may be described by a set of four parameters to be explained below; these values describe the performance of the transistor only when its input signal is changing, thus causing a changing or ac output. [Similarly, a vacuum tube may be described by three interrelated parameters—μ (a voltage ratio), r_p (a resistance), and g_m (a conductance).]

Many different kinds or sets of parameters have been used in recent years; the *h* or hybrid parameters are most popular and are used here. (Sets of Z parameters or *r* parameters have been used generally; these values are difficult to measure under certain required open-circuit conditions. Only two of the *h* parameters are measured with open circuit, while the other two are measured with short circuit; this mixture of measurement requirements suggests the name of *hybrid* or *h parameters*.)

To help explain how parameters are determined, a transistor is regarded merely as a box, shown in Fig. 7-19, that has an input current i_i, an output current i_o, an input voltage v_i and an output voltage v_o; each of these is only the ac or changing current or voltage that results from a varying signal. The dc supplies or bias batteries previously included serve only to set the operating point *Q* (in Sec. 5-5), and so they are omitted in this discussion and in Fig. 7-19.

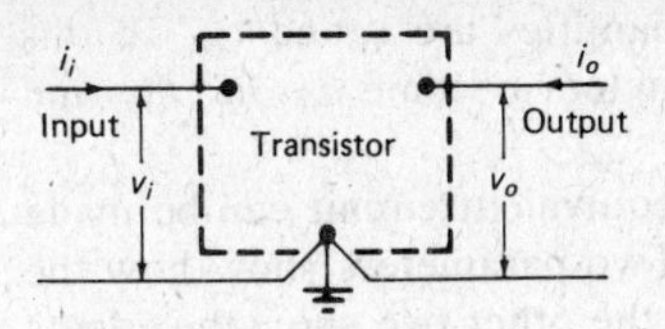

Figure 7-19 General treatment of transistor by input-output voltages and currents.

Based on these varying or changing values, the four h parameters are called:

h_i = input resistance (or impedance) $= v_i / i_i$

h_f = forward current transfer ratio $= i_o / i_i$

h_r = reverse voltage transfer ratio $= v_i / v_o$

h_o = output conductance (or admittance) $= i_o / v_o$

Sometimes the h parameters are shown having number subscripts instead of letters, such as h_{21} instead of h_f. Here the numeral 1 refers to the input side while 2 refers to the output side. Thus h_{21} indicates a change in the 2 side (or output) that is caused by a change in the 1 side (or input). So

$$h_i = v_1 / i_1 = h_{11} \qquad h_f = i_2 / i_1 = h_{21}$$

$$h_r = v_1 / v_2 = h_{12} \qquad h_o = i_2 / v_2 = h_{22}$$

When a transistor is operated in a common-base circuit, Fig. 7-20*a* identifies the input quantities as i_e and v_{eb}, while the output quantities are i_c and v_{cb}. To show that the parameter values apply to the transistor while it is used in this common-base circuit, a second subscript b is added, thus forming h_{ib}, h_{fb}, h_{rb}, and h_{ob}. Similarly, for the common-collector circuit in Fig. 7-20*c*, the parameters become h_{ic}, h_{fc}, h_{rc}, and h_{oc}.

A PNP transistor may be used in place of the NPN unit shown in Fig. 7-20, since the bias or dc values are not shown in the equivalent circuit of Fig. 7-21.

The following discussion uses the same transistor, but it is used in the common-emitter circuit; here Fig. 7-20*b* shows that the input quantities

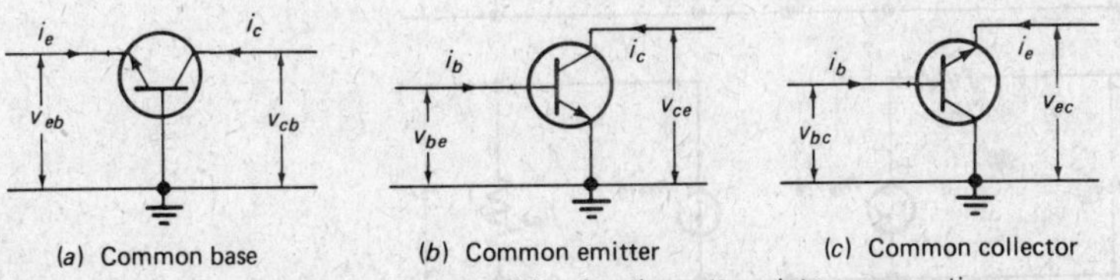

Figure 7-20 Input and output quantities for three transistor connections.

now become i_b and v_{be} while the output quantities are i_c and v_{ce}. In this common-emitter circuit the transistor parameters become h_{ie}, h_{fe}, h_{re}, and h_{oe}.

By the use of these four parameters, an equivalent circuit can be made that represents the transistor in operation. Two parameters show how the transistor reacts to changes in input current; the other two show the effects of a varying output voltage. Depending on current variation, Fig. 7-21*a* shows the parameters h_{ie} and h_{fe}, now to be described.

When the tiny changing voltage v_{be} is applied directly between base and emitter, a changing current flows through the base-to-emitter junction. By Ohm's law ($V = IR$), $v_{be} / i_b = h_{ie}$ or the *input resistance*. Further, when i_b is the changing base current or input signal, a much larger current flows in the transistor collector circuit. In Sec. 7-11 the signal i_b is said to cause an output i_c that is β times as large as i_b. In Fig. 7-21, the parameter h_{fe} is the same as β; therefore, the collector of the transistor acts as a current generator that produces a constant current that flows in the direction of the arrow and is equal in size to $h_{fe}i_b$. Thus h_{fe} shows the ratio between currents i_b and i_c, whereby the effect of the input current is transferred forward into the output; so h_{fe} is called the *forward current transfer ratio*.

Neither h_{ie} nor h_{fe} includes any effect caused by a variation in collector-to-base voltage; thus v_{ce} is considered to be constant, as though any variation in v_{ce} is short-circuited through a large capacitor C_1. This is why h_{ie} and h_{fe} are called *short-circuit parameters*.

If the output voltage v_{ce} now is permitted to vary, as it does in a useful

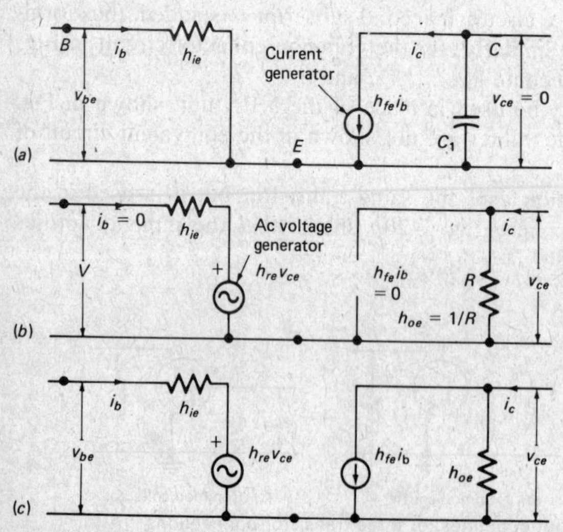

Figure 7-21 Equivalent circuit showing h parameters.

circuit, two more effects must be included in the equivalent circuit, by the addition of parameters h_{oe} and h_{re}. As is shown by typical transistor performance curves (such as Fig. 5-10 and again in Fig. 7-22), the collector current I_C increases slightly as V_{CE} is increased, even though I_B is held constant at 100 μA, or 0.1 mA. Therefore, the total output current includes not only a fixed value of $h_{fe}i_b$, but also a current that increases at greater values of V_{CE}; such an increase is like the current that flows through a resistor R, added across v_{ce} in Fig. 7-21b. The amount of this added current $= v_{ce} / R$ or $= v_{ce} \times$ conductance. Although a resistor symbol is added in the equivalent diagram, the added current is indicated by the parameter h_{oe}, which is the conductance of this added circuit. To measure h_{oe}, the varying i_b must be made zero so that the generator $h_{fe}i_b$ produces no current; then *output conductance* $h_{oe} = i_c / v_{ce}$.

It is known also that the varying v_{ce} affects the input circuit by feeding back a small ac voltage; this effect is included in Fig. 7-21b by a generator that produces the voltage $h_{re}v_{ce}$. Here h_{re} is the portion of the ac output voltage that is transferred in the reverse direction to the input; so h_{re} is called the *reverse voltage transfer ratio*. This ratio usually is less than $^1/_{1000}$ but can be determined by measurement of v_{ce} and the base-to-emitter voltage at V, provided that no ac voltage exists across h_{ie}; for this purpose the varying i_b must be zero.

Since the values of both h_{re} and h_{oe} are measured while no variation occurs in the base current, these parameters specify that the total base current I_B shall be constant (and thus may consist of only the dc bias). To remove the variation in I_B, the input signal is made zero by opening the ac input circuit. This is why h_{re} and h_{oe} are called *open-circuit parameters*.

The complete equivalent circuit appears in Fig. 7-21c, so as to represent the transistor when it is used in the common-emitter circuit. This same equivalent circuit is used for the common-base or common-collector arrangements, but the input and output values must be changed, as indicated in Fig. 7-20; the numerical values of the parameters will differ for the various arrangements, as is discussed further in Sec. 7-15.

7-14 GRAPHICAL MEANING OF *h* PARAMETERS

Typical curves are shown in Figs. 7-22 and 7-23 for an NPN transistor operating in a common-emitter circuit. Using these curves, the approximate values of the h parameters may be determined by graphic methods. In the input or collector curves of Fig. 7-22, a load line is plotted for $V_{CC} = 16$ V and $R_L = 1000\ \Omega$. The base current is adjusted to a dc value of 0.15 mA so that the transistor operates at point Q, at a steady collector current of 10 mA.

Based on the discussion in Sec. 7-13, the forward current ratio is found to be the *change* or difference in I_C that is caused by a certain *change* in I_B, provided that the output voltage V_{CE} remains constant. Along vertical line

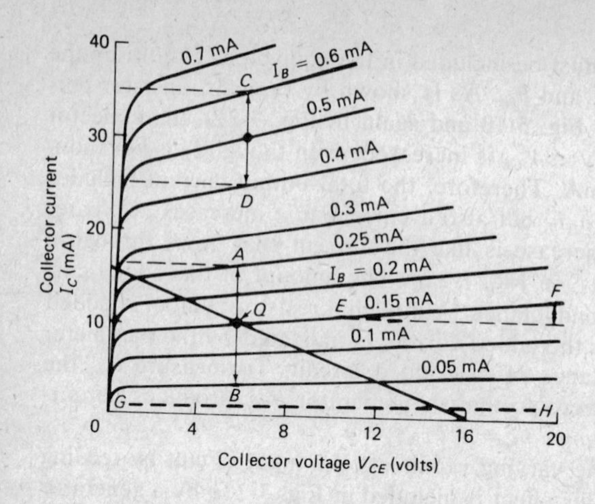

Figure 7-22 Graphic means for finding parameters h_{fe} and h_{oe}.

AB in Fig. 7-22, I_B varies from 0.25 mA at A to 0.05 mA at B and causes I_C to change from 16.5 mA down to 3.5 mA; meanwhile, V_{CE} is the same at both A and B. Thus ΔI_C (or difference in I_C) is caused by ΔI_B, while V_{CE} is constant. The forward current ratio is

$$h_{fe} = \frac{\Delta I_C}{\Delta I_B} = \frac{16.5 - 3.5}{0.25 - 0.05} = \frac{13 \text{ mA}}{0.2 \text{ mA}} = 65$$

If the biasing current is increased to 0.5 mA, between C and D, the new value of h_{fe} is $(35 - 25)/(0.6 - 0.4) = 50$.

Above, the output conductance h_{oe} is shown to be the change in I_C that is caused by the change in V_{CE}, while I_B remains constant. Passing through Q in Fig. 7-22, the line marked $I_B = 0.15$ mA has a small upward slope; at all points on this line, I_B is constant. At E, V_{CE} is 10 V and I_C is 11 mA; at F, where V_{CE} has increased to 20 V, I_C is 13 mA. The slope of this line is equal to the output conductance, and

$$h_{oe} = \frac{\Delta I_C}{\Delta V_{CE}} = \frac{13 - 11}{20 - 10} = \frac{2 \text{ mA}}{10 \text{ V}} = \frac{0.002 \text{ A}}{10 \text{ V}}$$

$$= 0.0002 \text{ mho} = (0.0002 \text{ siemen}) = 200 \ \mu\text{mhos (micromhos)}$$

To show that h_{oe} becomes much smaller at lower current values, a line GH is added near the bottom of Fig. 7-22. Here V_{CE} changes through a range of 20 V while I_C increases from 1 mA at G to only 2 mA at H. The new h_{oe} is 1 mA / 20 V = 0.00005 mho = 50 μmhos.

To show the remaining parameters h_{ie} and h_{re}, the input curves of Fig. 7-23 are needed; here the tiny base current I_B rises as the small base-to-emitter voltage is increased. [Before this forward bias V_{BE} is applied, Sec. 7-8 mentions that the base current consists only of I_{co} (or I_{CBO}) flowing through the reverse-biased collector-to-base junction. As V_{BE} is increased, this I_{co}

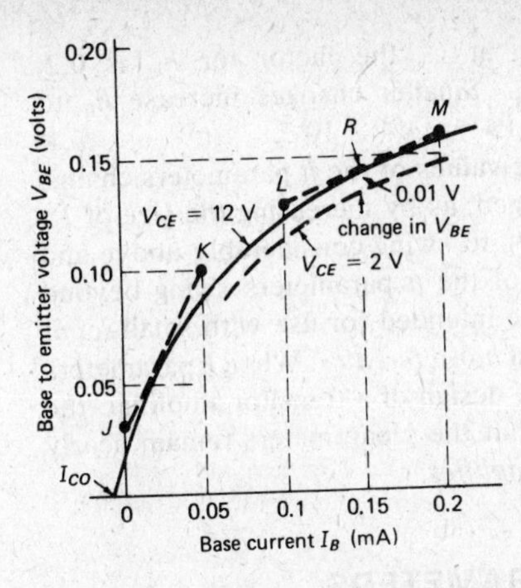

Figure 7-23 Graphic means for finding parameters h_{ie} and h_{re}.

must be offset before I_B can rise to higher values.] In Sec. 7-13, the input resistance h_{ie} is seen to be the ratio between the change in input V_{BE} and the corresponding change in I_B, while V_{CE} remains constant; thus h_{ie} may be measured in Fig. 7-23 by the slope of the solid curve, drawn for a constant value of $V_{CE} = 12$ V. At small V_{BE} the curve slope is shown by the tangent line JK. Here

$$h_{ie} = \frac{\Delta V_{BE}}{\Delta I_B} = \frac{0.1 - 0.025}{0.05 - 0} = \frac{0.075 \text{ V}}{0.05 \text{ mA}} = 1500\ \Omega$$

But when the bias current I_B is raised to 0.15 mA, the slope of the line is decreased, as is shown at LM; now $h_{ie} = (0.16 - 0.13) / (0.2 - 0.1) = 0.03 \text{ V} / 0.1 \text{ mA} = 300\ \Omega$.

The parameter h_{re} is too small to be seen easily in Fig. 7-23. The small vertical distance between the dashed line (drawn for $V_{CE} = 2$ V) and the longer solid line (for $V_{CE} = 12$ V) shows at R that this 10-V difference in output voltage V_{CE} has changed the input voltage V_{BE} by about 0.01 V. While I_B remains constant at 0.15 mA,

$$h_{re} = \frac{\Delta V_{BE}}{\Delta V_{CE}} = \frac{0.01 \text{ V}}{10 \text{ V}} = 0.001$$

which is the reverse voltage ratio in this example.

Instead of using curves like Figs. 7-22 and 7-23, the performance of a transistor often is described by stating its parameters at one value of emitter current, accompanied by a graph such as Fig. 7-24 that shows (on logarithmic scales) how much each parameter changes as I_E is varied. As an example, characteristics may be given as $h_{ie} = 1500\ \Omega$, $h_{fe} = 50$, $h_{re} = 7 \times 10^{-4}$, and $h_{oe} = 40\ \mu$mhos, when $I_E = 1$ mA. At $I_E = 1$ mA, point A in Fig. 7-24 shows a factor of 1.0; but if the size of I_E is increased to 10 mA, the graph shows at B that h_{oe} is increased 8 times, so that the new

$hoe = 8 \times 40 = 320$ μmhos. Similarly, at C, the factor for h_{ie} is 0.2, so the new $h_{ie} = 0.2 \times 1500 = 300\ \Omega$. Smaller changes increase h_{fe} to $1.3 \times 50 = 65$ and raise h_{re} to $2 \times 7 \times 10^{-4} = 1.4 \times 10^{-3}$.

The curves in Fig. 7-24 warn that the values of the h parameters change greatly if the operating point Q is changed, as by increasing the size of I_E. Further, if the incoming signal causes I_E to swing considerably above and below the chosen Q point, the values of the h parameters swing beyond useful limits. Since these parameters are intended for use with small input signals, they are called the *h small-signal characteristics*. When h parameters and an equivalent circuit are used in the design of a transitor amplifier, the input signal is assumed to be small so that the h parameters remain nearly constant; this is called a *small-signal amplifier*.

7-15 CHANGE OF h^b to h^e PARAMETERS

Often the transistor characteristics are given only as common-base parameters; for example, h_{11} or $h_{ib} = 30$ ohms (Ω), h_{21} or $h_{fb} = -0.98$, h_{12} or $h_{rb} = 6 \times 10^{-4}$, h_{22} or $h_{ob} = 1.4 \times 10^{-6}$ mho. Before the performance of this transistor can be calculated when operating in a common-emitter circuit, the above h^b values must be converted into the corresponding h^e common-emitter parameters. The following relations are used for this purpose; the resulting h^e values are calculated for the above example.

$$h_{ie} = \frac{h_{ib}}{1 + h_{fb}} \qquad \frac{30}{1 - 0.98} = \frac{30}{0.02} = 1500\ \Omega = h_{ie}$$

$$h_{fe} = \frac{-h_{fb}}{1 + h_{fb}} \qquad \frac{0.98}{1 - 0.98} = 49 = h_{fe}$$

$$h_{re} = \frac{h_{ib}h_{ob}}{1 + h_{fb}} - h_{rb} \qquad \frac{30 \times 1.4 \times 10^{-6}}{1 - 0.98} - 6 \times 10^{-4} = 15 \times 10^{-4} = h_{re}$$

$$h_{oe} = \frac{h_{ob}}{1 + h_{fb}} \qquad \frac{1.4 \times 10^{-6}}{1 - 0.98} = 70 \times 10^{-6} \text{ mho} = 70\ \mu\text{mhos} = h_{oe}$$

7-16 TRANSISTOR AMPLIFIER GAIN

When the correct parameters are known, the gain produced by a transistor circuit may be found by the equations shown below, obtained from the equivalent circuit. When two or more transistor stages are combined (as in Fig. 6-14) so as to produce greater gain, the input signal to stage 2 is a varying current that must be supplied by the output of stage 1; for greater gain, the input resistance R_i of stage 2 should be nearly the same number of ohms as the output resistance R_o of stage 1 (a requirement called *impedance matching*, as described in Sec. 6-15). Whereas a vacuum tube gives only voltage gain, each transistor stage may provide current gain A_i as well as

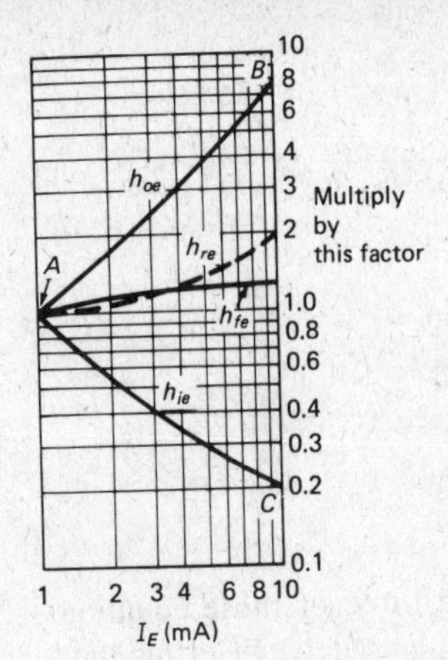

Figure 7-24 Variation in h parameters versus I_E.

voltage gain A_v; the product of A_i and A_v gives the power gain G of the transistor stage (as in an example in Sec. 5-6).

Figure 7-25 shows one stage of a common-emitter amplifier, together with its equivalent circuit. In the example calculations that follow, the transistor has the h^e parameters calculated in Sec. 7-15; the preceding stage acts as a source resistance $R_s = 500\ \Omega$, while the following stage acts as a load $R_L = 20{,}000\ \Omega$.

The input resistance R_i of the stage in Fig. 7-25 is the ac resistance measured between B and E, while the output is connected to R_L (which includes the input resistance of the following stage). By writing circuit equations around the equivalent circuit, it is found that input resistance

$$R_i = \frac{v_{be}}{i_b} = \frac{h_{ie} + (h_{ie}h_{oe} - h_{fe}h_{re})R_L}{1 + h_{oe}R_L}$$

Similarly, the output resistance R_o of this stage is the ac resistance measured between C and E, while the source R_s is connected to the input.

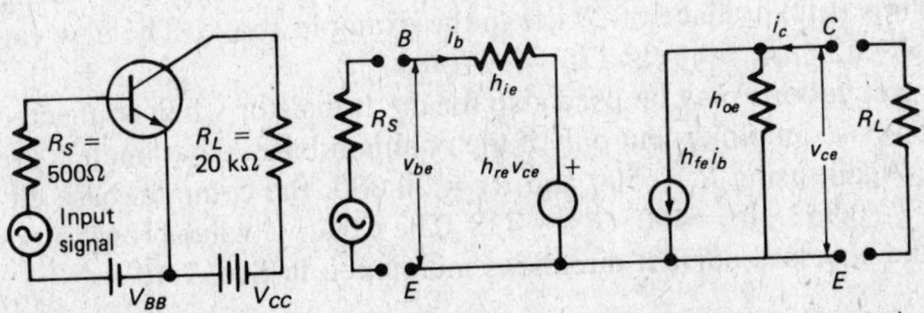

Figure 7-25 Equivalent circuit used to obtain amplifier resistances and gains.

Thus

$$R_o = \frac{v_{ce}}{i_c} = \frac{h_{ie} + R_s}{(h_{ie}h_{oe} - h_{fe}h_{re}) + h_{oe}R_s}$$

The voltage gain in Fig. 7-25 is

$$A_v = \frac{v_{ce}}{v_{be}} = \frac{-h_{fe}R_L}{h_{ie} + (h_{ie}h_{oe} - h_{fe}h_{re})R_L}$$

Current gain:

$$A_i = \frac{i_c}{i_b} = \frac{h_{fe}}{1 + h_{oe}R_L}$$

Since the quantity $(h_{ie}h_{oe} - h_{fe}h_{re})$ appears in three of these equations, this quantity often is called Δh^e and is calculated separately. Inserting the h^e parameter values calculated in Sec. 7-15, for this example $\Delta h^e = (1500\ \Omega)(7 \times 10^{-5}\text{ mho}) - (49)(1.5 \times 10^{-3}) = 0.105 - 0.0735 = 0.0315 = \Delta h^e$.

$$R_i = \frac{h_{ie} + \Delta h^e R_L}{1 + h_{oe}R_L} = \frac{1500 + 0.0315 \times 20{,}000}{1 + (7 \times 10^{-5})(2 \times 10^4)} = \frac{2130}{2.4} = 888\ \Omega$$

$$R_o = \frac{h_{ie} + R_s}{\Delta h^e + h_{oe}R_s} = \frac{1500 + 500}{0.0315 + (7 \times 10^{-5})(500)} = \frac{2000}{0.0665} = 30{,}000\ \Omega$$

$$A_v = \frac{-h_{fe}R_L}{h_{ie} + \Delta h^e R_L} = \frac{-49 \times 20{,}000}{1500 + 0.0315 \times 20{,}000} = \frac{-980{,}000}{2130} = -460$$

$$A_i = \frac{h_{fe}}{1 + h_{oe}R_L} = \frac{49}{1 + (7 \times 10^{-5})(2 \times 10^4)} = \frac{49}{2.4} = 20.4$$

This current gain A_i is smaller than h_{fe} and depends on the size of R_L external to the transistor; but the current ratio h_{fe} is a characteristic of the transistor alone, obtained when $R_L = 0$.

Power gain $G = A_iA_v = (20.4)(-460) = -9384$. This negative sign results from A_v, which is shown as negative merely to indicate that the output voltage wave is shifted 180° from the input voltage wave. The sizes of A_v and gain G are positive quantities.

The effect of using a smaller load resistance may be shown by using $R_L = 2$ kilohms (kΩ) in place of 20 kΩ in the example above. The new values are $A_v = -62.6$, $A_i = 43$, and $G = -2700$.

The above equations may be used also for the transistor when connected as a common-base amplifier, but only if the common-base h^b parameters are substituted. Again using $R_s = 500$ and $R_L = 20{,}000$, the common-base circuit has $A_i = -0.953$, $A_v = 460$, $G = -438$. The negative values result from the use of the standard current directions mentioned in Sec. 7-10.

7-17 SOLID-STATE DEVICES AT HIGH FREQUENCIES

When tubes, solid-state diodes, or transistors are used in industrial equipment at power frequencies [up to 10 kHz (or 10 kc)], it is customary to ignore the capacitive effects within these devices; thus no internal capacitors appear in Fig. 7-21 or the discussion above. However, at the higher frequencies used in communication circuits (and including fast switching actions in computing circuits), the usefulness of a transistor or tube is limited by its internal parts that act as tiny capacitors. Since the plate, grid, and cathode of a tube are made of metal surfaces separated by small distances in a vacuum, such interelectrode (grid-to-plate) capacitance may measure only 5 micromicrofarads ($\mu\mu$F), or 5 picofarads (pF), yet it may act like a short circuit when operating in the megahertz range (millions of cycles per second).

Further, a reverse-biased PN junction in a diode or transistor consists of two surfaces that are not separated in space yet contain a depletion region (Fig. 7-10) that acts electrically like an insulation between the surfaces. Thus the average PN junction has greater capacitance than a tube, and this tends to limit transistor operation to frequencies lower than those permissible with vacuum tubes. (The point-contact diode shown in Fig. 5-1 has much smaller areas in contact; the smaller capacitance lets such diodes be useful at higher frequencies.) Newer methods of making junction transistors decrease these capacitances, so that high-frequency transistors are available.

7-18 SPECIAL DIODES—THE ZENER DIODE

Four-layer PNPN devices are described in Sec. 9-1. However, by abnormal doping of the silicon material, special two-layer PN devices are made, such as the Zener diode and the tunnel diode.

The usual silicon PN diode, made with small amounts of doping or impurities, normally is used for the conduction of forward current; if reverse-biased, it is expected to operate well below the breakdown voltage shown in Fig. 5-3. However, many diodes are made with the purpose of operating often or continuously at a desired value of breakdown voltage; such a diode may be used so as to limit or regulate the amount of voltage applied to a load circuit.

If more than the usual amounts of impurities are added when the PN junction is made, the value of breakdown voltage is decreased. Thus curve A in Fig. 7-26 applies to a 50-volt (V) breakdown or Zener diode; when reverse voltage is applied across it [(+) at its N side], only a tiny leakage current flows until this reverse voltage has increased to 50 V. At this point the action of the diode changes abruptly, so that much greater current now can pass through it; the amount of this current must be limited by an external resistor R, so as not to exceed the rated current of the diode. A reason for this abrupt change is suggested by scientists, as given next.

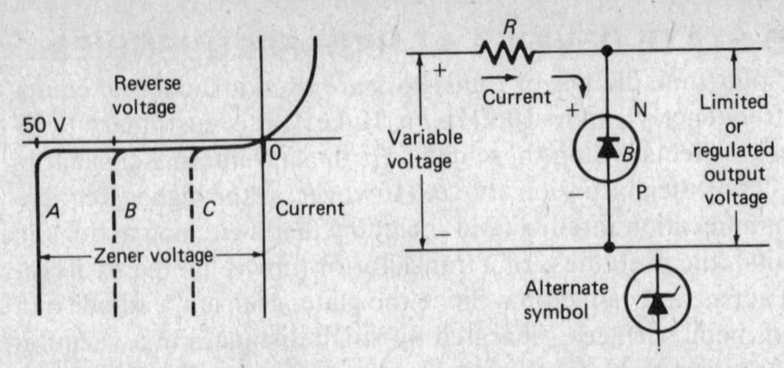

Figure 7-26 Circuit and behavior of a Zener or breakdown diode.

Reverse voltage across this PN junction produces the depletion region shown in Figs. 5-4 and 7-10; the voltage, applied across this narrow depletion region, produces a large electric field which can accelerate the few electrons (minority carriers) that exist in the P-type material at room temperature. At 50 V applied in this certain material, these speeded electrons gain enough energy to break other atoms upon collision, so as to form more electrons and holes; these new electrons also are speeded by the electric field so as to break still more atoms. This increasing "avalanche" effect makes the material become conductive, but only as this critical 50-V limit is reached; this also is called the *Zener voltage*, named for a scientist.

If a diode is substituted, wherein the PN junction is made of materials containing a much heavier (greater) doping of impurities, the breakdown voltage occurs at still lower level, as shown by curve *B* or *C* in Fig. 7-26. It is known that a greater doping decreases the width of the depletion region; thus a smaller voltage, applied across this narrower space, can produce the same size of electric field needed to speed the electrons and break atoms.

If the voltage terminals to such a Zener diode are interchanged, a very small forward voltage causes a large flow of current. Such action as an ordinary rectifier is not expected from a Zener diode; so conventional current normally is not permitted to flow in the direction of the arrow shown in its symbol. The useful avalanche electrons flow in the direction of the symbol arrow.

Thus the careful control of manufacturing processes makes available a wide variety of Zener (breakdown or reference) diodes, in small voltage steps between 2 and 1000 V and in sizes from 250 mW ($^1/_4$ watt) to 50 W. The use of Zener diodes as voltage regulators is discussed in Sec. 17-6, where calculations for an example circuit are shown. On ac circuits, two such Zener diodes are joined back to back, as in Figs. 27-2 and 27-5.

7-19 THE TUNNEL DIODE

This newer type of PN device is obtained when the doping or concentration of impurities is increased to more than 1000 times the amount used in an ordinary rectifier. By comparison with curves *A*, *B*, and *C* in Fig. 7-26, this great increase in doping reduces to zero the reverse breakdown voltage; therefore, the tunnel diode is used with a small forward applied voltage. Its symbol and characteristic curve are shown in Fig. 7-27; because of this unusual pattern wherein the tunnel-diode current decreases as the voltage across it rises, this PN device can act like a triode or a transistor. In its action as an amplifier, an oscillator, or an ON-OFF switch, this simple rugged diode performs faster than most transistors and is less affected by temperature or radiation.

The dashed curve in Fig. 7-27 shows how the current increases gradually in an ordinary PN diode, as the forward voltage across it rises; this is shown also in Fig. 5-3. In the tunnel diode, the solid line in Fig. 7-27 shows that a very small forward voltage (about 0.05 V) causes the current to increase to a peak point I_P. Then, while the forward voltage is rising to about 0.3 V, the tunnel-diode current decreases gradually to a valley point I_V. With further increase of forward voltage, the tunnel diode acts much like the ordinary rectifier, so that the current of either device rises to large values that must be limited by an external resistor. The tunnel diode has its greatest use and value in the range below 0.4 V, so as to take advantage of the negative-resistance or downslope part of the curve.

In the portion of the curve between peak I_P and valley I_V, this downslope indicates that the tunnel diode has negative conductance or negative ac resistance, since an increasing voltage causes a decreasing current (a negative increase). The amount of resistance is equal to the reciprocal of the slope of the curve.

The cause of the peak-point and valley-point current in the tunnel diode may be explained with the use of energy-level diagrams. Figure 7-9 shows the diagram for an ordinary PN junction before any voltage is applied across it; here the equalizing of the Fermi levels (shown separately in Fig. 7-7 for each type of material) has produced a small conduction hill and valence hill. But in the tunnel diode, the excessive doping in each material causes the Fermi level of the N type to lie within the conduction band; the Fermi level of the P type lies within the valence band. When these materials meet at a

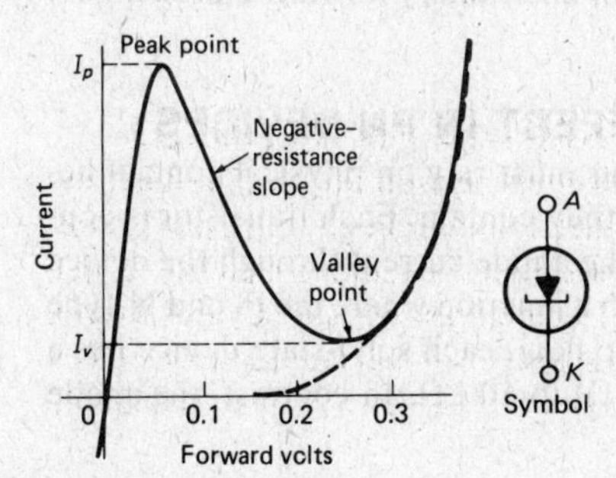

Figure 7-27 Behavior of a tunnel diode.

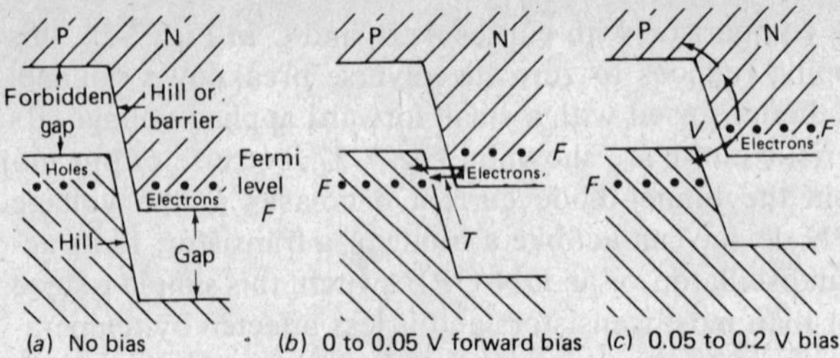

Figure 7-28 Energy levels in a tunnel diode.

junction, the Fermi level in P must become equal to the Fermi level in N; therefore, the energy levels are displaced greatly, as is shown in Fig. 7-28*a*. Since no voltage yet has been applied across the diode, no current flows.

When a very small forward bias is applied to the tunnel diode, Fig. 7-28*b* shows that the energy level of the N side has been raised, but it still overlaps, at *T*, a portion of the energies of the P side. As yet no electrons have enough energy to climb the "hill" from the N side into the P side of the conduction band. But here the new process of tunneling occurs; physicists suggest that many of the electrons cross at *T* into the valence band of the P-type material by seeming to tunnel through the hill or barrier gap between P and N. Thus the tunneling current increases toward the I_P value as the forward voltage rises to 0.05 V; this result is called the *Esaki current*, named for the discoverer of the tunnel-diode principle.

As the forward bias is increased above 0.05 V, Fig. 7-28*c* shows that the amount of *T* overlap is decreasing, so that fewer electrons can tunnel at *V* through to the P material. Therefore, the tunneling current decreases gradually toward the valley current I_V. But the size of the hill between P and N is decreasing meanwhile, so that more electrons may be able to climb into the P conduction band; this forms a normal diode current, as shown by the dashed curve in Fig. 7-27.

At forward voltages greater than 0.3 V, the decrease in tunneling current is more than offset by the increase in normal diode current: the energy-level diagram becomes like that of Fig. 7-11 for an ordinary forward-biased diode.

7-20 INTRODUCING FIELD EFFECT IN PN DEVICES

All solid-state devices described so far must rely on physical contact between the P- and N-type materials that they contain. Each transistor is controlled by a *flow* of electrons or holes; the anode current through the device is varied by a current that passes through a junction where the P- and N-type materials meet. To allow such current to flow, each solid-state device has a low input resistance, such as 50 ohms (Ω) to 10 kΩ. In contrast, the anode current through the average vacuum tube may be varied, not by a flow of grid current, but mainly by the potential applied at the grid; this produces an electric field that controls the amount of electrons flowing to the anode. As explained in Sec. 2-13, the input circuit (between tube grid and cathode) requires no flow of current; therefore, the input resistance to the tube circuit may be high, such as 10 kΩ to a few megohms.

To duplicate more closely the action within a vacuum tube, the PN field-effect transistor is used. Here the P- and N-type materials need not make physical contact; if they do join, they are reverse-biased, so that no current needs to flow between P and N. As is explained in Sec. 7-23, the main current of the field-effect transistor (between source and drain) is controlled by the *effect* of the electric *field* produced by the *voltage* applied between source and gate.

7-21 THE FIELD-EFFECT TRANSISTOR (FET)

Figure 7-29 shows a circuit using a field-effect transistor made of a block of N-type material that has a P insert on each side (as shown in Fig. 7-31). The two ends of the N block are marked *S* (source) or *D* (drain) and are connected in series with a load R_L; the voltage V_{DS} appears across the FET, from *D* to *S*. The load current is also I_D, which flows through the *channel* of the N block; in contrast to the earlier transistor,[7-8] this current does not cross any PN junction. The two P inserts are connected together to form the gate *G*; the voltage V_{GS} provides negative bias, so that no current flows in the gate as long as *G* is held more negative than *S*.

As shown in Fig. 7-29*b*, this certain FET conducts about 8 milliamperes (mA) through its N channel when V_{GS} is zero; but if V_{GS} is made −4 V, I_D is reduced to 2 mA. These amounts of current change very little when V_{DS} varies. These curves closely resemble those for a pentode tube. To show how this voltage at gate *G* (without any current through *G*) can control the amount of I_D that flows through R_L, the following details are given.

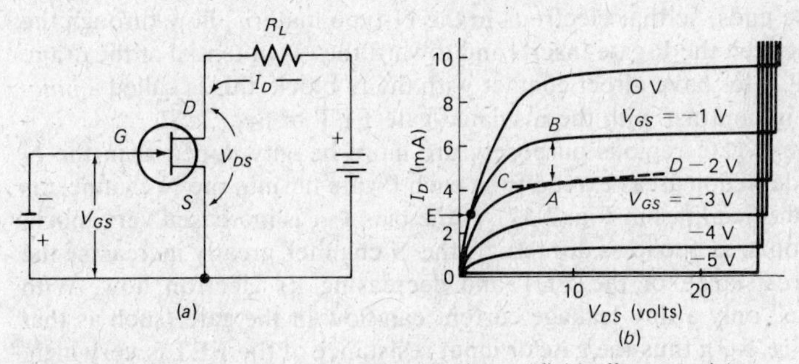

Figure 7-29 Circuit and performance of N-channel field-effect transistor.

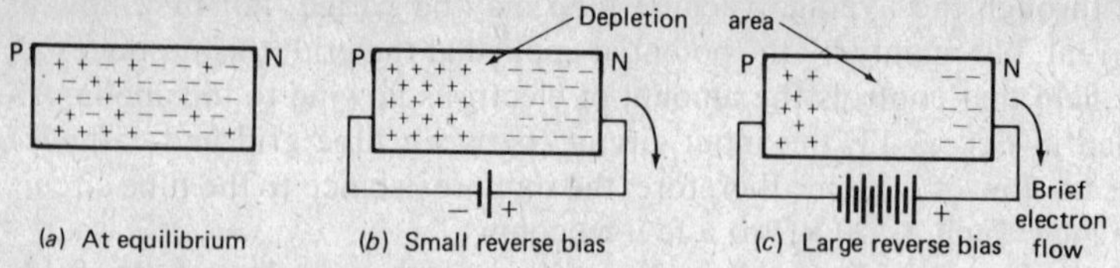

(*a*) At equilibrium (*b*) Small reverse bias (*c*) Large reverse bias

Figure 7-30 Large reverse bias increases the depletion area.

7-22 THE PN DEPLETION AREA

The field-effect transistor controls its amount of channel current by varying the depletion area within the N channel between the P inserts shown in Fig. 7-31. In Sec. 7-7, the region near a PN junction is described as a *depletion area* when the junction is reverse-biased. Further, Fig. 7-30 shows that this area increases in width when the reverse bias is increased. In Fig. 7-30*a*, without any bias, some electrons (−) appear among the countless holes (+) in the P material. When a small reverse bias is applied, Fig. 7-30*b* shows that all holes have withdrawn into P, and all electrons into N, leaving the center area depleted of charges and therefore less able to conduct current. When the reverse bias is increased, electrons flow briefly from N to the (+) battery terminal; electrons from the (−) terminal enter the P region and combine with holes. Fewer total charges remain in Fig. 7-30*c*, and the width of the depletion or nonconducting region has increased.

7-23 THE JUNCTION FET

When two such PN junctions are located on opposite sides of the N bar, as in Fig. 7-31, this forms a N-channel FET. Here the two P regions are connected together to act as the gate; the battery V_{GS} (voltage from gate to source) applies the reverse-bias voltage; this voltage produces the electric field that causes the depletion areas. In Fig. 7-32 the two ends of the N block are called the *source* and the *drain;* a second battery V_{SD} is connected between these ends, so that electrons in the N-type material flow through the channel between the P-gate inserts and toward the (+) potential at the drain. Since the P gates have direct contact with the N block, this is called a *junction* FET, in contrast with the insulated-gate FET of Sec. 7-27.

Since the P-gate regions purposely are more heavily doped than the N block, the depletion areas extend from each P gate far into the N channel (as shown by dashed lines in Fig. 7-32). If the bias V_{GS} is increased very much, the depletion area occupies or restricts the N channel, greatly increasing the electrical resistance of the FET and decreasing its electron flow. With reverse bias, only a tiny leakage current can flow in the gate (such as that shown in Fig. 5-3); thus the gate or input resistance of the FET is very high. As shown by the curves in Fig. 7-29, this N-channel FET acts like a pentode tube, in that the controlling input signal is a voltage V_{GS} instead of a current.

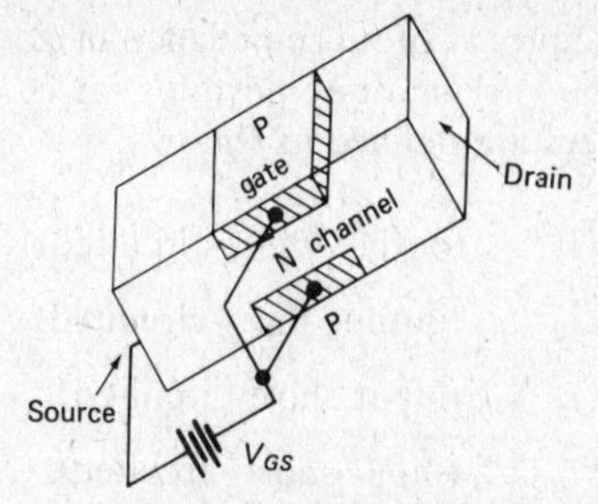

Figure 7-31 The N-channel FET.

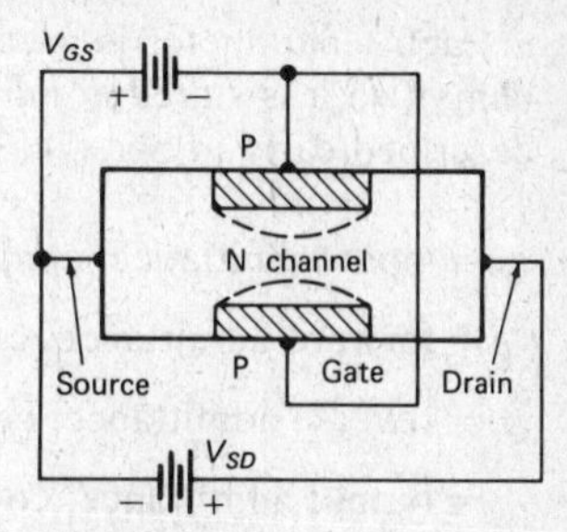

Figure 7-32 Depletion areas controlled by bias V_{GS}.

[Such a vacuum-tube pentode may be replaced by inserting a pair of junction FETs (N-channel) called a *Fetron.*] Also, its conduction consists of a stream of electrons only, which flow directly from a source (like a cathode) to a drain (like an anode) without crossing any PN junction.

In contrast, the main flow through the usual transistor must pass through both a forward-biased and a reverse-biased junction. As mentioned in Sec. 7-2, the common transistor is considered to be *bipolar*, since its conduction is formed of both majority and minority carriers. But the FET is *unipolar*; both holes and electrons are present, but the main conduction is formed of majority carriers only (such as electrons in N-type material).

At the right in Fig. 7-29, near $V_{DS} = 25$ volts (V), the sudden upturn of the curves shows that a breakdown voltage has been reached; this occurs between gate and drain, where the greatest voltage difference exists. This breakdown value is called BV_{DGO}; values to 50 V are commonly available.

7-24 FET PARAMETERS AND EQUIVALENT CIRCUIT

The parameters used for describing FET performance are like those used for a vacuum tube. Instead of using the transistor h parameters of Sec. 7-13, it is more practical to use y or admittance parameters, which are better suited to these high-impedance FETs. Using y parameters, the FET equivalent circuit is shown in Fig. 7-33, based on the common-source connection. (This resembles Fig. 7-21 of the usual bipolar transistor.)

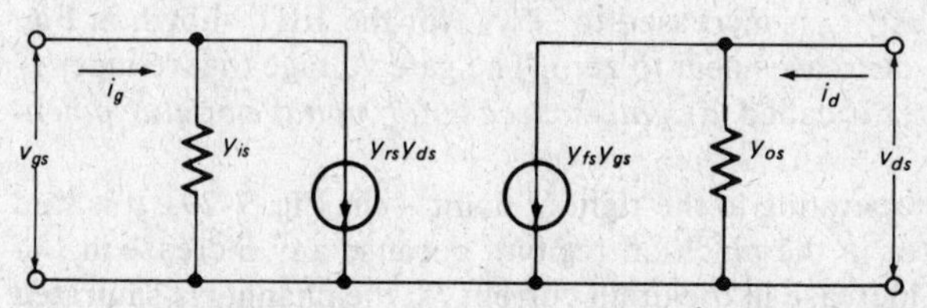

Figure 7-33 Equivalent circuit of FET, showing y parameters.

Each y parameter is an admittance (or reciprocal of an impedance of Z ohms); so it is stated in mhos. Using only the varying or ac portions (as is described early in Sec. 7-13), the y parameters are defined as follows:

y_{is} = input admittance, common source $= i_g / v_{gs}$ (output short-circuited)

y_{fs} = forward admittance, common source $= i_d / v_{gs}$ (output short-circuited)

y_{rs} = reverse admittance, common source $= i_g / v_{ds}$ (input short-circuited)

y_{os} = output admittance, common source $= i_d / v_{ds}$ (input short-circuited)

With output short-circuited, v_{ds} is constant; with input short-circuited, v_{gs} is constant.

At frequencies below 100 kHz (or kc/sec), y_{fs} and y_{os} are the more important. (The forward admittance y_{fs} also is called g_m and corresponds to mutual conductance g_m in a vacuum tube. The output admittance y_{os} also is called g_{ds}, which corresponds to $1 / r_p$ in a vacuum tube.)

7-25 GRAPHICAL MEANING OF y PARAMETERS

These two parameters can be shown graphically on the common-source drain characteristic curve, as in Fig. 7-29*b*. The method explained in Sec. 7-14 is used again here.

Points A and B in Fig. 7-29 have the same V_{DS} but lie on V_{GS} curves that are 1 V apart. The corresponding values of I_D differ by 2 mA. So the forward admittance near $A - B$ is

$$y_{fs} = g_m = \frac{\Delta I_D}{\Delta V_{GS}} = \frac{2\text{ mA}}{1\text{ V}} = 0.002 \text{ mho (siemens), or } 2000\ \mu\text{mhos}$$

The output admittance (at A) is gotten from the slope of the V_{GS} curve as it passes through A; in Fig. 7-29 this is shown by the dashed line CD. For a horizontal length of 10 V, this line rises about 0.4 mA. So the output admittance at A is

$$y_{os} = g_{ds} = \frac{\Delta I_D}{\Delta V_{DS}} = \frac{0.4\text{ mA}}{10\text{ V}} = 0.000040 \text{ mho (siemens), or } 40\ \mu\text{mhos}$$

The reciprocal of this admittance is the resistance through the channel, or $1 / g_{ds} = r_{ds} = 25\text{ k}\Omega$. This is the dynamic or ac resistance.

As the reverse bias V_{GS} is increased to -5 V, for the FET shown in Fig. 7-29, the value of I_D decreases near to zero. The gate voltage that reduces I_D to a few microamperes is called the *gate-source cutoff voltage* or *gate pinch-off voltage* V_P

When the FET is operating to the right of point A (in Fig. 7-29), it is said to be in saturation (or in the pinch-off region), because any increase in V_{DS} causes only a small increase in the drain current I_D; the channel is saturated with about as many current carriers as it can possibly contain at that certain gate voltage V_{GS}. But when this FET operates near point E, it is in the unsaturated region, where the FET is said to be ON. (Here the terms *saturated* and *unsaturated* refer to the condition of the channel; this usage differs from the use of the same terms for bipolar transistors.)

In Fig. 7-29, point E lies on the curve of $V_{GS} = 0$; from the slope of this curve at E, the value of drain resistance is obtained as $r_{ds,ON}$ or $r_{ON} = 2.5$ V / 5 mA = 2000 Ω. This is the lowest drain resistance that can be obtained for this certain depletion-type FET.

7-26 THE P-CHANNEL FET

Just as the FET described above has a channel of N-type material and is called an N-channel or N FET, there is also a P-channel FET having heavily doped N gate inserts into a channel block of P material. For such a P FET, Fig. 7-34 shows that both batteries are reversed, as compared with Fig. 7-29. The main current now consists of a flow of holes through the P channel; this flow is decreased when gate G is made more (+) to increase the reverse bias and the depletion area. As this V_{GS} bias is increased further, a point is reached where the conduction portion of the channel is made so narrow that all flow stops; this value of V_{GS} is called the *pinch-off* voltage. In contrast, if V_{GS} goes more negative than −0.5 V in Fig. 7-34, this forward bias lets the gate conduct so that all field-effect amplification stops; this gate current may damage the FET unless limited by resistance in series with the gate.

Adopted standards state that the drain and the gate are positive with respect to the source, and that all conventional currents flow *into* the FET; so in Fig. 7-34*b* values of I_D and V_{DS} are shown as (−).

Whereas the NPN transistor and the N-channel FET have electron streams, as do vacuum tubes, there is no tube equivalent for the PNP transistor or the P-channel FET, both of which use a stream of holes.

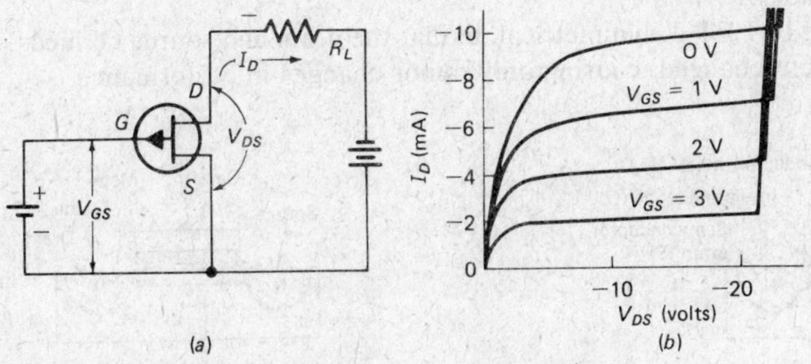

Figure 7-34 Circuit and performance of P-channel FET.

7-27 THE INSULATED-GATE FET; THE MOSFET

The junction types of FET described above use gates that have direct electrical contact with the channel; but reverse bias is used so as to prevent a flow of gate current, and thus the gate acts as though it is insulated from the channel. (Since the usual signal applied to the gate depletes the channel of current carriers, the junction FET operates in what is called the "depletion mode.")

In place of this insulating action by the reverse bias, another type of FET uses a definite layer of insulating silicon dioxide, formed between gate and channel; in this way there is no junction, and we remove its disadvantages of leakage current and the need for reverse bias. Since this insulated gate now can be forward-biased without any flow in the gate, another method or mode of operation is possible. In Fig. 7-35 a channel of N material has been diffused into the top of a block of P bulk semiconductor; enlarged ends of this N channel form the source and drain. The gate is neither P nor N, but is merely a layer of conducting metal; it is insulated from the channel by a layer of silicon dioxide. As before, if the metal gate is made more negative, its voltage produces a field effect that enlarges the depletion zone in the N channel so as to decrease the flow of electrons through the channel. (This isolated gate acts much like the control grid of a vacuum triode tube.)

But if the gate in Fig. 7-35 now is made more positive, it produces an electric field that attracts the minority electrons contained in the P bulk material; these electrons are pulled into the N channel so as to increase or enhance the total number of carriers, and thus to increase the current conduction of the FET. (Since the carriers in the channel are enhanced by those available in the bulk P material, this FET now operates in what is called the "enhancement mode.")

Figure 7-37 shows the insulated-gate FET or IGFET circuit. Its characteristic curves show that a single IGFET may be operated through a wider range of gate voltage. When V_{GS} is negative, the output I_D is reduced toward zero or pinch-off, using the depletion mode; but positive values of V_{GS} increase I_D, using the enhancement mode. Thus the IGFET acts like a vacuum pentode tube.

Usually, the IGFET is symmetrical, in that the drain and source connections can be interchanged, causing only minor changes in performance.

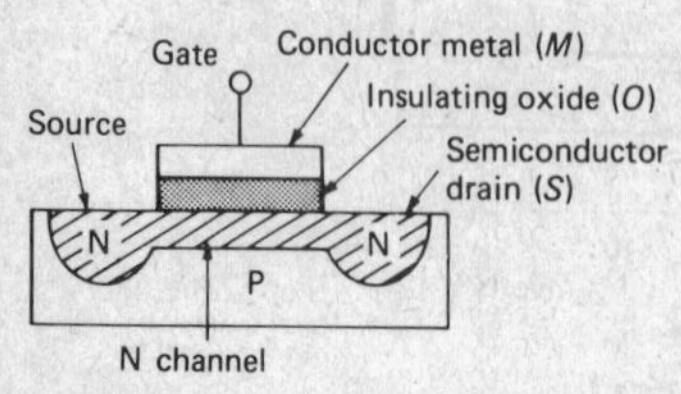

Figure 7-35 Insulated-gate FET; the MOSFET.

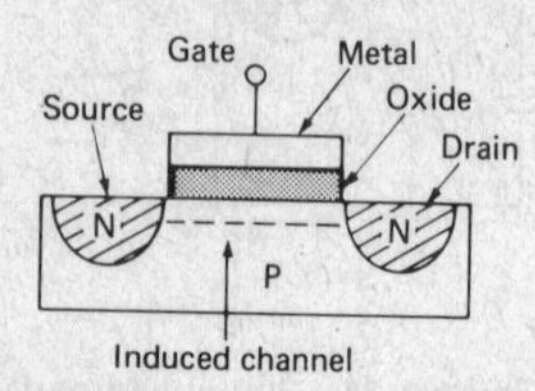

Figure 7-36 Induced-channel FET.

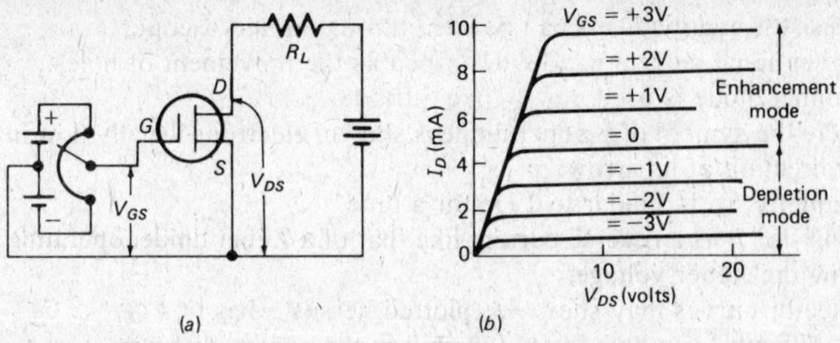

Figure 7-37 Circuit and performance of insulated-gate FET.

The arrangement of P and N regions in Fig. 7-35 makes it possible to produce the IGFET entirely on one surface of P bulk semiconductor material; thus many FETs can be produced at one time, using a diffusion process like that in Sec. 12-1. In the IGFET, the process of placing *metal* on top of *oxide* insulation on top of a *semiconductor* is given the term MOS. (Similarly, MNS describes the use of a *nitride* insulation instead of an oxide.)

The quantity-production advantage of the MOSFET often is offset by the ease of damage by static electricity; the insulating layer may break down at 35 to 50 volts. The gate resistance is so high that static accumulates; its discharges can puncture the insulation; so special handling and protective features may be needed, as is discussed in Sec. 11 = 11.

7-28 THE INDUCED-CHANNEL FET

A further modification of a MOSFET, as shown in Fig. 7-36, provides an induced channel and adapts this FET particularly for switching circuits. When no voltages are applied, this FET has no channel whatever; the resistance from source to drain may be 500 kΩ. This resistance decreases to a few kilohms as the gate is raised to to +5 V. The field produced by this (+) gate attracts electrons from the bulk P-type material toward the gate so that they act as carriers in a new induced channel, as shown by the dashed path in Fig. 7-36. The induced-channel FET operates in the enhancement mode only, since the gate never is reverse-biased so as to form depletion areas. Meanwhile the input or gate resistance is very large (above $10^{13}\Omega$).

Problems

7-1 True or false? Explain why.

(a) As shown by their atomic structure, carbon and tin should be useful in making transistors.

(b) Transistor energy levels can be seen through a microscope.
(c) Conventional current can be described as the movement of holes.
(d) A tunnel diode is used mostly like a triode.
(e) Where the symbol of a Zener diode is shown, electrons usually flow in the direction of its arrow.
(f) Parameter h_{oe} is similar to $1 / r_p$ for a tube.
(g) Transistor I_C is a reverse current like that of a Zener diode, operating below the Zener voltage.
(h) Collector curves may show $-I_C$ plotted versus $+V_{CB}$ or V_{CE}.
(i) It is difficult for a hole to go downhill in the energy diagram.
(j) A material that has greater work function also has a larger forbidden gap.
(k) Majority carriers in the emitter become minority carriers in the base.
(l) An electron in the valence band can be raised into the conduction band by any amount of added energy.
(m) If h parameters are used, the equivalent circuit is the same for common-base as for common-emitter connection.

7-2 The collector characteristics of a transistor consist of straight lines between the following points:

	At $V_{CE} = 2$ V	At $V_{CE} = 10$ V
When $I_B = -80$ μA	$I_C = 1.0$ mA	$I_C = 1.2$ mA
When $I_B = -160$ μA	$I_C = 2.0$ mA	$I_C = 2.4$ mA
When $I_B = -240$ μA	$I_C = 3.2$ mA	$I_C = 4.0$ mA
When $I_B = -320$ μA	$I_C = 4.6$ mA	$I_C = 6.2$ mA
When $I_B = -400$ μA	$I_C = 6.1$ mA	$I_C = 8.9$ mA

At an operating point $I_B = -240$ μA, $V_{CE} = 6$ V, find (*a*) β and (*b*) α. (*c*) Operating in a circuit like Fig. 5-6, and at the Q point given above, determine the maximum R_L so that V_{CC} need not exceed 15 V.

7-3 These transistor characteristics are given and are straight lines between the following points:

	At $V_{CB} = -2$ V	At $V_{CB} = -20$ V
When $I_E = 0$	$I_C = -10$ μA	$I_C = -30$ μA
When $I_E = 1$ mA	$I_C = -0.9$ mA	$I_C = -1.1$ mA
When $I_E = 3$ mA	$I_C = -2.84$ mA	$I_C = -3.04$ mA

At an operating point $I_E = 2$ mA, $V_{CB} = -11$ V, find (*a*) α and (*b*) dynamic resistance of the collector, $= 1 / h_{ob}$. (*c*) State whether this is a PNP transistor and give reasons.

7-4 These common-base parameters are given:

$$h_{11} = 24\ \Omega \quad h_{12} = 3 \times 10^{-4} \quad h_{21} = -0.97 \quad h_{22} = 0.8\ \mu\text{mho}$$

Find (*a*) the h^e parameters, (*b*) Δh^b for common base, and (*c*) Δh^e for common emitter.

7-5 Repeat Prob. 7-4 using these common-base parameters:

$$h_i = 32\Omega \quad h_r = 3 \times 10^{-4} \quad h_f = -0.95 \quad h_o = 1.0\ \mu\text{mho}$$

7-6 Use the transistor of Prob. 7-5 in a common-emitter circuit, with $R_L = 2$ kΩ. Find (*a*)A_i, (*b*) A_v, and (*c*) power gain G.

7-7 Repeat Prob. 7-6 using the transistor of Prob. 7-4, with $R_L = 20$ kΩ.

7-8 For the conditions of Prob. 7-7, find (*a*) R_i and (*b*) the value of R_s so that R_o is 80 times as large as R_i.

7-9 Use the transistor of Prob. 7-5, with $R_L = 2$ kΩ and $R_s = 500$ Ω. For the common-base configuration, find (*a*) R_i and (*b*) R_o. For the common-emitter configuration, find (*c*) R_i and (d) R_o.

8

SENSING OF TIME, VOLTAGE, LIGHT: THE UNIJUNCTION TRANSISTOR

The time-delay action described in Chap. 3 is used here in several commercial circuits that provide an adjustable time delay, in the range between 0.1 and 120 sec.

8-1 ELECTRONIC DELAY TIMER (GENERAL ELECTRIC 3S7504ET560)

In this book, all type numbers refer to units made by the General Electric Company unless stated otherwise. Figure 8-1 shows the circuit of a time-delay relay that is manufactured for general-purpose use in industry; it includes a dial P_1, which is turned for selection of the length of time delay. The circuit starts its time-delay action at the instant when switch S is opened (at upper left); at the end of the desired time delay, the transistor Q_3 current energizes or picks up relay CR, whose contacts are used to close some other circuit, or to open that circuit if preferred. In Fig. 8-1, relay CR has two contacts as shown. The n-o contact is *normally-open*, meaning that it is open when CR is not energized, which also is the condition if all electricity is removed from the entire circuit; under this same condition, the n-c contact is *normally-closed*. When CR is picked up, the n-o contact closes and the n-c contact opens.

The power supply in Fig. 8-1 is 115 volts (V) 60 Hz (or cps) ac, and the transformer T_1 decreases this to about 16 V. A half wave of current passes through diode D_1 to keep the large capacitor C_1 charged to 20 V dc, thus

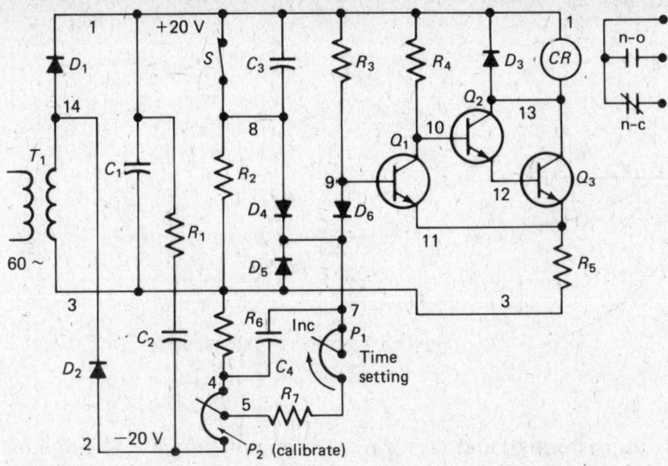

Figure 8-1 Circuit of delay timer using transistors (3S7504ET560).

holding top line 1 about 20 V more positive than centerline 3. During the other half wave, when T_1 terminal 14 is more negative than 3, diode D_2 conducts and charges C_2, holding bottom line 2 about 20 V more negative than centerline 3.

With switch S closed, electrons flow from the lower capacitor C_4 to terminal 7 and through diode D_4 and S, charging C_4 to more than 20 V between top line 1 and terminal 4 (at the top of P_2, and held a little more negative than centerline 3 by the voltage-divider action of R_6 and P_2). Since 7 is near +20 V, diode D_6 is reverse-biased and acts as an open circuit, letting the base of Q_1 be held positive (through R_3), thus turning on Q_1; its collector current, flowing through R_4 and R_5, holds negative the base 10 of Q_2, so that this transistor passes no current through base 12 of Q_3. Thus no collector current passes through Q_3 or the coil of relay CR; CR is not energized.

When S is opened (to start the time-delay action in Fig. 8-1), the potential at 7 drops slowly as capacitor C_4 discharges through the resistance of R_7 and time adjuster P_1. The point-7 potential heads toward the more negative potential of point 5 at the slider of P_2 (as shown in Fig. 8-2); meanwhile, the emitter of Q_1 is held slightly above 0 V, at the top of R_5. When point 7 reaches about 0 V, diode D_6 conducts and lowers base 9; this turns off Q_1 and decreases the current through R_4. Base 10 rises, turning on Q_2; current in base 12 turns on Q_3, whose collector current picks up relay CR.

As P_1 is turned clockwise and increases its resistance, the discharge of C_4 becomes slower and causes longer delay before CR is energized. When S again is closed, Q_1 and Q_3 are turned off and CR drops out. Energy stored in the inductive CR coil may be dissipated by forcing current through diode D_3.

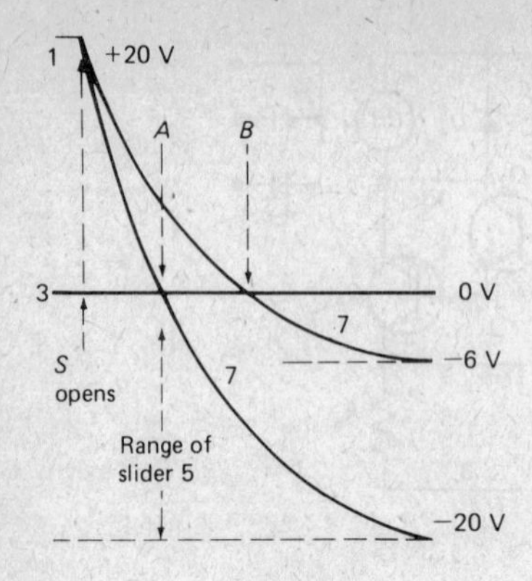

Figure 8-2 Effect of calibration by P_2 in Fig. 8-1.

In Fig. 8-1, transistors Q_2 and Q_3 form a Darlington circuit[6-7] to provide large current amplification so that Q_3 can supply enough current to pick up *CR*.

To calibrate this timer, the slider 5 of P_2 may be moved through a wide voltage range, as shown in Fig. 8-2. If P_2 is turned counterclockwise to touch at 2, the potential at 7 (top of C_4) moves toward a final value of −20 V and thus quickly ends the time delay at *A*. But if P_2 is turned clockwise (in an adjustment by the manufacturer), point 7 then drops toward, perhaps, only −6 V; the time delay ends at *B* and is longer (for the same setting of P_1).

8-2 A RESISTANCE-SENSITIVE RELAY (3S7511RS570)

The circuit in Fig. 8-3 is controlled by the tiny current that may flow through a microcontact, a moist thread, or through any resistance R_x up to perhaps 0.1 megohm (MΩ); it responds to a flow of current far too small to operate an ordinary relay such as *CR*.

Transformer *T* in Fig. 8-3 supplies 18 V ac, which, changed by D_2 and C_2, gives to the top line 1 a steady potential 20 V above centerline 3; D_3 and C_3 hold line 2 at 20 V below 3. At the left, voltage divider R_1-R_2-R_3-R_4 serves to keep terminal 4 at about +9 V, while terminal 6 is about −4 V. Between terminals 4 and 6, the external microcontact or R_x is in series with sensitivity adjuster *P*. While R_x has a low value (below 50 kΩ or because of a closed contact), the potential at point 5 is positive, at the base of NPN transistor Q_1, so that electrons flow from 3 through R_7, Q_1, and R_6. The voltage across R_6 holds base 7 of Q_2 below emitter 8; so Q_2 passes no current to the coil of relay *CR*.

But if R_x becomes much larger (or the contact opens), the voltage across *P* decreases, so that the point-5 potential falls below line 3; this stops the Q_1 collector current through R_6, letting the base 7 rise, so that Q_2 collector current picks up relay *CR* and operates its contacts shown. Even a slow change

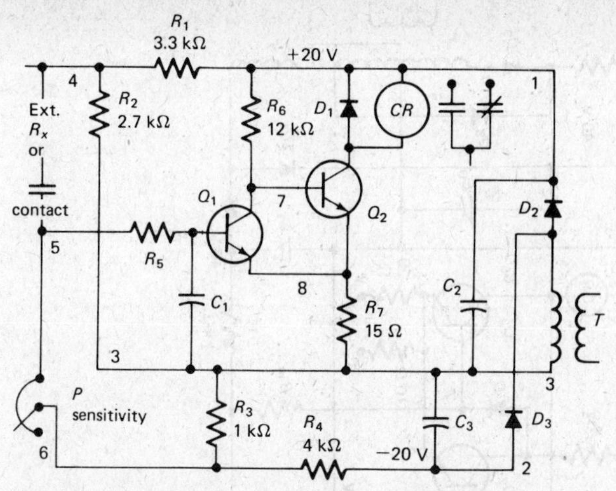

Figure 8-3 Resistance-sensitive relay (3S7511RS570).

in point-5 potential causes a sudden change in Q_2 current, since Q_1 and Q_2 act as a Schmitt trigger, as described in Sec. 6-8. When Q_2 current stops, to drop out *CR*, the energy stored in the coil inductance is dissipated as its current continues to flow through diode D_1.

8-3 A VOLTAGE-SENSITIVE RELAY (3S7511VS580)

The circuit of Fig. 8-4 may be adjusted by *P* to operate at a desired value or level of input voltage *V*, at the left. If *V* falls below this level, relay *CR* is picked up or energized, operating its large contacts (not shown) to cause desired action in some separate circuit; *CR* drops out when *V* rises above this level.

At the right, a center-tapped winding of transformer *T* acts through D_8 and D_9 to provide full-wave voltage that charges C_5 to 34 volts (V), for the *CR* coil and transistors Q_2 and Q_3. A lower winding of *T* acts through D_{11} to charge C_6 to 40 V; this is applied across divider R_7-R_8-R_9, so that top line 1 is 6 V above centerline 3. During the other half cycle, *T* charges C_7 (through D_{10}) to −40 V; this is applied through bottom resistor R_{15} to the Zener diode *Z*. As described in Sec. 7-18, this certain Zener holds bottom line 2 steadily at 22 V more negative than 3; thus the voltage across part of adjuster *P* serves as a reference voltage that remains constant even though the voltage supplied by *T* may vary.

At the left in Fig. 8-4, voltage *V* (to which the whole circuit responds) is applied across divider R_1-R_2-R_3-R_4; the portion across $R_2 + R_3$ is connected across a bridge rectifier (diodes D_1 to D_4) so that a dc voltage *W* appears across R_5. (Thus *V* may be an ac voltage, or dc of either polarity.) If adjuster

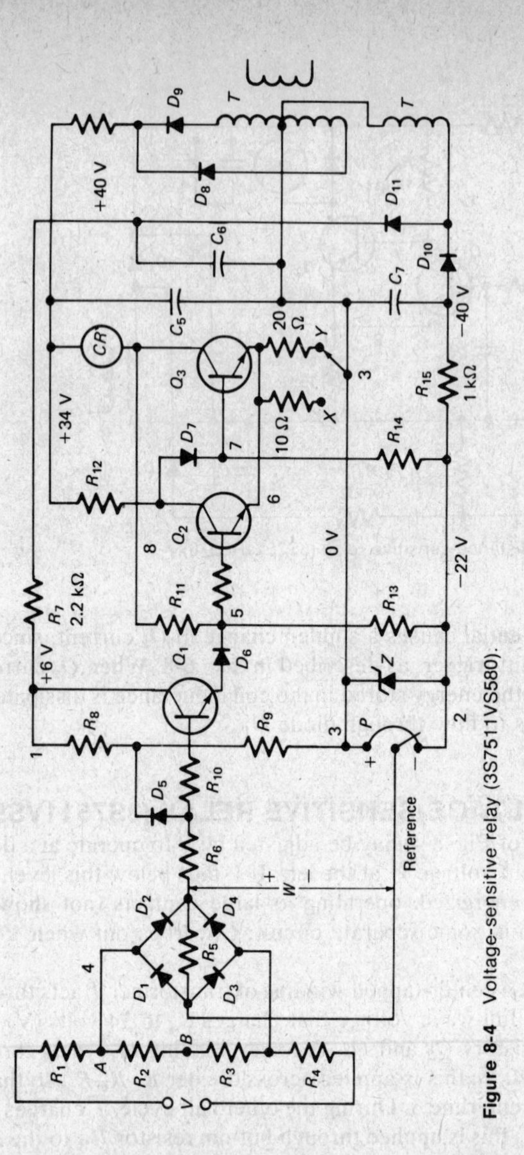

Figure 8-4 Voltage-sensitive relay (3S7511VS580).

P has been turned clockwise to touch at bottom line 2, the slider of P is 22 V below centerline 3. Now if V is so small that W is less than 22 V, the base of transistor Q_1 is more negative than 3. Since Q_1 is connected as an emitter follower,[5-10] the voltage across R_{13} also must be less than 22 V, and thus holds negative the base of NPN transistor Q_2. Since Q_2 passes no collector current through R_{12}, the base 7 of Q_3 is at a potential much higher than 3 (as electrons flow through large R_{14}, D_7, and smaller R_{12}); so Q_3 collector current energizes relay CR. [At very low V levels, diodes D_5 and D_6 act as open circuits. The Q_2 base is at the negative potential of point 5 on a divider (large R_{11} and smaller R_{13}); since CR is energized, its terminal 8 is near the zero potential of point 3.]

Now let input V increase, thus raising voltage W to greater than the 22-V setting of P. This raises the base of Q_1 until D_6 conducts; the increased current through R_{13} also raises base 5 until Q_2 starts to pass collector current through R_{12}. This lowers the potential at the Q_3 base; by action as a Schmitt trigger,[6-8] the decreasing Q_3 emitter current lessens the voltage drop across the 20-ohm (Ω) resistor at Y and lowers the potential of Q_2 emitter 6. Thus Q_2 turns on quickly, turning off Q_3 and dropping out CR. (While CR is energized and Q_3 current flows in 20-Ω Y, this holds emitter 6 of Q_2 at a potential somewhat higher than 3; therefore, V must rise higher to turn on Q_2. But now the Q_2 current in Y is much less than was the Q_3 current, and lowers the Q_2 emitter closer to 3 potential; thus V must decrease to a lower level before Q_2 can be turned off, to again make Q_3 pick up CR. This differential, between V values that pick up or drop out CR, can be lessened if the connection from 3 to Y is moved instead to the 10-Ω X.)

If adjuster P (low in Fig. 8-4) is turned halfway until only 11 V remains between its slider and line 3, now CR is operated when input V is at a voltage level only half as great as before. If voltage W greatly exceeds the value selected by P, diode D_5 clamps the Q_1 base to R_8 at less than +6 V. If V ranges above 20 V, terminal 4 (at the R_1-to-R_4 voltage divider) is to be moved from A to B, so that the W voltage corresponds to a smaller fraction of V.

8-4 A REFLEX PHOTOELECTRIC RELAY (3S7505PS510)

This simple compact relay includes a light source within its enclosure, and is used for counting or an alarm when some external object interrupts its steady beam of light. As shown low in Fig. 8-5, the lamp's beam passes through a lens in the enclosure, to a plastic reflector mounted up to 10 ft distant, from which the beam returns through the lens to shine on the photosensitive detector PD. This PD is a silicon photovoltaic cell, which generates a small voltage in proportion to the total light it receives.[23-15] Here the PD voltage is shown (+) at the left; therefore, as light increases at PD, its right-hand terminal 4 becomes more negative, lowering the base of NPN transistor Q_1 so as to decrease its collector current.

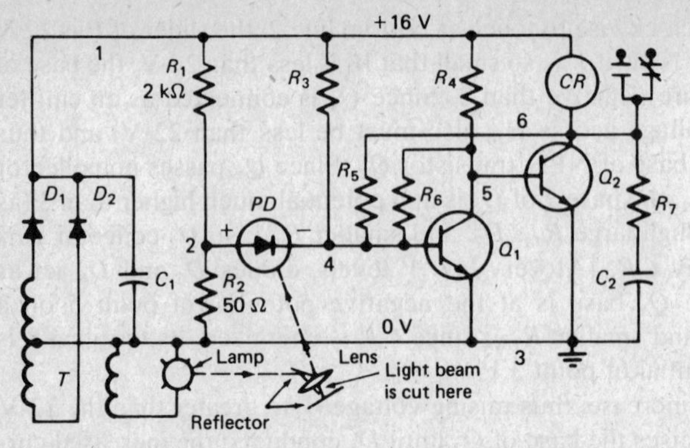

Figure 8-5 Reflex photoelectric relay (3S7505PS510).

At the left in Fig. 8-5, a center-tapped winding of transformer T supplies 12 V ac, which, through diodes D_1 and D_2, charges C_1, so that top line 1 is 16 V above the grounded lower line 3. The divider R_1-R_2 keeps point 2 at 0.4 V above 3. With no light at *PD*, base 4 of Q_1 also is more positive than its emitter 3; so Q_1 passes collector current through R_4. The voltage drop across R_4 holds the base-5 potential so low that Q_2 passes too little current to energize relay *CR*. The lower *CR* terminal 6 is near +16 V, which is fed back through R_5 to raise base 4, thus completely turning on Q_1.

When the external reflex light beam is not interrupted but shines on *PD*, the voltage generated by this cell drives the Q_1 base more negative; less Q_1 current through R_4 lets point 5 rise nearer top line 1 so as to increase the Q_2 current through the *CR* coil. As the potential of *CR* terminal 6 drops and (through R_5) lowers the Q_1 base 4, the Q_1 current stops and Q_2 is turned on completely and picks up *CR*. Thus light on *PD* energizes relay *CR*; interruption of the light beam drops out *CR*.

8-5 A MODULATED LIGHT SIGNAL USING A LIGHT-EMITING DIODE (LED)

Note above that Fig. 8-5 uses a steady beam of light produced by a hot-filament lamp, as is used by most early photoelectric control relays. In contrast, the photorelay of Fig. 8-7 uses a flickering or modulated light for the following reason: photoresistor *PT* (at the left in Fig. 8-7) generates a larger voltage when greater *total* light shines on it; so its accuracy is reduced by sunlight or other steady light that may be as bright as the signal being received from the lamp. (Earlier, such a problem was solved mechanically by modulating the light beam by using a rotating disk to interrupt the beam about 10,000 times per second; there the photorelay circuit was designed so as to respond to the flickering light signal but to be "blind" to the steady daylight.) But now an electronic device can produce such a flickering light. As is described also in Sec. 23-15, a light-emitting diode (LED) can produce up to a million separate flashes per second. For this purpose, the circuit of Fig. 8-6 receives 120-V 60-Hz power through transformer T_1, whose center-tap low-voltage output is rectified through diodes D_1 and D_2 (as in Fig. 4-2), and is filtered by large capacitor C, so as to supply 12 V dc between upper line 1 and bottom line 3. (At lower left, a duplicate rectifier supplies about 13 V dc for Z at the top of Fig. 8-7.)

At the right, Fig. 8-6 is a transistor multivibrator (also like Fig. 24-8) which produces 15 kHz from transformer T_3 at the top. Transistors Q_1 and Q_2 have identical common-emitter circuits; at first they may have equal collector currents; above Q_1, capacitor C_1 is charged to the voltage between Q_1 collector 2 (+) and Q_2 base 6 (−). But this current cannot remain in such a stable condition; any momentary disturbance can slightly increase the Q_1 collector current, thus increasing the voltage drop across the left-hand winding of T_3. This lowers Q_1 collector 2; acting through C_1 (which cannot change its charge or voltage instantly), this lowers base 6 of Q_2; diode 4 conducts, limiting the reverse voltage applied to Q_2). With less base current, the Q_2 collector current decreases through the right-hand T_3 winding, letting collector 5 rise; fed back through C_2 and R_2, this raises base 4 of Q_1, turning on Q_1 completely. Such large Q_1 current lowers points 2 and 6 so quickly that Q_2 is completely off; its collector 5 is near +12 V, charging C_2 through R_2 and Q_1.

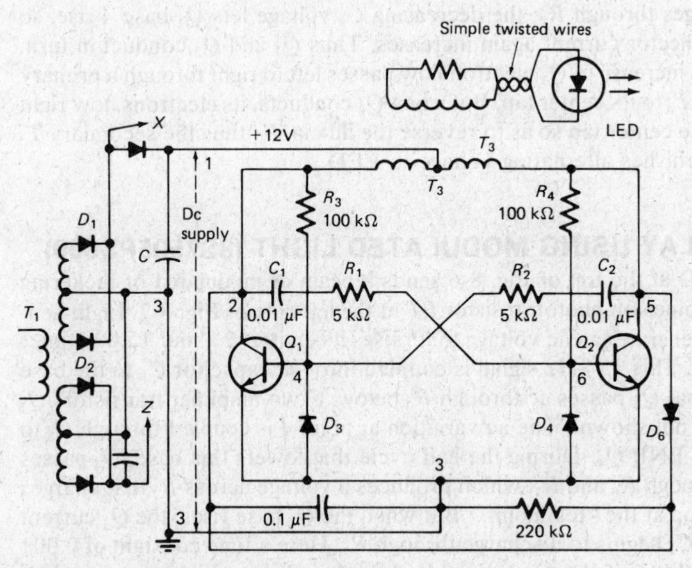

Figure 8-6 15-kHz light source for Fig. 8-7.

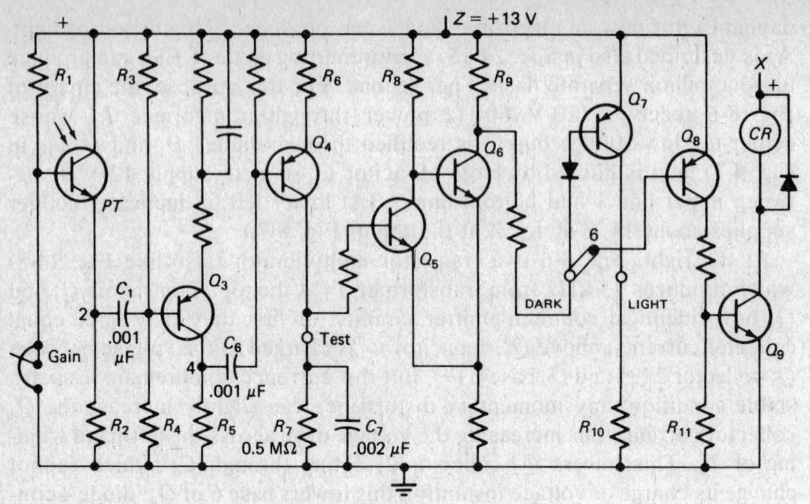

Figure 8-7 Photorelay using modulated light (3S7505PS800).

But conditions change as C_1 discharges through R_1 (with time constant of 0.00005 sec); soon D_4 stops conducting and base 6 becomes slightly positive (on the R_1-R_4 voltage divider); so Q_2 starts to pass current through T_3, lowering collector 5 and (through C_2 and R_2) lowering the base of Q_1. Very quickly this positive feedback turns Q_1 off and Q_2 on. Again the circuit waits while C_2 discharges through R_2; the decreasing C_2 voltage lets Q_1 base 4 rise, so that the collector current again increases. Thus Q_1 and Q_2 conduct in turn. The abrupt increase of Q_1 electron flow passes left to right through a primary winding of T_3 to its center tap. But when Q_2 conducts, its electrons flow right to left to the center tap so as to reverse the flux in T_3; thus the secondary T_3 winding furnishes alternating voltage to LED.

8-6 RELAY USING MODULATED LIGHT (3S7505PS800)

The LED at the top of Fig. 8-6 sends a beam of modulated or flickering light that shines on phototransistor *PT* at the left side of Fig. 8-7. Light-sensitive PT generates an ac voltage that raises its emitter 2 about 15,000 times per second. This 15-kHz signal is coupled through capacitor C_1 to the base of Q_3, so that Q_3 passes ac through R_5 below. (Two amplifier transistors Q_1 and Q_2 are not shown.) The ac variation at point 4 is coupled through C_6 to the base of PNP Q_4. During the half cycle that lowers this base, Q_4 passes current through R_6 and R_7, which produces a voltage across R_7 that charges C_7 (+) on top at the "test point." But when the Q_4 base rises, the Q_4 current stops, and C_7 begins to discharge through R_7. Here a time constant of 0.001 sec lets so little of the C_7 voltage be lost that the test point remains (+).

Applied to the base of NPN Q_5, this (+) causes more Q_5 collector current through R_8, lowering the base of Q_6; less Q_6 current through R_9 raises the terminal marked DARK and (through a jumper to 6) raises the base of PNP transistor Q_8. As this stops the Q_8 collector current through R_{11}, the base of Q_9 is too low to permit Q_9 collector current; thus relay coil CR is not energized.

When anything interrupts the flickering LED beam, PT no longer causes rapid changes at point 2; C_1 charges to a steady value and passes no signal to Q_3; C_6 also charges to a steady value which raises the base of Q_4, stopping its collector current. Within $^1/_{300}$ sec the test point drops toward ground and turns off Q_5; this turns on Q_6, which lowers the point marked DARK; since this is jumpered to 6, it turns on Q_8 and Q_9, to energize or pick up relay CR. When opposite operation is desired (by moving the jumper to connect point 6 to LIGHT) the presence of LED light causes the test point to be (+) as before, turning Q_5 on and Q_6 off. The DARK terminal still is positive; this turns off Q_7, which lowers the terminal LIGHT, now jumpered to point 6. As 6 drops, it increases the Q_8 collector current through R_{11}, thus increasing the Q_9 current, which picks up CR. In this mode of operation, the interruption of the LED light beam deenergizes or drops out relay CR.

8-7 THE UNIJUNCTION TRANSISTOR (UJT)

This device is used to apply a sudden pulse of power to energize a relay (or to fire an SCR, as in Sec. 9-5) when the voltage applied to the UJT emitter reaches a desired value, such as is applied by a capacitor being charged during a time delay. A UJT thus is used in the delay timer of Sec. 8-9; it is bistable[17-2] and is also a thyristor.[9-18]

A unijunction transistor, shown in Fig. 8-8, consists of a small bar or crystal of N-type silicon of high resistance (about 10,000 Ω); an ordinary ohmic or nonrectifying contact is made at each of the ends, which are called base 1 and base 2. A piece of P-type material is formed near the middle of the N bar; thus a single alloy PN junction is made on the crystal bar and acts also as an emitter. The UJT is not like most transistors, but is used as a switching device.

Internally, the UJT acts like a voltage divider consisting of the two series resistors R_A and R_B, while the PN junction acts like the diode D. When the interbase voltage V_{BB} is applied, a portion V_E appears between the emitter and base 1. This portion $\eta = R_A / (R_A + R_B)$, and is called the *standoff ratio*. (η = eta.)

If now an external voltage is applied which makes emitter E more positive than base B_1, no current flows through the emitter, so long as this applied voltage is less than V_E, which is ηV_{BB}. However, when this applied voltage exceeds V_E by a fraction of a volt, current flows through the emitter to quickly decrease the resistance of R_A, by a process known as conductivity modulation, as next described.

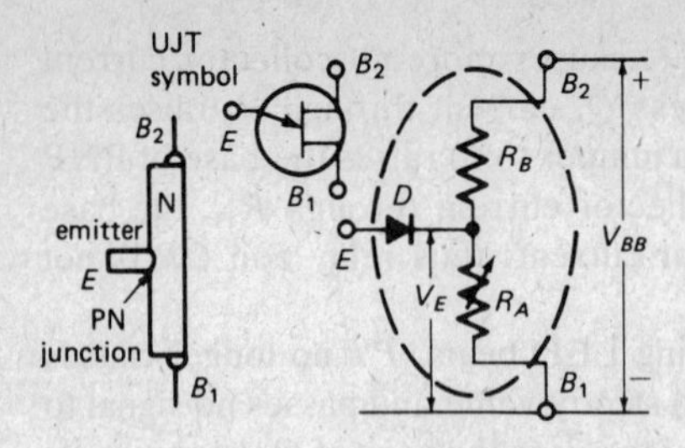

Figure 8-8 UJT, the unijunction transistor.

So long as no current flows through the emitter, the electric flow in the N-type bar consists almost entirely of its excess electrons (majority carriers) moving from B_1 to B_2; relatively few electrons flow, because of the small doping and high resistance of the bar. When the potential of emitter E is raised so that current flows through the PN junction, this is a flow of excess holes (which are majority carriers in the P-type emitter material) that pass through the N-type bar toward base 1. The entering by these holes causes a corresponding greater flow of electrons into B_1; this sudden increase in the number of available carriers quickly decreases the resistance of the R_A portion of the UJT so that current, once started, flows easily between E and B_1. Thus the conductivity of R_A is modulated or varied by the flow of emitter current.

The UJT is a consistent operator, and trips reliably always at the same value of V_E (determined by its standoff ratio η).

8-8 DELAY TIMER USING A UJT (3S7504ET550)

As shown in Fig. 8-9, this timing unit operates from a 115-volt (V) ac supply. When switch S is raised to its upper position, autotransformer T supplies 16 V between lines 2 and 3; current through diode D_1 charges C_2 and raises line 4 about 20 V above 3. A small current flows through R_4 and the CR coil, but not enough to pick up this relay. Capacitor C_1 now is being charged by electrons flowing through the resistance of time adjuster P and R_3 to line 4. The voltage increases across C_1, gradually raising the potential of the C_1 terminal 6. At that instant, when 6 becomes more positive than emitter E, current flows through diode D_2 and UJT. As described in Sec. 8-7, there is a sudden decrease in resistance within UJT between E and base 1. The energy stored in C_1 forces a surge of current through UJT and the CR coil large enough to pick up CR; although this surge soon ends as C_1 discharges, CR easily is held in by the current flowing through R_4. So, at the end of the time delay selected by P, UJT is triggered and the CR contact connects 115 V across the external load.

When switch S is returned to its lower position in Fig. 8-9, removing voltage from the UJT and CR circuit, the CR contact removes voltage from the

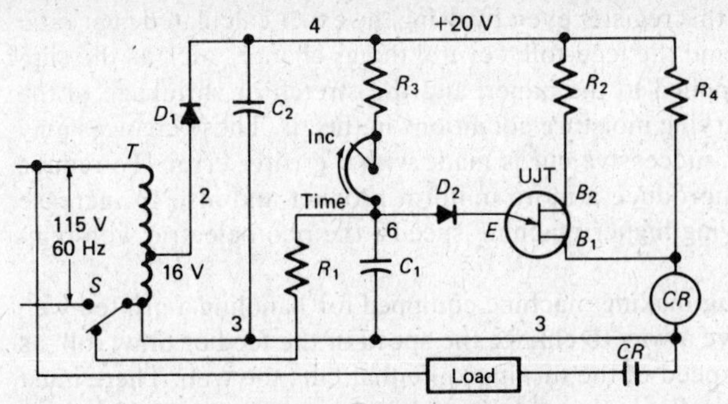

Figure 8-9 Delay timer using a UJT (3S7504ET550).

load. Any charge on C_1 is drained through R_1 and the S contact so that C_1 has 0 V at the start of each timing operation.

8-9 REGISTER CONTROL

Many applications that require high-speed photoelectric relays can be operated by very rapid changes in light, lasting perhaps one-thousandth of a second. These light-operated circuits may be used to control the cutting or handling of a continuous strip of paper as it comes off large rolls at high speed. This "web" of paper already is printed with a recurring design, which includes also rectangular spots placed at the edge of the web, to be scanned by the phototube. The web is fed into machines that make it into bags or wrap it around boxes, so that the printed design is aligned with the box corners or the bag edge. This is a web-register control; similar systems are used also for multicolor printing. At each instant when the moving paper web is in the correct position, the web is "in register"—now the added design or cut is made exactly right.

The design printed on the web is usually in sections and must be cut between these sections. With such a unit design, it costs less to print on a continuous web of paper than on separate precut sheets; it is hard to handle certain stocks (such as cellophane) unless web printing is used. Such web stock is printed and then wound on a roll, to be fed later into the packaging or bag-making machine; there is no definite "tie-in" between the timing of the drive roll that feeds the web into the machine. Therefore, if the feed-roll travel (per machine revolution) differs slightly from the spacing of the printing on the web, the knife will soon cut into the printed design. Even though the error of each cut may be only $^1/_{100}$ in., or $^1/_{10}$ of 1 percent, after cutting 500 sheets the cut will occur in the middle of the printed design rather than at the end—and it requires a very short time to make 500 cuts on a highspeed packaging machine.

It is hard to keep this register even by using the exact calculated gear ratio between the cutter and the feed roll; several things change, such as the slippage, the tension applied to the paper, and the stretch or shrinkage of the paper, caused by varying moisture conditions in the air. These changes may add up so that each successive cut is made with a greater error. To reduce these spoilages and produce a more uniform product and also to increase production by allowing higher machine speeds, the photoelectric web-register control is used.

A packaging or bag-making machine equipped for handling a printed web should therefore have a way to change the speed of the feed or draw roll, as compared with the speed of the turning knife that cuts the web. There must also be some way to tell whether the printed design is in exact register with the cutter. This can be done well by using a photoelectric device to "see" the printing and to compare its relative position with that of the cutter.

The design already printed on the paper must be made to line up (usually within $^1/_8$ to $^1/_{32}$ in.) with the edge of the package or with the cutoff device; this is done by the photoelectric register control, while the printed web moves past. This photoelectric equipment, whose circuit is discussed next, must respond to a printed spot perhaps $^1/_8$ in. (measured in the direction of travel) by $^1/_2$ in. wide, moving past the phototube at speeds from 150 to 1000 ft/min. To "see" this spot, which passes in approximately $^1/_{2000}$ sec, the photoelectric control or relay must be able to respond to these very rapid changes of light.

8-10 ONE-WAY REGISTER CONTROL (CR7515CT105)

Most of this light-operated circuit is shown in Fig. 8-10. This relay is called a *one-way register* control, for its acts only in one direction, to retard or decrease the speed of the web of material that it cuts. Usually, the driving motor is geared to the draw rolls so as to feed this strip or web into the wrapping or bag-making machine slightly faster than the desired average speed. Spots have been printed at the edge of the strip to permit this paper to be cut at the right point. As each such spot passes beneath the scanning head (which contains the phototube and is connected by cable to the control panel), an electric signal is produced. Meanwhile, just as the cut is made, a cam on the cutter shaft operates a selector switch, shown as S at the center of Fig. 8-10. If the spot is "on time" or "in register," the selector-switch contact opens and prevents the spot signal from reaching the SCR; there is no further action. However, when the spot arrives early, ahead of the cutoff knife, the spot signal occurs before the selector switch opens, thus firing SCR to pick up relay CR; a CR contact operates a solenoid or a motor which, through a differential gear, acts to retard or slow the web and keep the following spots in register.

At the left in Fig. 8-10, windings of transformer T furnish low ac voltages; rectified by a four-diode bridge, top line 3 is kept at +28 volts (V); rectified

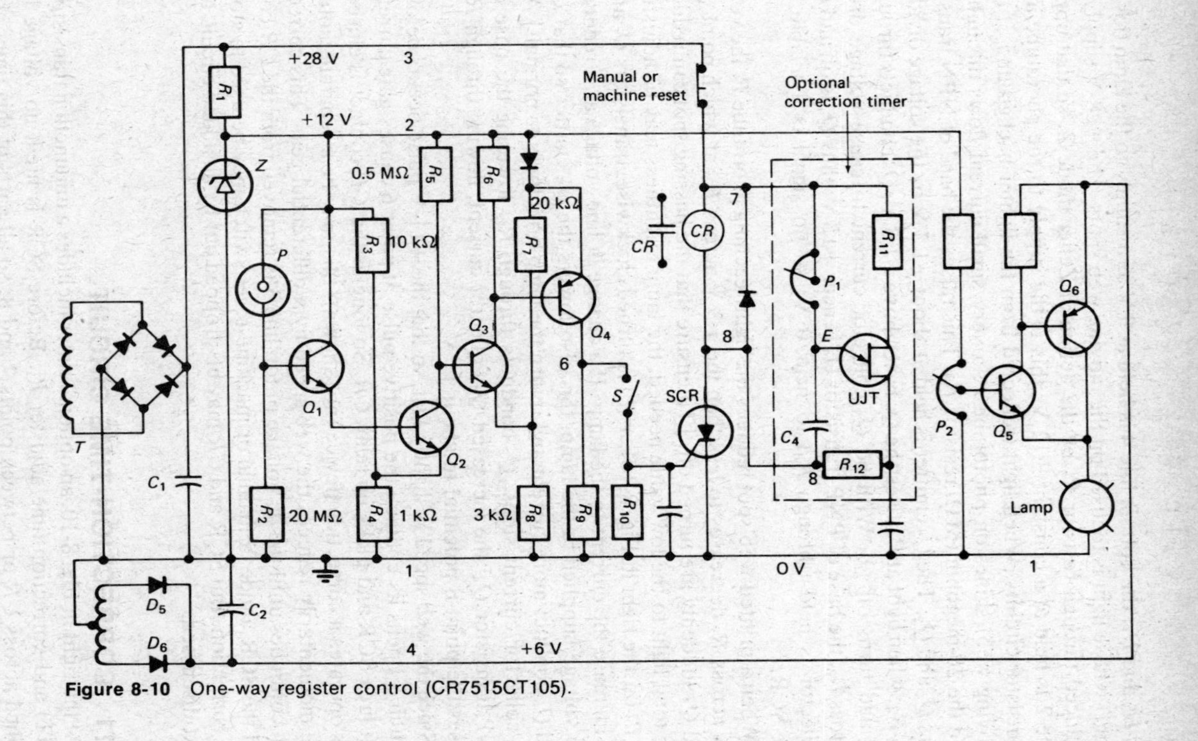

Figure 8-10 One-way register control (CR7515CT105).

by D_5 and D_6, the bottom line 4 is held at +V as a supply to the lamp (lower right) whose light is focused on the moving web spots. The +28-V supply is reduced through resistor R_1 by the action of Zener diode Z, so that upper line 2 is held at a constant +12 V; this is the supply to the phototube and transistor circuits. When light (reflected from the lighter background of the moving web) shines on phototube P, a very small current flows through P and the 20-megohm (M Ω) resistor R_2. This raises the base of NPN transistors Q_1 and Q_2. The Q_2 emitter is held at about +1.3 V by the voltage divider R_3-R_4; when light at P raises the Q_2 base above +1.3 V, Q_2 conducts through R_5 and turns off Q_3. With no Q_3 collector current to cause voltage drop across R_6, the base of PNP transistor Q_4 is near +12 V; thus Q_4 is off and its collector is held (through R_6) to near 0 V; so no signal is available to fire SCR.

When a printed web spot reduces the light reaching phototube P, the voltage across R_2 decreases to less than the 1.3 V across R_4, at which point Q_1 and Q_2 suddenly are turned off. [To ensure that the passing spot can reduce the total light to the low value needed, the lamp brightness may be adjusted by P_2 (at the right in Fig. 8-10); as P_2 is turned clockwise, transistors Q_5 and Q_6 increase the current to the lamp. If a change in line voltage at T reduces the voltage supplied to the lamp, this also lowers the Q_5 emitter so that Q_5 and Q_6 conduct more current and return the lamp brightness to normal.] As Q_2 collector current stops, Q_3 conducts through R_6, lowering the base of PNP transistor Q_4; the increased Q_4 collector current, flowing through R_9, raises the point-6 potential to about 11 V.

Since the web speed is slightly fast, so that the +11-V pulse occurs before switch S opens its contact, the positive pulse at point 6 causes gate current that fires SCR and picks up relay CR. So long as the CR contact is closed, this operates a correction device (not shown); this may be a separate motor that momentarily reduces the web speed by a differential gear. This correction continues until the dc voltage of top line 3 is removed from the CR coil and the SCR anode; a manual or machine-reset switch may be used to stop the correction. But SCR and CR may be dropped out by an added circuit, as next discussed.

8-11 CORRECTION-TIME CIRCUIT

At the right in Fig. 8-10, an optional timer includes a unijunction transistor (UJT) and correction-time adjuster P_1. Before SCR is fired, no voltage is applied across CR or between points 7 and 8; so all parts of this timer are near +28 volts (V); capacitor C_4 has no charge. The firing of SCR suddenly lowers point 8 to about +1 V, so that C_4 starts to charge through the resistance of P_1. By action similar to that of Fig. 9-8, emitter E of UJT soon is raised to the potential that lets emitter current fire UJT; C_4 discharges, forcing electrons through R_{12} and UJT. The resulting voltage drop across R_{12}

drives the SCR anode 8 more negative than its cathode at 1, long enough to turn off SCR and drop out CR to end the correction time.

Problems

8-1 True or false? Explain why.

(a) The symbol for an n-o contact shows always the contact position that exists when no electricity is applied to the entire circuit.

(b) When S closes in Fig. 8-1, thus turning off Q_3, all voltage instantly disappears from across the CR coil.

(c) A transformer ac voltage, aided by pairs of diodes and capacitors, can produce both a (+) and a (−) voltage.

(d) The major result when one moves slider 5 (of P_2 in Fig. 8-1) is that the RC time constant is changed.

(e) In Fig. 8-3, Q_2 is either all on or all off.

(f) The differential between pickup and dropout of a Schmitt trigger can be adjusted by a simple change in circuit resistance.

(g) In Fig. 8-5, if the polarity of PD is reversed, an interruption of the light beam picks up CR.

(h) In Fig. 8-7, a changing light to PT causes relay CR to drop out.

(i) The UJT acts like an NPN transistor.

(j) All relay circuits in Chap. 8 apply filtered dc to the transistor circuits.

(k) A UJT is reset or turned off by decreasing V_{BB} to zero.

(l) A UJT can be turned on gradually.

(m) In Fig. 8-9, if R_4 is short-circuited, the time delay becomes zero.

(n) The hold-in current of a relay is less than the pickup current.

THYRISTORS: THE SCR AND TRIAC

The on-off switching of small currents may use a transistor, operated first in saturation and then below cutoff (as is described in Secs. 5-7 and 10-2). The transistor is the solid-state equivalent of a high-vacuum triode, described in Sec. 2-7. To control larger currents, the thyratron tube (Chap. 20) is closely duplicated by its solid-state equivalent, the SCR. The SCR is one kind of thyristor, as explained in Sec. 9-18.

9-1 THE SILICON CONTROLLED RECTIFIER

Known as the SCR (and also called a *solid-state controlled rectifier*), this PNPN device is made of four layers of P- and N-type silicon, as shown in Figs. 9-1 and 9-2; its three terminals are called the anode A, cathode K, and gate G. The SCR is fired or is turned on by a pulse of current flowing through its gate; usually it must be turned off externally by decreasing its anode current nearly to zero. The SCR in Fig. 9-1 is inverted from the symbol of Fig. 9-2; the top cable is the cathode, while the anode connects to the threaded metal stud at the bottom. Standard SCRs are available to carry to 1000 amperes rms each.

The operation of an SCR is explained as though it consisted of one NPN and one PNP transistor interconnected as shown in Fig. 9-2. The combined unit acts as an open circuit between A and K until a current i_1 is inserted at gate G, whereupon the entire unit acts as nearly a short circuit between A and K, so that the anode current must be limited by a load resistance. Whenever A is more positive than K, each of the emitter-base junctions is forward-biased; but so long as gate current i_1 is zero, the junction 2 acts as an open circuit, so that i_2 and i_3 are practically zero (leakage current only).

In Fig. 9-2, when gate G is made more positive than cathode K, a small current i_1 flows through G and between base and emitter of transistor Q_1; by usual transistor action, a large current i_2 flows through the Q_1 collector. But

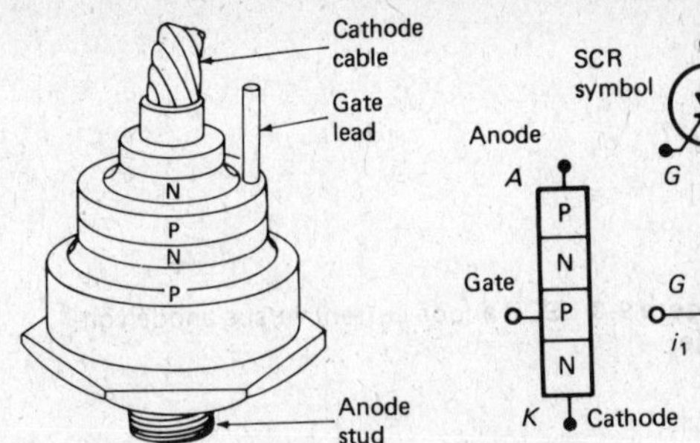

Figure 9-1 Parts of a large SCR.

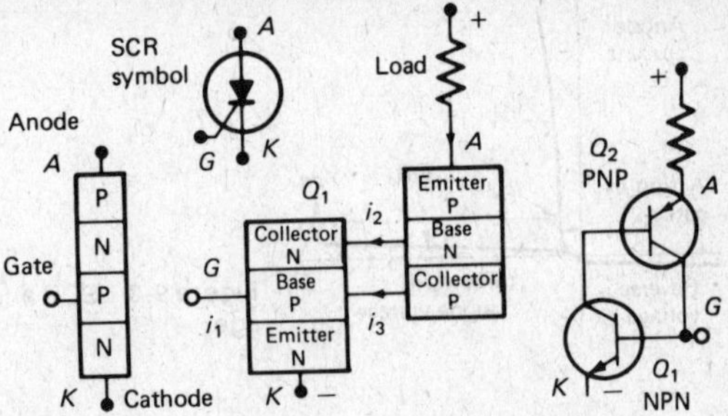

Figure 9-2 The SCR acts like these two transistors combined.

this i_2 is also the base current of Q_2; flowing through this N-type base, it causes greater current i_3 to flow through the Q_2 collector. Since this i_3 flows also in the base of Q_1, it serves as a larger gate current, thus increasing the conduction of both transistors into their saturation state; this is a form of feedback. Even if the original gate signal i_1 is removed, the SCR continues to conduct as a simple rectifier until its anode potential is removed or its anode current is decreased to less than a certain holding level. (Similar to an SCR, a GTO switch can be turned off by short negative pulse at its gate; this is the gate turnoff feature, which also needs larger gate current and uses extra power. This not used in any SCR circuit described in this text.)

In a typical SCR, a rated anode current of many amperes thus can be started by a momentary pulse (4 μsec) of a few milliamperes of gate current. When used in an ac circuit, the gate-current pulse can be timed so as to fire the SCR at the desired angle within each positive half cycle, thereby producing phase control, as described in Sec. 9-5. Thus the SCR acts like a thyratron tube of Chap. 20, except that the SCR is controlled by a pulse of gate current instead of by a change of grid voltage. If dc anode voltage is applied to the SCR, special means are needed to remove the anode voltage momentarily so as to turn off or *commutate* the SCR (as in Sec. 9-9).

9-2 SCR BEHAVIOR AND RATING

The current-voltage behavior of the SCR is shown in Fig. 9-3. In the OFF condition there is a small leakage current; without gate current, the transistor α values[7-9] are so low that this leakage current is not important. If a large forward voltage is applied between anode and cathode, a breakover voltage V_{BR} may be reached which fires the SCR. Normally, the SCR is used where the circuit voltage is much less than V_{BR}. A flow of gate current forces the SCR into the ON region; fired by this i_1, the forward curve of the SCR becomes like that of an ordinary PN diode. The load current passing through the SCR must be maintained larger than a holding-current value I_H, which is

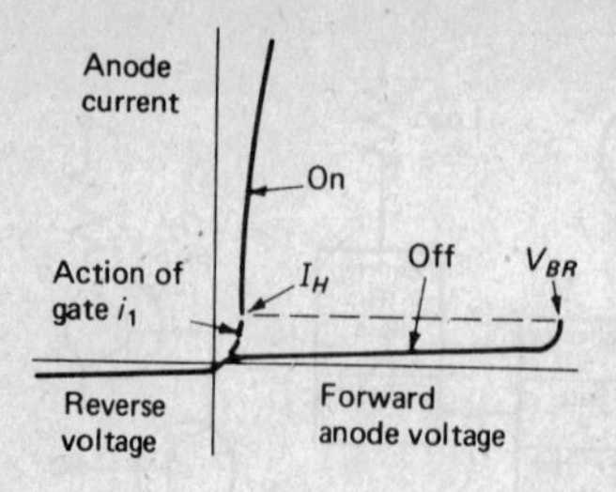

Figure 9-3 SCR anode current versus anode voltage.

about as large as the required gate pulse i_1; if this anode current becomes less than I_H for more than about 20 μsec, the SCR is turned off.

Enlargement of the ON portion of Fig. 9-3 shows that the voltage drop across the SCR during conduction is nearly constant, at about 1 volt. (This action resembles the constant 10- to 15-V arc drop of a thyratron.[17-3]) When reverse anode voltage is applied (stopping the anode current), the SCR regains its original OFF condition within about 20 μsec, and thus it can be used at higher frequencies of anode voltage than can most thyratrons.[20-3]

The SCR must be able to dissipate or get rid of the heat produced within it; at every moment this heat is i^2R_t. But the internal resistance of the SCR decreases as the current i through it increases, for their product iR_t is a nearly constant voltage drop, as shown during ON in Fig. 9-3. Therefore, heat $= i \times$ constant drop; thus the current rating of the SCR may be determined by the average value of i instead of by i^2 or the rms value. However, certain resistive parts within the SCR, such as leads and joints, develop heat that is related to i^2, so that most SCRs are given ratings in amperes rms.

Standard sizes of SCR range from 1 to 300 A of average anode current, and at reverse voltages from 25 to 1200 V. The corresponding rms anode current (for half-wave operation) is 0.5/0.318, or 1.57 times the I_{avg}; thus a 16-A (avg) SCR is rated 25 A rms, and a 70-A (avg) SCR is rated 110 A rms. A pair of back-to-back water-cooled SCRs rated 1200 A rms is shown in Figs. 18-2 and 18-8, and is used in Sec. 19-6.

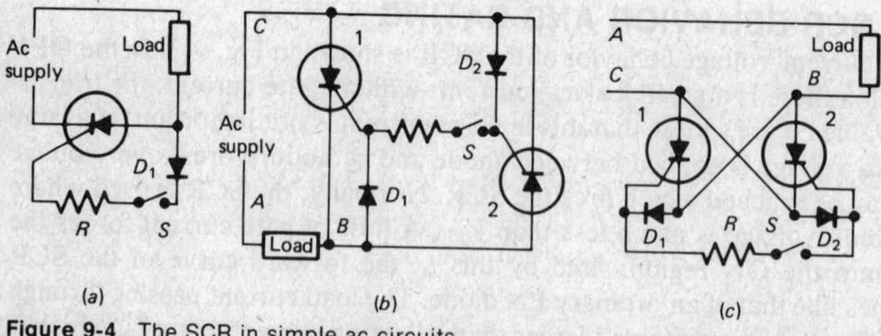

Figure 9-4 The SCR in simple ac circuits.

9-3 THE SCR IN SIMPLE AC CIRCUITS

Simple circuits for switching the power to an ac load are shown in Fig. 9-4. Loads of many amperes can be switched by only 10 mA flowing through switch *S*. Resistor *R* serves to limit the peak gate current to less than 2 A. Since *S* connects the gate circuit to the anode, in Fig. 9-4*a* the gate voltage drops to about 1 V as soon as the load current starts; thus current flows in the gate only long enough to fire the SCR. Diodes are added to prevent reverse gate current. Figure 9-4*b* and *c* shows two arrangements of the same circuit whereby two SCRs are connected back to back or in inverse parallel so that the complete wave of ac voltage appears across the load when *S* is closed. (The arrangement in Fig. 9-4*c* is similar to circuits using two SCRs or two ignitrons, in Fig. 18-4.) When line *C* is positive, there is a small electron flow from *A* and *B* to the cathode of SCR 1 and from its gate through *R*, switch *S*, and D_2 to *C*. This gate current quickly fires SCR 1, causing large electron flow through the load, cathode to anode through SCR 1 to *C*; since the *B*-to-*C* voltage falls to about 1 V, the gate current stops quickly.

A half cycle later, when line *A* is positive, electrons first flow from line *C* to the cathode of SCR 2, and from its gate through *S*, *R*, and D_1 and through the load; as this fires SCR 2, the main electron flow passes through it, and the gate current through *S* and D_1 stops. (If the load is inductive like a welding transformer, certain protective circuits must be added to ensure turnoff.[9-12])

In the bridge circuit shown in Fig. 9-5*a*, a single SCR controls both halves of the ac wave applied to the load. When line 1 is more positive than line 2, electrons flowing through the load must pass also through diodes *D* and *A* and up through SCR. Similarly, when line 2 is the more positive, load electrons must pass also through diodes *C* and *B* and up through SCR. Here the SCR must be fired by a pulse of gate current that occurs in each half cycle.

In Fig. 9-5*b*, incandescent lamps may be dimmed gradually by turning R_1. In each half cycle the rising ac voltage (applied through either diode *A* or *B*) charges C_1 through R_1; as voltage increases across C_1 it charges the larger C_2 more slowly. If R_1 is set midway, C_2 discharges through R_3 and the SCR gate near the middle of each half cycle; this fires SCR so that the lamps receive voltage for the latter part of each half cycle. If R_1 is turned clockwise

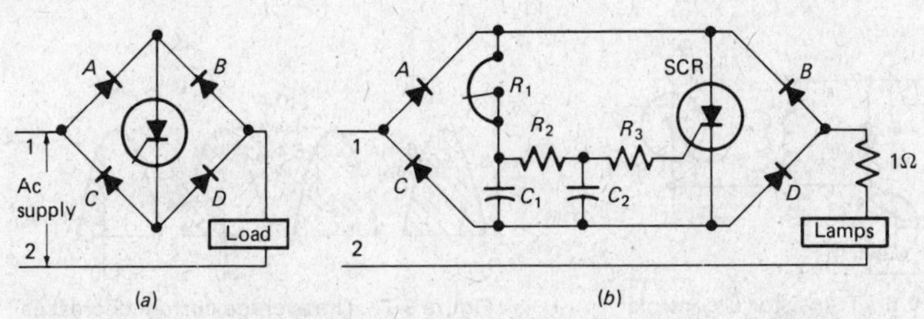

Figure 9-5 (*a*) One SCR controls both ac half waves; (*b*) a light dimmer.

to zero ohms (Ω), C_1 and C_2 charge quickly, so that SCR is fired near the start of each half cycle; the bright lamps receive nearly full ac line voltage. (A 1-Ω resistor limits the inrush current drawn by cold lamps at starting.) With R_1 set near greatest resistance, C_1 charges so slowly that SCR fires very late in the half cycle or not at all. (Other light dimmers are in Sec. 9-16.)

9-4 A TRANSISTOR MAY FIRE AN SCR

By the circuit shown in Fig. 9-6, SCR may be fired by transistor *Q*. If a steady value of *Q* collector current passes through the primary winding of transformer *T*, its secondary winding produces no voltage and SCR receives no gate current. But when a signal applied at base *B* causes *Q* suddenly to increase its collector current, the resulting change in transformer flux produces a pulse of voltage, forcing a momentary flow of gate current that fires SCR.

Since the rise of *Q* current stores energy in the transformer inductance, any following decrease of *Q* current causes the primary winding of *T* to generate a voltage [(+) at its lower terminal] that tries to continue this current flow and prevent SCR from turning off. Therefore, diode *E* is added to let this current continue to circulate until the energy stored in *T* is dissipated in the circuit resistance.

9-5 PHASE CONTROL OF THE SCR; FIRING BY A UJT

When operating on ac voltage as shown in Fig. 9-4, each SCR conducts throughout a complete half cycle, since it receives a pulse of gate current immediately after its anode becomes positive. The resulting current is limited only by the load and cannot be varied by the amount of gate current. However, we can reduce and vary the *average* current that SCR conducts into a constant-resistance load, by delaying the time in each half cycle when SCR is fired. If a load receives through SCR a peak current of 10 amperes (as shown in Fig. 9-7), the average current in each half cycle is 6.4 A when SCR is fired at 0°. If the firing of SCR is delayed to the 90° point in the half cycle, the average current (or average height of the shaded area) is reduced a half, or to 3.2 A. Further delay of the SCR firing to 120° reduces the average cur-

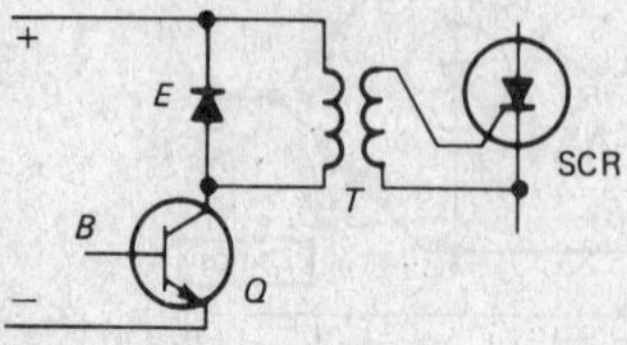

Figure 9-6 Transistor *Q* controls SCR.

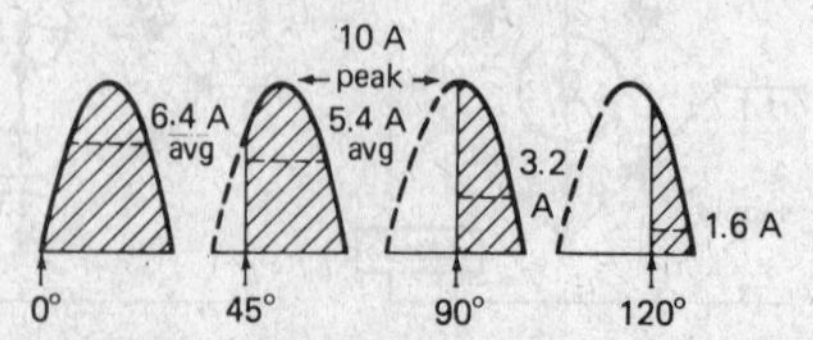

Figure 9-7 The average current decreases as SCR is fired later in wave.

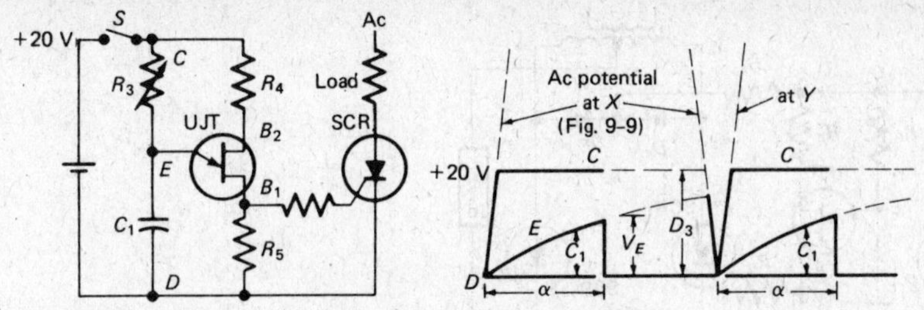

Figure 9-8 UJT fires SCR after a delay set by R_3 and C_1.

rent to 1.6 A. This method of gradual control of an SCR (by delaying its firing point within each half cycle) is called *phase control.*

Since an SCR usually is fired by a short-time pulse of gate current, a circuit is needed that can delay and control the instant that such a pulse occurs within each half cycle. Thus we use[8-6] a unijunction transistor (UJT) to fire the SCR as is shown in Fig. 9-8; it is used again as a part of Fig. 9-9. No part of the UJT receives voltage until switch S is closed so as to apply +20 volts (V) at C. Then, as capacitor C_1 charges through R_3 toward this +20 V, the increasing voltage across C_1 is also the voltage between emitter E and B_1 of UJT. When this voltage across C_1 exceeds V_E (across R_A in Fig. 8-8), current starts to flow through the emitter, and "triggers" the UJT. The resulting decrease in resistance of R_A permits a sudden surge of current as C_1 discharges through R_A and the external R_5. Part of this discharge becomes a pulse of gate current sufficient to fire the SCR.

While S remains closed, the Fig. 9-8 circuit acts as a relaxation or sawtooth oscillator, as C_1 repeats its charge-discharge cycle.

9-6 ONE UJT FIRES TWO SCRs ALTERNATELY

In Fig. 9-9, SCR 1 is to be fired during the ac half cycle when supply terminal X is more positive than center tap W. This increasing (+) voltage passes through diode D_1 and R_1, but the potential at C is limited to a value of 20 volts across the breakdown or Zener diode Z; thus a nearly square-wave voltage suddenly is applied between points C and D, at the start of each half cycle (and thus it acts like the closing of switch S in Fig. 9-8). The voltage across C_1 increases toward +20 V until, quickly, it is discharged through UJT and R_5 (as is described above and shown in Fig. 9-8). The rising voltage across R_5 produces a pulse of current through R_6 and the gate so as to fire SCR 1. [Current flows also in the gate of SCR 2; R_6 and R_7 serve to equalize these two gate currents. However, SCR 2 cannot be fired at this time, for its anode (at Y) is more negative than W.] Since all the supply voltage now is applied across the load (except for about 1 V across SCR 1), the voltage between C and D also has disappeared; so the discharged C_1 does not recharge

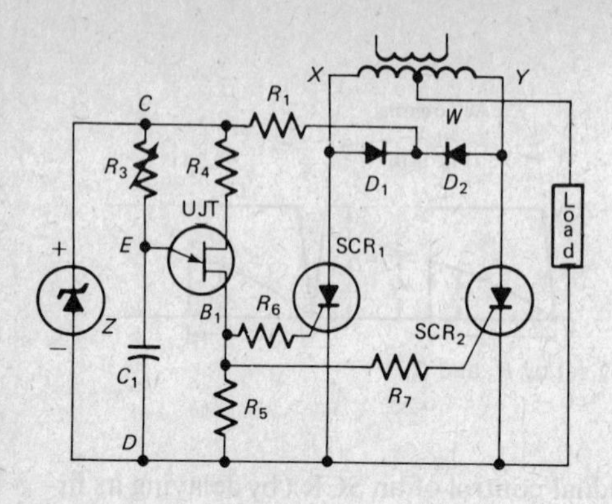

Figure 9-9 One UJT fires two SCRs in alternate half cycles.

within that half cycle. At the end of that half cycle, as the X potential and load current decrease to zero, SCR 1 is turned off.

In the following half cycle, SCR 2 is to be fired while terminal Y is more positive than center tap W. As point C again rises to +20 V, C_1 charges through R_3 and thus delays the firing of SCR 2 by the same angle α that delayed the firing of SCR 1.The resistance of R_3 may be varied so as to adjust the time delay within each half cycle; thereby R_3 can change the phase angle at which each gate current occurs, to fire the SCR.

9-7 PHASE CONTROL BY PEDESTAL AND RAMP

The preceding circuits may be improved, as shown in Fig. 9-10, by adding diode D and voltage divider R_3 and P and by connecting the top of R_5 directly to the ac supply at line 1. As before, at the start of each positive ac half cycle, Zener diode Z limits the point-3 potential to +20 V, and holds this limited voltage across the UJT. A portion of 20 V appears across adjuster P, holding point 5 at, say, +2 V. Although the top of capacitor C_1 is negative during the preceding half cycle, point 6 now rises rapidly as C_1 charges toward line 1 and electrons flow through D and the small resistors R_3 and R_1. As line 1 rises in its half cycle and as point 6 reaches the +2-V level of point 5 (shown at A in Fig. 9-10), diode D becomes reverse-biased and disconnects 6 from 5. Point 6 continues to rise, but much more slowly, as electrons flow through the large resistor R_5 toward the high potential of line 1. At F the C_1 voltage raises emitter E of UJT above the V_E that triggers UJT; this occurs late in the half cycle, firing SCR so that only the last portion of the ac voltage wave is applied to the load. When the ac line voltage reverses, SCR is shut off; the +20 V disappears, letting the UJT current stop; C_1 charges through R_5 toward the potential of line 1, now negative.

In Fig. 9-10, if P is turned clockwise, increasing its resistance and raising point 5 to +6 V (shown at G), C_1 charges rapidly to this adjustable dc value (called the pedestal); then follows the lesser slope (called the ramp) toward

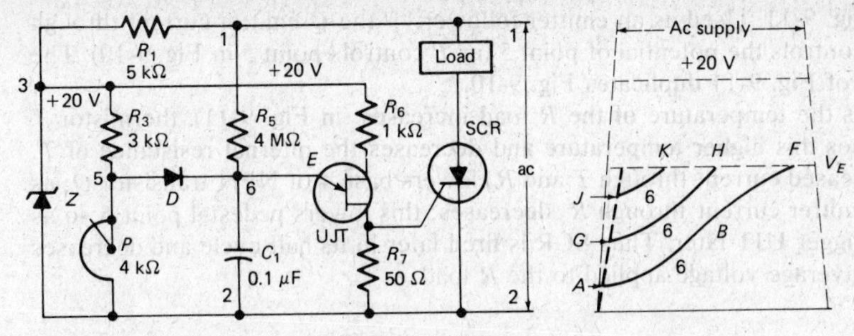

Figure 9-10 Phase control of SCR by pedestal and ramp.

H, at which point the UJT is triggered, thus firing SCR about midway (90°) in the half cycle. When further increase of the *P* resistance raises pedestal point 5 to +10 V (shown at *J*), the slow rise of point 6 along its ramp triggers UJT at *K*, firing SCR quite early in the ac half cycle. (This pedestal-and-ramp feature is used in Sec. 21-1.)

The manual turning of *P* changes the amount of dc voltage between 2 and 5 and thereby varies the trigger point of UJT so as to provide phase control of SCR. Similarly, a change in dc voltage caused by another device may produce phase control, as next described.

9-8 SCR PHASE CONTROL BY TEMPERATURE OR LIGHT

In Fig. 9-11 a thermistor *T* senses a temperature (such as that of a resistive load) and controls SCR so as to hold that temperature constant. A thermistor is a semiconductor (metallic oxide) made so that its internal resistance decreases greatly as its temperature rises and thus generates additional electron-hole pairs. So sensitive a device usually would not directly replace adjuster *P* in Fig. 9-10; instead, thermistor *T* is used to control transistor *Q*

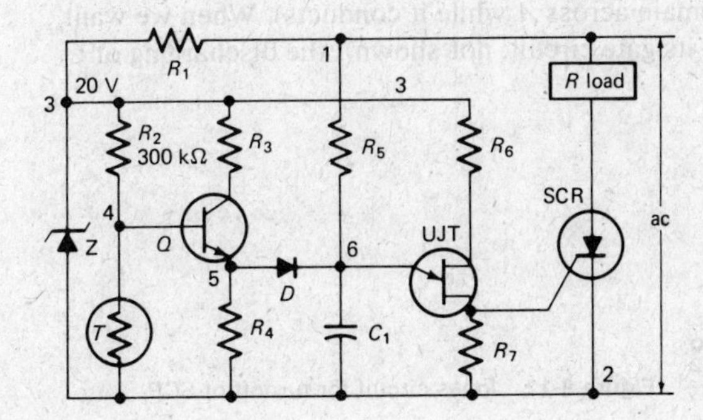

Figure 9-11 Phase control of SCR by thermistor *T*.

in Fig. 9-11. Used as an emitter follower,[5-10] the Q emitter current through R_4 controls the potential of point 5 (as P controls point 5 in Fig. 9-10). The rest of Fig. 9-11 duplicates Fig. 9-10.

As the temperature of the R load increases (in Fig. 9-11), thermistor T senses this higher temperature and decreases the internal resistance of T. Increased current through T and R_2 lowers base 4 of NPN transistor Q; as Q emitter current through R_4 decreases, this lowers pedestal point 5 so as to trigger UJT later. Thus SCR is fired later in its half cycle and decreases the average voltage applied to the R load.

9-9 TURNOFF OF SCR; JONES CIRCUIT

So long as anode current flows, the central or base regions of the SCR (as shown in Fig. 9-2) are saturated with stored charges (holes and electrons). When anode current stops, time is needed for these charges to diffuse or recombine; after these stored charges have been removed, the center junction 2 regains its ability to block forward voltage. (This recombination or turnoff time is similar to deionization time in a thyratron.[20-3])

Using ac voltage at the SCR anode, this voltage reverses and stops anode current during each negative half cycle. If higher-frequency voltage is used, this voltage wave may return positive before the stored charges are fully removed; thus the SCR again conducts, even though there is no gate current.

When the SCR operates with dc anode voltage, a special circuit is added to turn off the SCR, by momentary removal of its anode voltage or by reducing its anode current below the holding value. One of many available methods, the Jones circuit, is shown in Fig. 9-12; here A is the SCR that conducts current to the load (when its gate receives a firing pulse from another circuit, not shown). To turn off A, the second SCR B is fired, as follows.

Each time that A is fired, current increases rapidly through A, winding E, and the load. Since E and F are two windings on the same core (acting as an autotransformer), this sudden current increase through E induces in F a voltage that is (+) at its end connected to diode D. As D conducts, capacitor C becomes charged to perhaps 30 V, (+) at its lower terminal 4; this charge remains, and serves to hold anode 4 of B more positive than the B cathode at 3 (since only a few volts remain across A while it conducts). When we want to turn off A, we fire B (by its gate circuit, not shown); the discharging of C

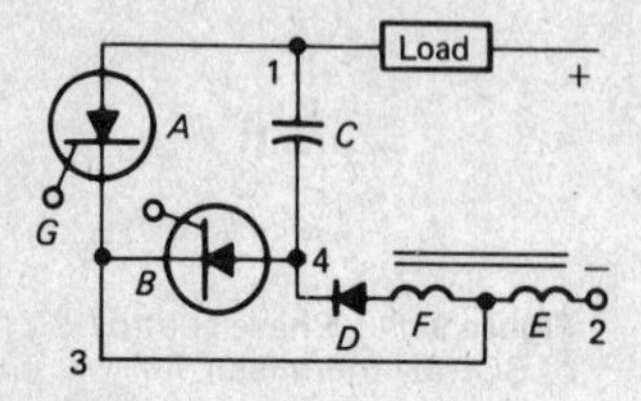

Figure 9-12 Jones circuit for turnoff of SCR.

forces electron flow from top line 1 down through *A*, and from cathode to anode of *B*. In *A* this flow opposes the load current, thereby momentarily reducing the total flow below the holding-current value in *A*, so that *A* stops conducting. The voltage across *C* reverses, thus stopping current in *B*; the *C* voltage is restored the next time *A* fires.

9-10 SCRs OR THYRATRONS WITH RESISTANCE LOAD OR INDUCTIVE LOAD

In Fig. 9-13, the SCR *S* is connected in series with load *R* (noninductive) across the ac supply voltage. (Sections 9-10 to 9-13 apply also to thyratron tubes when used with the kinds of load shown in Figs. 9-13 to 9-21.) So long as the SCR receives no turn-on pulse at its gate *G*, the entire supply voltage appears between anode *A* and cathode *K*. When gate current fires the SCR at *F*, the anode potential *A* drops at once to a few volts above *K*. In Fig. 9-13, the anode current in SCR *S* and resistance load *R* rises abruptly at *H*, then follows a sine wave which reduces to zero at *J*, when the supply voltage also is zero. Anode *A* immediately becomes negative at *L* as the supply voltage becomes negative; no current flows while *A* is below *K*. If *S* is fired again at *M*, anode current flows again until the supply voltage reverses, at *N*.

There are differences when the load is assumed to be inductive (such as a transformer winding or a reactor *X*, as shown in Fig. 9-14). When the SCR is fired (at *V*), the anode current in *S* and load *X* rises more slowly and reaches a lower value (at *U*); moreover, owing to the energy stored because of this current flowing in the inductive load *X*, the current does not decrease to zero at *W*, but continues to flow for some time after the supply voltage has reversed. So long as this anode current flows, the voltage drop across the SCR remains at a few volts; the potential at anode *A* remains positive far into the following half cycle, as shown at *Y* and at *Z*.

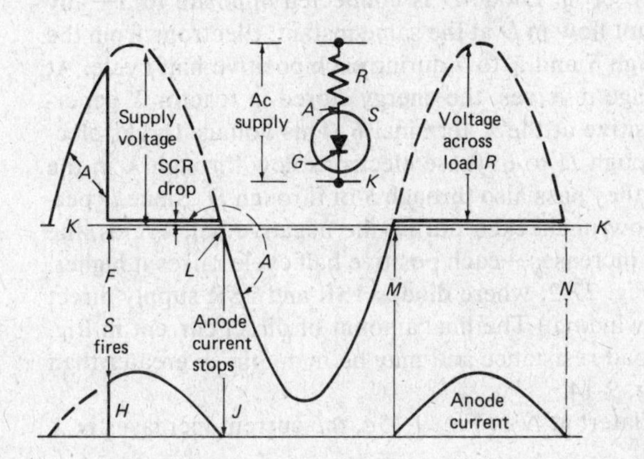

Figure 9-13 Action of SCR or thyratron with resistance load.

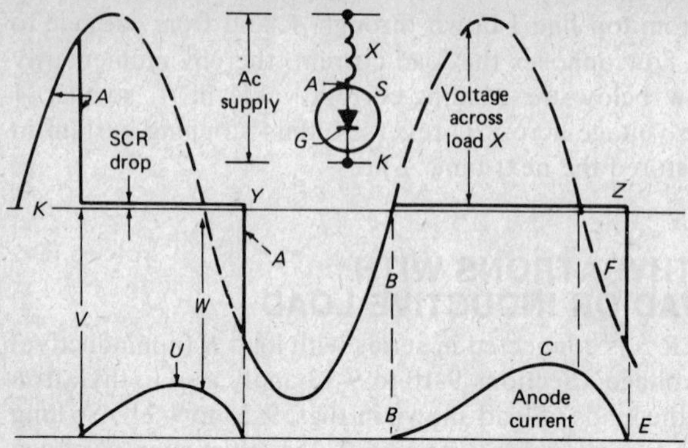

Figure 9-14 Action of SCR or thyratron with inductance load, showing effect of stored energy at *Y* and *Z*.

Starting at *B* (in the second cycle shown in Fig. 9-14), the SCR current increases only to an amount *C* before the supply voltage reverses. As long as current flows in the SCR, it connects load *X* to the ac voltage, even though that voltage has become negative, at *F*, so that it opposes the current and finally decreases it to zero. The energy stored by this current in reactor *X* must be removed by this reverse voltage *F* before the current can stop, at *E*. Thereafter, at the start of each positive half cycle, a similar wave of current begins, no larger than the first.

9-11 SCRs WITH DIODES IN AC INDUCTIVE CIRCUITS

If now a diode *D* is added across *X* (as shown in Fig. 9-15) and *S* is fired at the start of each cycle, Fig. 9-15*b* shows that the current through *S* and *X* continues to increase, cycle after cycle, until the amount of current is limited only by the dc resistance of *X*. Diode *D* is connected opposite to *S*—any current flowing in *S* cannot flow in *D* at the same instant. Electrons from the ac line flow from 5 through *S* and *X* to 7 during each positive half cycle. At *P*, when the supply voltage reverses, the energy stored in reactor *X* generates a voltage that is positive at the *X* terminal 6. This voltage forces electrons to flow from 7 through *D* to 6; these electrons flow through *X* in the same direction, whether they pass also through *S* or through *D*. Since *D* permits this *X* current to flow unchecked during the negative half cycles, the amount of direct current increases—each positive half cycle raises it higher. (This circuit is used in Fig. 27-2, where diodes 1SR and 2SR supply direct current to a motor field winding.) The final amount of direct current in Fig. 9-15 is limited only by load resistance and may be many times greater than the current pulses in Fig. 9-14.

If now SCR *S* is fired later, at *N* in Fig. 9-15*c*, the current increases in *X*

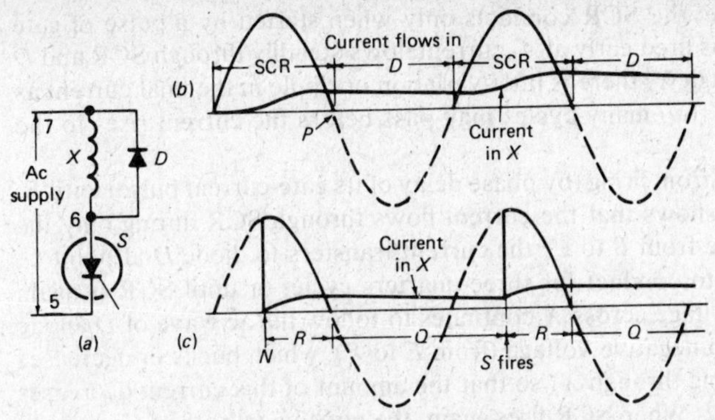

Figure 9-15 With diode D added, SCR S controls average current in X.

during only the brief intervals R. During the longer intervals Q, diode D conducts; this D current decreases slowly, owing to the resistance and a small heat loss in this circuit. The final amount of direct current in Fig. 9-15c is less than in Fig. 9-15b, because the firing point of S is delayed.

A single SCR and its companion diode D may be arranged as shown in Fig. 9-16 for gradual control of the direct current in an inductive load X; here, by phase control of the SCR, the current is varied in both SCR and D. (This arrangement may be used to vary the current in the dc field circuit of a generator or a dc motor. If such a circuit was not inductive, maximum current would flow in D; the load current could not be influenced greatly by SCR.) Diode D always passes current during that entire half cycle when its

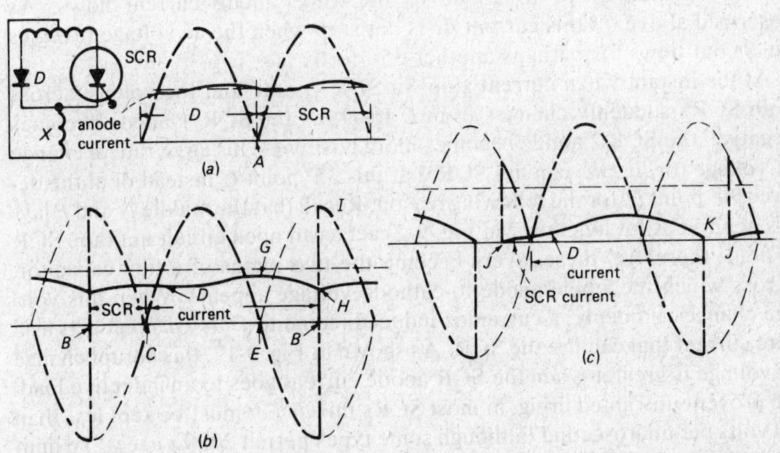

Figure 9-16 Phase control of one SCR changes the current through diode D also.

anode is positive; the SCR conducts only when started by a pulse of gate current. If SCR is fired early at *A*, current flows steadily through SCR and *D* in turn and through *X;* there is little variation or ripple in the final current as shown in Fig. 9-16*a;* many cycles may pass before the current rises to the amount shown.

If SCR is kept from firing (by phase delay of its gate-current pulse) until *B*, then Fig. 9-16*b* shows that the current flows through SCR during only the one-quarter cycle from *B* to *C;* the current transfers to diode *D* at point *C*. So *D* continues to conduct for three-quarters cycle, or until SCR is again fired; at *E* the voltage across *X* continues to follow the ac wave of *D* anode voltage—this is a negative voltage (from *E* to *F*), which bucks or decreases the current flowing through *X*, so that the amount of this current decreases between *G* and *H*. When SCR fires again, the positive voltage at *I* increases the current flow, which may not rise to the full amount before it is again decreased by the delayed firing of SCR. The average direct current in Fig. 9-16*b* is less than that in Fig. 9-16*a*.

If the firing of SCR is further delayed to *J*, then Fig. 9-16*c* shows a further decrease of average dc; the result is nearly the same as if diode *D* were being used alone, giving a voltage wave as shown in Fig. 9-14.

9-12 VOLTAGE CHANGE, *dv/dt*

When two SCRs are connected back to back as shown in Fig. 9-17 (and also like Fig. 9-4*c*), the anode-to-cathode voltage of SCR 1 is also the cathode-to-anode voltage of SCR 2. If phase control is added so as to delay by 90° the firing of each SCR, Fig. 9-17 shows the waveshapes of current and voltage across these SCRs while they energize an inductive load (thus extending the case of the single SCR of Fig. 9-14). At *A*, as SCR 1 fires, its anode potential drops to about 1 volt while anode current flows. As described above,[9-10] this current does not stop when the ac voltage reverses (at *B*) but flows for perhaps another 35°, to *C*.

At the instant when current stops in SCR 1, note that the voltage across both SCRs suddenly changes from *C* to *D;* as the SCR 1 anode becomes negative, the SCR 2 anode becomes more positive. This large rate of change of voltage (or dv/dt) can fire SCR 2 at this 35° point *C* instead of at the desired 90° point *E*, for the following reason. Recall that the middle *N* and *P* layers of an SCR (at junction 2 in Fig. 9-2) act as an open circuit until the SCR is fired; therefore, these layers become the two plates of a tiny capacitor, across which the whole anode-to-cathode voltage appears. When this voltage changes suddenly, a current is induced (equal to $C\,dv/dt$) that acts as a gate current that can fire the SCR. As shown in Fig. 9-17, this abrupt change of voltage is greater when the SCR anode current goes to an inductive load. To prevent unwanted firing, in most SCRs this dv/dt must be kept less than 40 volts per microsecond (although some types permit 200v / μsec). To limit such changes of voltage across SCRs in ac inductive circuits, we may con-

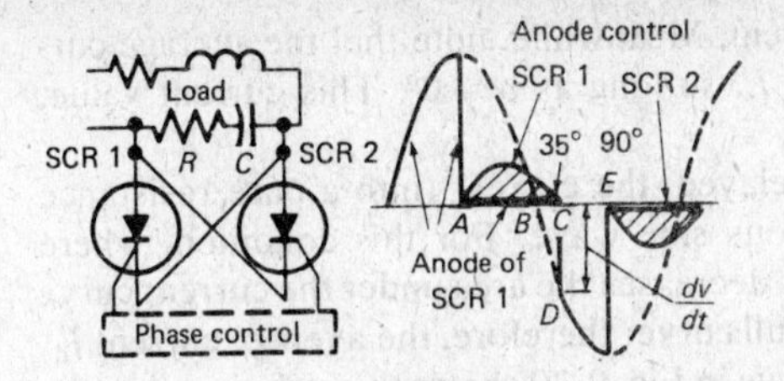

Figure 9-17 Use of *RC* to reduce sudden voltage changes in ac inductive circuit.

nect resistor *R* and capacitor *C* (in series) between anode and cathode of the SCR.

The triac of Sec. 9-15 likewise must be protected against high values of dv / dt lest the triac current may not stop, even when its gate current is removed; in Fig. 9-25, we add R_2 and C_2 for this purpose. Such features often are omitted from circuit diagrams in later chapters.

9-13 TWO-SCR RECTIFIER WITH COMBINED *R* AND *L* LOAD

When SCRs or thyratrons, with phase control, supply to the load only certain portions of the sine wave of ac voltage, the resulting average load current I_{dc} and its waveshape depend on the amount of load inductance, or rather, the ratio of X_L to R (where $X_L = \omega L$ or $2\pi fL$). (Note the case of a one-SCR rectifier in Sec. 9-10.)

Consider the biphase half-wave rectifier of Fig. 9-18, and assume that the SCR or tube drop is zero. When fired at zero phase delay ($\alpha = 0°$), as though they were diodes, Fig. 9-19 shows the resulting waves of load current. For pure resistive load, where $\omega L / R = 0$, the current i_0 is a rectified sine wave that reaches a peak value of $\sqrt{2}\ V / R$, and whose average or dc value $= (2 / \pi)\ (\sqrt{2}\ V / R) = 0.9V / R$. If load inductance is added until $\omega L = R$, the dashed curve i_1 shows that the current wave now has less variation. For a more inductive load, such as $\omega L / R = 4$, the variation of cur-

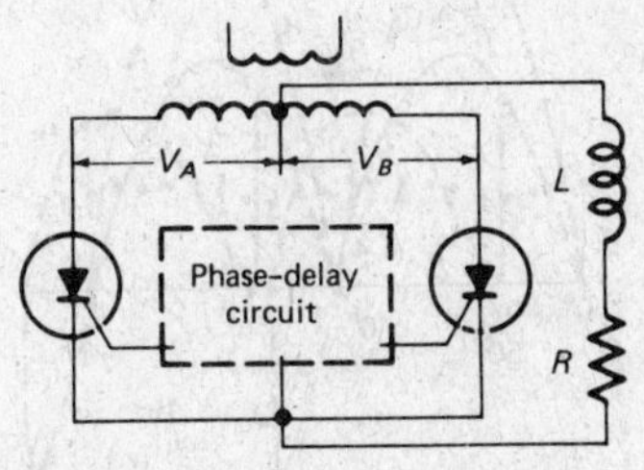

Figure 9-18 Rectifier with *R and L* load.

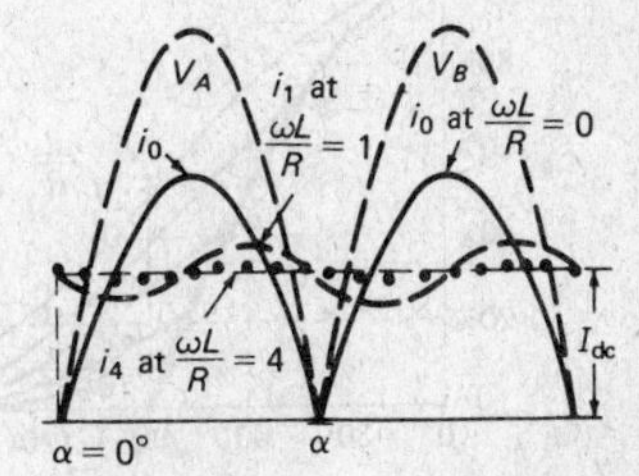

Figure 9-19 Waveshapes for *RL* load in Fig. 9-18, with zero firing delay.

rent i_4 (dotted) is only a few percent. Meanwhile, note that the average current value I_{dc} is not affected by L, so long as $\alpha = 0°$. This current value, $0.9V/R$, here is called I_{full}.

If the firing of each SCR is delayed, the current (into a pure resistance load) rises instantly to its previous sine wave. For this condition, where $\omega L/R = 0$, firing the SCRs at 90° decreases the area under the current curve to just half of the area under the full curve; therefore, the average current I_{dc} is 50 percent of I_{full}; the upper curve in Fig. 9-20 shows this value at point D. For other firing angles, the area under the current curve can be measured so that the ratio I_{dc}/I_{full} can be found.

If the firing of each SCR is delayed until $\alpha = 50°$, Fig. 9-21 shows zero current between 0° and α. The average current can be determined by the calculus, and its new value is shown at E in Fig. 9-20.

$$I_{dc} = \frac{1}{\pi}\int_{50°}^{180°} \frac{\sqrt{2}\,V \sin \omega t}{R}\, d(\omega t) = 0.74\frac{V}{R} = 0.82 I_{full}$$

The current is discontinuous also for $\omega L/R = 1$ (for $\alpha = 50°$), and i_1 is zero between about 45° and α: here the load inductance forces each SCR or tube to conduct for 45° after its supply voltage has gone negative; this current wave is not part of a sine function. For $\omega L/R = 4$, the current i_4 is continuous but it decreases to a minimum value at α, where current transfers from one SCR to the other.

When the load is inductive, the calculation of the average value of load current or I_{dc} is more difficult; the results appear in Fig. 9-20, expressed in percent of I_{full}. At small angles of firing delay α, the values of I_{dc} are read from the heavy line ABC. For $\omega L/R = 1$, this is between A and B, for $\alpha < 45°$. Within this range the load current is continuous; as α increases toward 45°, more of the negative part of the ac supply voltage is connected across the load (as shown at F in Fig. 9-21), decreasing I_{dc} quite rapidly.

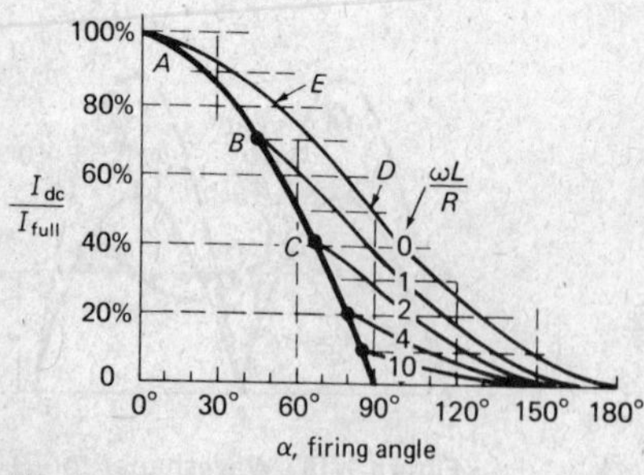

Figure 9-20 Average load current in Fig. 9-18 versus firing delay α.

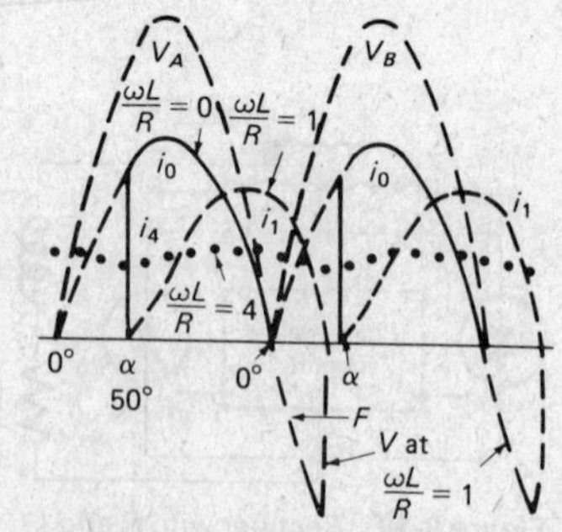

Figure 9-21 Waveshapes for Fig. 9-18 when firing is delayed to α.

However, when $\alpha < 45°$, values of I_{dc} are read from the lighter curve (at the right of B) labeled $\omega L / R = 1$. Here it is seen that I_{dc} does not decrease so quickly when α increases, for neither SCR is conducting later than angle B in the following half cycle; therefore, negative supply voltage cannot reach the load later than B. Similarly, for $\omega L/R = 2$, Fig. 9-20 shows that the load current is continuous up to 63° firing angle, at C.

9-14 RECTIFIER WITH BACK-EMF LOAD

When the biphase rectifier of Fig. 9-18 supplies power to a battery or to the armature of a dc motor, the back emf or counter emf V_g of the armature greatly affects the size of I_{dc} and its waveshape. (This cemf V_g is discussed in Sec. 21-3.) As is shown in Fig. 9-22, each half wave of voltage V (from anode to center tap) is applied across one SCR in series with the armature, which may be viewed as a load R and L, including cemf V_g. Meanwhile, the motor field is separately excited; since field flux ϕ is constant, the motor torque is proportional to I_{dc}. As V_g increases with armature speed, it raises the cathode potential, so that the only voltage that can force current through the load is the difference between the applied voltage $v = \sqrt{2}\, V \sin \omega t$ and $V_g + V_t$. (V_t is the small voltage across SCR, or about 10-V drop in a thyratron.)

Even if the SCRs are replaced by diodes, Fig. 9-23 shows that they cannot fire earlier than the angle $\alpha_e = \sin^{-1} (V_g + V_t) / \sqrt{2}V$. Also, if the armature inductance L is considered negligible, current will not flow later than α_1, which also is $\pi - \alpha_e$.

If the firing of each SCR now is delayed until α (and $L = 0$), the voltage that causes current flow in each half cycle is shown shaded in Fig. 9-23, and the average value of armature current is

$$I_{dc} = \frac{1}{\pi} \int_{\alpha}^{\pi - \alpha e} \frac{\sqrt{2}\, V \sin \omega t - (V_g + V_t)}{R}\, d(\omega t)$$

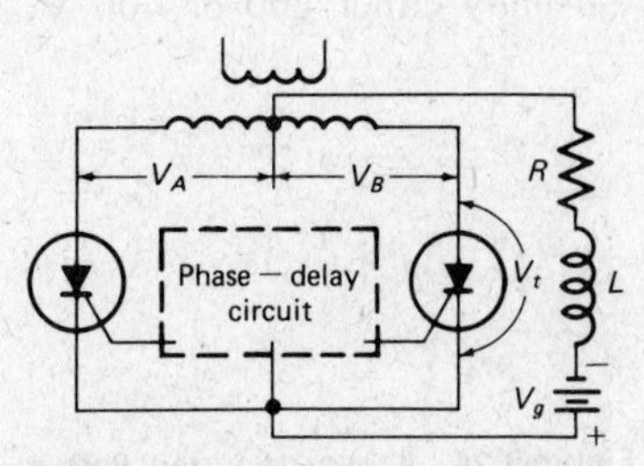

Figure 9-22 Circuit of Fig. 9-18, with addition of back-emf load.

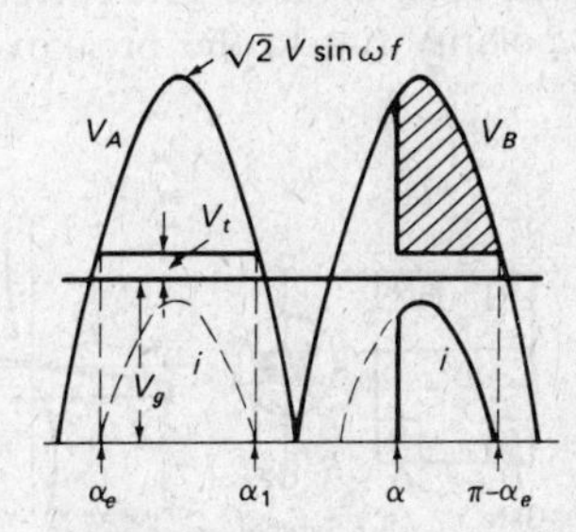

Figure 9-23 Waveshapes for back-emf load in Fig. 9-22.

or $$I_{dc} = \frac{1}{\pi R} [\sqrt{2}\, V(\cos \alpha_e + \cos \alpha) - (V_g + V_t)(\pi - \alpha^* - \alpha_e^*)]$$

where * indicates the angle in radians.

Thus, for 230 volts (V) at V_A or V_B, if tube drop is 12 V and the armature has 6 ohms of R and generates 105 V cemf, then $\alpha_e = 21°$. If each tube is fired at $\alpha = 60°$, the motor armature current is 14 amperes (A); each tube conducts an average of 7 A. However, if the motor speed doubles so that cemf becomes 210 V, then $\alpha_e = 43°$. With $\alpha = 60°$, the armature current is only 5.4 A.

9-15 THE TRIAC

The conventional SCR, as shown in Fig. 9-2, is a PNPN device that is controlled by a pulse of electrons out of its P base; this permits a large electron flow from cathode K to anode A. There is also a *complementary* SCR, which has a gate connection to its N base; here a pulse of electrons *into* its gate can start electron flow from A to K when K is more positive than A; larger gate current is needed. Both of these actions are combined in the SCS (silicon controlled switch) having two gates, in Sec. 9-18.

A more recent device is the triac (triggers on ac), which can block voltage of either polarity but which starts electron flow in either direction by means of an electron pulse in or out of its single gate. The triac has four major layers NPNP, but several N regions are fitted into its lower P layer, as shown in Fig. 9-24; one of these N regions serves as terminal T_1, and the other is the gate. Meanwhile, the upper P layer is made to protrude through part of the top N layer to form terminal T_2. These layers are formed by the film techniques described in Sec. 12-1.

Figure 9-24 shows the triac symbol and its curves of anode current versus anode voltage. Either T_1 or T_2 can be the anode. When T_2 is positive, the triac curve nearly duplicates the SCR curve of Fig. 9-3; a current pulse into (or electrons out of) the gate starts the main electron flow from T_1 to T_2. When T_2 is negative, the mirror-image curve shows that very little main or anode current flows until there is a pulse of current out of (or electrons into) the gate. With no gate current, the triac resists the applied voltage of either polarity (up to the breakover voltage V_{BR}, usually either 200 or 400 V,

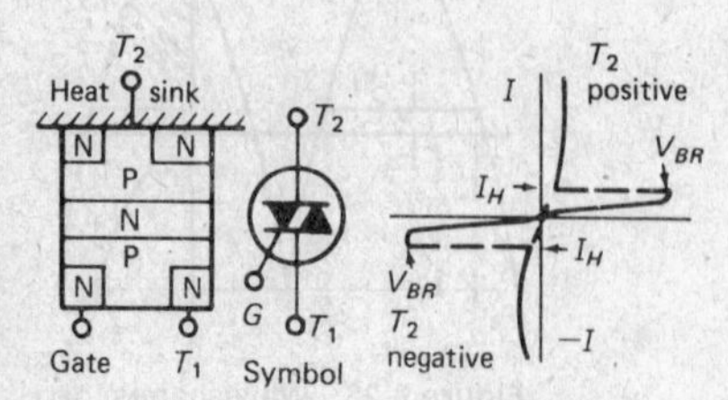

Figure 9-24 A triac; its current versus voltage.

which must be higher than the peak of the applied ac voltage). Only a few volts drop remains across the triac while it is conducting its rated 6 or 10 A in either direction; the rest of the applied ac voltage appears across the load. The triac protects itself against damage caused by transient overvoltages of either polarity, merely by conducting at V_{BR}; this does not protect the external circuit from the effects of undesired firing of the triac.[9-12]

While most SCRs can be turned off by voltage reversal during the negative half cycle of the ac supply [up to 30 kilohertz (kHz or kc / sec)], such rapid voltage reversal across a triac does not turn it off, for the triac merely conducts in the opposite direction. But when a triac is used in ac circuits of 60 Hz or less, the rate of change of voltage (near the zero point of the sine wave) is low enough to permit commutation or turnoff of the triac, during a cycle when there is no pulse of gate current.

9-16 TRIAC CIRCUITS

A switching circuit is shown in Fig. 9-25, where a tiny contact *S* is closed so as to pass gate current that fires triac *T* near the start of each half cycle, thus applying ac voltage to the load. When *T* fires, only a few volts remain across *T*; so the pulse of gate current stops. (For loads up to 10 A, this is a simple alternative to the use of two SCRs, as in Fig. 9-4.) If the controlled load is inductive, R_2 and C_2 are added to limit the rate of voltage rise (dv / dt) across the triac when its current stops, thus helping to turn it off.[9-12]

A light-dimmer control for incandescent lamps (up to 700 watts) is shown in Fig. 9-26; this is a phase control, wherein R_3 is turned clockwise to increase the light. At the start of each half cycle (before triac *T* is fired), the ac voltage causes point 3 to rise as C_1 is charged through the resistance of R_3 and the lamp load. (The diac shown is a trigger diode that abruptly conducts full current, just as the voltage across it rises above a set breakover value, such as 30 V.) When point 3 reaches this 30-V level, the diac conducts, letting C_1 discharge through the gate of triac *T*, which applies ac voltage across the lamps for the rest of that half cycle. During the next negative half cycle, points 1 and 3 are negative and C_1 charges to the opposite polarity; the diac is triggered at the same 30-V level, firing *T* at the same

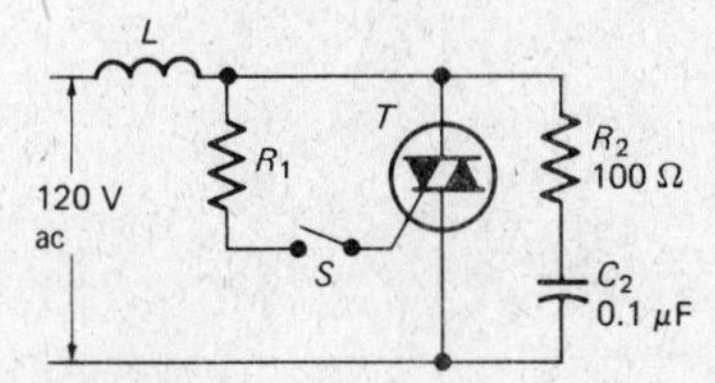

Figure 9-25 Full-wave ac is across *L* when *S* closes, firing the triac.

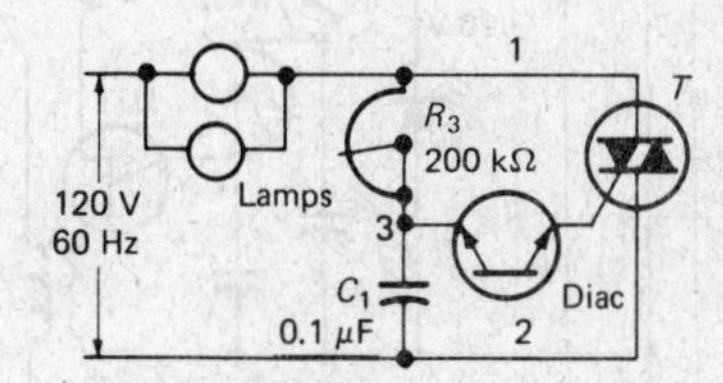

Figure 9-26 Phase control of a triac as a light dimmer.

phase delay as in the positive half cycle. If the resistance of R_3 is increased, C_1 charges more slowly, reaching the 30-V trigger point later in each half cycle, so that a smaller portion of the ac voltage wave is applied thus dimming the lamps.

The circuit of Fig. 9-26 will control a furnace blower motor instead of lights if a thermistor is used in place of rheostat R_3 (as described also in Sec. 9-8). At a low furnace temperature the thermistor passes little current; so triac T is not fired. When a hotter furnace is sensed by the thermistor, its decreased resistance lets C_1 charge so that T fires earlier in each half cycle, applying ac voltage to run the blower motor.

A more complete light dimmer, shown in Fig. 9-27, adds the feature of slow turn-on or "soft start" when ac power first is applied to the lamps. When cold, the resistance of large incandescent lamps is very low; if full line voltage suddenly is applied, the resulting inrush of current can blow a fuse or damage circuit parts before the lamps reach their hot resistance.

Diodes D_1 to D_4 form a bridge rectifier that supplies full-wave voltage between points 1 and 2; this voltage is reduced across R_1, so that 20 V is held by Zener diode Z between 3 and 2. Like the action described in Sec. 9-6, point 3 in Fig. 9-27 drops to zero potential at the end of each half cycle, so as to discharge C_1 and reset UJT.

When ac power first is applied to the circuit, the large capacitor C_2 charges slowly through R_2 so that 8 or 10 cycles elapse before point 4 approaches the 20-V potential of point 3. At first, the C_2 voltage (applied across R_3 and C_1) is not large enough to let C_1 charge fast enough to fire UJT much before the end of the ac half cycle (regardless of the setting of light adjuster R_3). After a few cycles, the increased voltage across C_2 charges C_1 more quickly, thus raising emitter E sooner, so that UJT fires the triac earlier in the half cycle. The pulse of UJT current, flowing in the primary winding of transformer T, produces a T-secondary voltage that forces a gate-current pulse to fire the triac during each half cycle, of either polarity.

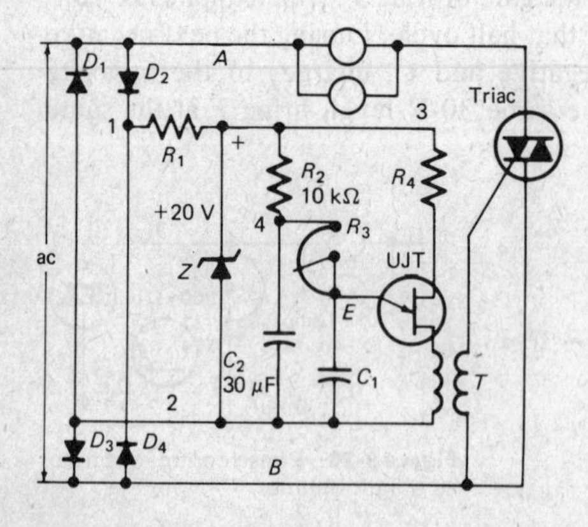

Figure 9-27 Triac light dimmer with slow turn-on.

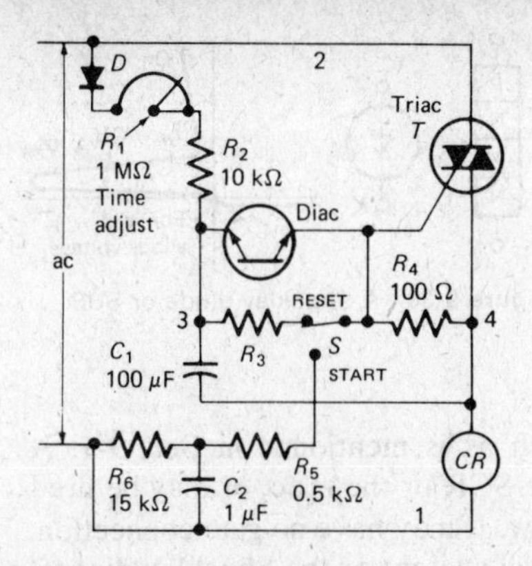

Figure 9-28 Triac time-delay relay.

9-17 A TRIAC TIME-DELAY RELAY

Figure 9-28 shows triac T that energizes relay CR at the end of a time delay, as set by $(R_1 + R_2)$ and C_1. Whenever top line 2 is more positive, electrons flow from 1 through the CR coil to charge C_1, continuing through R_2, R_1, and diode D to 2. But while switch S touches at RESET, the triac cannot fire, since its gate is held near cathode 4 by small resistor R_4, acting as part of the voltage divider R_1-R_2-R_3-R_4. When S is moved to START, the potential at C_1 terminal 3 rises further during each positive half cycle, at a rate adjusted by R_1. After the desired delay, 3 reaches the breakover voltage of the diac (as also occurs in Fig. 9-26), letting large C_1 discharge slightly, sending an electron pulse through the triac gate and the diac; the triac fires at the start of each following half cycle when its top terminal 2 becomes positive, thus picking up relay CR.

Before the triac fires, no voltage is applied across C_2 or R_5 (at the bottom of Fig. 9-28). When the fired triac applies positive voltage across the CR coil, this voltage appears also across C_2 and R_5. By the time the line voltage reverses, C_2 is being charged by electrons flowing through R_5, switch S, and into the triac gate; this current continues after the top of the triac becomes negative and thus fires the triac again at the start of each negative half cycle. The CR coil continues to receive the entire wave of ac voltage until S is moved to RESET; then C_1 discharges through R_3 and R_4, so that point-3 potential cannot cause diac current to fire the triac during the next positive half cycle. Thus no voltage exists across the CR coil and there is no C_2 charging current to fire the triac in the negative half cycle. Relay CR drops out.

9-18 THYRISTORS—PNPN DEVICES

Thyristors are a group or class of solid-state devices that include the SCR and the triac described above. A thyristor is a PNPN device having four layers (as in Figs. 9-2 and 9-24); it is bistable and is either all on or all off,

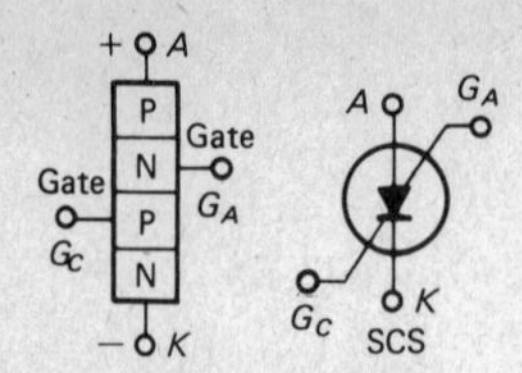

Figure 9-29 SCS, the silicon controlled switch.

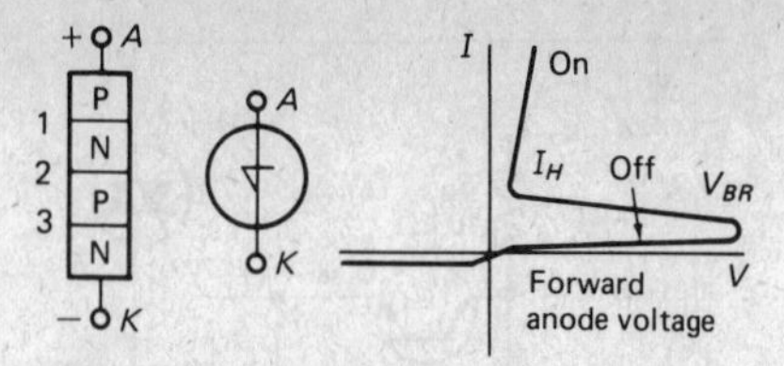

Figure 9-30 A Shockley diode or SUS.

caused by internal feedback action such as is mentioned in Sec. 9-1. A thyristor may have a single gate, like the SCR or the triac, or may be fired by either of two gates like the SCS, below. It may have no gate connection, like the diac or the SUS (silicon unilateral switch) or the Shockley diode.

The silicon controlled switch (SCS, Fig. 9-29) is like a small SCR rated less than 1 ampere; it is turned on and off as described in Sec. 9-2 and Fig. 9-2. The SCS firing characteristic is extremely sensitive; thus its anode current may be used for firing a larger SCR.

The SCS has two gates, as shown in Fig. 9-29; current flowing in either gate fires the SCS. If no connection is made to G_A, the unit acts like the SCR, fired by G_C. By the use of G_A instead, the SCS may be inverted so that it becomes a NPNP device, fired by making G_A more negative.

A Shockley diode is a four-layer silicon PNPN device that uses no gate connections; it is made to conduct when the voltage across it is raised to a breakover V_{BR} or tripping potential. Figure 9-30 shows that this diode acts like the SCR that has no gate current; until its rated value of V_{BR} is reached or exceeded, only a small leakage current flows. Here the PN junctions 1 and 3 are forward-biased; the leakage current is limited only by junction 2, which is reverse-biased, while anode A is (+). At V_{BR}, an avalanche breakdown occurs at junction 2 so that much greater current can flow through the diode. Owing to the special design of this junction, after V_{BR} is reached, the size of voltage needed to cause this rising current decreases abruptly until only a few volts remain across the conducting diode. Within 1 μsec the Shockley diode switches on and continues to conduct until the voltage across it is reduced so that its anode current becomes less than I_H, the required holding current.

Because the curve between V_{BR} and I_H in Fig. 9-30 indicates a negative resistance (shown by an increasing current caused by a decreasing voltage), this diode can operate only in the on or the off state; it switches very quickly from one state to the other.

The silicon unilateral switch (SUS) is like a Shockley diode but has a single gate that is used mainly to synchronize its discharge with the applied ac voltage (as in Fig. 21-11) or for lockout or other special signals. The SUS breaks down and conducts always at a specified value near 10V applied to its anode [whereas a UJT trips when its emitter reaches a fraction η of whatever voltage is applied across it (V_{BB} in Fig. 8-7)]. The SUS is used in Secs. 21-8 and 24-11.

9-19 ZERO-VOLTAGE SWITCHING CIRCUIT

In Secs. 9-13 to 9-16 we see how SCRs or triacs may be used to turn on an ac load gradually. In general, when a thyristor is used to turn on a resistive load late in the cycle, a great electromagnetic interference (EMI) is generated because of the very fast rise of current, as shown at H in Fig. 9-13. In applications where the thyristor is to turn the load either on or off, we desire to make sure that the thyristor starts conducting at the beginning of the ac voltage wave, at the zero crossover point. So we use the zero crossover or zero-voltage switching circuit shown in Fig. 9-31 to determine when the voltage is passing through zero so that we turn on the thyristor at that instant. In Fig. 9-31, if either Q_1 or Q_2 is conducting, the collector voltage of these transistors (and hence the gate voltage of SCR 1) is too small to fire the SCR. Switch S may be closed to prevent Q_1 from conducting. Q_2 starts to conduct as soon as the voltage of upper line A becomes 0.5 V more positive than line B, for this is the voltage on the base of Q_2. But just as line A starts to go positive, a few microseconds elapse before A reaches 0.5 V, during which time Q_2 does not conduct; assuming that S has been opened, the gate of SCR 1 receives +10 V through 100-ohm resistor R_5 and D_2. Thus SCR 1 must conduct within this first instant when line A begins to go positive, or SCR 1 must wait until the next cycle.

Thus SCR 1 will turn on the load for a complete half cycle. If the load requires full-wave conduction, SCR 2 is added. While SCR 1 is conducting, capacitor C is being charged toward the maximum positive voltage to appear across the load. When line B next is positive, SCR 2 conducts for the next half cycle. C is discharged by the gate of the turned-on SCR 2 and thus must be recharged when SCR 1 is turned on.

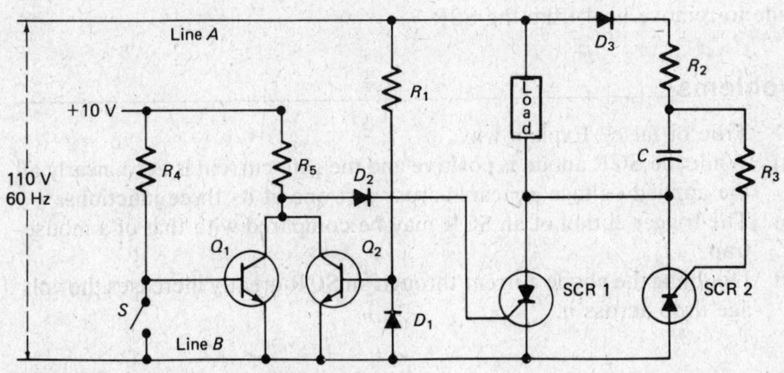

Figure 9-31 Zero-voltage switching circuit.

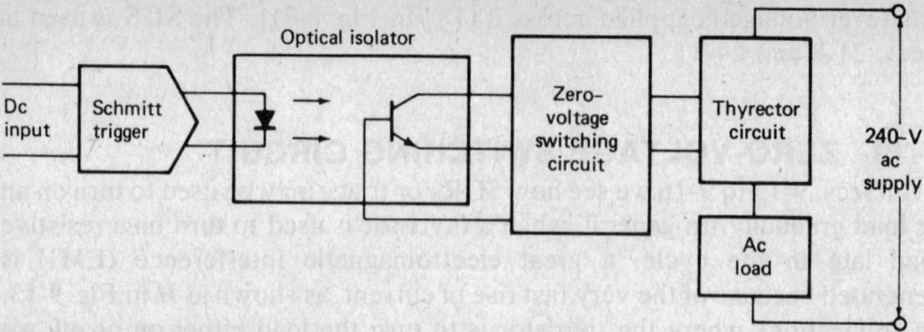

Figure 9-32 Solid-state relay.

9-20 OPTICALLY COUPLED ISOLATOR—SOLID-STATE RELAY

In all the above thyristor circuits (except Fig. 9-6) the portion of the circuit that controls the gate must be connected to the cathode side of the thyristor; thus the low-voltage control circuit cannot be isolated from the 115-V line (or 230 or 460 V). In Fig. 9-6 transformer *T* is used in the gate circuit so that the controlling transistor *Q* is not connected to the power circuit. Another device that electrically isolates the controlling circuit from the power circuit is the optically coupled isolator, as shown in Fig. 9-32. As the name implies, this device uses a lamp—typically a light-emitting diode (LED, Sec. 23-15)—focused onto a phototransistor or a photodiode. Many versions of this device have been developed wherein punched cards may pass between the lamp and the sensor. A type often used in machine-tool control is the solid-state relay (SSR); this device replaces the single normally open contact of an electromechanical relay.

In the SSR shown in Fig. 9-32, a slowly increasing dc signal causes the Schmitt trigger[6-8] to rapidly turn on the lamp in the optical isolator. The zero-voltage switching and trigger circuits are like that in Fig. 9-31 except that switch *S* is replaced with a phototransistor. The current-carrying capacity of the SSR is like that of the SCR in Sec. 9-2. Usually some provision must be made to remove heat from the SSR.

Problems

9-1 True or false? Explain why.

(a) While the SCR anode is positive and the gate current is zero, nearly all the applied voltage appears across just one of its three junctions.

(b) The trigger action of an SCR may be compared with that of a mousetrap.

(c) Doubling the anode current through an SCR greatly increases the voltage drop across it.

(d) After being fired, the SCR cannot continue to carry current of only a few milliamperes.

(e) After being fired, the amount of instantaneous SCR current can be varied by its gate current.

(f) With $R_1 = 0$ ohms (Ω) in Fig. 9-5 *b*, the lamps receive nearly full ac line voltage.

(g) In Fig. 9-6, a sudden decrease of transistor *Q* current can fire SCR.

(h) In Fig. 9-9, if Zener *Z* is replaced by a 20-volt battery, UJT still fires twice each cycle.

(i) In Fig. 9-10, if diode *D* is short-circuited, SCR fires early in each half cycle.

(j) No *RC* time delay is used in the Jones circuit, Fig. 9-12.

(k) In Fig. 9-13, when the watts loss in SCR is halved, the loss in *R* is reduced to one-fourth.

(l) In Fig. 9-14, as the load is made more inductive, there is more recombination time to assist the turnoff of SCR.

(m) Both the UJT and the Shockley diode operate entirely ON or entirely OFF.

(n) If a pure resistance load replaces *X* in Fig. 9-15, zero current flows in diode *D*.

(o) In Fig. 9-16, no current flows in diode *D* if SCR is removed.

(p) The *R* and *C* in Fig. 9-17 make this circuit useful for time-delay purposes.

(q) The voltage ηV_{BB} affects current flow in the UJT as V_{BR} does in the SCR.

(r) The speed with which a voltage is reapplied across an SCR, just after its anode current stops, is not important.

9-2 A single-phase transformer supplies 220 V 400 Hz per leg to a two-SCR rectifier. SCR drop = 0. The load has $R = 88\Omega$, $L = 0.07$ H. (*a*) Find the firing angle α when a dc ammeter reads 0.75 A in the load. (*b*) When $\alpha = 40°$, find the load current. (*c*) Find the largest value of α at which the load current does not become zero momentarily.

9-3 A two-SCR rectifier has zero internal drop, and is connected to an anode transformer that supplies 240 V 60 Hz per leg. The load resistance equals its inductive reactance. When the SCRs fire with zero delay, a dc ammeter reads 5.4 A in the load. (*a*) Find the ammeter reading when the firing angle α is 75°. (*b*) Find the henrys of the load. (*c*) Find the largest value of α at which the load current does not become zero momentarily. (*d*) When the ammeter reads 0.81 A, find α.

9-4 Using a circuit sketch, explain whether a single two-anode rectifier tube (like Fig. 4-3) can be used to replace or to give the same results as both SCR (with 0 phase delay) and *D* in Fig. 9-15.

9-5 This PN diode has negligible drop. The dc ammeter A reads 21 A. Motor M has a 160-V cemf. The motor armature has negligible inductance. (*a*) For how many degrees does the diode conduct, per cycle? (*b*) Find the armature resistance.

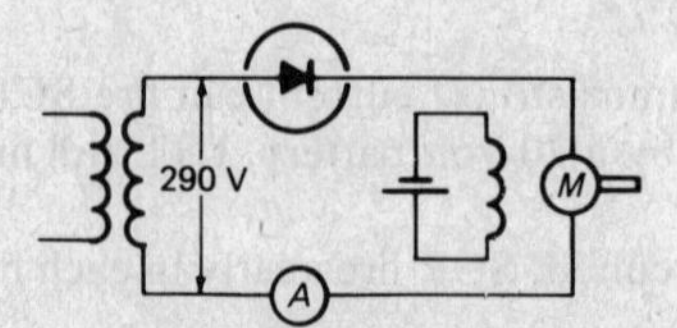

Figure Problem 9-5

9-6 Using the above circuit and diode, the transformer supplies 145 V. The armature of motor M has 3 ohms of R and negligible inductance. The motor runs at such speed that its armature current flows for only 140° during each ac cycle. Find (*a*) the cemf of motor, and (*b*) the reading of dc ammeter A.

10

SWITCHING AND COUNTING CIRCUITS

10-1 COMPUTERS AND BINARY COUNTING

A general discussion of electronic computers is not attempted here; that subject is covered by many textbooks.

An analog computer contains circuit elements wherein voltages vary in a pattern that simulates or represents the action of parts of complete electrical or mechanical systems. A digital computer consists of circuits that count numbers in the form of consecutive electrical pulses, which may be stored or combined at very high speed. Since such computing or counting circuits are used for the direct control of many industrial machines (including the welder control in Sec. 19-1), it is desirable to present here the methods by which they count.

Most people count a number in tens or multiples of ten; this is the decimal system. But circuits for counting are simplified when their devices (such as transistors, tubes, or magnetic cores) operate in only two conditions, either entirely on or entirely off; thus these devices recognize or respond only to two numbers. If the OFF condition is called a zero or 0, while the ON condition is called a one or 1, then these electric circuits count in terms of 0 or 1 only; this is called a two-unit or binary system.

In the familiar decimal system, the number 3728.5 consists of the following parts:

3 thousand	or	3×1000	or	3×10^3	$= 3000$
7 hundred		7×100		7×10^2	$= 700$
2 tens		2×10		2×10^1	$= 20$
8 units		8×1		8×10^0	$= 8$
5 tenths		5×0.1		5×10^{-1}	$= 0.5$
					3728.5

Thus each column, given a value by its position to the left of the decimal point, represents a certain power of 10 (which is the number of times that 1 is multiplied by 10). The first of these columns, or 10^0, indicates a multiplication by 1. (When any number is raised to the zero power, it is equal to 1). A number such as 3×10^3 is said to be larger than 7×10^2 by one *order of magnitude*. Such an order of magnitude implies roughly a 10-to-1 ratio.

In comparison, in a binary system the number 1001101.1 consists of

$$\begin{aligned}
1 \times 2^6 &= 1 \times 64 = 64 \\
0 \times 2^5 &= 0 \times 32 = 0 \\
0 \times 2^4 &= 0 \times 16 = 0 \\
1 \times 2^3 &= 1 \times 8 = 8 \\
1 \times 2^2 &= 1 \times 4 = 4 \\
0 \times 2^1 &= 0 \times 2 = 0 \\
1 \times 2^0 &= 1 \times 1 = 1 \\
1 \times 2^{-1} &= 1 \times {}^1/_2 = \underline{0.5} \\
& \qquad\qquad\quad 77.5
\end{aligned}$$

Thus the familiar number 77.5 is equal to the binary number 1001101.1. The following table compares small numbers as shown by each system.

Decimal	Binary	Decimal	Binary	Decimal	Binary
0.25	0000.01	8	01000	17	10001
0.5	0000.1	9	01001	18	10010
1	0001	10	01010	19	10011
2	0010	11	01011	20	10100
3	0011	12	01100	21	10101
4	0100	13	01101	22	10110
5	0101	14	01110	23	10111
6	0110	15	01111	24	11000
7	0111	16	10000	32	100000

Each vertical column in a binary number contains either 0 or 1, and thus it can be represented in a counter by a single device that is either off or on. Using computer language, the first pulse counted makes a transistor or tube "flip" into the on position; as the next pulse is being counted, the transistor or tube "flops" back to its off position. Thus a circuit that is suitable for the two actions of "flip" and "flop" is commonly called a *flip-flop*.

Since such a flip-flop circuit can remain steadily in either of only two conditions, it has two stable states and so it is bistable. Four such bistable flip-flops are combined into the industrial type of counter shown in Fig. 10-3. By counting the number of pulses (produced once in each cycle of the ac supply voltage) this counter measures and controls the length of time during certain welding operations in Sec. 19-1.

10-2 THE FLIP-FLOP CIRCUIT

A flip-flop is a tube or transistor circuit (also called a *bistable multivibrator*) used in counting and computer applications. Many kinds are described in various manuals; one form of flip-flop is shown in Fig. 10-1, wherein (*a*) shows the circuit as it may appear in a manual, while (*b*) presents the same kind of circuit, in the form used in the industrial type of decade counter shown in Fig. 10-3. In Fig. 10-3, two NPN transistors are connected in common-emitter circuits; such a transistor is turned off when its P-type base is made more negative.

This kind of circuit is designed so that each transistor is either fully on (having maximum collector current as it operates in saturation) or is off (having negligible collector current as it operates in the cutoff region); the transis-

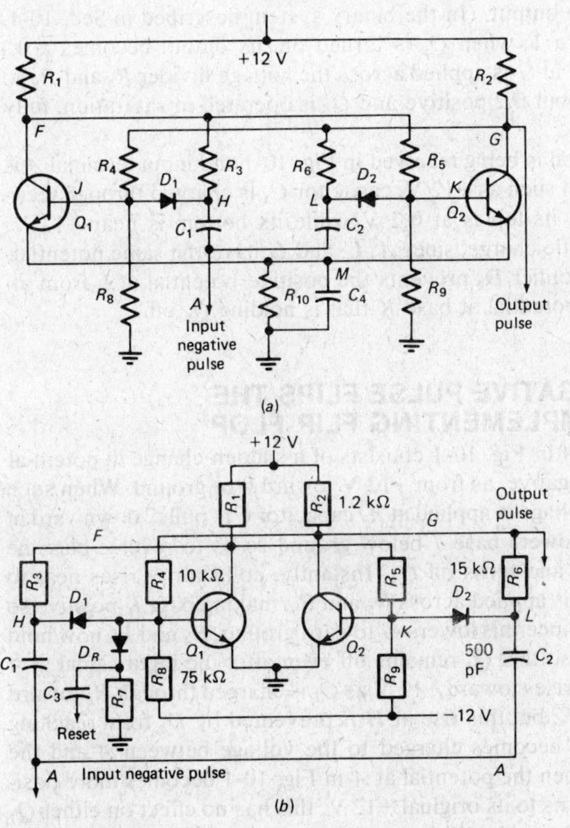

Figure 10-1 Basic flip-flop circuit as shown (*a*) in transistor manual and (*b*) in industrial counter.

tor is switched on or off, as described in Sec. 5-7. Moreover, when transistor Q_1 is on, Q_2 is off; when Q_1 is off, Q_2 is on.

While transistor Q_1 is on in Fig. 10-1*a*, electrons flow from ground through bias resistor R_{10}, emitter to collector of Q_1 and through R_1 to +12 volts. While Q_1 is in saturation, or on, the voltage difference between its collector and emitter is very small, so that F is at the same potential as M; current flowing through R_{10} holds M about 1 V above ground. Meanwhile K, the base of Q_2, is at a potential between F and ground; a voltage divider, R_5 and R_9, holds K more negative than M so that Q_2 is off.

A resistor such as R_{10} is not needed in Fig. 10-1*b;* instead the emitters are at ground potential and a separate supply of −12V is available for holding the base negative. When Q_1 is on, its collector F is very near ground potential; thus the output F is said to be zero. A voltage divider, R_5 and R_9, holds base K slightly below ground so that Q_2 is off; its collector G is near +12V; so Q_2 is providing an output. (In the binary system described in Sec. 10-1, this output is called a 1; when Q_2 is turned on, its output becomes a 0.) Moreover, this +12V at G is applied across the voltage divider R_4 and R_8 so that base J is held about 0.2 positive and Q_1 is operated in saturation, fully on.

When no input signal is being received in Fig. 10-1 and input terminal A is at a constant potential such as +12 V, capacitor C_1 is charged through rectifier diode D_1 so that its top is at 0.2 V while its bottom is near +12 V; meanwhile, C_2 has little charge, since A, L, and G have the same potential, near +12 V. Here rectifier D_2 prevents the positive potential at L from affecting the negative potential at base K that is holding Q_2 off.

10-3 EACH NEGATIVE PULSE FLIPS THE CIRCUIT; A COMPLEMENTING FLIP-FLOP

An input signal at A in Fig. 10-1 consists of a sudden change in potential that drives A more negative, as from +12 V toward 0 or ground. When such a "negative-going" voltage is applied at A, capacitor C_1 "pulls" downward at H and, through D_1, lowers base J below ground so as to reverse-bias the emitter-base junction and turns off Q_1. Instantly, collector F rises near to +12 V. This rise at F is applied across R_5 and R_9, making base K positive so that Q_2 is turned on; since this lowers G toward ground, R_4 and R_8 now hold base J below ground so that Q_1 remains off even after the input signal at A has stopped. Point H rises toward +12 V as C_1 is charged through R_3 toward the high potential at F; but this rise at H is prevented by D_1 from reaching base J. Capacitor C_2 becomes charged to the voltage between A and the +0.2 V at base K. When the potential at A in Fig. 10-1 becomes more positive as the signal returns to its original +12 V, this has no effect on either Q_1 or Q_2, since D_1 and D_2 isolate this "positive-going" voltage from J or K.

Now Q_1 is off and Q_2 is on in Fig. 10-1. When the next negative-going or "trigger" pulse appears at A, capacitor C_1 again lowers H and J; but Q_1 al-

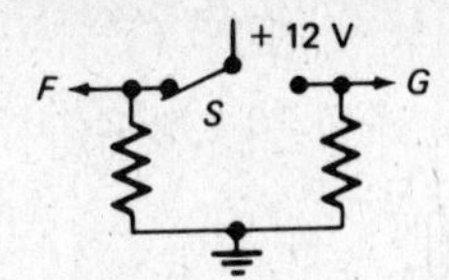

Figure 10-2 Flip-flop action shown by switch S.

ready is off. So C_2 lowers L and, through D_2, also lowers K so as to turn off Q_2; as G rises toward +12 V, base J also is raised, turning on Q_1. As F is lowered, base K is held negative so that Q_2 remains off even after the signal at A has stopped.

This flip-flop changes state (or complements) each time it receives an input pulse, and thus it is called a complementing flip-flop.

This circuit is bistable—it remains steady when Q_2 is either fully on or fully off. This flip-flop action resembles that of a double-throw switch S shown in Fig. 10-2. While S is at the left as shown (as when Q_1 is off and Q_2 is on), a 12-V output appears between F and ground; G is at ground potential, with 0 output. When a signal pulse moves switch S to the right, the output disappears from F, but G now has a 12-V output.

Just as a negative-going pulse is used as the input signal at A in Fig. 10-1, a corresponding output signal is produced whenever G becomes more negative, as it decreases from +12 V toward ground. This negative-going output at G is produced only half as often as the input signal at A; this G output may be used as the input signal to a second flip-flop circuit, as shown in Fig. 10-3. When such circuits are combined in cascade (i.e., one follows another), they can be used to count the total number of input pulses at A, or to cause a certain result after a chosen number of A pulses. When used in this way, the circuit must include means for resetting the transistors so that the same transistor is on when each count begins. Such a RESET circuit is added at the base of Q_1 in Fig. 10-1*b*. Whereas either Q_1 or Q_2 may be on at the end of a previous count, a negative RESET pulse (applied through C_3 and D_R) lowers base J of Q_1 so that the next count starts with Q_1 off and Q_2 on. At the end of the RESET pulse, D_R isolates the rising potential so that it has no effect on Q_1.

10-4 FLIP-FLOPS IN A COUNTER

To count as many as ten electric pulse signals, the circuit in Fig. 10-3 is used; here eight transistors are paired into four flip-flop circuits like the one discussed above. (This counter is used also in Sec. 19-1 as part of a sequence weld timer. A "ring counter" of ten is described in Sec. 19-7.) Figure 10-3 shows complete circuits (like Fig. 10-1) for transistors Q_1 to Q_4, but the circuits of Q_5 to Q_8 omit parts not needed for explanation of overall sequence.

If the input pulses, applied at the lower left corner in Fig. 10-3, are made to occur once each cycle 60 times per second, this counting circuit also

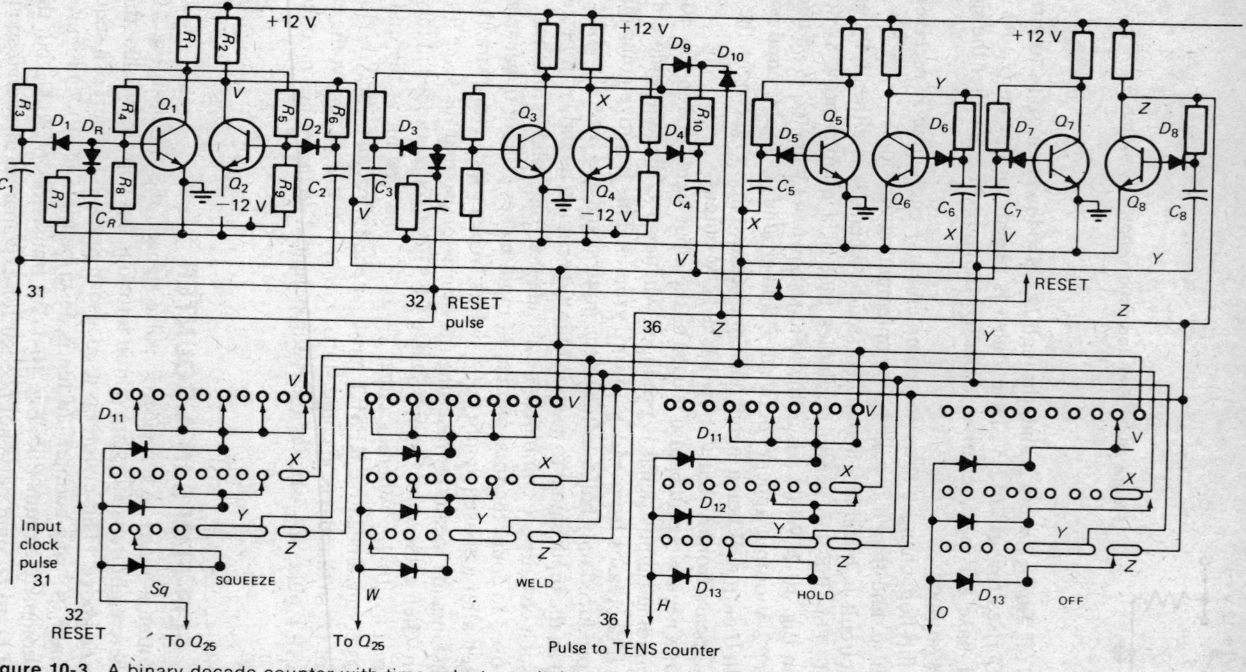

Figure 10-3 A binary decade counter with time-selector switches.

measures time; 10 pulses = $^1/_6$ sec. After every ten pulses this circuit produces a negative output pulse at terminal 36 (bottom of Fig. 10-3), which is used later as the input pulse to a second circuit exactly like Fig. 10-3; this second circuit counts *tens* of pulses, so that the two circuits together form a digital timer that counts accurately any number of cycles from 1 to 100, or a time range from $^1/_{60}$ to $1^2/_3$ sec.

At the start of any count, the transistors first are reset by a negative pulse at bottom terminal 32; this RESET pulse is applied to the base of the left-hand transistor of each flip-flop pair, so that Q_1, Q_3, Q_5, and Q_7 are off, thus turning on Q_2, Q_4, Q_6, and Q_8. When thus reset, this circuit gives a count of 1 cycle to the four selectors below; the first input pulse at line 31 shifts the count to 2 cycles. (In many counters, this first pulse at 31 is counted as 1.) Table 10-1 shows which transistors are on as each number is counted; the circuit operations summarized in this table are discussed in Sec. 10-5.

The lower half of Fig. 10-3 shows the internal circuits of the four identical time selectors; sliding parts within each selector circuit may be moved toward the right to set the desired number of cycles' duration of SQUEEZE, WELD, HOLD, or OFF,[18-16] as described in Sec. 10-7.

10-5 COUNTER OPERATION

At input 31 (lower left in Fig. 10-3) a rising potential has no effect, because of D_1 and D_2 [except that it charges C_2 (−) on top, (+) at bottom]; but a negative-going pulse at 31 acts through C_2 and D_2 to lower the base of Q_2 so it is turned off. The Q_2 collector V rises to +12 and (through R_4) turns Q_1 on; this rise at V also reaches C_3 and C_4 in the second flip-flop but has no effect on Q_3 or Q_4 or Q_7, because of D_3, D_4, and D_7. Thus, at this count of 2, Q_1 is on and Q_2 is off, but other transistors are not affected.

The next negative pulse, at a count of 3, turns off Q_1, again turning Q_2 on; as the potential of Q_2 collector V falls toward ground, it serves as an input signal to the second flip-flop. By lowering the bottom of C_3 and C_4 and acting through D_4, this V pulse turns Q_4 off; the rising potential of Q_4 collector X

TABLE 10-1

Cycles counted (RESET pulse = *count of 1*)										
1	2	3	4	5	6	7	8	9	10	11
Transistors ON										
Q_2 Q_4 Q_6 Q_8	Q_1 Q_4 Q_6 Q_8	Q_2 Q_3 Q_6 Q_8	Q_1 Q_3 Q_6 Q_8	Q_2 Q_4 Q_5 Q_8	Q_1 Q_4 Q_5 Q_8	Q_2 Q_3 Q_5 Q_8	Q_1 Q_3 Q_5 Q_8	Q_2 Q_4 Q_6 Q_7	Q_1 Q_4 Q_6 Q_7	Q_2 Q_4 Q_6 Q_8

turns Q_3 on but cannot affect Q_5 or Q_6. (The V connection to C_7 has no effect on Q_7 at this time.) At 4 count, the pulse turns Q_2 off, so that Q_1 goes on; there are no other changes.

At a count of 5, the input pulse at line 31 turns Q_1 off; as Q_2 goes on, the falling potential at V acts through D_3 to turn Q_3 off. As this turns Q_4 on, the falling potential at X serves as an input signal to the third flip-flop. By lowering the bottom of C_5 and C_6 and acting through D_6, this X pulse turns Q_6 off; the rising potential of Q_6 collector Y turns Q_5 on but cannot affect Q_8. At 6 count (as at 4 count) the pulse turns Q_2 off and Q_1 on without affecting other transistors.

At a count of 7, the sixth pulse at line 31 turns Q_1 off; as Q_2 goes on, the falling V potential acts through D_4 to turn Q_4 off; so Q_3 is on. The X potential rises and has no effect on Q_5 or Q_6. On 8 count, Q_2 is turned off, so that Q_1 is on; there are no other changes.

At a count of 9 (which is the eighth input pulse at 31) Q_1 is turned off; so Q_2 is on. The falling V potential turns Q_3 off; as this turns Q_4 on, the falling X potential acts through D_5 to turn Q_5 off. As Q_6 is turned on, its collector potential Y falls, thus serving as an input signal to the fourth flip-flop; by lowering the bottom of C_8 and acting through D_8, this Y pulse turns Q_8 off. The rising potential of Q_8 collector Z turns Q_7 on; this +12 V at Z now feeds back through D_{10} and R_{10} to raise the base of Q_4 so that Q_4 will not be turned off by further pulses. (Without this feedback from Z, and without the V connection from Q_2 to Q_7, this circuit would be called a scale-of-16 counter, since 16 pulses would be needed before Q_7 would turn off and Q_8 turn on, so as to give a negative-going output pulse at bottom circuit line 36.)

10-6 A BINARY COUNTER OF TEN PULSES

To produce a decade counter, Fig. 10-3 adds the connection from Q_2 collector V to C_7 at the base of Q_7; also, it includes the feedback circuit from Q_8 collector Z through D_{10} and R_{10} to the base of Q_4. These have no effect until Q_8 is turned off at a count of 9, thus turning Q_7 on. The next pulse (count of 10) merely turns Q_1 on and Q_2 off.

At the tenth input pulse at line 31 (count of 11) Q_2 is turned on; the falling potential at V acts through D_7 to turn Q_7 off. Thus Q_8 is turned on; the falling potential at Q_8 collector Z produces a negative-going pulse to terminal 36. Occurring at the end of each ten pulses, this signal at 36 is the output of this decade counter; it is used in Sec. 19-1 and Fig. 19-3 as the input signal to a counter of *tens*.

At the same time when the output pulse is given at 36, we may see above (and at 11 count in Table 10-1) that every transistor has returned to the state that existed after the RESET pulse and before the first input pulse at 31; thus Q_2, Q_4, Q_6, and Q_8 are on and the circuit is in the proper condition to receive and count another ten pulses.

10-7 TIME-SELECTOR SWITCHES

In addition to one output signal (at 36) for each ten input pulses received at 31, each time selector (in the lower portion of Fig. 10-3) makes it possible to obtain a useful output signal for any desired count between 1 and 10. If the weld-time selector is set for 1 cycle, the movable portion of the selector circuit is exactly as is shown low near the center in Fig. 10-3. In the upper row of circle terminals, no one of the five pointed contacts is touching at *V*; below, in the middle row, no one of three contacts touches at *X*; the single contact in the bottom row touches neither *Y* nor *Z*. Bottom line *W* has no connection to any stationary terminal *V*, *X*, *Y*, or *Z*; thus line *W* (connected to the base of Q_{25} in Fig. 19-3) is not clamped or controlled by the counter, but it permits Q_{25} in the welder control to turn on (as described in Sec. 19-3) to give the signal that ends the weld time after 1 cycle.

If the squeeze-time selector is set for 2 cycles, all the pointed contacts have been moved one step to the right (as shown at the lower left in Fig. 10-3); an upper contact now touches *V*, which connects to the Q_2 collector. During cycle 1, Q_2 is on; so its collector potential is near ground, low enough to let diode D_{11} conduct, thus holding the *Sq* line near ground (so as to hold Q_{25} off in Fig. 19-3). When the cycle-2 pulse has turned Q_2 off and Q_1 on, the collector of Q_2 rises enough to reverse-bias D_{11} so that it acts as an open circuit; this lets line *Sq* rise so that Q_{25} turns on.

When the dial is turned to set the selector for 4 cycles, each pointed contact is moved three steps to the right. The result is shown by the HOLD selector in Fig. 10-3; an upper contact touches at *V*, a middle-row contact touches at *X*, but the bottom contact touches neither *Y* nor *Z*. During cycles 1 and 2, bottom line *H* connects through diode D_{12} and *X* to the Q_4 collector; since Q_4 is on, its collector potential is near ground, letting D_{12} conduct. During cycle 3, Q_2 is on; so D_{11} conducts. When cycle 4 is reached, both Q_2 and Q_4 are off; so both D_{11} and D_{12} are reverse-biased, disconnecting line *H* from ground (so that Q_{25} turns on in Fig. 19-3).

If the off-time selector is set for 9 cycles (as shown at the lower right in Fig. 10-3), no upper contact touches *V* and no middle-row contact touches *X*. The bottom contact touches *Z*, which connects to the Q_8 collector. Since Q_8 always is on until a count of 9, Q_8 and diode D_{13} hold line *O* at ground during the first eight cycles; at 9, the turn off of Q_8 reverse-biases D_{13} so that line *O* is permitted to rise and turn Q_{25} on.

Whereas the preceding binary counter uses transistor flip-flops, a different form of counter using PUTs is described in the ring counter of Sec. 19-7.

10-8 BASIC CIRCUITS FOR COMPUTERS

An electronic computer performs complex mathematics by doing simple arithmetic (like addition or subtraction) in a certain order or sequence. To multiply 3 by 4, the first number (3, called the multiplicand) is added to 0 four times (where 4 is called the multiplier), so that $3 + 3 + 3 + 3$ gives the desired result of 12. Here the computer must have a counting circuit to set the number of additions to be made. It also must "remember" or store the result of $3 + 3$, to which it then adds another 3; this result 9 again is stored until the fourth 3 is added to produce the final answer. This need for a computer's "memory" or storage of information is like the action of a man who, when faced with $6 \times 3 + 4 \times 7 = ?$, will jot down 18 while he figures $4 \times 7 = 28$ to add to this stored 18. The computer circuit that stores information is called a *register*, described further in Sec. 10-16.

Similarly, to divide 20 by 5, the computer repeatedly subtracts the number 5 from 20, and counts how many times this subtraction can be done before the remainder is brought to 0; thus $20 - 5 - 5 - 5 - 5 = 0$. Since 5 is subtracted four times, the desired answer is 4.

These examples show that computer circuits must (*a*) add or subtract pulses, (*b*) store information, and (*c*) control the sequence of these operations by giving orders to other circuits. Such addition is discussed in Sec. 10-15, wherein "gate" circuits are used. Such gates are next discussed.

10-9 GATE CIRCUITS; THE AND GATE

Some of the simple "building blocks" used in making a computer are called *gate* circuits, of which there are many kinds. The AND gate and the OR gate are next described.

Figure 10-4 shows an AND circuit that uses diodes; this gate does not "open" to permit a useful voltage output at *D* unless the desired input voltages are applied at *A* AND at *B* AND at *C*. In computers, such action is described in terms of a voltage +V (called a 1) or a lack of voltage (called a 0). Moreover, when +V appears at output *D*, this output is said to be true; but if 0 voltage appears at *D*, this output is false.

In Fig. 10-4, if input *A* is near 0 volts (thus it is false), electrons flow through diode D_1 and through resistor *R* to +V. Since the diode has negligible voltage drop while it conducts, the output at *D* also is near 0 (so it is false). Similarly, if input *B* or input *C* is near 0 volts (false), a different diode conducts; output *D* still is false. Now if input *A* is made true by raising it near to +V, this has no effect so long as either *B* or *C* is near 0 (false). But if all three inputs are raised near to +V (thus becoming true), this reverse-biases all three diodes so that no one of them conducts; since no current now flows in resistor *R*, there is no voltage drop across *R*; thus output *D* rises to +V and becomes true (or a 1). So for this AND gate, all inputs (*A* AND *B* AND *C*) must be true before output *D* can be true.

For even this very simple circuit, a computer engineer uses a "truth table," as shown in Fig. 10-4*b*; this gives a list of all possible input conditions and the resulting output signals. Here the bottom line shows the only condition that lets output *D* become 1 (or true); all three inputs must be 1 before *D* can be 1.

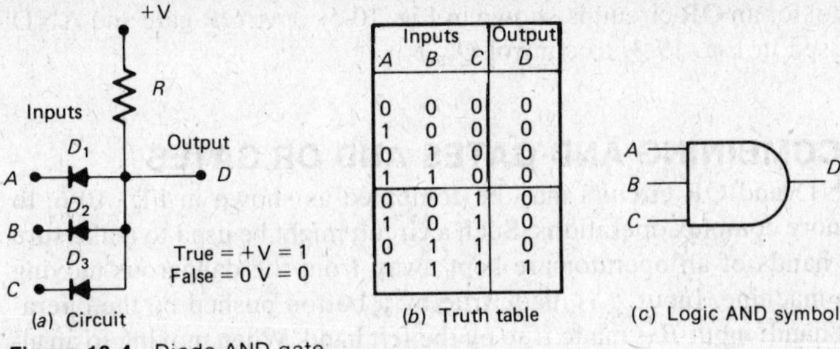

Inputs			Output
A	B	C	D
0	0	0	0
1	0	0	0
0	1	0	0
1	1	0	0
0	0	1	0
1	0	1	0
0	1	1	0
1	1	1	1

(*a*) Circuit (*b*) Truth table (c) Logic AND symbol

Figure 10-4 Diode AND gate.

The symbol shown in Fig. 10-4*c* is a simplified way of showing any AND gate. This symbol always means that *A* AND *B* AND *C* produces *D*. In practice there are several different circuits that can perform as AND gates; each of these circuits is represented by this same symbol. In a schematic diagram of a computer (which may contain hundreds of gates) these simple symbols are used so that the engineer can more quickly analyze the interaction within a large system.

10-10 THE OR GATE

Figure 10-5 shows an OR circuit which also uses diodes. The circuit output at *D* is at + V volts if any input *A* OR *B* OR *C* is at + V volts. For example, if *A* is true (at +V), then diode D_1 is forward-biased; electrons flow from 0 through *R* and D_1, so that *D* rises close to +V volts, causing the output *D* to be true. When all the input voltages are false (at 0 volts), no diode conducts. Since there is no current through resistor *R*, the output *D* is also at 0 volts.

The truth table in Fig. 10-5*b* lists all the possible input conditions; it shows that if any input is true (shown as a 1), then the output *D* also is true. There is only one condition (the top line) for which the output is false; this is when all inputs are 0 (false). But the output is true if *A* OR *B* OR *C* is true.

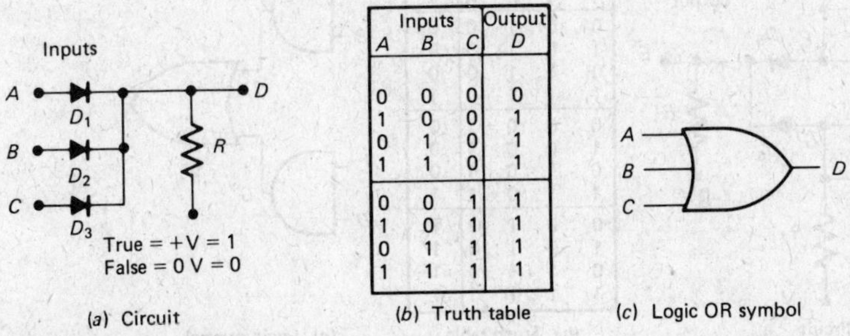

Inputs			Output
A	B	C	D
0	0	0	0
1	0	0	1
0	1	0	1
1	1	0	1
0	0	1	1
1	0	1	1
0	1	1	1
1	1	1	1

(*a*) Circuit (*b*) Truth table (*c*) Logic OR symbol

Figure 10-5 Diode OR gate.

The symbol for an OR circuit is shown in Fig. 10-5*c*. (An OR gate and AND gate are used in Fig. 19-3, to control Q_{25}.)

10-11 COMBINING AND GATES AND OR GATES

The AND and OR circuits may be combined as shown in Fig. 10-6, to perform more complex operations. Such a circuit might be used to make sure that both hands of an operator are kept away from the dangerous moving parts of a machine. Input A is made true by a button pushed by the operator's right hand; input B is made true by the left hand. When moving to an alternate operating position the same person presses buttons that cause inputs C and D.

Diodes D_1 and D_2 and resistor R_1 form the first AND circuit in Fig. 10-6, which has an output F. The second AND circuit is composed of D_3, D_4, and R_2 and has the output at G. Either F or G operates the OR circuit composed of D_5, D_6, and R_3. The whole circuit of Fig. 10-6 has the truth table shown in Fig. 10-6*b*. This circuit has four inputs, thus giving 16 possible combinations. A truth table of this size rarely is used; instead, a smaller truth table for each basic type of circuit is preferred. The logic diagram shown in Fig. 10-6*c* combines the two symbols already presented.

10-12 TRANSISTOR GATE CIRCUITS; NAND; NOR

When many diode gates are used in a single machine, we need to place an amplifying transistor between each pair of gate circuits. Figure 10-7 shows such a transistor Q_1 with common-emitter connection; therefore, the collector output of Q_1 is inverted. (The term *inverted* means that, when the base voltage goes positive, the collector voltage drops from +V to near 0; when

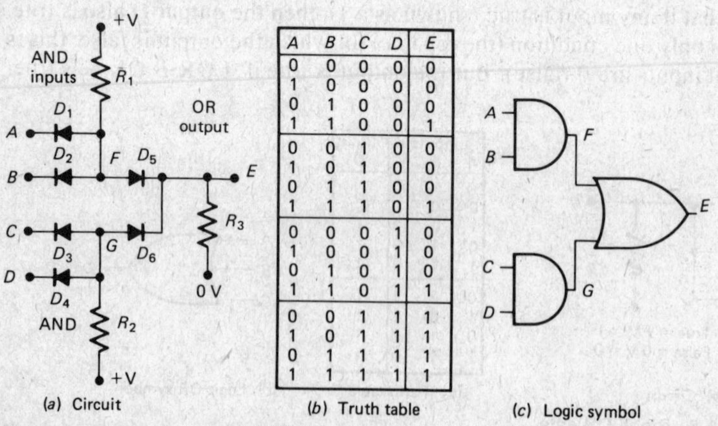

A	B	C	D	E
0	0	0	0	0
1	0	0	0	0
0	1	0	0	0
1	1	0	0	1
0	0	1	0	0
1	0	1	0	0
0	1	1	0	0
1	1	1	0	1
0	0	0	1	0
1	0	0	1	0
0	1	0	1	0
1	1	0	1	1
0	0	1	1	1
1	0	1	1	1
0	1	1	1	1
1	1	1	1	1

(*a*) Circuit (*b*) Truth table (*c*) Logic symbol

Figure 10-6 Combined diode gates.

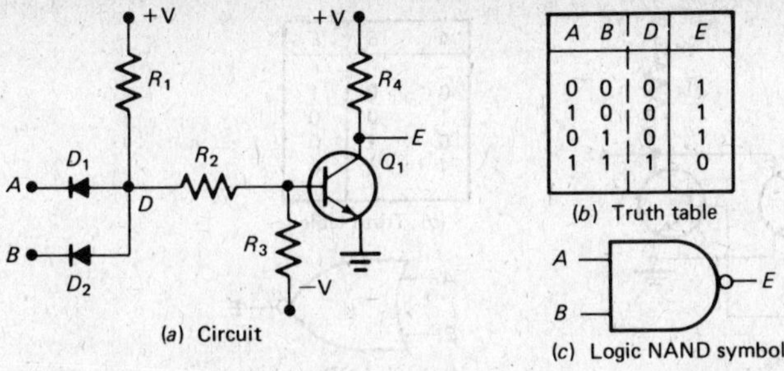

A	B	D	E
0	0	0	1
1	0	0	1
0	1	0	1
1	1	1	0

Figure 10-7 NAND gate.

the base goes negative, the collector goes positive.) Such a circuit having an inverting transistor is called a NAND gate (meaning NOT-AND).

In Fig. 10-7*a*, diodes D_1 and D_2 with resistor R_1 act like the AND gate of Fig. 10-4. When inputs A and B are made many volts positive, point D also rises to a positive voltage sufficient to turn transistor Q_1 on. But if either A or B is near 0 volts, the $-$V applied through resistor R_3 ensures that Q_1 turns fully off.

The logic symbol of the NAND gate, as shown in Fig. 10-7*c*, consists of the AND gate to which a small circle is added at E; this circle denotes that the output is inverted. With this type of gate we say that, when A AND B are true, this makes E false. (Should we desire a true output when A and B are true, then we use a second transistor to invert the output E.)

Columns A, B, and D of the truth table in Fig. 10-7*b* show the normal action of a diode AND gate. Column E, the output from the transistor, shows the inversion that has occurred. (The usual truth table does not show the intermediate point D, added here for clarity.)

The NOR gate (or NOT-OR) includes a transistor for each input, as shown in Fig. 10-8. Here the grouping of transistor Q_1 with resistors R_2, R_3, and R_4 is the same as the right-hand portion of Fig. 10-7*a*. In the NOR circuit, as input A rises to +V, transistor Q_1 turns on and the output at E goes near to 0 volts. Likewise, a positive voltage at input B turns Q_2 on, producing the same result at E. Thus output E becomes 0 (false) when either A or B or both inputs are positive (true).

Four gates now have been described; they act in these ways:

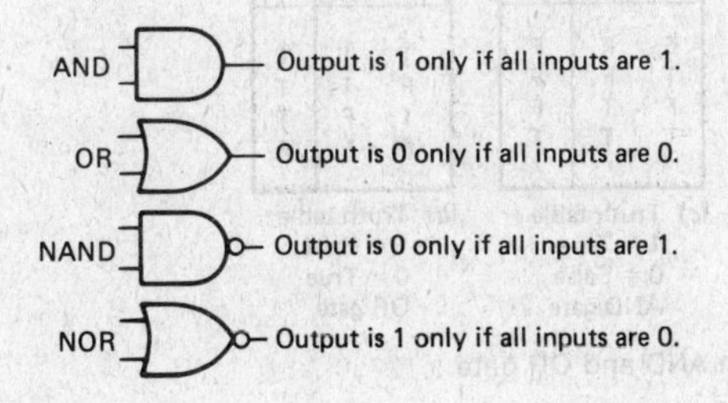

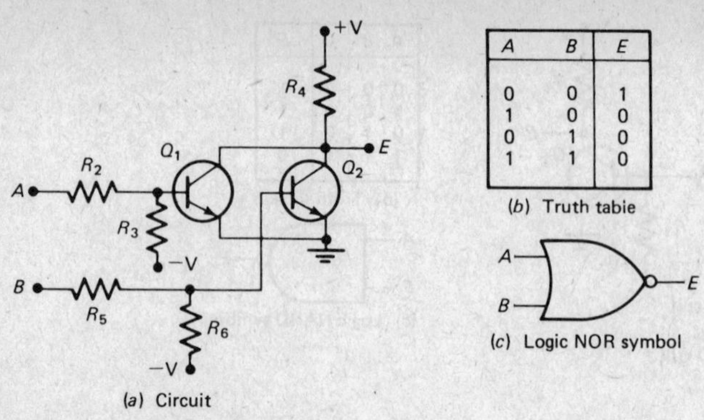

A	B	E
0	0	1
1	0	0
0	1	0
1	1	0

(*a*) Circuit

(*b*) Truth table

(*c*) Logic NOR symbol

Figure 10-8 NOR gate.

10-13 INVERTING THE LOGIC

Inverted logic is used in Sec. 10-14; so it is described now.

The diode AND circuit of Fig. 10-4 is redrawn in Fig. 10-9*a*, but using only two inputs, for simplification. As shown in Fig. 10-9*b*, the truth table usually presents its information by giving values of voltage, expressed as 0 or 1. If a 1 voltage also is defined as being true (as stated in Fig. 10-4), then the truth table in Fig. 10-9*c* uses T or F to match the 1 or 0 voltages in Fig. 10-9*b;* these statements of true and false also are called the *logic* that is used in studying the circuit. The statements used in Fig. 10-9*c* are known as *positive logic*.

But this AND circuit can be used as an OR circuit, by inverting the logic. To do this, we must invert the previous statements so that 0 volts is defined as true, while a 1 voltage is false. The truth table in Fig. 10-9*d* shows this condition (and is called *negative logic*); table (*d*) is obtained from table (*c*) merely by interchanging T and F. The output at *D* is true when either *A* OR *B* (or both) is true. Thus the AND circuit of (*a*) also performs the OR operation when the logic is reversed or inverted.

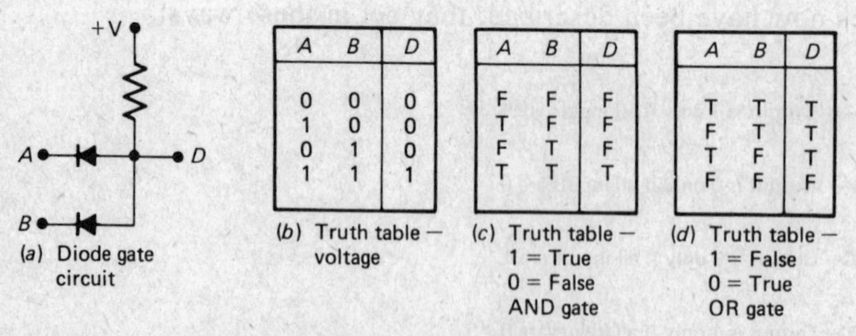

(*a*) Diode gate circuit

A	B	D
0	0	0
1	0	0
0	1	0
1	1	1

(*b*) Truth table — voltage

A	B	D
F	F	F
T	F	F
F	T	F
T	T	T

(*c*) Truth table — 1 = True 0 = False AND gate

A	B	D
T	T	T
F	T	T
T	F	T
F	F	F

(*d*) Truth table — 1 = False 0 = True OR gate

Figure 10-9 Same circuit may be both AND and OR gate.

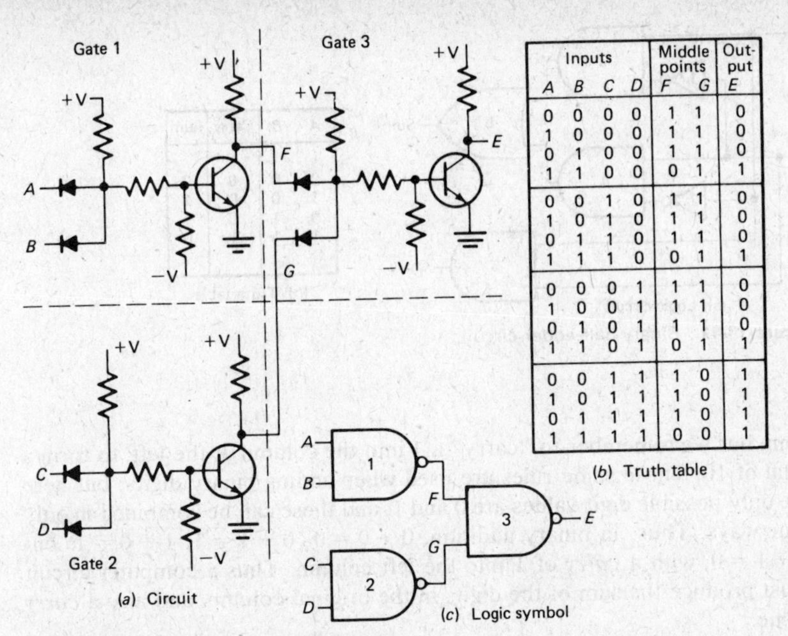

Inputs				Middle points		Out-put
A	*B*	*C*	*D*	*F*	*G*	*E*
0	0	0	0	1	1	0
1	0	0	0	1	1	0
0	1	0	0	1	1	0
1	1	0	0	0	1	1
0	0	1	0	1	1	0
1	0	1	0	1	1	0
0	1	1	0	1	1	0
1	1	1	0	0	1	1
0	0	0	1	1	1	0
1	0	0	1	1	1	0
0	1	0	1	1	1	0
1	1	0	1	0	1	1
0	0	1	1	1	0	1
1	0	1	1	1	0	1
0	1	1	1	1	0	1
1	1	1	1	0	0	1

(*b*) Truth table

Figure 10-10 Combined transistor gates.

10-14 COMBINED TRANSISTOR GATES

Transistor gates also may be combined, to perform complex requirements in computers. Similar to Fig. 10-6 (which joins two AND gates and one OR gate), Fig. 10-10 shows the same operation being performed by the combination of three transistor NAND gates. Here the transistors of gates 1 and 2 invert the logic, so that gate 3 performs a NOR operation. This inverted logic, as described above for the diode AND circuit, is equally valid for the transistor NAND circuit. Thus the same transistor circuit can perform the NAND operation or the NOR operation. Columns *A*, *B*, *C*, *D*, and *E* in Fig. 10-10*b* show the same values as the truth table in Fig. 10-6, proving that either circuit gives the same result. The advantage of the transistor circuit of Fig. 10-10 is that it amplifies, so that it can furnish more current to the output than can the Fig. 10-6 diode circuit. Column *F* in Fig. 10-10 shows the output of gate 1; this duplicates the behavior shown in Fig. 10-7*b*; similar action is shown again in column *G*, giving the output of gate 2.

10-15 BINARY ADDITION

As mentioned in Sec. 10-8, a computer must be able to add numbers; these usually are the binary numbers described in Sec. 10-1.

When the decimal digits 7 and 3 are added, the sum is 0 in that same col-

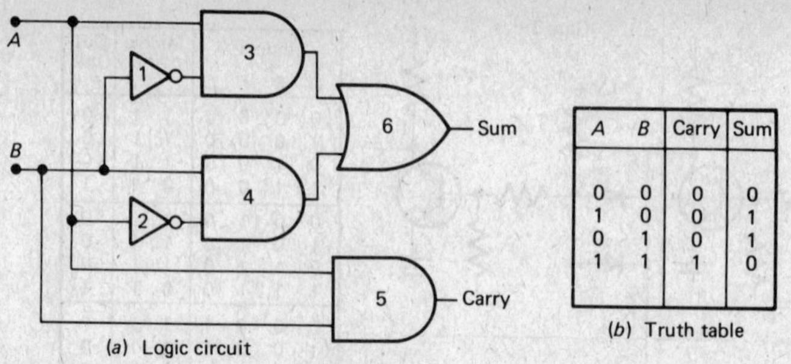

(a) Logic circuit

A	B	Carry	Sum
0	0	0	0
1	0	0	1
0	1	0	1
1	1	1	0

(b) Truth table

Figure 10-11 Binary half-adder circuit.

umn, but we remember to "carry" a 1 into the column at the left, to form a total of 10. These same rules are used when adding binary digits; but here the only possible digit values are 0 and 1, and these can be combined in only four ways. Thus, in binary addition, $0 + 0 = 0$; $0 + 1 = 1$; $1 + 0 = 1$; but $1 + 1 = 0$, with a *carry* of 1 into the left column. Thus a computer circuit must produce the sum of the digits in the original column, and also a *carry* value.

The circuit in Fig. 10-11 produces these desired binary results; its AND and OR gates are shown in symbolic form, as also in Figs. 10-4 to 10-6. A new symbol appears in Fig. 10-11, consisting of a triangle with a small circle; this is the logic symbol for an *inverter*. (This inverter is like the NAND gate shown in Fig. 10-7, except that it has only one input.) It serves only to provide a 0 or false output when its input is 1 or true; a 0 input causes a 1 output. Thus, when input *A* in Fig. 10-11 is 1, it applies its 1 directly to gate 3, but this 1 is changed by inverter 2 so that gate 4 receives a 0.

The truth table in Fig. 10-11 lists all the possible additions of the binary values applied at *A* and *B*. When both *A* and *B* are 0, the output of each AND gate (3, 4, 5) is 0; both the sum (output of gate 6) and the *carry* are 0. Lines 2 and 3 of the truth table show that if *either A* or *B* is 1 (true), but both are not 1, then the sum is 1. (Here, if *A* is 0 and *B* is 1, gate 3 receives a 0 from *A* and a 0 from inverter 1; gate 3 gives 0 output. Meanwhile, gate 4 receives a 1 from *B* and a 1 from inverter 2, so that gate 4 gives a 1 output. Since a 1 is applied at an input to the OR gate 6, its output shows a *sum* of 1. Also, since only one input to the AND gate 5 is a 1, its output shows a *carry* of 0.)

This circuit in Fig. 10-11 is called a "half adder" because it performs only part of the addition; it adds only the two digits *A* and *B*, but does not include any *carry* value that may remain from a previous column or operation. (As a decimal example, in the addition of 547 and 235, we add digits 4 and 3 in the center column, but also must include the *carry* value of 1 obtained from the addition of 7 and 5 in the right-hand column.)

The total addition, including the *carry*, is performed in the next circuit,

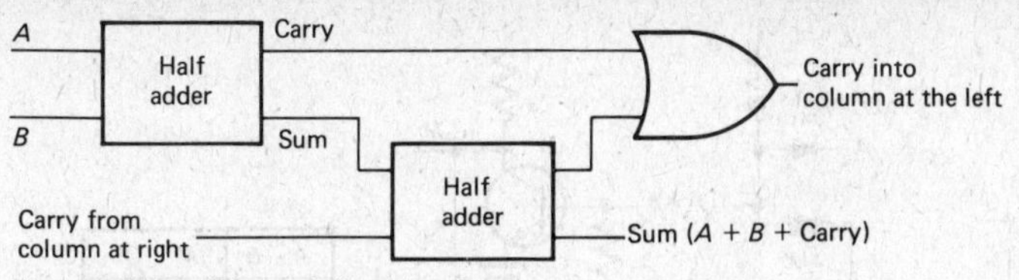

Figure 10-12 Binary full adder.

called a "full adder" in binary logic; this circuit is made by combining two *half-adder* circuits as shown in Fig. 10-12.

10-16 INFORMATION STORAGE

The gate circuits and their combinations produce desired results only when the input signals continuously are present. But some input signals may occur only briefly and must be "remembered" by electronic circuits. This is like the button that calls an elevator car to a desired floor; the button need not be pressed continuously (although some may choose to do so), since a circuit remembers that the button has been pushed. The example of 4 × 3 in Sec. 10-8 also shows that circuits must remember numbers for future use; such a feature is called a *memory*.

A flip-flop is the circuit most frequently used for "remembering." A single flip-flop can store one *bit* of information (since its output stays either as a 1 or as a 0). Several flip-flops are combined into a *register* to store a larger number. The flip-flop of Sec. 10-2 is one of many circuits used for storing information. The counter circuit in Fig. 10-3 contains four such flip-flops and is called a 4-bit-counting register, because it both counts and stores 4 bits of information. (It also is called a decade counter, because it counts up to 10.)

10-17 A BASIC FLIP-FLOP USING TWO NAND GATES; RS FLIP-FLOP

A flip-flop may be formed by combining two NAND gates; this is called a SET-RESET flip-flop (shortened to RS flip-flop), and is shown in Fig. 10-13. Its electric circuit acts like the flip-flop shown in Fig. 10-1. No action occurs in the circuit when both inputs A and B are 1 (or +V). This is shown by the bottom line of the truth table; here M^n means that the M output remains the same as it was before, either a 0 or a 1. But $\overline{M^n}$ shows that the value at P is equal to the inverted value of M^n; thus, if M is 0, P is 1, but if M is 1, P is 0.

When input A is made 0 in Fig. 10-13, diode D_1 conducts and lowers the voltage at point F; transistor Q_1 is turned off and output M becomes 1 (+V). This +V at M is fed back so as to reverse-bias diode D_3. This lets base G rise (since input B at D_4 still is a 1); this turns Q_2 on, thus making output P become a 0 (thus agreeing with NAND gate operation as

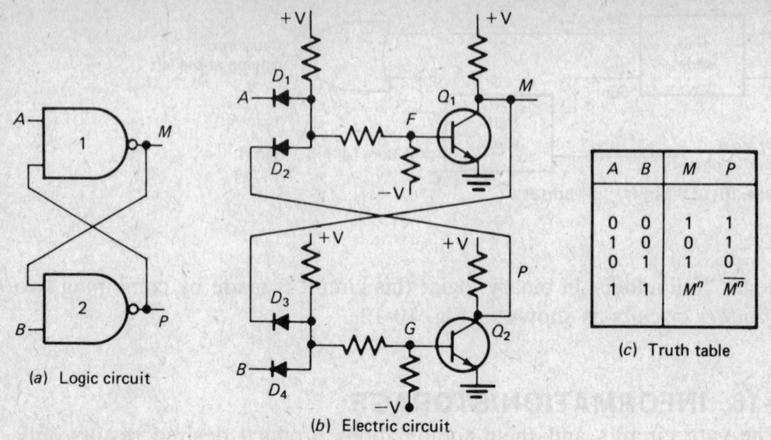

A	B	M	P
0	0	1	1
1	0	0	1
0	1	1	0
1	1	M^n	$\overline{M^n}$

Figure 10-13 Flip-flop formed by two NAND gates.

described in Sec. 10-12). When input *A* again becomes a 1, this flip-flop remains in this state. Output *P* is 0, letting D_2 conduct and continue to hold Q_1 off.

A resetting action occurs when both inputs are 1 (+ V) and input *B* then momentarily is made 0.

If both inputs should be 0, both Q_1 and Q_2 are off and both outputs are 1; if both inputs then are made 1 (+V), we cannot determine which transistor will turn on. Therefore, circuit designers avoid any operation that can cause both inputs to go from 0 to 1 simultaneously.

10-18 SYNCHRONIZING BY A CLOCK PULSE

Many forms of flip-flop circuit are used in computers and other machines; but a common addition to such memory circuits is a timing or synchronizing system, which makes all flip-flops change state at a definite time. These times of switching are governed by a "clock," which usually is a pulse-generating oscillator (such as the multivibrator in Fig. 24-6); it sends timed pulses throughout the machine. During these clock pulses the flip-flops are allowed to switch. (Similar but negative pulses are used at the left in Figs. 10-3 and 19-3.)

To make a clock-controlled RS flip-flop, two NAND gates 3 and 4 are added to Fig. 10-13, giving the result in Fig 10-14. Here the flip-flop remains unchanged so long as the *S* and *R* inputs are 0. When input *S* is at 1 (+V) and a positive clock pulse is received at NAND gate 3, its output *A* goes to 0 for the duration of the clock pulse. Gates 1 and 2 now react as shown in Fig. 10-13*c*; as point *A* momentarily goes to 0, it *sets* the flip-flop so that *M* is 1 and *P* is 0. Similarly, when input *R* is 1 and a positive clock pulse is received,

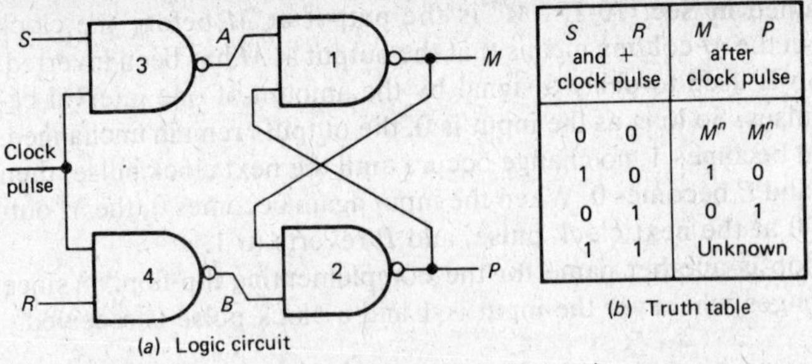

S and + clock pulse	R	M after clock pulse	P
0	0	M^n	M^n
1	0	1	0
0	1	0	1
1	1	Unknown	

(b) Truth table

Figure 10-14 RS flip-flop triggered by (+) clock pulses.

this *resets* output M to 0, and P to 1. The truth table of Fig. 10-14 covers operation of all four gates. As shown in the bottom line (and mentioned in Sec. 10-17), we avoid letting both S and R be 1 simultaneously, since the next clock pulse either sets or resets the flip-flop, unpredictably.

10-19 OTHER TYPES OF FLIP-FLOP; JK FLIP-FLOP

In addition to RS flip-flops[10-17] and complementing flip-flops,[10-3] there are other flip-flop circuits to give different kinds of action. A sophisticated flip-flop in present use is called the JK flip-flop. It overcomes the limitation of the RS flip-flop, since, if both inputs are true simultaneously, the JK gives definite predictable resulting outputs.

The truth table of the JK flip-flop in Fig. 10-15*a* matches that of the RS flip-flop in Fig. 10-14; but the bottom line of the JK truth table shows that, when both inputs are true, the next clock pulse changes or inverts the out-

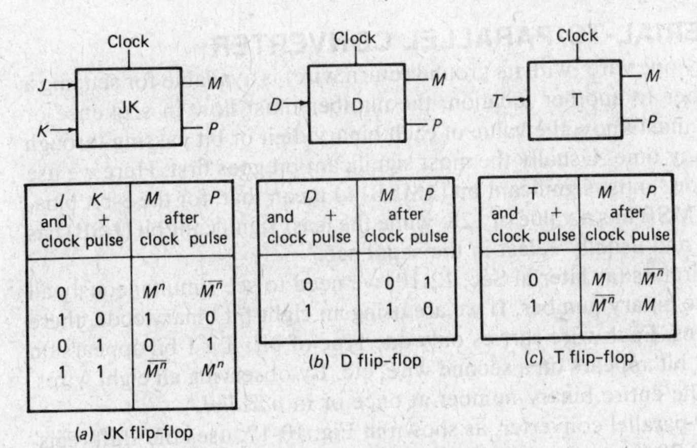

J and + clock pulse	K	M after clock pulse	P
0	0	M^n	$\overline{M^n}$
1	0	1	0
0	1	0	1
1	1	$\overline{M^n}$	M^n

(a) JK flip-flop

D and + clock pulse	M after clock pulse	P
0	0	1
1	1	0

(b) D flip-flop

T and + clock pulse	M after clock pulse	P
0	M	$\overline{M^n}$
1	$\overline{M^n}$	M

(c) T flip-flop

Figure 10-15 Truth tables for more types of flip-flop.

put. As explained in Sec. 10-17, M^n is the output at M before the clock pulse; but M^n in the M column means that the output at M has been inverted.

A D flip-flop is used to delay a signal by the amount of one interval between clock pulses. So long as the input is 0, the outputs remain unchanged. When the input becomes 1, no change occurs until the next clock pulse; then M becomes 1 and P becomes 0. When the input again becomes 0, the M output reverts to 0 at the next clock pulse, and P reverts to 1.

The T flip-flop is another name for the complementing flip-flop,[10-3] since the output changes whenever the input is 1 and a clock pulse is received.

10-20 SHIFT REGISTER

Six of above type-D flip-flops (Fig. 10-15*b*) are combined to form the six-stage shift register in Fig. 10-16. The shift register remembers a given sequence of 1s and 0s, and will repeat this sequence at its output after a specified number of clock pulses. At clock pulse number 1, the signal input to D_1 is 0 and thus the output of D_1 is also 0. At clock pulse 2, the input is 1; so the output of D_1 becomes 1 also. At clock pulse 3 the input to D_2 reverts to 1; so the output of D_2 becomes 1. With successive clock pulses, we see that the sequence of 1s and 0s is moved into the shift register. At the sixth clock pulse the same sequence begins to emerge from the output of D_6.

Thus this six-stage shift register has stored as many as six bits of information during six clock-pulse times. Most of the hand-held calculators use several shift registers to store the numbers that are entered by means of the keyboard. Each shift register often has more than 40 stages, sometimes up to 1000 stages in one shift register. Some shift registers make the output of each stage available so that the stored sequence of 1s and 0s can be observed at one time.

10-21 SERIAL-TO-PARALLEL CONVERTER

When only one wire (with its ground return wire) is available for sending a binary number to another location, the number must flow in sequence or serially. We must know the value of each binary digit or bit passing through the wire at any time. Usually the most significant bit goes first. Here we use the expression "most significant bit" (MSB) to mean that, for the 8-bit binary code, the MSB has a value of 128, while the least significant bit (LSB) has a value of 1 and usually is last in the sequence.

In some circuits (as later in Sec. 12-10) we need to see simultaneously all the bits of the binary number. If we are using an eight-bit binary code, there are eight wires. Each wire carries only one type of bit; if a 1 bit appears on one wire, a 2 bit appears on a second wire, etc. By observing all eight wires, we can see the entire binary number at once or in *parallel*.

A serial-to-parallel converter, as shown in Fig. 10-17, uses the shift register of Sec. 10-20 to receive serially the binary number on a single input line.

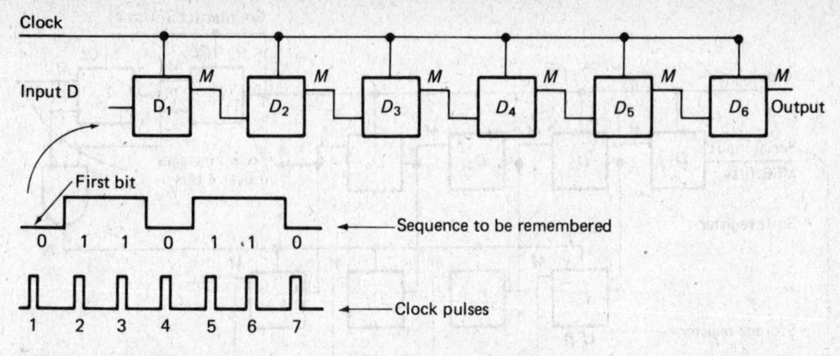

Clock pulse number	Status of output of flip-flops					
	D_1	D_2	D_3	D_4	D_5	D_6
1	0	0	0	0	0	0
2	1	0	0	0	0	0
3	1	1	0	0	0	0
4	0	1	1	0	0	0
5	1	0	1	1	0	0
6	1	1	0	1	1	0
7	0	1	1	0	1	1
8	0	0	1	1	0	1
9	0	0	0	1	1	0
10	0	0	0	0	1	1
11	0	0	0	0	0	1

First bit to arrive at the output (pulse 6, D_6)
Last bit to arrive at the output (pulse 11, D_6)

Figure 10-16 D flip-flops in a shift register.

(Only four bits are shown for simplicity; so further explanation applies to a four-bit binary code.) Here the shift-register section makes all conversion; the rest of the circuit must ensure that we observe the shift-register outputs at the proper time. Consider that the binary number 1101 (13) is being received serially on the single input to D_1 (at upper left in Fig. 10-17). The 8 bit (MSB) arrives first and, with the first clock pulse, enters the D_1 flip-flop. With the second clock pulse the 4 bit arrives and enters the D_1 flip-flop at the same time that the previous D_1 bit is shifted to D_2. At this time the outputs of the shift register do not show properly the binary number; we must have two more clock pulses (a total of four) before the entire binary number is properly placed in the shift register. So a count-to-four circuit (consisting of two type-T flip-flops of Fig. 10-15*c*) is used to generate a pulse on line *A* (at upper right in Fig. 10-17) at clock pulse 4 when both *P* outputs are at 1. The clock line is connected to the input of T_1 and also the clock terminals of T_1 and T_2; thus T_1 complements with each clock pulse while T_2 complements with every second and fourth pulse, as is shown by the table in Fig. 10-17. Both T_1 (*P*) *and* T_2 (*P*) must be 1 to let line *A* be 1. When line *A* is 1, the contents of the shift register (D_1 through D_4) are loaded into the storage register

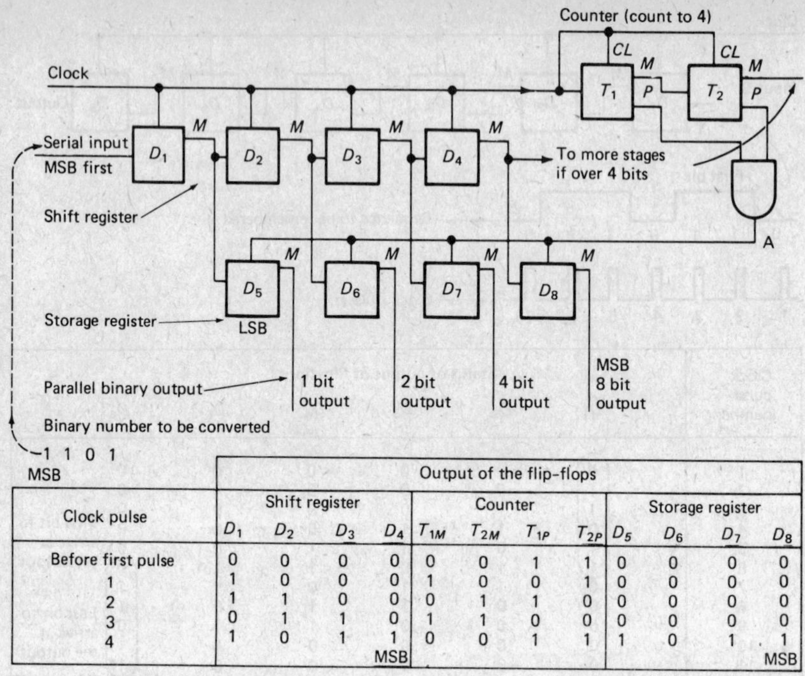

Clock pulse	Output of the flip-flops											
	Shift register				Counter				Storage register			
	D_1	D_2	D_3	D_4	T_{1M}	T_{2M}	T_{1P}	T_{2P}	D_5	D_6	D_7	D_8
Before first pulse	0	0	0	0	0	0	1	1	0	0	0	0
1	1	0	0	0	1	0	0	1	0	0	0	0
2	1	1	0	0	0	1	1	0	0	0	0	0
3	0	1	1	0	1	1	0	0	0	0	0	0
4	1	0	1	1	0	0	1	1	1	0	1	1
				MSB								MSB

Figure 10-17 Serial-to-parallel converter.

consisting of D_5 through D_8. Now the 8 bit is properly placed and appears on the 8-bit output line; all other bits likewise are properly placed. The output of the storage register remains constant for the next three clock pulses even while a new serial binary number is being shifted into the shift register. Here note that the clock rate at which the serial binary number enters the converter is four times as fast as the rate at which the parallel binary numbers leave the converter. (This is like having a single toll booth for a four-lane highway—it can be the element that limits the speed of the whole system.) Thus, in systems where speed is critical, we prefer to transmit binary numbers in parallel instead of transmitting them serially.

In practice, all flip-flops used in this converter (and in most other flip-flop applications) include an R (reset) input so that, with a single R signal, all flip-flops can be reset to 0. When power first is turned on in such a circuit, we cannot be sure that all flip-flops will turn on in the 0 condition; thus the R line is momentarily energized to do this.

Problems

10-1 True or false? explain why.

(a) In Fig. 10-1, a flip and a flop are caused by two different kinds of input signal.

(b) Six flip-flops are needed, to count from 1 to (*a*) 30 or (*b*) 34.

(c) 1×2^8 is four times as large as 1×2^6.

(d) Transistors used in binary counters operate mostly in the active region (see Fig. 7-14).

(e) In the binary system (using 2 as the base), a shift of the decimal point by one place either doubles or halves the value of the number.

(f) The binary sum of 00111 and 10101 is 11100.

(g) If a third AND gate replaces the OR gate in Fig. 10-6*c* any 0 input causes a 0 output.

(h) If an AND gate replaces each NAND gate in Fig. 10-10, two or more horizontal lines of the truth table (*b*) still are correct.

(i) The total number of components in a binary full adder is just twice those in a half adder.

10-2 List the transistors whose collectors are connected by selector contacts to Q_{25} (at the bottom of Fig. 10-3) when the weld-time selector is set for (*a*) 3 cycles, (*b*) 5 cycles, (*c*) 6 cycles, (*d*) 8 cycles, and (*e*) 10 cycles.

10-3 Give decimal-system numbers equal to the following binary numbers: (*a*) 11010, (*b*) 111000, (*c*) 1010.1, (*d*) 1001001, (*e*) 100100.1, (*f*) 10010.01, (*g*) 1100011000, (*h*) 100000100000.

10-4 Repeat Prob. 10-3 for (*a*) 101111, (*b*)10101010, (*c*) 11011.01, (*d*) 1011011.1, (*e*) 10011.11, (*f*) 110011100, (*g*) 11101101.1, (*h*) 111100001111.

10-5 Express the following numbers in binary form: (*a*) 36, (*b*) 14.75, (*c*) 65.5, (*d*) 85, (*e*) 250.25, (*f*) 819, (*g*) 1000, (*h*) 1999.

10-6 Repeat Prob. 10-5 for (*a*) 29.5, (*b*) 5[illegible] (*c*) 70, (*d*) 150, (*e*) 1021, (*f*) 1275, (*g*) 333, (*h*) 555.5

10-7 Find each binary sum and check by conversion to decimal numbers.

(*a*)	(*b*)	(*c*)
1101101	111111	100010
0110010	100001	010001
1001001	010001	001101

11 INTEGRATED CIRCUITS FOR SWITCHING

Integrated circuits (called ICs) permit the presence of hundreds of transistors, diodes, and resistors within the size of an aspirin pill; all these circuit elements are made at the same time, on the same tiny wafer of silicon. In contrast, circuits described in earlier chapters use separate or *discrete* circuit elements; each resistor, capacitor, diode, or transistor is made separately, and these then are connected together. Printed circuits (PCs) provide ways to interconnect hundreds of discrete elements on a single board, when hundreds of identical PC boards are to be made. Certain film and hybrid types of integrated circuit often are merely subminiature assemblies of discrete parts; thus they use circuit designs like those found in earlier large assemblies. In complex equipment, many ICs may be mounted on a single PC board.

But the completely new device is the *monolithic* integrated circuit, wherein hundreds of diodes, transistors, and resistors are formed or "grown" by the same processes, at the same time, by chemically treating certain parts of the surface of one tiny peice of silicon; some of these methods were learned in the making of transistors alone. In this chapter, IC is to mean mainly the monolithic integrated circuit.

11-1 THE NEED FOR INTEGRATED CIRCUITS

The main needs for ICs lie in their saving of space, improved reliability, and reduction in cost, when made in large quantities. Thus ICs permit the design of more complex and compact circuitry; as in aircraft and satellites, the IC now appears in industrial equipment, automobiles, TV sets, and hearing aids.

A 1954 computer used tube flip-flops, each requiring 30 cubic inches (500 cm^3); the transistor flip-flop in a 1963 computer needed 3.3 cu in.; but the IC flip-flop uses $^1/_{40}$ cu in. (0.4 cm^3), thus fitting within a metal case formerly used by a single transistor. The entire counter shown in Fig. 10-3, with four flip-flops and interconnections, is available in one IC of $^1/_4$ cu in. (4 cm^3). A single IC does all the adding, subtracting, multiplying, and dividing in a compact hand-held calculator. A circuit of this complexity (using over 800 transistors or 100 gates) is called LSI (large-scale integration); a circuit of medium size is MSI.

As is described in Sec. 12-1, hundreds of ICs are made on the surface of each wafer of silicon, in less than 1 sq in. (6.5 sq cm). Fully made and tested, this wafer then is sliced into chips; each *chip* contains one IC (or perhaps 50 transistors) and is mounted individually in a case, such as the "dual in-line package" or DIP, shown in Fig. 11-1. The case encloses also the leads from the chip to the external plug-in terminals; the case also carries away the heat generated in the chip.

There is no access to parts within the IC; should failure occur, the entire IC is replaced. Since many ICs are made from the same wafer under close control, the ICs are closely matched and show excellent life.

11-2 INSIDE THE IC

The IC became possible in 1966 when methods were developed for making the *planar epitaxial passivated* transistor; these same methods are included in making the IC. ("Epitaxial" refers to the means used for arranging or locating a growth of N layer onto the wafer of P-type silicon; "passivated" refers to the use of an inert protecting layer as the top surface of the

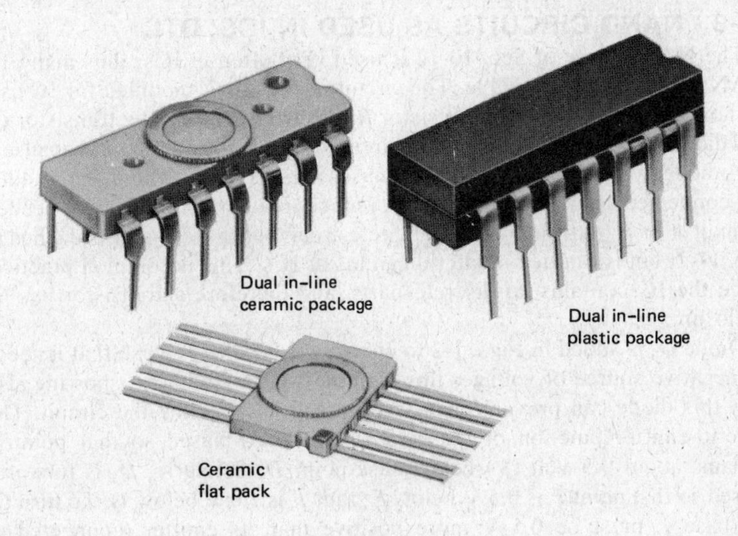

Figure 11-1 DIP (or dual in-line package) containing IC. (*Radio Corporation of America.*)

wafer.) By the photographic and chemical etching procedures described in Sec. 11-10, parts of a grown N layer are removed, leaving behind elongated portions of N-type silicon to act as resistors. Also, since three P or N layers have been formed, one above another, tiny portions of these touching metal sandwiches may be isolated so as to become individual diodes or transistors.

While observing these results, the designer learns that a circuit element within the IC costs more if the element needs more surface area in the chip. Since each chip has a fixed surface area, it can be used to make many more diodes than resistors. On a chip whose surface is 0.05 × 0.05 in., each diode needs a space of 4 × 3 mils, a bipolar transistor 4 × 6 mils, and 2 × 12 mils for a 1000-ohm resistor. A capacitor is costly and rarely is used in ICs, since 100 picofarads (pF), or 0.0001 microfarad (μF), needs 10 × 30 mils, or enough space for 12 transistors.

Notice how the above relative costs influence the modern circuit design of ICs. Recall that a circuit based on discrete elements uses many resistors and capacitors, for they are less costly than transistors. Here resistors, capacitors, and also inductors are called passive devices because they do not contain continuous sources of power. In contrast, the designer of ICs uses many extra transistors and diodes if this will eliminate the more costly capacitors or larger resistors. A transistor is an active device because there are power sources within its equivalent circuit, as shown in Figs. 7-21 and 7-25. Thus the monolithic IC employs many new circuit designs not found in discrete-element circuits; some of these IC designs are next discussed.

11-3 NAND CIRCUITS AS USED IN ICS; DTL

The NAND gate of Sec. 10-12 is used very often in ICs; thus many IC NAND circuits are available. The circuit of Fig. 10-7, modified for IC use, is shown in Fig. 11-2; former resistor R_2 has been replaced by transistor Q_2 and diode D_3. This is called a DTL circuit (diode transistor logic) because it uses diodes at the inputs A and B, and uses a transistor amplifier. This added Q_2, connected as an emitter follower, reduces the amount of current needed at input A or B, to turn Q_1 off. The circle around each transistor is dashed in Fig. 11-2, but is omitted in later diagrams of ICs. This is common practice, since the IC contains no discrete parts, and therefore a transistor has no enclosure.

Diode D_3 is added in Fig. 11-2 to change the biasing of Q_1 so that it needs no negative source of voltage; this method is discussed next, showing also how this diode can prevent electrical noise from affecting the circuit. The base-to-emitter junction of Q_2 always is forward-biased so that point E remains about 0.5 volt (V) below base point D. Similarly, D_3 is forward-biased so that point F is 0.5 V below E; thus F is 1.0 V below D. To turn Q_1 on, base F must be 0.5 V more positive than its emitter (connected to ground). The addition of these voltages shows that Q_1 does not turn on if

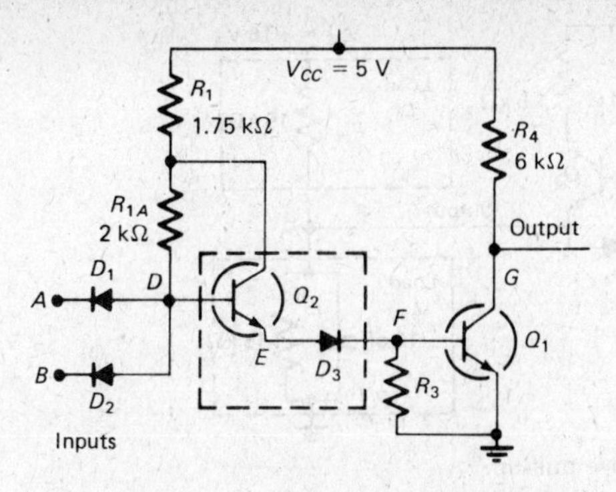

Figure 11-2 DTL NAND gate.

point D remains less than 1.5 V above ground. For Q_1 to be off, either input diode D_1 or D_2 must be conducting. When this diode's forward voltage drop of 0.5 V is subtracted from 1.5 V, we see that the input voltage at A or B has an upper limit of 1.0 V, in order to hold Q_1 off.

The inputs to this NAND gate usually are connected to the outputs from similar gates in preceding stages within the IC system. For example, the input A connects to the collector of an earlier transistor like Q_1; when turned on, its collector voltage is guaranteed to be less than +0.5 V; thus input A is held below 0.5 V. This is well below the 1.0-V limit that ensures cutoff of Q_1; thus no source of negative voltage is needed to hold Q_1 off.

This difference (between the greatest voltage from the conducting transistor driving the input A, as compared with the 1.0-V threshold allowed at point A) here amounts to 0.5 V, and is called the *noise margin*. This permits as much as 0.5-V electrical-noise distrubance on the wires feeding into A or B, without falsely turning Q_1 on.

11-4 HIGH-THRESHOLD LOGIC OR HTL

The noise margin of the preceding DTL NAND gate may be increased to 4 V by replacing its D_3 by a Zener diode (of about 8 V), as shown at Z in Fig. 11-3. With Z, the input at A or B must exceed 8.5 V to turn Q_1 on. However, the output voltage (from similar gates ahead of A or B) is near 12.5 V; this provides an excess of 4 V above the 8.5 V needed to turn Q_1 on. Thus this circuit is immune to electrical noise as great as 4 V.

Some HTL circuits are modified further by adding Q_3, D_4, and R_5, as shown at the right in Fig. 11-3; this forms a circuit called "active pull-up." This feature is useful where the circuit output is connected to a highly capacitive load, such as the stray capacitance of many long wires closely bound together. Or the output may connect to a grounded load such as the load L_2 at the right in Fig. 11-3. When Q_1 is fully on, load terminal F is held about 0.8 V above ground; thus current flows through load L_1, D_4, and Q_1.

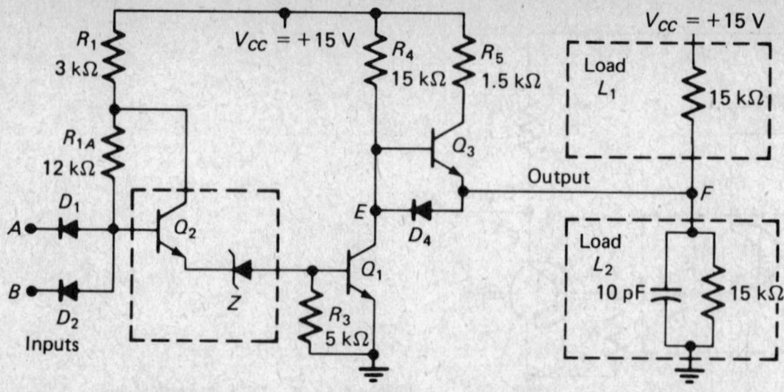

Figure 11-3 HTL NAND gate with "active pull-up."

As D_4 conducts, it holds point E about 0.5 V below F; this holds Q_3 off. Now when Q_1 is turned off, base E of Q_3 rises near to +15 V; as Q_3 turns on, it raises point F near to 13 V. Load L_2 now receives a large electron flow that passes also through Q_3 and R_5 to +15 V; here diode D_4 is reverse-biased.

Thus, because of Q_3, the load L_2 voltage can be varied from 13 V down to 0.8 V. In comparison, if R_5, Q_3, and D_4 are removed (as when D_4 is short-circuited), then the maximum voltage across L_2 (with Q_1 off) is only 10 V; moreover, the voltage across L_1 cannot be reduced to below 5 V. By pull-up the circuit pulls the output voltage from 10 V up to 13 V, because of Q_3, an active device.

11-5 TRANSISTOR-TRANSISTOR LOGIC OR TTL; NAND GATE

Previous NAND circuits use diodes for the AND part of the input gate as shown in Fig. 11-4*a*. But transistors are used for this same purpose in Fig. 11-4*b*; these allow the NAND circuit to switch faster, which is very important in large high-speed computers. In Fig. 11-4*b*, the bases of the transistors are connected together (as also are their collectors); here the IC designer may save space by combining these into a single transistor having two emitters, as shown by Q_4 in Fig. 4*c*. The truth table for Q_4 is the same as in Fig. 10-7*b*.

When both the Q_4 inputs A and B are at 0 V (and up to eight such inputs may be used), the base at point D is held near 0 V because both base-to-emitter junctions are forward-biased. This turns Q_4 on into saturation so that its collector E also is near 0 V. But E also is the base of transistor Q_2, which now is turned off; Q_2 operates as an emitter follower. Since no current flows in R_3 to raise base F, Q_1 is turned off; thus its collector G is (+), near V_{CC}. Since Q_2 is off, the potential at its collector H is near V_{CC}; so Q_3 is turned on. Thus the resistance from V_{CC} to the output G consists mainly of the 130 ohms of R_5.

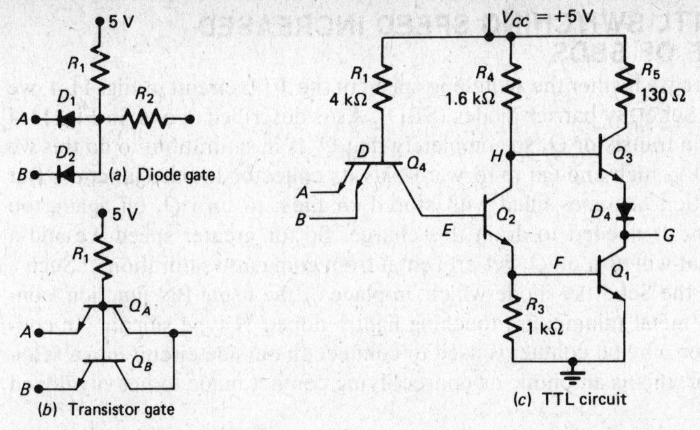

Figure 11-4 TTL NAND gate.

In Fig. 11-4*c*, transistor Q_3 and D_4 form an active-pull-up circuit, but not like that in Fig. 11-3. If Q_3, D_4, and R_5 were replaced by one resistor (in the way that R_4 is used in the DTL circuit shown in Fig. 11-2), this resistor would need to be more than 1.6 kilohms (kΩ) to safely limit the Q_1 current in saturation. But the IC designer prefers to add Q_3, as shown in Fig. 11-4*c*. Here the conduction in Q_2 turns Q_1 on but also turns Q_3 off; this reduces the greatest Q_1 current to only that which passes through the output line *G*. Meanwhile, the resistance from output *G* to ground or to V_{CC} never exceeds 130 Ω. (Thus the IC designer adds Q_3 and D_4 so as to decrease the resistance of a resistor.)

In Fig. 11-4, when either *A* or *B* input to Q_4 becomes (+), the output is not changed, so long as the other input is at 0 V. [Whichever input becomes (+) reverse-biases its base-to-emitter diode so that it cannot affect Q_4.] When *both* inputs *A* and *B* are raised several volts, base *D* of Q_4 also becomes (+). The Q_4 collector *E* rises to about +1.0 V, limited by the 0.5-V drop between base and emitter of Q_2, plus an equal drop at Q_1. Thus both Q_4 emitters are reverse-biased. Base *D*, in turn, is more positive than collector *E*; this is an unusual situation for an NPN transistor, in that the base-to-collector junction is forward-biased. Thus the base-to-collector current of Q_4 becomes the base current of Q_2 and turns Q_2 on. The Q_2 emitter current turns Q_1 on so that the output *G* (collector of Q_1) is nearly 0 V. Since Q_2 is on, point *H* is about 1.0 V, which turns Q_3 off. Diode D_4 ensures that Q_3 turns off when the output voltage at *G* is above or below 0.5 V.

The transistor Q_2 often is called a "phase splitter" because its outputs (at collector *H* and emitter *F*) are used separately for the following stages Q_3 and Q_1. The output at *F* is in phase with the base-*E* signal; the output at *H* is 180° out of phase with the base-*E* signal.

11-6 TTL SWITCHING SPEED INCREASED BY USE OF SBDS

To increase further the switching speed of the TTL circuit in Fig. 11-4, we may add Schottky barrier diodes (SBD). As is described above, in Fig. 11-4 we turn on transistor Q_1 so completely that Q_1 is in saturation; to do this we raise its V_{BE} high enough to forward-bias its collector-to-base junction. But this junction becomes filled with stored charges; to turn Q_1 off again, too much time is needed to drain this charge. So for greater speed we add a device that will turn on Q_1 yet prevent it from going into saturation.[5-7] Such a device is the Schottky diode which, in place of the usual PN junction, consists of a metal (aluminum) touching lightly doped N-type silicon. (In contrast, when a metal contact is used to connect an outside circuit into a semiconductor, this is an ohmic or nonrectifying contact made to heavily doped silicon.)

Because of this aluminum-to-N junction, the current consists of majority carriers only (forming electron flow in the N-type silicon). These charges are quickly cleared out, so that this Schottky diode can turn itself off in about one-third of the time needed by the usual PN junction. Also important, the Schottky barrier or voltage drop is only 0.24 V while conducting (compared with 0.5 V across a PN diode). When this SBD is connected collector-to-base across a transistor such as Q_1 as shown in Fig. 11-5*a*, it lets Q_1 turn on without putting Q_1 into heavy saturation. Since fewer charges gather at this 0.24-V barrier, the switching time is reduced about one-half. The low 0.24-V drop decreases the heat loss so that the SBD is more efficient; it is widely used in IC devices.

The separate SBD and Q of Fig. 11-5*a* are combined into the symbol shown in Fig. 11-5*b*. Figure 11-5*c* shows again the TTL circuit using Schottky diodes at Q_1, Q_2, Q_3, and Q_4.

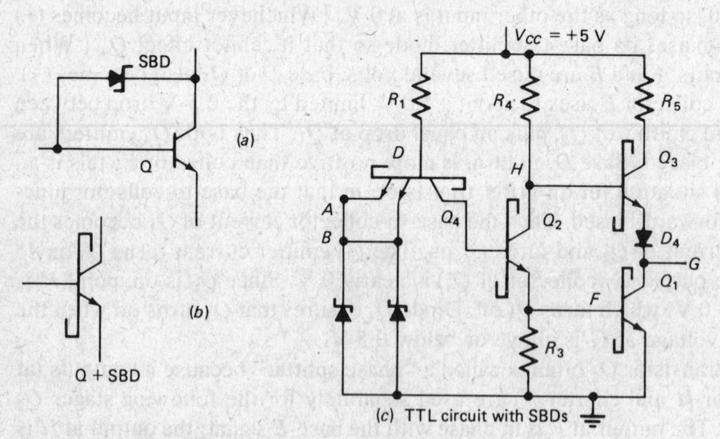

Figure 11-5 TTL switching speed increased by use of SBDs.

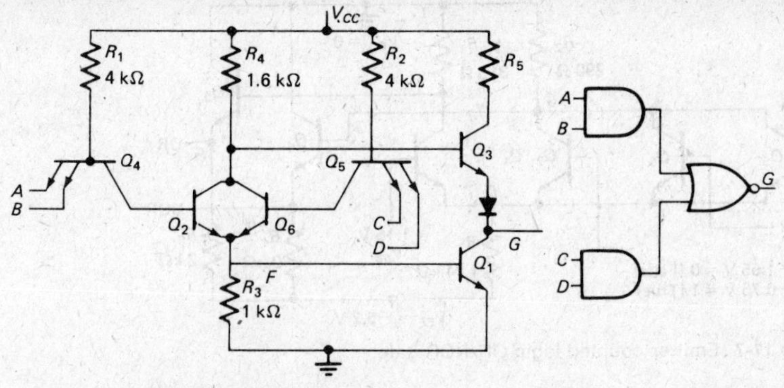

Figure 11-6 TTL AND-OR-INVERT gate.

11-7 COMBINATION OF GATES IN ONE IC

Makers of ICs place more elements on each chip so as to reduce the cost of each circuit element; thus different combinations of gates are built into one IC. As an example, the AND-OR-INVERT gate is shown in Fig. 11-6. At the left, Q_4, R_1, and Q_2 form an AND gate and are the same as those used in Fig. 11-4, and operate in the same way. The added elements Q_5, R_2, and Q_6 operate as a duplicate AND section of the gate, having the inputs C and D. In Fig. 11-6, as *either* Q_2 or Q_6 turns on, this turns Q_1 on and Q_3 off. But if both Q_2 and Q_6 are off, this turns Q_1 off and Q_3 on. Therefore, when either A AND B or C AND D are +V, Q_1 is on so that the output G is 0 V. If inputs B and D are not present, this circuit then is called a NOR gate. The logic symbol in Fig. 11-6 is like that in Fig. 10-6, except that the output G is inverted.

11-8 EMITTER-COUPLED LOGIC OR ECL

This type of circuit is very fast, since no transistor is allowed to operate in its saturated region.[5-7] When excessive numbers of minority carriers (which are electrons for NPN transistors) are not permitted to accumulate in the transistor bases, this permits switching speeds as short as 10 nanoseconds. (In 10 nsec, light travels about 10 ft.)

The circuit in Fig. 11-7 is basically a differential amplifier formed by Q_1, Q_2, R_1, R_2, and R_3.[6-10] The base of Q_1 is held constant by a source of −1.15 V; the forward drop between Q_1 emitter and base holds point D at −1.65 V, applied to the emitters of Q_2, Q_5, and Q_6. So long as inputs A, B, and C are held more negative than −1.55 V (or false), transistors Q_2, Q_5, and Q_6 do not conduct. But Q_1 is on, and its current flow in R_1 makes point E more negative than point G. Since E also is the base of Q_3 (an emitter follower), this makes output point F more negative than −1.55 V (or false).

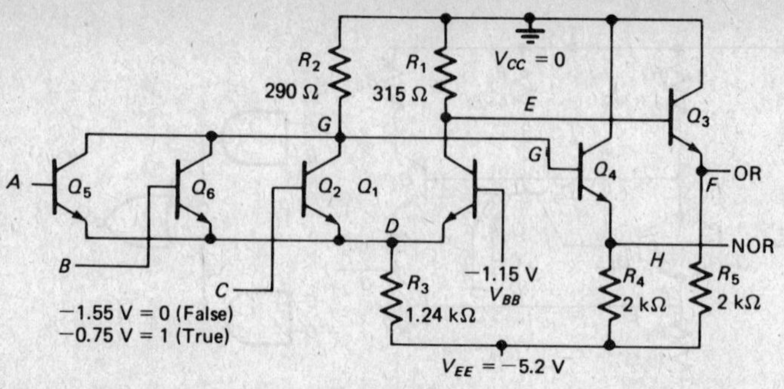

Figure 11-7 Emitter-coupled logic OR/NOR gate.

Meanwhile, little current flows in R_2 (since all transistors below it are off); so G rises near to 0 or ground. Point G is also the base of transistor Q_4, an emitter follower; Q_4 is on, making output point H more positive than −0.75 V (or true). Thus, when no inputs are true, this circuit produces a false OR output and a true NOR output. Hence this is called an OR/NOR gate.

If any input (such as C) is true (or more positive than −0.75 V), this turns on its transistor (such as Q_2). Its emitter D becomes −1.25 V, because of the 0.5-V drop between base and emitter of Q_2. Since D is also the Q_1 emitter and now is only 0.1 V more negative than its base (held at −1.15 V), Q_1 is turned off. The Q_1 collector E now is near 0 V, making point F more positive than −0.75 V (which is a true OR output). But G is more negative than E, and drives point H more negative than −1.55 V (which is a false NOR output). Thus, when any input is true, it causes the OR output to be true and causes the NOR output to be false.

11-9 MOS GATES

The MOSFET (described in Sec. 7-27, and meaning metal on oxide on semiconductor field-effect transistor) is more easily made than the bipolar transistor and needs less area on the chip. The FET commonly used for switching circuits is the P-channel enhancement type, using the induced channel. This transistor does not turn on until its gate becomes 5 volts more negative than the source, as shown in Fig. 11-8*a*.

The MOSFET acts like an open switch so long as the gate-to-source voltage is less negative than −5V. But when the gate is more negative than −5V, this FET passes full current and acts as though the switch has closed. The MOSFET substrate (the underside of the chip) is connected to ground potential as shown in Fig. 11-8*b*. This shows also the standard accepted symbol for the P-channel enhancement-mode MOSFET; but many users of these devices simplify the symbol to that in Fig. 11-8*c*, which shows three duplicate FETs. The MOSFET works equally well in either direction; the

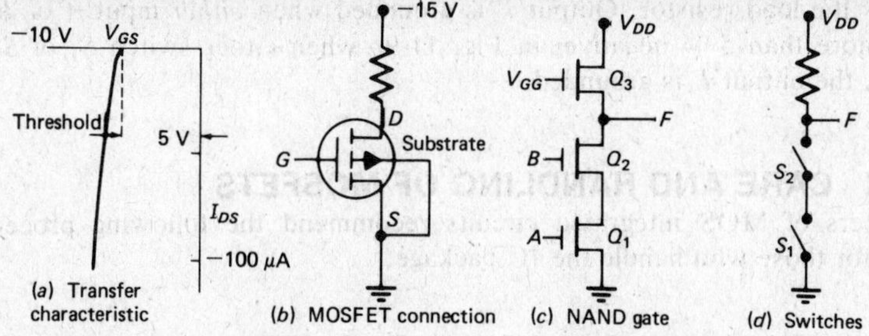

Figure 11-8 Enhancement-type MOSFETs used as NAND gate.

source is defined as that end which is the most positive potential (the lower or ground terminal in Fig. 11-8 since V_{DD} is negative).

Within the IC, a MOSFET acts as a resistor when its gate is held about 25 V more negative than the source. Thus, in Fig. 11-8*c*, Q_3 becomes the load resistor for the NAND gate when V_{DD} is −15 V and V_{GG} is −25 V. (These voltage values vary among manufacturers. Here Q_3 has a long narrow channel to give it the desired resistance characteristic.) The MOSFET used here acts so much like a switch that its NAND circuit is more simple than the bipolar circuits in Secs. 11-3 to 11-8. In Fig. 11-8*c*, if input *A* becomes more negative than −5V, Q_1 turns on acting like the closing of switch S_1 in Fig. 11-8*d*. But this does not affect the output *F* until input *B* also becomes more negative than −5V; this turns Q_2 on (acting like the closing of switch S_2), so that output *F* now is connected to ground and becomes a false output. (Negative true logic is used here.)

11-10 A MOS NOR GATE

The NOR circuit also often is used, and is shown in Fig. 11-9*a;* its switch equivalent is shown in Fig. 11-9*b*. Again, V_{GG} is −25 V, so that Q_3

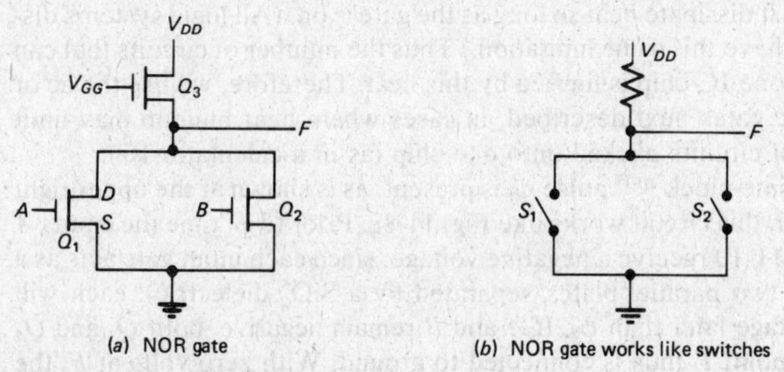

Figure 11-9 A NOR gate using MOSFETs.

acts as the load resistor. Output F is grounded when *either* input A or B goes more than 5 V negative; in Fig. 11-9*b* when either switch S_1 or S_2 closes, the output F is grounded.

11-11 CARE AND HANDLING OF MOSFETS

Makers of MOS integrated circuits recommend the following procedures for those who handle the IC package:

1. Keep all leads shorted together until after the IC is put into the circuit; this can be done by wrapping the entire IC with metallic foil, inserting the leads into conductive plastic, or setting all the leads on a metal sheet (like an oven baking sheet).
2. Ground whatever may touch the MOSFET including metal work benches, tools, soldering-iron tips; even a person should be grounded, by means of metal bracelets wired through a 1-megohm resistor to ground.
3. Avoid wearing synthetic-fiber clothing such as nylon aprons or shirts; on dry days these fibers can build high static charges.
4. Remove power before inserting MOSFET devices into circuit or removing them from circuit. Do not apply signal voltages to the inputs while the power supplies are turned off.
5. After MOSFET devices are installed on circuit boards, treat these subassemblies as you would an individual device until the board has been inserted into a complete system. Good practice is to short together all the external terminals of the subassembly until it has been installed into a complete system.

11-12 DYNAMIC MOS GATES

We say that the MOS gates described above use dc or static logic since they work so long as there are supply voltages and input signals. A major disadvantage of this type of circuit is that the resistor devices (such as Q_3 in Fig. 11-8) must dissipate heat so long as the gate is on. (All logic systems discussed so far have this same limitation.) Thus the number of circuits that can be placed on one IC chip is limited by this heat. Therefore, we use the ac or dynamic logic gates next described, in cases where heat buildup may limit the number of circuits packed onto one chip (as in a calculator IC).

When the time-clock [10-18] pulse ϕ_1 is present, as is shown at the upper right in Fig. 11-10*a*, this circuit works like Fig. 11-8*c*. Prior to ϕ_1 time the inputs A and B in Fig. 11-10 receive a negative voltage; since each input gate acts as a capacitor (of two parallel plates separated by a SiO_2 dielectric), each will store this voltage later than ϕ_1. If A and B remain negative, both Q_1 and Q_2 conduct and point F thus is connected to ground. With zero volts at F, the

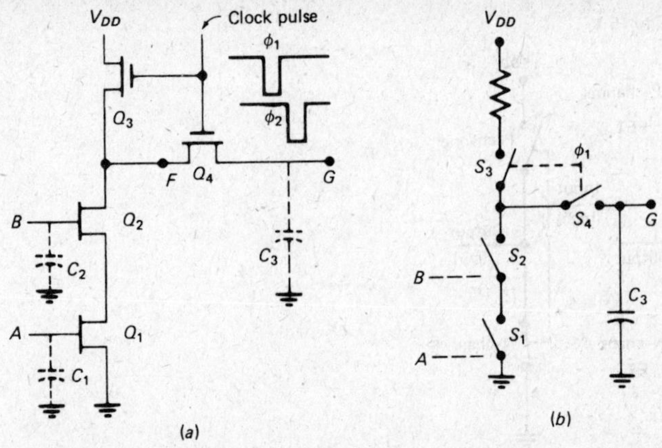

Figure 11-10 Dynamic MOS gate (a) circuit; (b) Switches act like Q_1 to Q_4.

next ϕ_1 pulse makes this zero volts pass through Q_4 to output G and now is stored on capacitor C_3. (In Fig. 11-10*b*, switches act like Q_1 to Q_4 above.)

If input A is zero volts prior to pulse ϕ_1 then Q_1 is not conducting. During the ϕ_1 pulse, transistors Q_3 and Q_4 turn on; Q_3 acts as the resistive device through which C_3 charges to voltage V_{DD}. Thus Q_3 dissipates heat only during the ϕ_1 clock pulse, which perhaps is only one-tenth of the total time. Since there always is some leakage across C_1, C_2, and C_3, less than 100 microseconds elapse between the ϕ_1 clock pulses.

Output point G may connect to the input of another NAND gate; this second gate uses a ϕ_2 clock pulse that occurs after ϕ_1 but does not overlap it; this forms what commonly is called a two-phase clock. When many such gates are connected in series to form a logical string, it requires a long time (compared with dc logic) for an input signal to emerge from the last gate; such delay may be used when a time delay is desired, as in a shift register.

11-13 COMPLEMENTARY MOS OR CMOS

If we form both N-channel and P-channel MOS transistors on a single IC chip, this combination is called *complementary* MOS. It has very low power loss (a fraction of a microwatt per gate) which lets it be used in hand-held calculators; more important, it is more immune to noise than are most other logic systems.

Let us start with a CMOS inverter such as Fig. 11-11*a* (a circuit that merely inverts a high-level input into a low-level output, or vice versa). We know that a P-channel enhancement-type FET[7-27] does not turn on until its gate is a few volts more negative than its source; similarly, an N-channel enhancement-type FET does not turn on unless its gate is a few volts more

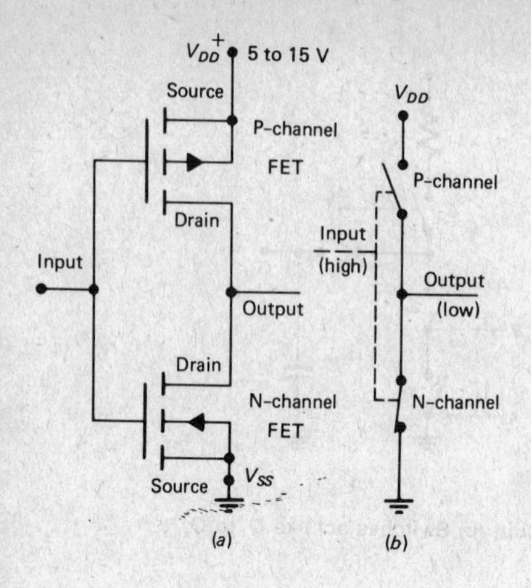

Figure 11-11 Complementary or CMOS using P-channel and N-channel FETs.

positive than its source. Thus, in Fig. 11-11*a*, the P-channel FET is turned on (to have about 1000 ohms between source and drain) when the input is near 0 V (since its gate is very negative compared with its source); this connects the output to V_{DD}. But when the input voltage is near V_{DD}, the P-channel FET turns off and the N-channel FET turns on. These FETs act like the two switches shown in Fig. 11-11*b*, where any high input closes the lower switch but a low input closes the upper switch. These switches are not both closed except during the very short changing period while each switch may be partially conducting.

Several such inverter circuits are combined to form the NAND gate in Fig. 11-12; here FETs Q_1 and Q_3 form one inverter; Q_2 and Q_4 form the other.

11-14 CMOS VOLTAGE TRANSFER CHARACTERISTICS AND NOISE MARGIN

The CMOS inverter (or NAND gate) has a graph of input voltage versus output voltage as shown in Fig. 11-13; this is called a voltage transfer characteristic. Since two circuits are rarely identical, this graph shows two limiting curves—at the left is the voltage for a circuit that has the lowest possible switching voltage; at the right, Fig. 11-13 shows the curve for a circuit having the highest switching voltage. All circuits provided for this logic function by the manufacturer will lie between these limits.

For a typical inverter, Fig. 11-13 shows (at point *L*) that an input voltage below 2.2 V corresponds to an output voltage greater than 9.2 V. Further, if the input voltage (at point *M*) is greater than 7.7 V, the output is less than 1.5 V. Here we wish to avoid an input voltage between 2.2 and 7.7 V, since we

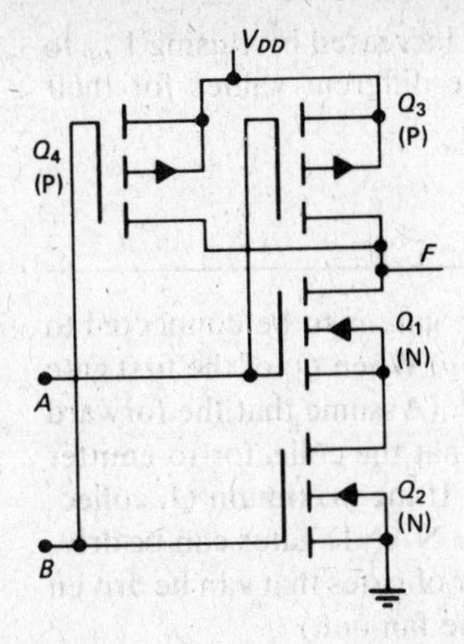

Figure 11-12 NAND gate formed by two CMOS inverters.

cannot closely predict the output voltage; also, the circuit can be in the process of changing state (from low to high or vice versa.)

If now the output of the above inverter is connected to the input of a second identical inverter, we see that, while the output of the first may normally be 10 V, yet the high input to the second needs to be between 7.7 and 10 V. This difference (between the second inverter's required 7.7 V and the 10V available from the first) is 2.3 V; this is called the *high-level noise margin*. Thus 2.3 V of noise can be introduced onto the line between inverters 1 and 2 without causing an erroneous output from inverter 2.

Similarly the low output of the first inverter normally is 0 V, but the low input to the second inverter must not be higher than 2.2 V. This difference of 2.2 V is the *low-level noise margin*. In this low-level condition, 2.2 V of

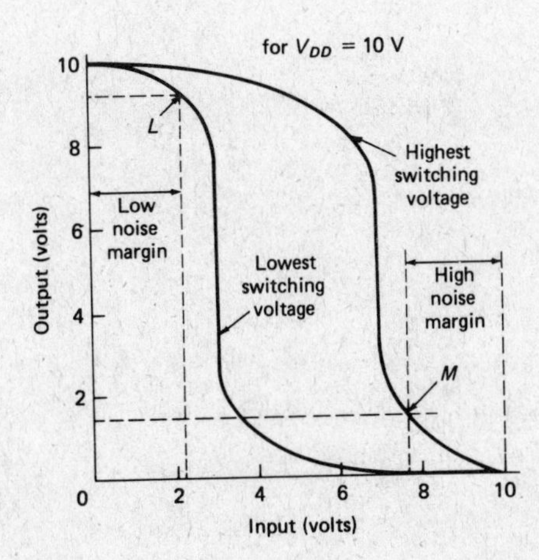

Figure 11-13 CMOS voltage transfer characteristic.

noise can be tolerated. The noise margin can be increased by raising V_{DD} to 15 V. Other families of logic (DTL, etc.) have different values for their noise margins.

Problems

11-1 In Fig. 11-2 the output (at G) of the DTL gate is to be connected to the A inputs of two duplicate DTL gates. (*a*) When Q_1 of the first gate turns on, determine its collector current I_C. (Assume that the forward voltage drop of diode D_1 is 0.5 volts and that the collector-to-emitter voltage drop of transistor Q_1 is 0.5 V.) (*b*) If the maximum Q_1 collector current is 10 mA, how many such DTL NAND gates can be driven to the off condition by Q_1? (This number of gates that can be driven from another of the same type is called the fan-out.)

11-2 Make a truth table for the circuit in Fig. 11-6. How does it differ from the table shown in Fig. 10-10?

12

INTEGRATED CIRCUITS FOR LINEAR APPLICATIONS

We obtain the many advantages of the IC (compared with discrete components) because large quantities of ICs are produced in each batch. By careful control of each step of the processing, the entire batch of ICs is made to have the same characteristics, with high reliability at economical cost. A single batch produces several thousand IC chips.

12-1 THE MANUFACTURE OF THE IC

The manufacture of ICs begins with an ingot of P-doped silicon, produced in such a way that the entire ingot (about 4-in. diameter by 15 in. long) forms only a single crystal. This ingot then is sliced into circular wafers that are polished and etched to a chemically clean mirrorlike finish. Each wafer is 8 to 10 mils thick and yields up to 400 ICs; many wafers are processed at the same time.

First the wafers are heated in an oven, during which time a gas deposits N-doped silicon on top of the P silicon. This is called the *epitaxial layer*, because this N-silicon deposit becomes part of the wafer crystal; the P section of the wafer now is called the *substrate*. Next a layer of silicon dioxide (SiO_2) is formed on the surface by heating the wafer at 1000°C in the presence of steam. At this point the resulting cross section of the wafer is shown in Fig. 12-1*a*. (The thickness of each layer is greatly exaggerated in these diagrams.) Thus far the process is the same as is used in producing the planar epitaxial passivated transistor (mentioned in Sec. 11-2).

The buried N^+ layer shown in Fig. 12-1*b* is a later addition to improve IC performance. This highly N-doped layer is produced before the epitaxial

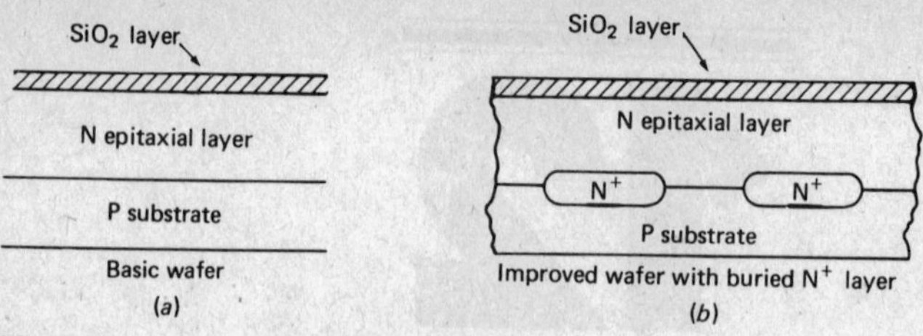

Figure 12-1 Early steps in making the IC.

layer is deposited. It requires photoetching and diffusion similar to the steps next described.

The SiO_2 layer is covered with a photosensitive paste called *photoresist*; wherever exposed to light, this material adheres to the SiO_2, but the unexposed regions can be washed away by a solvent. So at this point a pattern or *mask* is laid over the wafer; through this mask the photoresist surface then is exposed to ultraviolet light. Such a pattern for a single IC has been prepared by its designer at about 500 times the final IC size; it then is reduced photographically to the desired real size. This single IC pattern is duplicated perhaps 400 times to form the mask which covers the entire wafer.

After the unexposed parts of the photoresist have been washed away, the wafer is exposed to hydrofluoric acid; this has no effect on the remaining photoresist, but the acid etches and removes the SiO_2 layer wherever it is not protected by photoresist. The remaining photoresist then is removed. Next the etched wafer is treated in an oven with a gas that contains boron (which dopes silicon so as to produce P-type material, as in Sec. 7-5). This P dopant diffuses into the epitaxial silicon layer only in spots where the SiO_2 has been removed, and thus changes the N-type into P-type silicon in these spots. This diffusion is continued until the P dopant reaches the P substrate, as shown in Fig. 12-2. Arrows *B* and *F* point to regions where transistors, resistors, or diodes are to be formed. At *A* the P dopant has been diffused, so that a P region completely surrounds each area that is to become a circuit element. [In the completed IC, the P substrate is held at the most negative potential in the circuit. Since this produces a reverse-biased "diode barrier," it isolates the transistor (or diodes or resistors) from one another; therefore, this is called the *isolation diffusion*.] During the diffusion process another layer of SiO_2 is formed above the new P regions.

12-2 FORMATION OF TRANSISTORS IN THE IC

Further photoetching and diffusion are needed at *B* and *F* in Fig. 12-2 so as to form transistors and other circuit elements. A second mask is made that coincides with the areas that were isolated by use of the first mask. Smaller

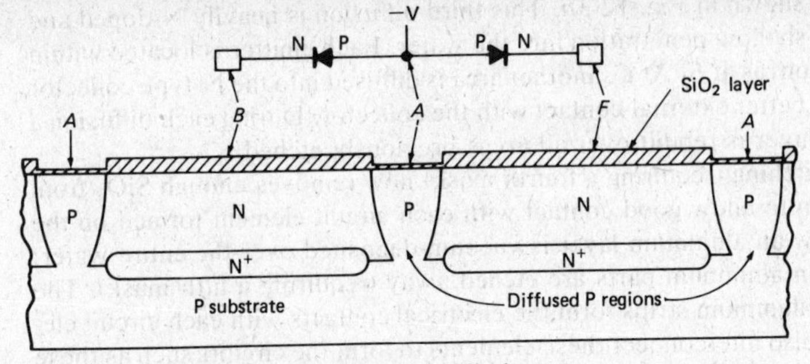

Figure 12-2 IC wafer after the isolation diffusion.

openings through the SiO_2 are formed by this second mask and etching, so that the P transistor bases may be diffused into the remaining epitaxial N regions; each N region surrounding a base becomes the collector for that transistor. (Resistors also are produced during this diffusion.)

In Fig. 12-3*a* is shown part of the wafer after the base regions are diffused into the collector regions at *B* and *F*. This second diffusion is made with P dopant, but for a shorter time than for the first; thus the new P region does not extend as far into the wafer as it did in the isolation diffusion. A new SiO_2 layer is formed above the P base.

The final diffusion requires a third mask so as to produce the emitter

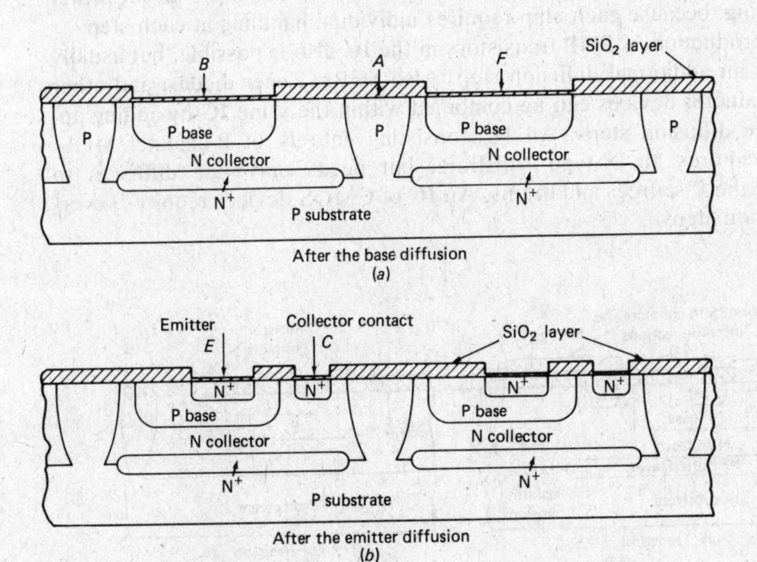

Figure 12-3 Formation of NPN transistor elements on the IC wafer.

regions as shown in Fig. 12-3*b*. This third diffusion is heavily N-doped and has only a shallow penetration into the wafer. Each emitter is located within a base region, as at *E*. At *C*, another area is diffused into the N-type collector to provide better external contact with the collector. During each diffusion a thin SiO_2 layer is rebuilt over all areas previously etched.

A final etching (requiring a fourth mask) now removes enough SiO_2 from each region to allow good contact with each circuit element formed on the wafer. Now an aluminum layer is vacuum-deposited over the entire wafer; then certain aluminum parts are etched away (requiring a fifth mask). The remaining aluminum strips form the electrical contacts with each circuit element, and also interconnect these elements to form the circuits such as those discussed earlier in this chapter.

A completed NPN transistor is shown in Fig. 12-4*a*. In Fig. 12-4*b*, a resistor is formed by altering the pattern of a transistor so as to obtain a long but narrow base region, having a contact at each end. A diode may be formed from either the collector-to-base or the emitter-to-base junction of a transistor.

After completion of the IC wafer, each IC is tested by automatic equipment that positions microprobes onto the contact terminals and electrically determines whether each IC meets required specifications. Any chips that fail are marked with drops of paint. The wafer now is cut into individual IC chips. Each good chip is attached into a ceramic package; leads are bonded to the contacts of the chip and then to the output leads of the package. After the package is hermetically sealed, the IC again is tested. The procedures described in this paragraph add more to the IC cost than do all the wafer processing, because each chip requires individual handling at each step.

The production of PNP transistors in the IC also is possible, but usually requires an additional diffusion step. Also SCRs, Zener diodes, and other semiconductor devices can be combined within the same IC by adding appropriate diffusion steps. An IC consisting entirely of P-channel MOSFETs requires an N-type substrate, but needs only one diffusion to produce the P sources and drains. An IC of CMOS devices requires several diffusion steps.

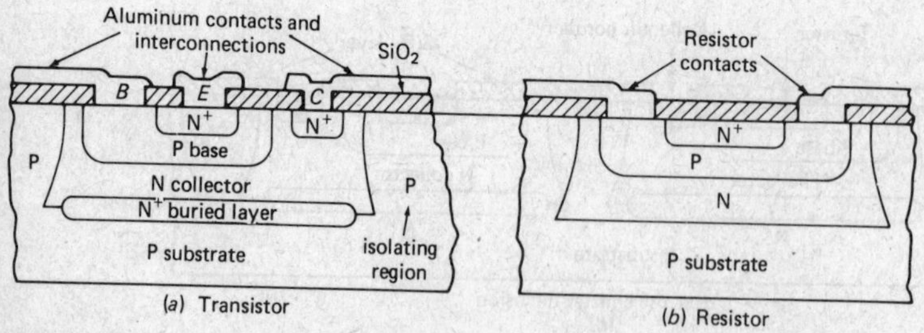

Figure 12-4 Completed circuit elements in the IC.

12-3 ARRANGEMENT PATTERN IN AN IC

The upper part of Fig. 12-5 is an enlarged photograph of an IC chip (0.05 in. square) that contains an amplifier (RCA type CA3020). The various circuit parts are marked by numbers that match those below in Fig. 12-5*b*, which is the circuit diagram of this amplifier chip, and is discussed in Sec. 12-4. The white portions of the photo show where the top metal layer is used to interconnect the IC devices underneath. Some of these devices appear as dim areas formed by vertical lines (caused by variations in thickness of the SiO_2 layer).

Small numbers (such as 4, 5, 6, and 7 at the top of the photo) mark the square areas or connection pads; to these pads are welded the fine wire leads from the outside case.

Transistor Q_1 (at the lower-left corner of the chip) is typical of all transistors on this chip, and is connected to three small rectangles. The base of Q_1 is the bottom rectangle, connected to terminal 10. The emitter is the middle rectangle and connects by a twisting path to terminal 1 at the lower-right corner of the chip; this long metal connection passes above many resistors but makes no connection to them. The Q_1 collector is the top rectangle of this transistor, connected to terminal 9.

A diode is made from a transistor by connecting its base to its collector, shown by the metal layer within D_1 or D_2 or D_3. As used in Sec. 12-4, each diode has a forward drop of about 0.7 V, since the emitter-to-base junction is being used.

To provide a transistor for greater current rating, we connect several transistor sections in parallel; thus, either Q_6 or Q_7 is a "power transistor" consisting of six small transistors in parallel. These IC transistors do not need emitter resistors (such as R_E shown in Fig. 6-3 or 6-11), since all these parallel transistors are close together on the same chip; each has the same V_{BE}.

To the right of terminal 10 in Fig. 12-5*a*, the small circle is used so as to position each mask while light exposes the desired parts of the photoresist beneath the mask. And between terminals 5 and 6 at the top of the chip is a single small transistor; this is used as a control standard during the production of the chip. Electrical characteristics of this transistor are tested after each diffusion and etching process.

12-4 THE LINEAR IC

The ICs of earlier sections are switching circuits (nonlinear or digital) that are well suited for computers. But the IC in Fig. 12-5 may perform linear operations such as amplification. To allow for such wider use, the chip is designed with several more connection points than those needed by switching circuits only. For example, users of this IC may choose to include transistor Q_1 only if it meets their needs; or they may short-circuit resistor R_{10} or R_{11}, depending on the amount of voltage received from the external power supply.

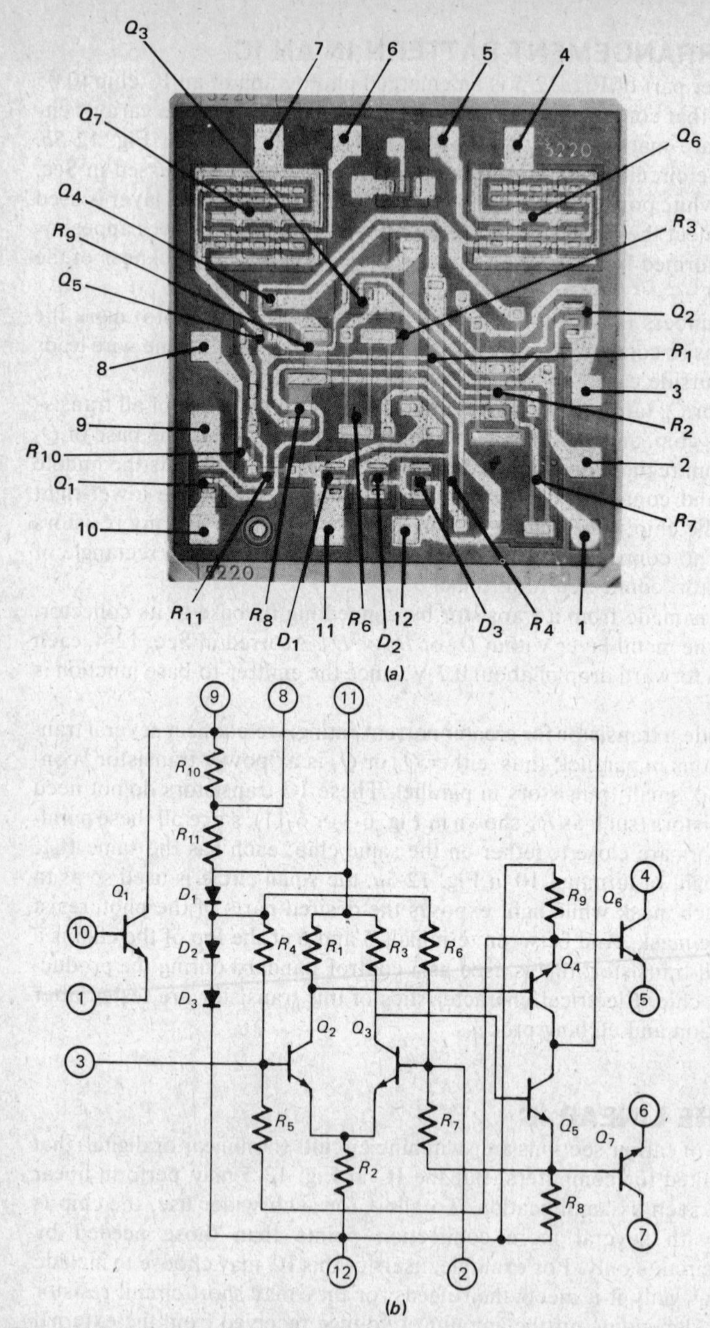

Figure 12-5 (*a*) Enlarged photograph of IC chip (RCA CA 3020); (*b*) circuit diagram of this chip (*Radio Corporation of America.*)

This IC of Fig. 12-5 includes several circuits described in Chap. 6. Terminals 2 and 3 are the inputs to a differential amplifier[6-10] consisting of the NPN transistors Q_2 and Q_3, with R_1, R_2, and R_3. If greater input sensitivity is needed, the signal input is connected instead to terminal 10, the Q_1 base; the emitter output of Q_1 (at point 1) then is connected through an external capacitor to terminal 3.

A regulated voltage source for this differential amplifier is formed by R_{10}, R_{11}, D_1, D_2, and D_3. Here the bottom terminal 12 is at 0 volts, while terminal 9 may be connected to a supply of +3 to +18 V. Although this input voltage may vary, the voltage at the D_2 anode remains at 1.4 V; this provides a 1.4-V bias for the bases of Q_2 and Q_3. Similarly, the D_1 anode provides a 2.1-V supply (through R_1 and R_3) for the collectors of Q_2 and Q_3.

When input terminal 3 becomes more positive, this increases the Q_2 current, thus lowering the Q_2 collector and the voltage at the Q_4 base; meanwhile, the Q_3 current decreases, thus raising the Q_5 base. Since Q_4 and Q_5 operate as emitter followers, the turnoff of Q_4 decreases the Q_6 current, while the turn-on of Q_5 increases the Q_7 current. Thus a push-pull action occurs like that in Sec. 6-3, since Q_6 and Q_7 act like Q_A and Q_B in Fig. 6-4a (there, transformer T_1 has been replaced by the differential amplifier). Input terminal 2 (bottom of Fig. 12-5) would be connected through a capacitor to ground so that the Q_3 base voltage does not vary.

Any unbalance in the differential amplifier is compensated by the negative feedback provided through resistors R_5 and R_7. Normally, Q_4 and Q_5 have equal collector currents when no signal is applied to either input 2 or 3. But if Q_5 should pass more current than Q_4, the increased voltage drop across R_8 raises the Q_5 emitter; this is fed back through R_7 so as to raise the Q_3 base, so that Q_3 conducts more current through R_3. This lowers the Q_3 collector and the Q_5 base, thus decreasing the Q_5 current toward the desired balance. Similar feedback from the Q_4 emitter through R_5 to the Q_2 base serves to compensate the Q_4 current.

To see how this amplifier can serve other purposes, depending on its external connections, note that this circuit can amplify the difference between two signals if one signal is applied to terminal 3 while the other signal is at terminal 2. Further, if the proper network is used that feeds a portion of the output back into the input, this circuit can serve as an oscillator.[24-4]

12-5 THE OPERATIONAL AMPLIFIER OR "OP AMP"

Figure 12-6 shows how a simple triangle may be used as a symbol to represent the whole amplifier circuit that is contained in an IC chip such as that in Fig. 12-5. The two input signals to the triangle appear at the left at 2 and 3; voltages are supplied (+) at top 9 and (−) at bottom 12; the resulting output appears at the right-hand side.

The operational amplifier, also called the "op amp," is a popular form of dc high-gain amplifier especially suitable for use in integrated circuits. It is so

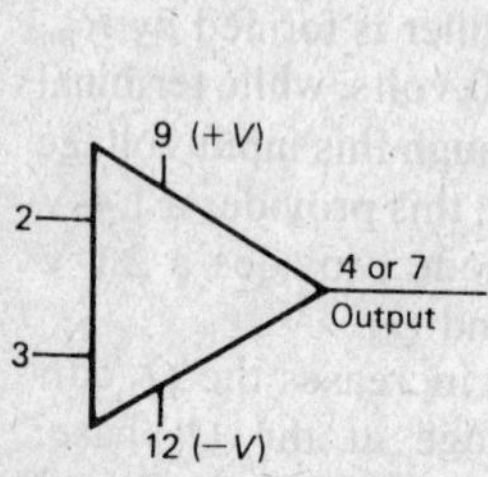

Figure 12-6 Symbol of an amplifier.

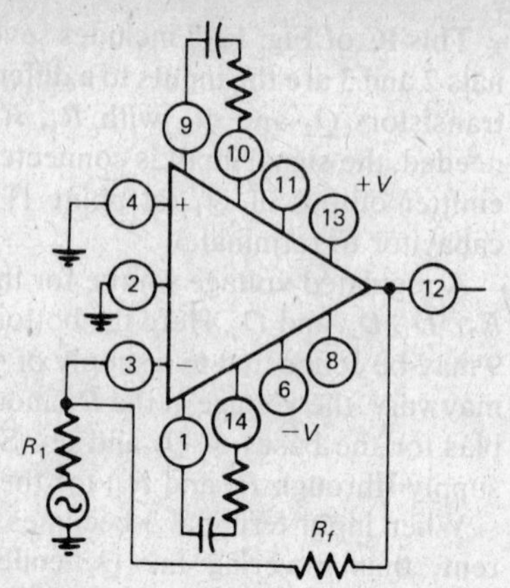

Figure 12-7 Op amp that multiplies and inverts.

named because early it was used in performing mathematical operations such as addition or integration. An op amp now refers to any very high gain direct-coupled amplifier circuit that uses external feedback[28-3] so as to control the output response. The design of such feedback circuits (including the resistors and capacitors located outside of the IC triangle) determines the success of the op amp. Several makers of ICs offer a variety of op amps, any of which can be represented by a triangle such as that shown in Fig. 12-7; Fig. 12-8 shows the circuits that are within a typical triangle, using the same numbered terminals; it is discussed below.

Usually the op amp triangle contains two differential amplifiers connected in cascade (so that the output of the first furnishes the input to the second); thus an op amp can produce extremely high gain such as 2000 or even 500,000. Often only a portion of this gain is used, as chosen by selecting the amount of resistance placed at R_f in the feedback circuit. In Fig. 12-7, if R_f is selected to be $500 \times R_1$, the voltage gain is near 500. When $R_f = R_1$, gain = 1.

In Fig. 12-7, connections at 9, 10, 1, and 14 are used for frequency compensation, so that the gain does not change when the input signal rises to a high frequency. Additional terminals often are provided for "offset" correction so that, when the voltage difference between the two input terminals is zero, the output voltage also is zero and is not offset to some other value. Devices within the amplifier also are employed to overcome this voltage offset, as are next described.

In Fig. 12-8, at terminals 4 and 3 the inputs to the op amp are applied to the bases of transistors Q_1 and Q_2, which form a differential amplifier (as is described in Sec. 6-10). The collector of Q_1 directly controls Q_4 while Q_2 controls Q_3; thus Q_3 and Q_4 act as a second differential amplifier (which is

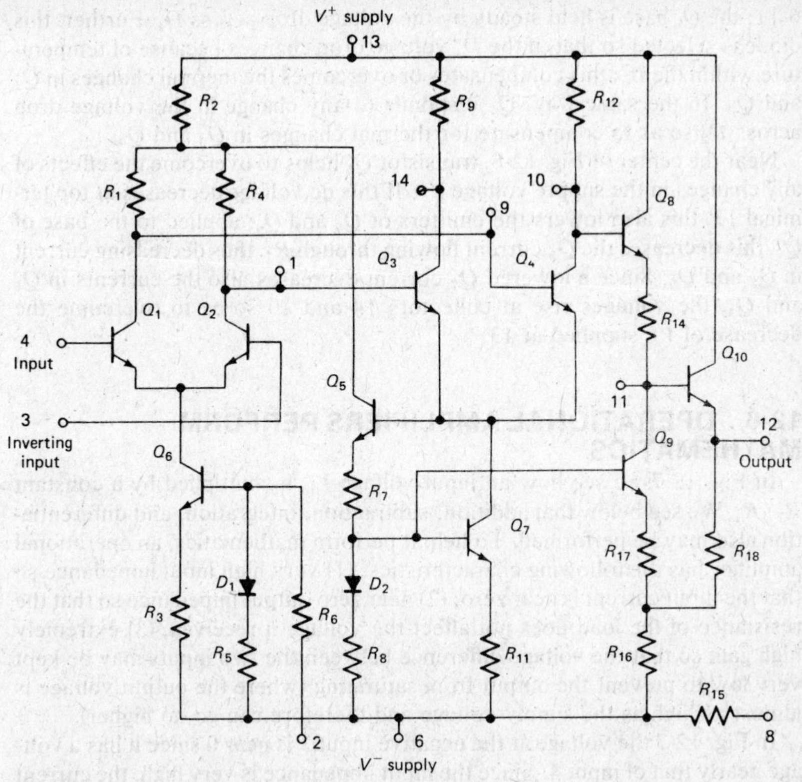

Figure 12-8 Circuits within an op amp chip.

driven push-pull from Q_1 and Q_2). The total current of Q_3 plus Q_4 is held constant by Q_7 (like Q_6 described below.).

First apply a rising signal at input 4 at the left of Fig. 12-8 (while input 3 is grounded); this increases the collector current in Q_1. As this lowers 9 (the base of Q_4), the current decreases in R_{12}, raising base 10 so as to increase the Q_8 current. This also increases current in Q_{10}, which acts as an emitter follower[5-10]; the output potential rises at terminal 12, and thus is in the same direction as the signal change at input 4.

Instead, now apply the rising signal at the "inverting" input 3 (while input 4 is grounded); this increases the collector current in Q_2, thus lowering base 1 of Q_3. Since the decreased Q_3 current causes the Q_4 current to increase, this lowers base 10 of Q_8. Current decreases in Q_8 and Q_{10} so that the output potential falls at terminal 12; thus a signal at input 3 causes an inverted output signal at 12.

Transistor Q_6 (below Q_1 in Fig. 12-8) acts as a source which holds constant the combined collector currents of Q_1 and Q_2 as is described in Sec.

6-11; the Q_6 base is held steady by the voltage drop across D_1. Further, this diode is selected so that, if the D_1 voltage drop changes because of temperature within the IC, this compensates or overcomes the thermal changes in Q_1 and Q_2. In the same way, Q_7 responds to any change in the voltage drop across D_2 so as to compensate for thermal changes in Q_3 and Q_4.

Near the center of Fig. 12-8, transistor Q_5 helps to overcome the effects of any changes in the supply voltage V^+. If this dc voltage decreases at top terminal 13, this also lowers the emitters of Q_3 and Q_4; applied to the base of Q_5, this decreases the Q_5 current flowing through R_7, thus decreasing current in Q_7 and Q_9. Since a lowered Q_7 current decreases also the currents in Q_3 and Q_4, the voltages rise at collectors 14 and 10 so as to overcome the decrease of V^+ supplied at 13.

12-6 OPERATIONAL AMPLIFIERS PERFORM MATHEMATICS

In Fig. 12-7 we see how an input voltage V_{in} is multiplied by a constant R_f / R_1. We see below that addition, subtraction, integration, and differentiation also may be performed. To help it perform mathematics, an operational amplifier has the following characteristics: (1) very high input impedance so that the input current is near zero; (2) near zero output impedance so that the resistance of the load does not affect the voltage it receives; (3) extremely high gain so that the voltage difference between the two inputs may be kept very low to prevent the output from saturating (where the output voltage is almost as high as the supply voltage and therefore can go no higher).

In Fig. 12-7 the voltage at the negative input 3 is near 0 since it has a voltage nearly that of input 4. Since the input impedance is very high, the current into input 3 is almost zero. Thus the current I_{in} (caused by V_{in}) must flow all the way through R_1 and R_f to the output terminal 12. Further, $V_{in} = R_1 I_{in}$ and $V_{out} = -R_f I_{in}$; thus $V_{out} / V_{in} = -R_f / R_1$, so that the output voltage is inverted from the input. (In Fig. 12-9 and later diagrams using op amps, only the input and output terminals of the op amp are shown even

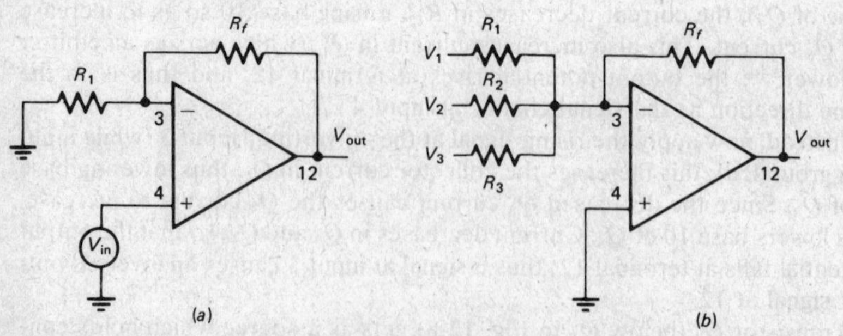

Figure 12-9 (*a*) Op amp that multiplies without inverting; (*b*) op amp adds inputs.

though the other connections to the op amp still may be needed.) In Fig. 12-9*a* V_{out} is not inverted (as it is in Fig. 12-6) since V_{in} is applied to the positive input. Since the current into input terminal 3 is near zero, the voltage at 3 is $V_{out}\,[R_1 / (R_1 + R_f)]$. The voltage at 4 is nearly the same as at 3. Thus

$$\frac{V_{out}}{V_{in}} = \frac{R_1 + R_f}{R_1} = 1 + \frac{R_f}{R_1}$$

The inverting op amp circuit in Fig. 12-7 may be modified to perform addition, as is shown in the summing circuit of Fig. 12-9*b*. Here the output voltage is the negative of the sum of each input voltage times its own resistor ratio, so that

$$V_{out} = -\left(V_1 \frac{R_f}{R_1} + V_2 \frac{R_f}{R_2} + V_3 \frac{R_f}{R_3}\right)$$

By using a capacitor C_2 in the feedback path as shown in Fig. 12-10*a*, the op amp circuit will integrate the input voltage. The rate of change of the output voltage is proportional to the input voltage, so that

$$\frac{V_{out}}{t} = -\frac{V_{in}}{R_1 C_2}$$

Figure 12-10*b* shows the output voltage for V_{in} that varies with time. Here $R_1 = 50{,}000\ \Omega, C_2 = 10\,\mu F$, and

$$V_{out} = V_{in} \times \frac{t}{R_1 C_2}$$

($R_1 C_2$ is the capacitive time constant, described in Sec. 3-3.) If the input voltage is not constant (or not in steps as shown in Fig. 12-10 *b*), we use the calculus equation

$$V_{out} = -\int_0^t \frac{V}{R_1 C_2}\,dt + V_{\text{initial value}}$$

The differential amplifier of Fig. 12-11 is used for instrumentation where

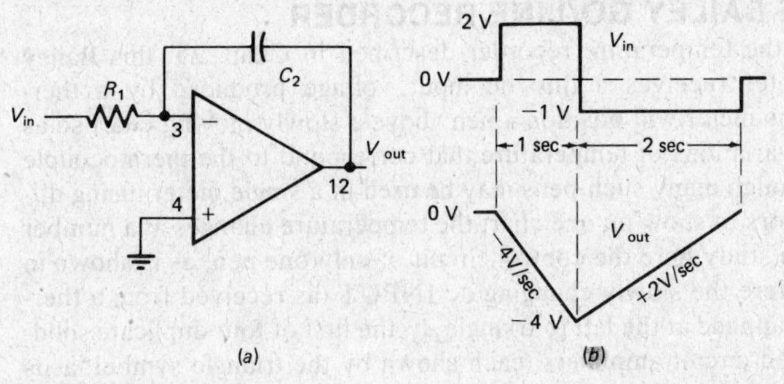

Figure 12-10 (*a*) Op amp integrates input; (*b*) Output voltage varies with time.

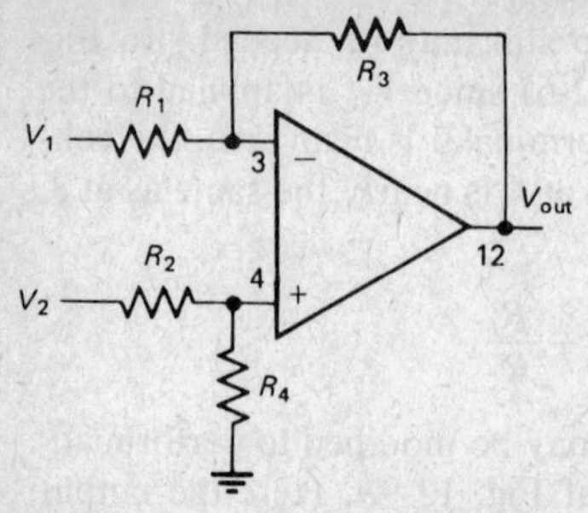

Figure 12-11 Op amp differential amplifier.

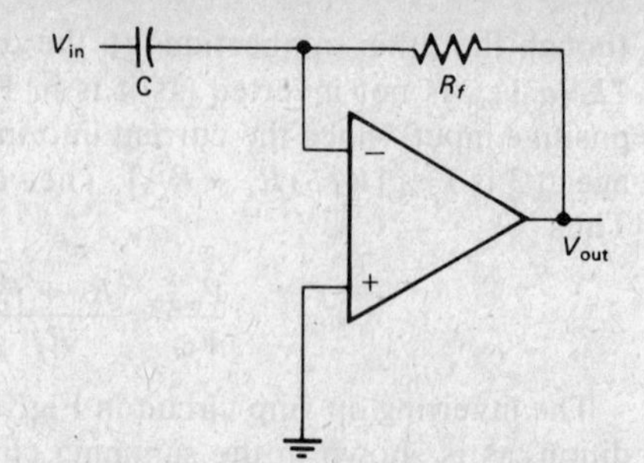

Figure 12-12 Op amp responds to derivative.

the two leads of a transducer (thermocouple, strain gage, or photodiode) are connected to inputs V_1 and V_2. Here the voltage difference between V_1 and V_2 is amplified while the voltage from V_1 or V_2 to ground is ignored. (This is called common-mode rejection.) Often the voltage produced by the transducer is very low compared with voltages that could appear between the transducer and ground. The output voltage is

$$V_{out} = V_2 \frac{R_4}{R_1}\left(\frac{R_1 + R_3}{R_2 + R_4}\right) - V_1 \frac{R_3}{R_1}$$

Also, if $R_4 = R_3$ and $R_2 = R_1$, then

$$V_{out} = \frac{R_3}{R_1}(V_2 - V_1)$$

In Fig. 12-12, the output voltage responds to the derivative of V_{in}. As V_{in} becomes more positive, V_{out} becomes negative. The faster V_{in} changes value, the further V_{out} goes negative. Usually another resistor is placed directly in series with C so that the circuit does not become unstable at high frequencies.

12-7 THE BAILEY GO/LINE RECORDER

Similar to the temperature recorder described in Chap. 25, this Bailey recording meter receives a tiny dc input voltage produced by a thermocouple; this meter will position a pen above a slowly moving chart so as to show the variations of temperature that correspond to the thermocouple voltage. Although many such pens may be used in a single meter (using different ink colors to show on one chart the temperature changes at a number of points), we study here the control circuit of only one pen, as is shown in Fig. 12-13. Here the slowly changing dc INPUT (as received from a thermocouple) is applied at the left to triangle A_1, the first of four duplicate solid-state integrated-circuit amplifiers (each shown by the triangle symbol, as is

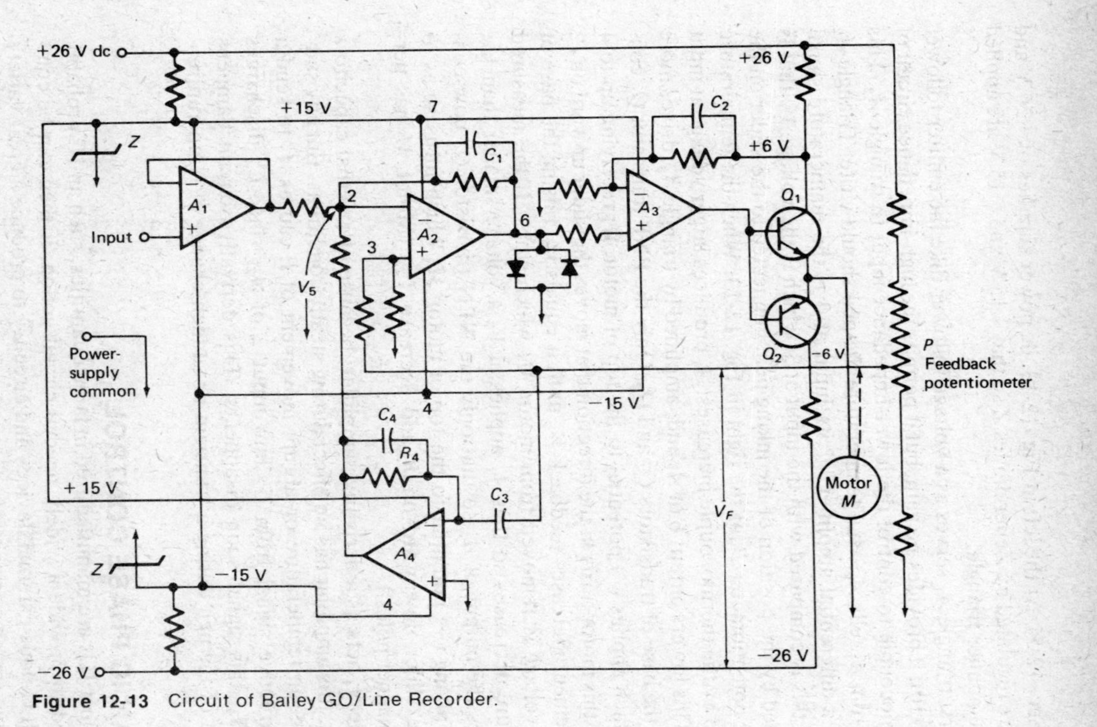

Figure 12-13 Circuit of Bailey GO/Line Recorder.

used in Sec. 12-5). At the left in Fig. 12-13, dc power supplies of +26 V and −26 V are regulated by Zener diodes Z so that +15 V and −15 V are applied to each amplifier triangle.

The first triangle A_1 serves as a voltage follower (like the emitter follower of Sec. 5-10); it provides no gain, but it permits the high-impedance circuit of the thermocouple to control the lower-impedance input to triangle A_2. This voltage from A_1 tells A_2 what temperature the pen should write. Triangle A_2 contains a differential amplifier;[6-10] its input at 2 is the temperature signal from A_1; this is compared with the input at 3, which is the voltage V_F that is determined by the position of the inking pen, connected to the slider on the feedback potentiometer P, at the right in Fig. 12-13. When the temperature measured by the thermocouple increases, A_1 produces larger voltage at input 2 of A_2. This lowers output 6 of A_2 and, amplified by triangle A_3, drives more negative the base of transistors Q_1 and Q_2. Only the PNP transistor Q_2 conducts, which applies (−) potential to the top of motor M; receiving up to 4 amperes, this motor turns in the direction that moves the slider upward on P; this movement increases feedback V_F until it equals V_5, raising the base of Q_2 until voltage is removed from motor M, which stops. If the measured temperature decreases so that A_1 applies at V_5 a voltage smaller than V_F, this raises the output of A_3 so that only the NPN transistor Q_1 now conducts, applying (+) potential to the top of motor M, which turns so as to move the slider downward on P and decrease V_F. (Motor M has permanent-magnet poles.)

Triangle A_4 acts as a derivative amplifier; because of external capacitors C_3 and C_4, this amplifier has no effect during steady conditions. But any sudden change in temperature or abrupt movement of P causes A_4 to send a sharp corrective signal from C_4 into input 2 of A_2; since C_4 discharges through R_4, this signal soon disappears. This derivative circuit dampens overshoot of the pen during a transient or sudden change of temperature.

12-8 AN IC PHASE CONTROL

Since most ICs are manufactured in large quantities, such an IC probably is designed to provide a widely needed circuit action; it then can be combined with various external devices and circuitry to produce a great variety of electronic systems or controls. For example, the dashed line in Fig. 12-14 encloses a General Electric PA436 Monolithic Integrated Phase Control Trigger circuit, which may be used for phase control of a triac. Here, as we turn P_1 clockwise at the right-hand side so as to apply more negative input at terminal 12 of the IC, we show later that this fires thyristors Q_1 and Q_2 (near the left-hand side), thus firing the triac earlier within each half cycle of the ac power supply; this gradually increases the rms value of ac voltage applied across the load, and provides phase control of this full-wave ac load voltage.

At the left in Fig. 12-14, the single-phase ac supply passes through R_S into

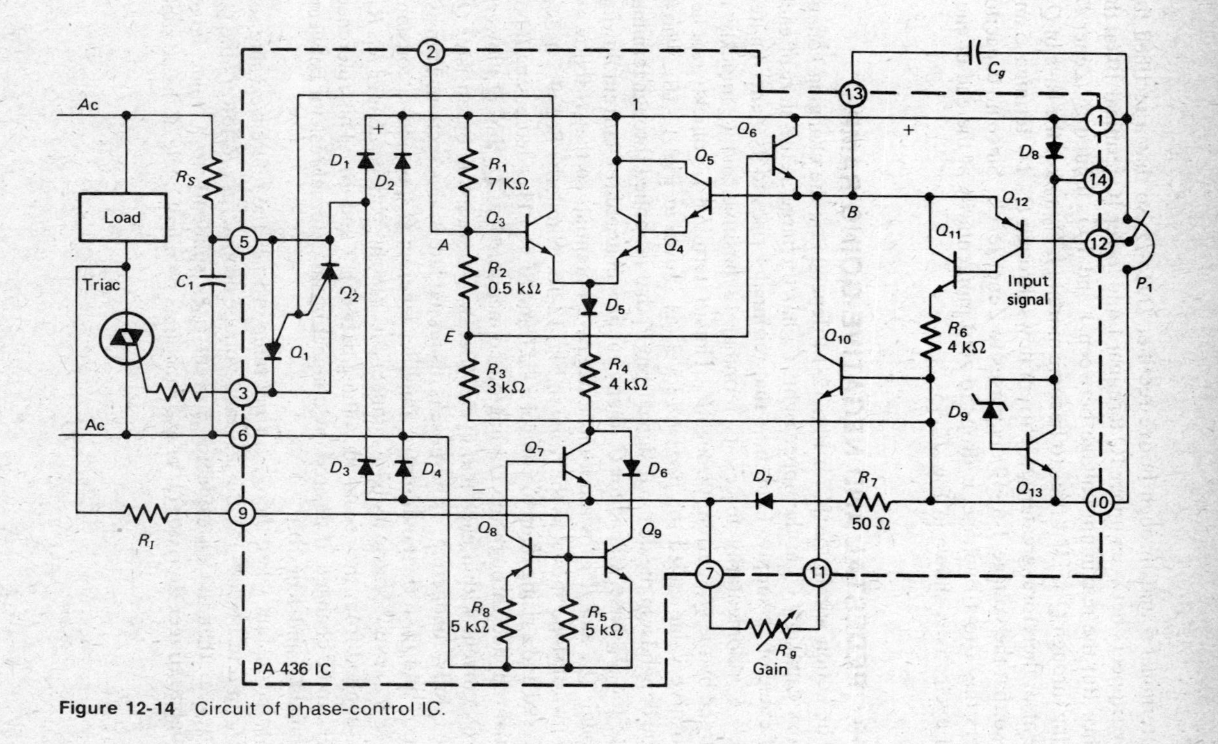

Figure 12-14 Circuit of phase-control IC.

IC terminal 5 and through bridge rectifier D_1-to-D_4 so that a rectified full wave appears between upper IC terminal 1 and lower IC terminal 10 (at the right). But the maximum voltage between 1 and 10 is limited by Zener D_9 acting through Q_{13}. [If 1 tries to become more (+), D_9 makes the base of Q_{13} rise also; therefore, greater Q_{13} current flows through D_8, D_1, terminal 5 and R_S so that the voltage 1-to-10 decreases to Zener level.] Since no capacitor filters this 1-to-10 voltage, it drops to zero momentarily at the end of each half cycle, as is shown in Fig. 12-15.

12-9 PEDESTAL AND NEGATIVE-GOING RAMP

The action within the IC of Fig. 12-14 depends on the changing voltage across capacitor C_g at the upper right; C_g has 0 charge at the start of each half cycle of ac supply. Each time that terminal 1 rises to its Zener-limited level, C_g momentarily forces its terminal 13 positive and C_g quickly is charged by the Q_{11} current through R_6. Thus B (terminal 13) quickly reaches a positive value called the *pedestal* level (as shown in Fig. 12-16), whose value depends on the dc input signal from P_1 that is applied through terminal 12 to the Q_{12} base. Capacitor C_g then becomes charged (by current flowing through Q_{10} and R_g) toward a more negative potential, so that B follows a downward slope shown as the *ramp* in Fig. 12-16. (Similarly, Sec. 9-7 uses a pedestal and a rising ramp to control a UJT and SCR.) This decreasing B potential (applied through the Darlington connection[6-7] of Q_5 and Q_4) lowers the Q_4 current within each half cycle. (Below Q_4, we assume transistor Q_7 here is fully conducting; its purpose is discussed late in this section. Transistors Q_3 and Q_4 form a differential amplifier wherein Q_3 provides a constant *reference* level because its base connects at A to the voltage divider R_1, R_2, R_3, supplied from the regulated voltage between 1 and 10. (This reference level can be changed, if desired, by connecting an external resistor between terminals 2 and 1 or 10.)

At that instant when the Q_4 current ramp crosses the reference value set by Q_3 (at α in Fig. 12-16), the lessened voltage drop across R_4 lowers the Q_3 emitter so that the Q_3 collector current rises suddenly to a value large enough to trigger thyristor Q_1 or Q_2, each in its own half cycle of the ac sup-

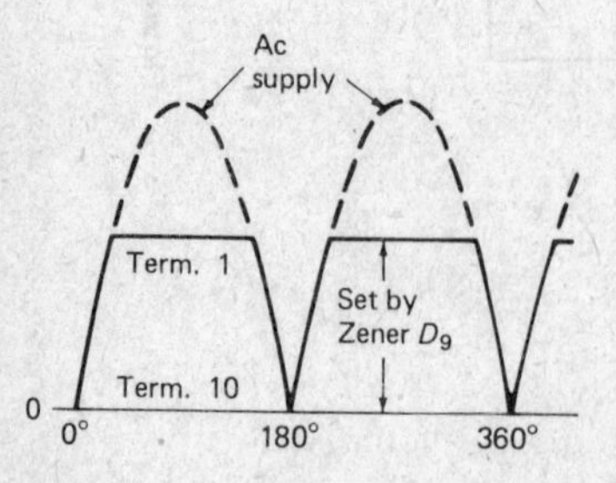

Figure 12-15 Zener-regulated supply in Fig. 12-14.

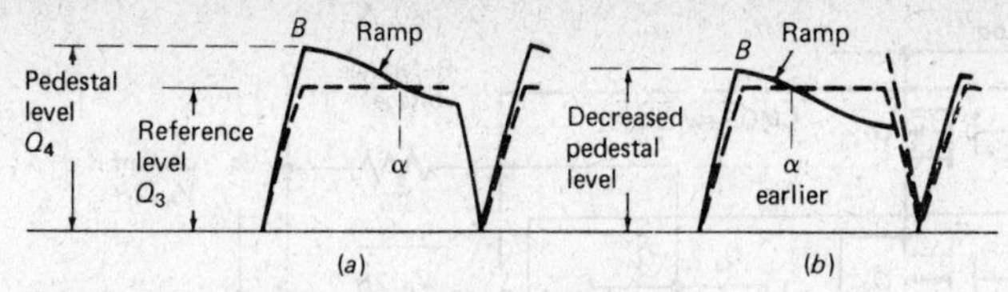

Figure 12-16 Ramp voltage fires IC at angle α.

ply. (At the left, the energy stored in capacitor C_1 is discharged through Q_1 or Q_2 in turn, into the gate of the triac.)

When P_1 is turned clockwise so as to lower the (+) input at terminal 12, this decreases the Q_{11} current through R_6. This lowers the pedestal level at B as shown in Fig. 12-16*b*; starting each half cycle at a lower B level, the ramp crosses the reference level earlier within each half cycle. Since Q_1 or Q_2 fires the triac at this earlier point α, the load receives a larger portion of each ac voltage wave, thus increasing the input to the load.

The downward ramp slope shown in Fig. 12-16 is formed as C_g charges through Q_{10} and R_g. But the base-to-emitter voltage of Q_{10} includes the voltage drop across R_7; this R_7 voltage, caused by the rectified sine-wave current flowing through it, makes Q_{10} pass greatest current near the middle of each half wave, so that the potential at B decreases most rapidly near the center of the half cycle.

When the IC of Fig. 12-14 provides for phase control of an *inductive* load, the measurement of firing angle α may start at 0° (the point where the voltage wave is 0), but the firing of thyristors Q_1, Q_2, and the triac must not occur until the *current* wave through the triac becomes 0. (Reference to Fig. 9-14 may help at this point.) This feature (that locks out the triac until its current stops) is provided by Q_7, Q_8, and Q_9 at the bottom of Fig. 12-14. So long as the triac continues to conduct the current of a previous cycle, very small voltage exists across the triac; its anode supplies such low potential (through R_I and IC terminal 9) to the base of Q_8 and Q_9 that no current can flow through R_4 and Q_3; so Q_1 or Q_2 cannot fire the triac. But at the instant the previous load current stops, the voltage across the triac returns to the entire ac supply voltage; this turns on Q_8 (and Q_7) or Q_9 so that Q_3 is able to conduct at subsequent point α in the wave, thus firing the triac. Figure 12-14 shows only one of the many external circuits that this certain IC can control.

12-10 DIGITAL-TO-ANALOG CONVERTER (DAC)

Frequently quantitative information is transmitted from one location to another in digital form since this is far more reliable than the sending of a voltage level or current level to represent this information. Once this digital

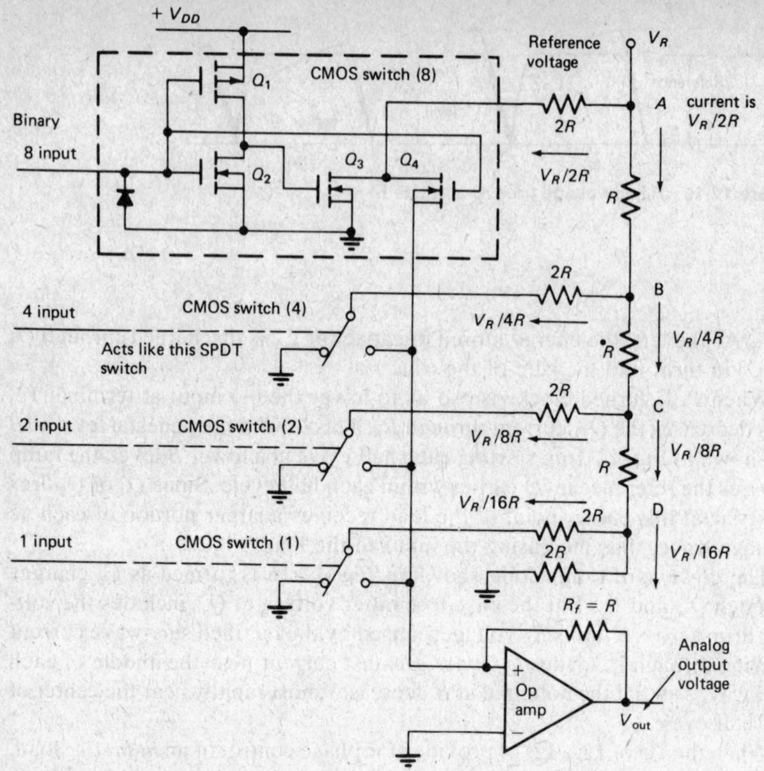

Figure 12-17 4-bit digital-to-analog converter using CMOS SPDT current-steering switches.

number is received, we may need to express it in analog form or in terms of a voltage level. This conversion is performed by the digital-to-analog converter, one form of which is shown in Fig. 12-17. Here note that digital information can be coded in different ways; the method described in Sec. 10-1 is the pure binary code frequently used. Other codes include the binary-coded decimal (BCD) or the octal code, as is discussed in Sec. 13-2. So the converter must be set up to receive the proper binary code.

For simplicity we show a 4-bit DAC, but in practice we add more CMOS switches and resistors to convert the 10 or more bits of a binary number into an analog quantity. A CMOS switch is used for the 8 binary input at the top of Fig. 12-17, but each of the 4, 2, and 1 inputs uses a simple single-pole double-throw (SPDT) switch that gives action equivalent to the CMOS. In the CMOS switch, Q_1 and Q_2 form an inverter similar to Fig. 11-11. When the 8 input is 0, now Q_1 and Q_3 conduct and thus they steer the current from V_R through the $2R$ resistor directly to ground. ($2R$ has twice the resistance of resistor R.) When the 8 input is 1, now Q_2 and Q_4 conduct, steering the current from V_R into the op amp input. This op amp input is held very near to ground potential so that, for either setting of the "switch," the current through the $2R$ resistor is at a constant value of $V_R / 2R$.

At the right in Fig. 12-17, the network of R and $2R$ resistors forces the current from V_R to divide into two equal parts at each right-hand junction A, B, C, or D. This division is easy to see at junction D; but at C note that the total resistance below C is equal to $2R$ so that the current divides into equal parts at C also.

As an example, if the binary input is 1011 (for the decimal number 11), this signal appears at the same time at each of the four inputs (as is explained in Sec. 10-21); this sets the switches for 8 input, 2 input, and 1 input so that they steer the current into the op amp (at bottom of Fig. 12-17). The current received is $I = V_R/2R + V_R/8R + V_R/16R$. All this current must pass through the feedback resistor R_f since almost no current can enter the input of the op amp. The output analog voltage is determined by the voltage drop across R_f, so

$$V_{out} = -R_f\left(\frac{V_R}{2R} + \frac{V_R}{8R} + \frac{V_R}{16R}\right)$$

When $R_f = R$ and V_R to ground is 10 volts, a binary input of 1011 produces the analog output

$$V_{out}\text{ (to ground)} = 10\ (^1/_2 + {}^1/_8 + {}^1/_{16}) = 6.875\text{ V}$$

12-11 ANALOG-TO-DIGITAL CONVERTER (ADC)

As a reverse of the situation of Sec. 12-10, we often need to obtain analog data (such as a temperature or pressure) but to transmit such data in digital form; thus an analog-to-digital or A/D converter is used. One such converter (for use with a digital voltmeter in Sec. 31-6) may be too slow for most industrial applications; so we often use a method called successive approximation, later in this section. We use here the expression "most significant bit" (MSB) to mean that, for the 8-bit binary code, the MSB has a value of 128 but the least significant bit (LSB) has a value of 1.

The A/D converter starts to act when the analog voltage is present at the input comparator (at top of Fig. 12-18) and the START pulse is received; this pulse resets all of the output-register flip-flops (type RS) and sets the converter-running flip-flop. The clock now produces pulses into the shift register. The START pulse also enters a pulse shaper whose only purpose is to ensure that just one pulse is sent to the input of the shift register at the same time when the clock sends its first pulse. Thus a single 1 bit is loaded into the shift register; with each successive clock pulse this 1 bit progresses through the register.

After the first clock pulse the output of the shift register is 1000, con-

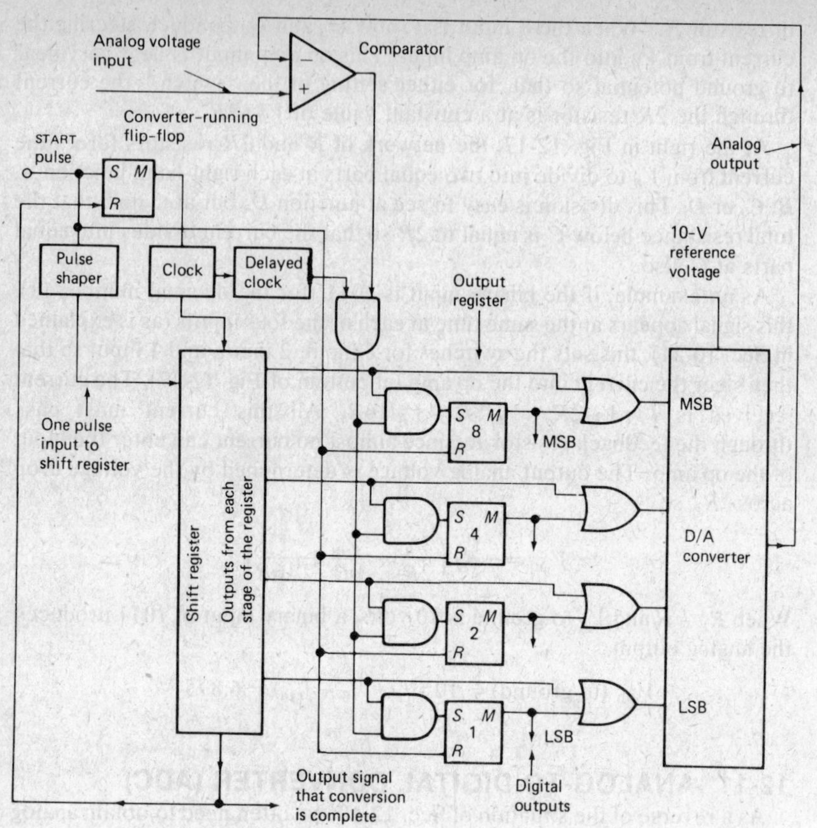

Figure 12-18 A 4-bit analog-to-digital converter using principle of successive approximations.

nected to a D/A converter like that in Sec. 12-10. Here 1000 is converted to a corresponding analog voltage (half of the reference voltage V_{CC} or 5 V) and is compared with the input analog voltage. If input is 6 V, the output of the comparator (an op amp without feedback) is very positive and sets flip-flop 8 in the output register. Note that the comparator output is led to an AND gate with a delayed clock pulse. (Because D / A converters cannot act instantly, there are times when the comparator is not receiving a correct analog voltage from the DAC; so some of the output-register flip-flops may get set unintentionally. Delaying the comparator output prevents this.)

The second clock pulse now shifts the 1 bit to the second stage so that 0100 is seen at the output of shift register. This 0100 goes to the DAC but flip-flop 8 of the output register is set so M is 1. Thus the DAC actually receives 1100 and its output is $(^1/_2 + {}^1/_4)$ 10 V or 7.5 V. In this case the comparator output is 0, since the input voltage is less than 0.5 V. Therefore, output-register flip-flop 4 will not be set, and we start another approximation.

The third clock pulse again shifts the register so that the output is 0010. The output register has 1000 stored in its flip-flops so the DAC receives an input of 0010 + 1000 = 1010 and its output now is $(^1/_2 + {}^1/_8)$ 10 V = 6.25V. Again the comparator output is 0; flip-flop 2 is not set. The fourth clock pulse changes the shift-register output to 0001 which, added to the 1000 output of the output register, puts 1001 into the DAC. The DAC output is now $(^1/_2 + {}^1/_{16})$ 10 V = 5.625 V, which is less than the input of 6 V. Therefore, flip-flop 1 is set. The next or fifth clock pulse shifts the register again so that the conversion-complete signal becomes true. (Note we do not use any binary output from the output register until the conversion-complete signal is true.) The error between the analog input voltage of 6.0 V and the binary 1001 equivalent of 5.625 V can be decreased by using more binary bits.

12-12 SAMPLE-AND-HOLD

During the time in which an A/D converter makes its conversion, the analog input signal voltage probably has changed. To prevent large resulting errors, the sample-and-hold circuit of Fig. 12-19 is used to store the analog input voltage signal, whatever its value may be, for a time long enough to complete the A-to-D conversion. Basically a high-quality capacitor can do this task as shown in Fig. 12-19*a*; however, this capacitor could draw too much current from V_{in}, and if the ADC input impedance is low, the capacitor would quickly discharge.

Thus we use op amp *A* in Fig. 12-19*b* to prevent overloading the source of V_{in} and use op amp *B* to prevent discharge from the capacitor. The gain of this circuit is 1, since $R_f = 0$ and, from Fig. 12-9,

$$\frac{V_{out}}{V_{in}} = 1 + \frac{R_f}{R_1} = 1$$

The action of switch *S* is performed by an FET.

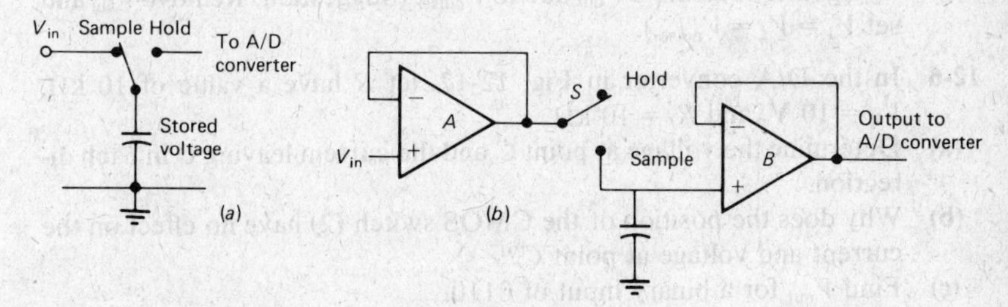

Figure 12-19 Op amps in a sample-and-hold circuit.

Problems

12-1 In an ideal op amp connected as shown in Fig. 12-7, let $R_1 = 20\text{k}\Omega$, $R_f = 40\text{k}\Omega$. $V_{in} = +2.0$ V. Find the magnitude and polarity of V_{out}.

12-2 For the connection shown in Fig. 12-9*a*, let $R_1 = 20\text{k}\Omega$, $R_f = 40\text{k}\Omega$, $V_{in} = 2.0$ V. Calculate the magnitude and polarity of V_{out}.

12-3 An ideal op amp is connected as shown in Fig. 12-9*b*, where $R_1 = R_2 = 200\text{k}\Omega$, $R_3 = 20\text{k}\Omega$, $R_f = 50\text{k}\Omega$. The power supply voltages to the op amp are $V+ = +10$ V and $V- = -10$ V.

(a) Calculate the magnitude and polarity of V_{out} when $V_1 = +10.0$ V, $V_2 = +8.0$ V, $V_3 = 0.5$ V.

(b) If $V_1 = -10.0$ V and $V_2 = 0.0$ V, determine the maximum plus value for V_3 without saturating the op amp. (For the ideal op amp, saturation occurs when the output voltage is almost equal to either supply voltage.)

12-4 An ideal op amp is connected as shown in Fig. 12-10*a*, where $R_1 = 500\text{k}\Omega$ and $C_2 = 1.0\ \mu\text{F}$. The supply voltages are +10 V and −10 V.

(a) Determine the magnitude and polarity of V_{out} after 1.0 sec if V_{in} turns on at 0 sec and remains constant at 1 V. The capacitor had no previous charge.

(b) How long can V_{in} be at 1 V until the op amp saturates? (see note in Prob. 12-3*b*).

(c) If we wish V_{out} to decrease at a uniform rate from +6 V to −4 V in 30 sec with $V_{in} = 0.2$ V and $R_1 = 500\text{k}\Omega$, calculate the value needed for C_2.

12-5 In the differential instrumentation amplifier in Fig. 12-11, let $R_1 = R_2 = 10\text{k}\Omega$, and $R_3 = R_4 = 100\text{k}\Omega$. A signal voltage $V_{sig} = 0.01$ V is connected across inputs V_1 and V_2. ($V_{sig} = V_2 - V_1$.)

(a) Calculate V_{out} caused by V_{sig}.

(b) Suppose R_4 is not properly matched to R_3, so R_4 is only $95\text{k}\Omega$. A noise voltage ($V_{noise} = 1.0$ V relative to ground) acts on both inputs V_1 and V_2 together. Calculate V_{out} due to V_{noise}. (Suggestion: Remove V_{sig} and set $V_1 = V_2 = V_{noise}$.)

12-6 In the D/A converter in Fig. 12-17, let R have a value of $10\ \text{k}\Omega$, $V_R = 10$ V, and $R_f = 10\ \text{k}\Omega$.

(a) Determine the voltage at point C and the current leaving C in each direction.

(b) Why does the position of the CMOS switch (2) have no effect on the current and voltage at point C?

(c) Find V_{out} for a binary input of 0110.

12-7 For the A/D converter in Fig. 12-18, (*a*) determine the binary output for an analog input of 4.0 V (reference is +10 V). (*b*) How much error exists between the 4.0-V input and the equivalent voltage represented by the binary output from part (*a*) ?

12-8 Repeat Prob. 12-7 for an A/D converter that converts to an 8-bit binary code instead of the 4-bit code used in Prob. 6.

13 INFORMATION CONVERSION

Information consists of data which presently are or will become useful to us in order to perform a task. In an industrial process this can be an amount of output or an input quantity of material, temperature, or pressure. This chapter describes how the information is transported to the place where it is useful or is converted into usable forms. This is like transferring printed information from this page into the mind of the reader; the whole page is available at one time but the reader must scan the page line by line. Printed words are converted to light patterns and into electrical pulses within the reader's head to be stored for future action.

In Secs. 12-10 and 12-11 we see how converters can change the form of information; but also we must be able to control the speed, voltage levels, and encoding systems in a reliable fashion.

13-1 INPUT-OUTPUT EQUIPMENT

In a typical machine (Fig. 13-1) using digital control circuits, we acquire data from several locations (such as limit switches, keyboards, and meters) and then send them to a central processing unit (CPU). Within the CPU we manipulate the data to determine what the machine should do next; then we send signals out to other locations (such as motor starters, valves, or solenoids) to make the machine work properly. The block diagram in Fig. 13-1 is simplified to show the basic parts of the system. All parts except CPU and the memory are called input-output equipment (I/O) or peripheral equipment. The CPU is discussed in Sec. 15-2.

In order to reduce the number of wires entering the CPU, a data bus (here consisting of a few wires) interconnects all the I/O equipment; therefore, the I/O equipment must speak the same language and also speak one at a time so as not to confuse the CPU. To select which device is talking into the data bus, and also which device is listening, another set of wires (called the

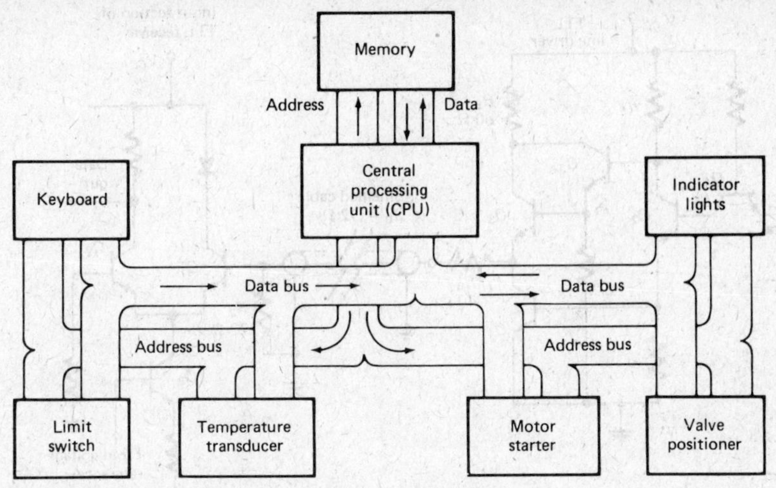

Figure 13-1 Block diagram of a machine-control system.

address bus) is interconnected to all I/O equipment. The address bus tells each I/O unit to speak or to listen only when properly addressed.

An *interface* is the boundary between two equipments. If these two equipments are not built to be directly connected together, then some type of interface circuit is needed so that data can pass from one equipment to the other. Interface circuits include serial-parallel converters, DACs,[12-10] ADCs,[12-11] and line drivers (special circuits used to send data through long wires).

13-2 SENDING SIGNALS OVER LONG LINES

It is difficult to send data at high speeds over lines longer than one meter without the aid of special line-driving circuits. Long lines add a large capacitive load on the sending circuit (see Sec. 11-3) and receive electrical noise from surrounding wires and equipment. Also, within long lines we have echoes or reflections that can be confused with the real signal. The problem is like trying to understand someone who speaks rapidly from the opposite end of a large noisy room. All wires have these effects, but they are significant only if the line is longer than a few centimeters. Thus driving and receiving circuits are used for lines longer than a few centimeters.

The single-transistor output circuit (seen as Q_1 in Fig. 11-2) is not suitable for sending signals over long lines; so we use circuits having active pull-up (as in Figs. 11-3 and 11-4) which are better able to drive the capacitance of the line. Active pull-up also ensures that the resistance of the line to ground or to V_{CC} is never more than that of R_5 (in Fig. 11-4c). This prevents a small amount of electrical noise energy from making a large voltage change in the

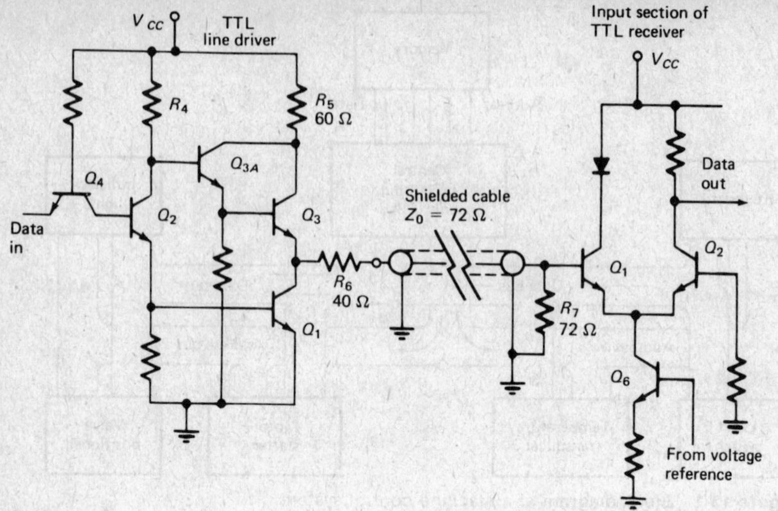

Figure 13-2 Line driver and receiver.

wire; a circuit that has low resistance to ground is little affected by electrical noise. However, to get even better isolation from noise, we wrap a grounded conductor around the insulation of the signal wire. This is called a shielded line; where special insulation and spacing are used, it is a coaxial cable. This type of cable can transmit high-speed data over long distances. Often merely twisting the signal wire with a ground wire gives good isolation from noise. All three types of conductor (signal wire and grounded conductor) have a characteristic impedance (Z_0 in Fig. 13-2) that is determined mainly by the diameters of the wires, their spacing from each other, and the insulating material. For a very great length of line, Z_0 is the impedance measured from the signal wire to the grounded wire, and usually ranges in value from 50 to 150 ohms. Though we think of fast movement of electrical signals, we still require a short time for a current to travel from one end of wire to the other end. The line-driver circuit of Fig. 13-2 sends a current pulse through a long line without knowing what is at the other end. If the line ends with an open circuit, the current pulse cannot go beyond this point; so it is reflected back, as when a thrown ball hits a solid wall, it bounces back. If we connect a resistor (equal to the characteristic impedance) at the end of the line, between the signal wire and ground, this prevents the reflection, for this is like trying to bounce the ball from a pile of feathers.

To prevent all such reflections, we must terminate both ends of the line with a resistor closely equal to the Z_0 of the line. Most line receiving circuits do not already provide the correct resistance; thus more resistors may be added, like R_7 in Fig. 13-2. This figure shows the output section of the driver circuit which is like that of Fig. 11-4 except that R_5 is lowered to 60 ohms; we add Q_{3A} to provide greater base current for Q_3, and we add R_6 of 40 ohms. (The forward drop of D_4 in Fig. 11-4 is replaced by the V_{BE} of Q_{3A}.) Here R_6 is a compromise value since Z_0 cannot be matched exactly for both conditions (as when Q_3 conducts or when Q_1 conducts); we accept this if $R_7 = Z_0$ on the receiving end of the line. At the receiving end, the input section of the receiver circuit shown in Fig. 13-2 is like the differential input section of the op amp in Fig. 12-8. Here the input impedance of the receiver is high; so R_7 must be added to terminate the line. In this system the ground potential must be exactly the same at both ends; where this is not true, we must use more complex systems.

13-3 THREE-STATE LOGIC

We must modify the line driver of Fig. 13-2 when we connect two or more drivers to a single line or bus. If the output of one driver (like that of Fig. 13-2) is high (with Q_3 on) and a second driver connected to the same line is low (with Q_1 on), a high-current path exists from V_{CC} to ground and Q_1 is destroyed. Therefore, we permit a third state in the driver in Fig. 13-3 (where neither Q_1 nor Q_3 is conducting); we say that the circuit is in the high-impedance (Hi-Z) state. Here the line can go high or low as demanded by one driver if all other drivers on the line are in Hi-Z state.

The circuit operates as in Fig. 13-2 while Q_7 is fully off. But a $+V$ voltage at the DISABLE input (at left in Fig. 13-3) raises the base voltage of Q_6,

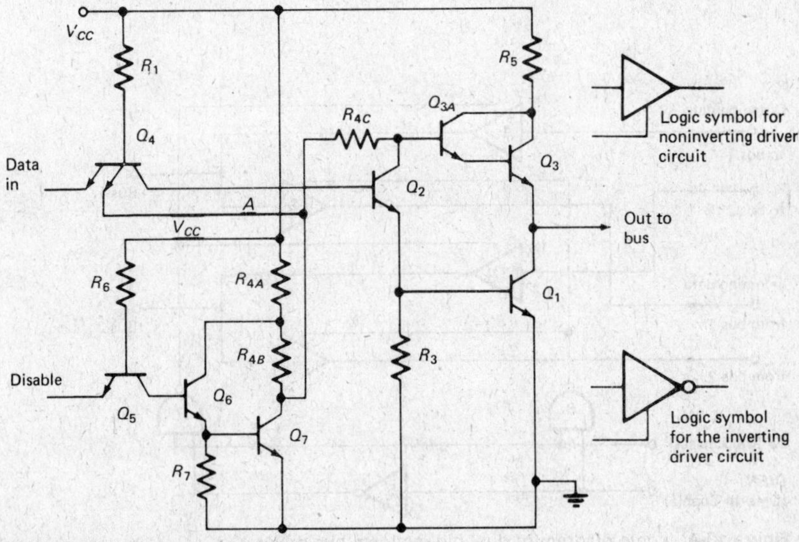

Figure 13-3 Three-state bus driver.

which also turns Q_7 on. While Q_7 conducts, the bases of Q_3 and Q_{3A} are held near 0.7 V; so they are off. Point A also is held near 0.7 V; so both Q_2 and Q_1 are off. Thus the +DISABLE signal prevents this three-state driver from affecting the data sent by other drivers on the same bus.

Since messages may be carried in either direction on the data bus, the same wires in Fig. 13-1, which at one moment send data out from the CPU, at another moment bring data in. Thus we must use a bidirectional bus driver to separate the incoming data from the outgoing data. In Fig. 13-4, such a driver for two buses uses the three-state driver circuit of Fig. 13-3 for drivers 1 and 3. But drivers 2 and 4 are receiving-type circuits (like that shown at the right of Fig. 13-2) with the addition of an output section having the three-state feature. The IC manufacturer places four such bidirectional bus-driver circuits on a single integrated-circuit chip and calls it a 4-bit parallel bidirectional bus driver. In Fig. 13-4 the entire chip is turned on by a true signal at the CS (chip select) input. Then a true signal at the DIEN (data-in enable) input lets the NAND gate 6 enable the drivers 2 and 4 to *receive* data from the bus. But a false signal at DIEN is inverted at inverter 5 so that, with CS true, the NAND gate 7 enables the drivers 1 and 3 to *send* data. Thus the CS and DIEN signals tell the chip when to speak and when to listen.

13-4 PARALLEL-TO-SERIAL CONVERTER

While Sec. 10-21 shows that we can send binary numbers faster over several wires in parallel, this method costs more when the sending distance exceeds about 50 meters. So we may need to send the binary numbers

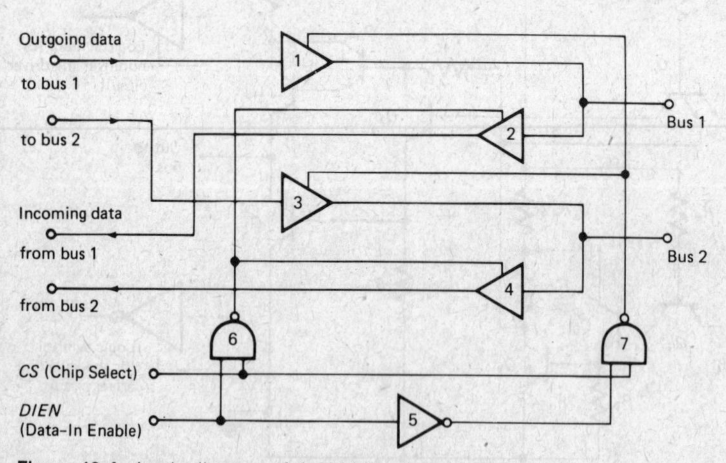

Figure 13-4 Logic diagram of dual bidirectional bus driver.

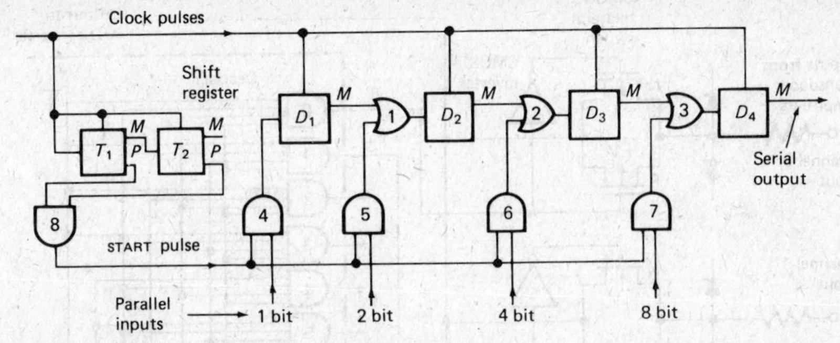

Figure 13-5 Parallel-to-serial converter.

serially where the amount of information to be sent per second is low enough so that one line can transmit it reliably.

The parallel-to-serial converter in Fig. 13-5 uses a shift register like that in Fig. 10-17 except that we place OR gates 1, 2, and 3 (Sec. 10-10) between each pair of D flip-flops so that each stage D_2, D_3, or D_4 receives an input from either the preceding stage (at M) or from the parallel-input lines. Initially the clock pulses cause the shift register to shift only 0s until the START pulse has occurred. The START pulse is the same as a clock pulse that occurs at a time when an 8-bit should enter the serial output. We obtain the START pulse from a count-to-four circuit like Fig. 10-17.

When we convert the binary number 1101 into serial form, the input lines representing the 8, 4, and 1 bits have the value of 1 at the time when a start pulse occurs. The outputs of AND gates 4, 6, and 7 become 1, and if the clock pulse occurs simultaneously with the start pulse, this shifts the bits into the D_1, D_3, and D_4 flip-flops. As soon as the clock pulse ends (as the clock line becomes 0) the output of D_4 causes the serial output line to go high, indicating that an 8 bit is present. No more start pulses occur during the next three clock pulses; thus these three clock pulses shift the contents of D_1, D_2, and D_3 out to the serial output.

13-5 MULTIPLEXERS (MUX)

In Fig. 13-1 the output signal of the temperature transducer is usually in analog form and is converted by an A/D converter (ADC) to a digital signal to be sent via the data bus to the CPU. In a large system there are several similar transducers, each needing A/D signal conversion. Most ADCs can make thousands of conversions per second, but most temperatures do not change fast enough to require such frequent readings. Thus one ADC can convert the analog signals of several transducers; we say it is *multiplexed*. The circuit of Fig. 13-6 switches the ADC input from one transducer to another; it is an *analog multiplexer*.

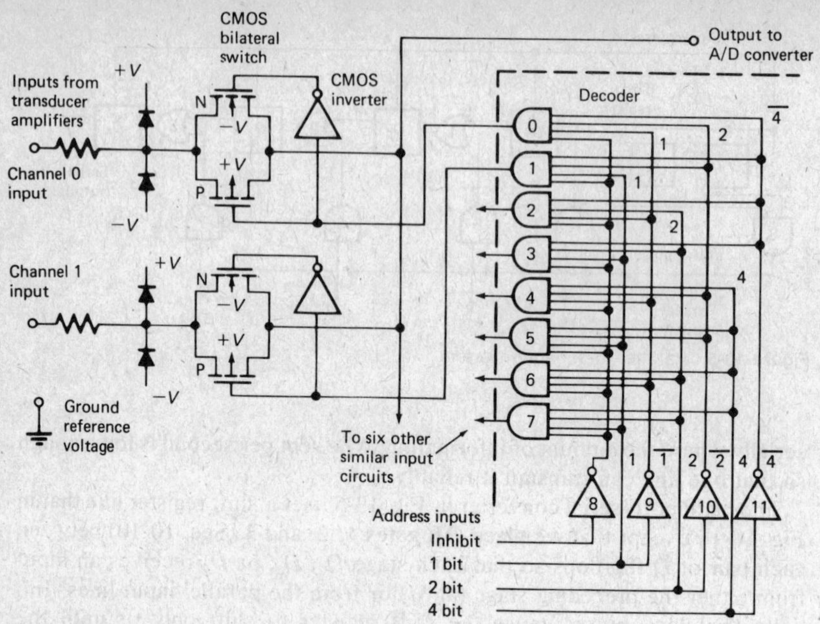

Figure 13-6 8-channel analog multiplexer.

At the left of Fig. 13-6, the CMOS switch section shows bilateral switches which allow current to flow equally well in either direction; this differs from the CMOS switch shown in Fig. 12-17 where current flows in one direction only. If we are assured of having analog voltages positive to ground only, then we need just the N-channel MOSFET. Since this is a CMOS switch, the P-channel device allows this circuit to be used without regard to the polarity of the analog signal. One of eight input analog channels is connected to the output at a time depending on which of the eight AND gates is true in the decoder section at the right.

The decoder in Fig. 13-6 converts a three-digit binary number (feeding in parallel into the address inputs) to a true signal from the AND gate and has the same number as the decimal equivalent. For example, the 1-bit and 4-bit address lines (at bottom) are connected to AND gates 5 and 7. A 0 input on the 2-bit address line is inverted by 10 to give the true signal to gate 5 but not to gate 7; thus a binary number of 101 converts to a true output from gate 5 and from no other gate. A true signal at the inhibit input is inverted (by inverter 8) to prevent any of the AND gates from becoming true; thus it inhibits any output from this circuit.

We can use this circuit for a digital multiplexer, although simpler circuits exist for this purpose. Here the digital multiplexer takes the place of three-state logic as shown in Fig. 13-7*a*, where two sources transmit digital infor-

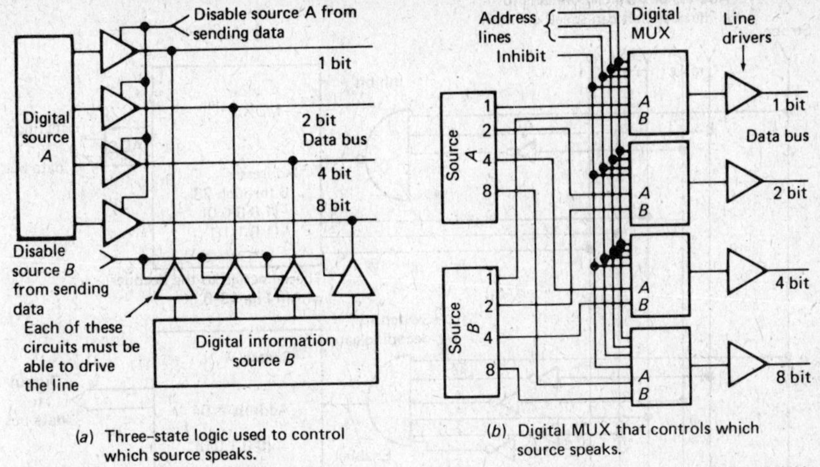

Figure 13-7 (*a*) Three-level logic used to control which source speaks; (*b*) digital MUX that controls which source speaks.

mation over one four-wire data bus; Fig. 13-7*b* shows how the multiplexer does the same job. One MUX is required for each outgoing line.

13-6 ADDRESSING

We address a system when we select the route of a binary message as it moves from a specified source until it reaches a specified point in the system. Section 13-1 shows that we need to select or control which source is to transmit information. In Fig. 13-6 the decoder section shows how a binary number sent on the address bus controls the sources. The complete address of a moderate-sized system may require eight binary digits (or 256 address locations). Each location has a decoding gate to convert the binary numbers to a YES or NO command to speak (or listen).

Figure 13-8 shows a simple five-line address bus (or 32 locations) and shows how the 8-input MUX of Fig. 13-6 is addressed. The MUX has an address for each input and has its own decoder for the 1-, 2-, and 4-bit lines. The input NAND requires a 16-bit signal, an $\overline{8}$ signal (where the bar above 8 means that the 8-bit signal is inverted, as in Sec. 10-17), and a strobe signal. This strobe signal becomes true after all the address lines have finished changing to the next address. (Some address lines change state faster than others and cause false addresses, but the strobe prevents any decoder or gate from reading the lines until they are stable.)

The decoding gate for switch *A* in Fig. 13-8 requires the input signals $\overline{16}$, $\overline{8}$, 4, $\overline{2}$, $\overline{1}$ (corresponding to the binary number 00100) to properly address switch *A* at (04). The separate input inverters transform 0s to 1s on the 1, 2, 8, and 16 address lines so that the AND gate will give an enable signal.

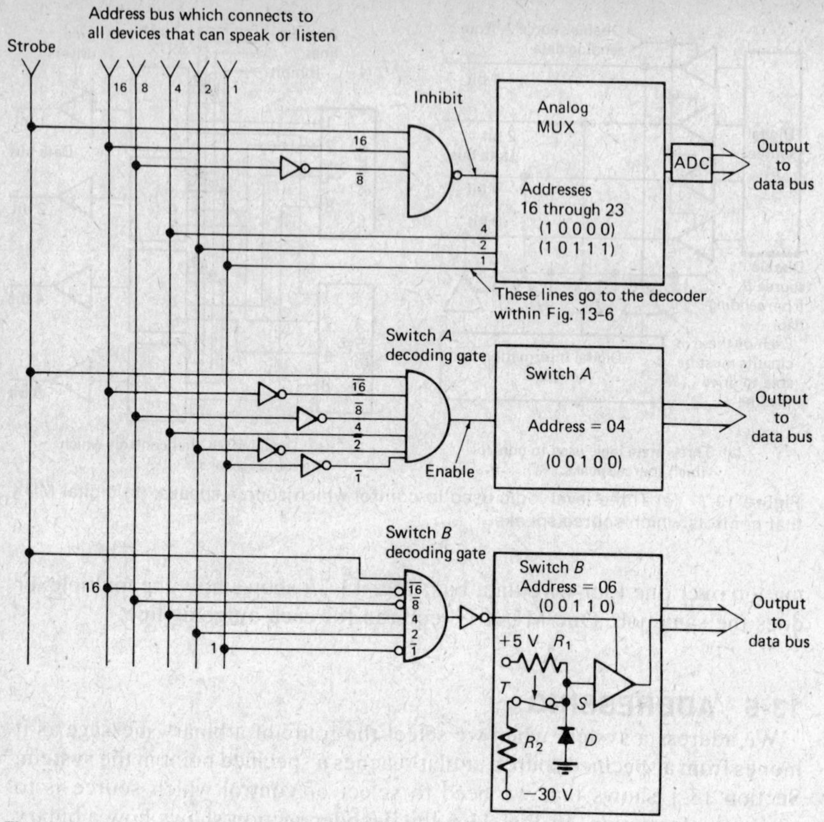

Figure 13-8 A method for addressing each I/O device.

The decoding gate at the left switch *B* in Fig. 13-8 requires the input signals $\overline{16}$, $\overline{8}$, r, 2, $\overline{1}$ to give the decimal address 06. The symbol for the AND gate used in the decoder shows small circles at some inputs. Such a circle means that the input is inverted (not by a separate inverter circuit as shown for switch *A*, but by an inverting transistor within the AND gate itself).

The circuit shown within switch *B* of Fig. 13-8 uses a noninverting three-state bus driver wherein the input comes from a mechanical switch. The three-state driver requires a low 0-V level to enable it (to take it out of the Hi-*Z* state); so we add the inverter to the output of the decoding gate. In low-voltage low-current circuits switches may not be reliable since the power level is too low to penetrate the oxides and atmospheric contaminants on the contact surfaces. So we gold-plate the contacts or seal them in inert gas so that the contact surfaces stay clean and conducting. But this is not possible for many heavy-duty industrial switches; so a voltage "wetting" circuit is used, as described next.

A mechanical switch used infrequently should be opened rather than closed to operate the circuit, because nonconducting particles can be caught on the open contact surfaces. While switch B is closed (at lower right in Fig. 13-8) points T and S are held slightly above ground by diode D; the output of the driver is 0 whenever switch B is addressed. When the switch is pushed open, point S now goes toward +5 V to make the driver output 1 when addressed. Meanwhile point T is at −30 V so that the voltage between the open contacts is 35 V, and sufficient to penetrate the oxides on the contacts when they reclose. (Diode D is a fast-acting type to prevent voltage damage to the input of the driver.)

13-7 BUFFERING

In general, a buffer is another name for an interface circuit; it allows signals to pass from one circuit to another when these circuits are incompatible without the buffer. A common example exists when two dissimilar types of logic must operate together, such as TTL and ECL. Circuits called *level translators* are used because the voltage that represents a 1 or 0 in ECL (typically − 0.75 V or −1.60 V) is different from those voltages in TTL (typically +2.0 V or +0.8 V). (But DTL and TTL families can work together, needing no translators.) Also many MOS and CMOS circuits are made to work with TTL so that system designers may obtain the best advantages of each logic family.

We need another type of buffering when there is a conflict in time. If we send data to a device faster than it can use them, those data must be stored temporarily in a buffer register. In Fig. 13-1 the motor in the valve positioner cannot move the valve as rapidly as the data are sent on the data bus. Thus the incoming data on all the lines are stored in flip-flops at the valve positioner so that the data bus can be used for other messages while the positioner is moving the valve to a new setting.

13-8 MONOSTABLE MULTIVIBRATOR REBUILDS A PULSE

Electrical signals sent from one circuit to another often become distorted (as in signal A in Fig. 13-9) and may cause improper operation of some logic circuits. So we use a monostable multivibrator circuit to restore the square edges to the pulse and to make all pulses have the same length or time duration, as shown in signal W below. The monostable vibrator in Fig. 13-9 is like the flip-flop in Fig. 10-13*a* (called a bistable multivibrator); but we alter it by placing capacitor C, resistor R, and diode F in the line between M and the input to gate 2. This combination of C, R, and F gives this circuit one stable state wherein gate 2 automatically turns off after each pulse at input A.

In Fig. 13-9, let a sequence of pulses enter the NAND gate 1 at input A. When the input level rises above the threshold voltage (shown as a dotted line

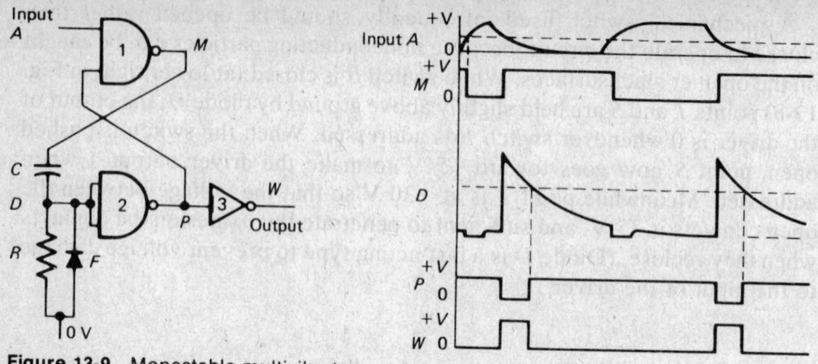

Figure 13-9 Monostable multivibrator.

in signal *A* at the right), the output of NAND gate 1 is 0 V (because the level at *P* is automatically set to +V when gate 2 is off). The resulting pulses at *M* have square edges but vary in length (which is not desirable in some logic circuits). Both sides of capacitor *C* are near zero volts when the output *M* of gate 1 goes to 0. So when gate 1 output *M* returns to +V, the input *D* of gate 2 also becomes +*V* momentarily. This causes gate-2 output *P* to become 0 V. The plus charge on capacitor *C* drains toward 0 V through resistor *R* so that, after a short time, the voltage at *D* drops below the threshold voltage of gate 2 (the dashed line shown with the *D*-signal waveform at the right in Fig. 13-9). So whenever gate-1 output is +*V*, then gate-2 output becomes 0 V for a short time as determined by the values of *R* and *C*. Thus gate-2 output is 0 V for a uniform time regardless of the length of the pulse at the input. (This fixed length of time or time delay causes some persons to call this a delay multivibrator.) In Fig. 13-9 we add inverter 3 so that the output at *W* consists of positive-going pulses, like input *A*. Each logic family has a special monostable-multivibrator chip that performs this same function.

13-9 BCD AND OCTAL BINARY CODES

Section 10-1 shows how the pure binary code can express a decimal number. But we also frequently use the binary-coded decimal (BCD) code and the octal code. (The BCD code requires more binary bits than the pure binary code; however, BCD is more convenient to convert from decimal numbers.) In the BCD code, the decimal numbers 1 to 9 use the same binary four-column numbers as are tabulated late in Sec. 10-1; these appear again here at the top of Table 13-1. Decimals 10 to 19 again use these same binary numbers, but each now is preceded by 0001; thus 13 has the BCD code value of 0001 0011. At decimal 20 to 29 we again repeat the binary four-column numbers but the preceding 0001 changes to 0010. At decimal 100 a third group of four digits is added before the other two columns, so

TABLE 13-1

Decimal number	BCD code	Decimal number	BCD code	Decimal number	BCD code
0	0000	10	0001 0000	20	0010 0000
1	0001	11	0001 0001	31	0011 0001
2	0010	12	0001 0010	42	0100 0010
3	0011	13	0001 0011	54	0101 0100
4	0100	14	0001 0100	65	0110 0101
5	0101	15	0001 0101	78	0111 1000
6	0110	16	0001 0110	94	1001 0100
7	0111	17	0001 0111	147	0001 0100 0111
8	1000	18	0001 1000	316	0011 0001 0110
9	1001	19	0001 1001	985	1001 1000 0101

that the decimal value 147 is shown as digital 0001 0100 0111. Thus each decimal digit is itself converted to binary form.

For the octal code we use Table 13-2, which (for the eight octal values 0 to 7) retains the same binary values as in Table 13-1. The decimal digits 8 and 9 are not permitted in the octal code. For octal values 10 to 17 we repeat the binary values used for 0 to 7, but we add 001 ahead in a new column; this becomes 010 at octal 20, or becomes 110 at octal 60.

To count nine items (decimal) we use the ninth numerical row or position in Table 13-2 which is at octal number 11 and whose binary code is 001 001; we note that this is the same as the 01001 shown for decimal value 9 in the table in Sec. 10-1 except that the binary digits now are arranged in groups of three.

A single binary digit is called a bit; it is the smallest possible division of in-

TABLE 13-2

Octal number	Binary code	Octal number	Binary code
0	000	10	001 000
1	001	11	001 001
2	010	12	001 010
3	011	13	001 011
4	100	14	001 100
5	101	15	001 101
6	110	16	001 110
7	111	17	001 111
		20	010 000
		60	110 000

formation.[10-1] A combination of bits (usually from 4 to 16) is called a binary word; in Sec. 15-3 a group of eight bits is called a byte. A byte can contain one alphanumeric character or two BCD digits or, in pure binary form, can represent decimal numbers up to 255. Binary information transmitted to another location is sent at a given number of bits per second (bps); for example, a standard telephone line can transmit binary data at 2400 bps.

So far we describe only numeric codes. In large systems we may desire to encode letters of the alphabet and punctuation into a binary code; this is called an alphanumeric code. We need seven binary digits to fully describe the complete set of letters (upper- and lowercase) and punctuation. A standard form of alphanumeric code is the ASCII code (American Standard Code for Information Interchange), which is used for communication between equipments made by different manufacturers. (A hexadecimal code is described in Sec. 15-5.)

13-10 NUMERIC DISPLAY OR LIGHTED NUMBER INDICATORS

Often the output number of a calculator or meter (such as the digital voltmeter in Sec. 31-6) will consist of several decimal digits. Each lighted digit is produced by energizing certain of the seven segments of light-emitting diodes (LEDs) shown (at the left in Fig. 13-10) as segment A, B, C, D, E, F, G (the decimal point DP is an eighth segment). Each segment requires a transistor driver circuit that supplies 20 to 100 mA to light the LEDs. To display four decimal digits, we need 4×8 or 32 driver circuits. To display more than four digits, the high cost (of a driver for each segment) makes us prefer a multiplexing system as is shown in Fig. 13-11; here only one digit is lighted at one instant, but other digits are lighted in rapid sequence so that the human eye receives the effect as if all digits are continuously lighted. Now we need only eight driver circuits S for the segments, but we need also a circuit P (at top of Fig. 13-11) to light each digit inthe proper sequence.

Near the center of Fig. 13-11, digit 1 shows the internal connections and diodes of a seven-segment decimal indicator. All the anodes inside digit 1 are connected through one wire to the anode driver transistor Q_1. To light the segment D (bottom of digit 1), we turn on Q_1 and Q_D in S (the segment decoder and driver IC). To light the numeral 5, we simultaneously turn on

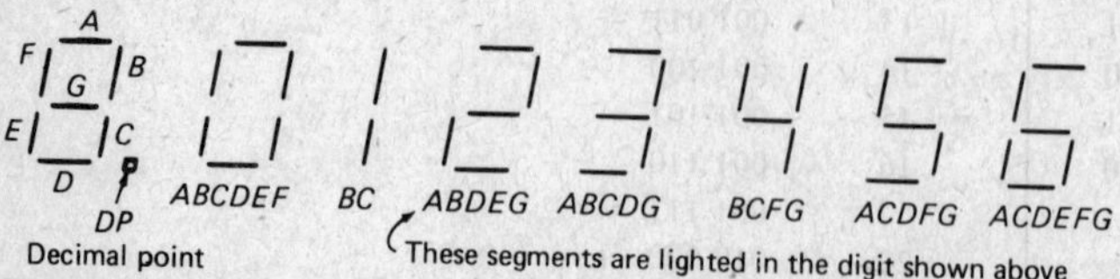

A
F B
G
E C
D DP
Decimal point

ABCDEF BC ABDEG ABCDG BCFG ACDFG ACDEFG

These segments are lighted in the digit shown above

Figure 13-10 This seven-segment indicator forms any single decimal digit.

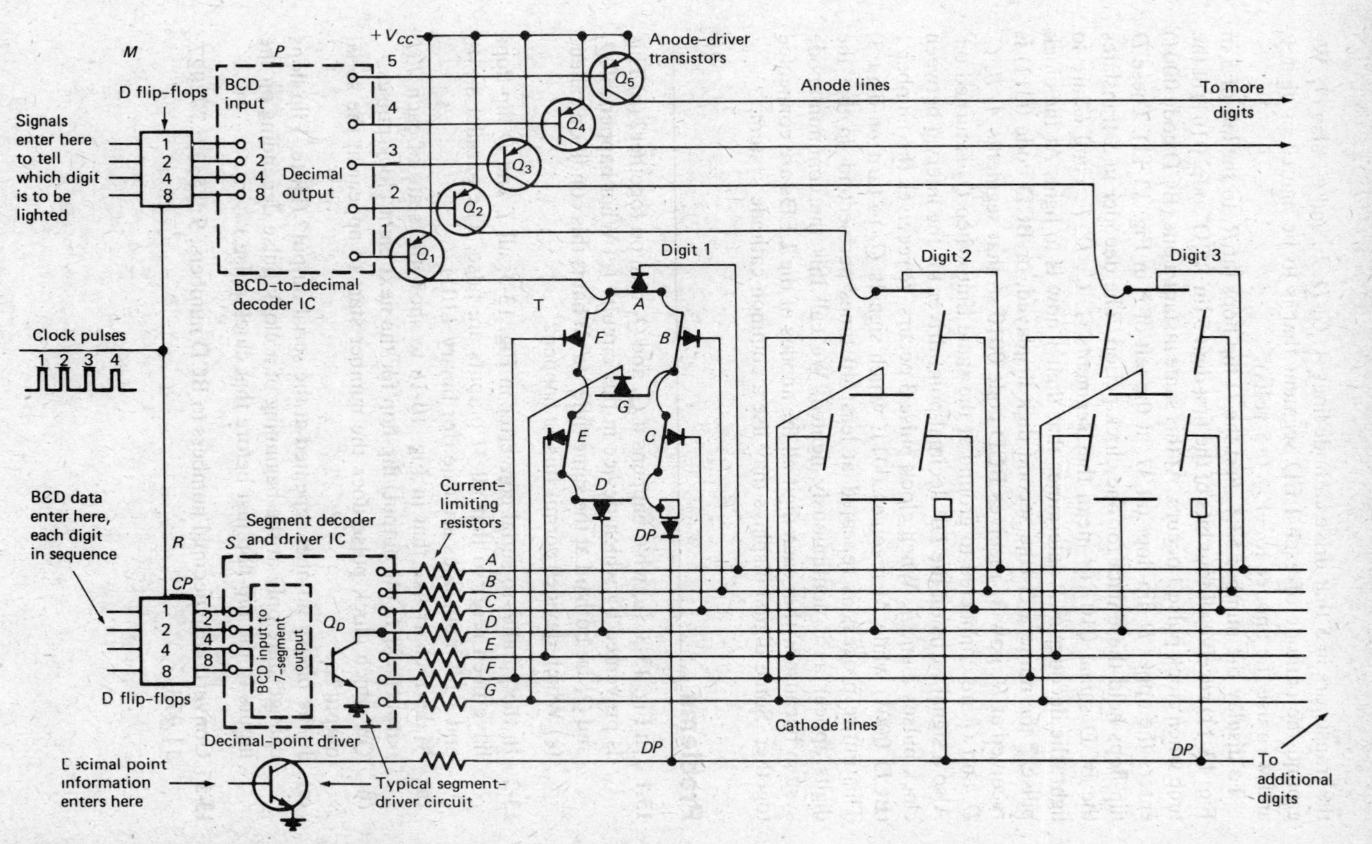

Figure 13-11 A multiplexed LED numeric display.

the transistors in S that drive cathode lines A, C, D, F, and G, also Q_1. We ground the cathode of each LED segment that is to be lighted in digit 1, and we raise the anodes to $+V_{CC}$ (+5 volts).

To display the number 53.1, first the D flip-flops (at R, to the left of S in Fig. 13-11) receive all four bits of the first digit 5 (in BCD code, 0101) at the time when clock pulse 1 occurs. At this same instant a one (BCD code 0001) enters the upper D flip-flops (at M, at the left of P in Fig. 13-11). These D flip-flops hold these data for one clock period. The decoder in S translates the BCD signal 0101 to mean that segments A, C, D, F, and G are to light; the decoder in P determines that digit 1 now is to light. At the clock pulse 2 the numeral 3 (the second digit displayed, or BCD code 0011) is received at R; now M receives BCD code 0010 so that segments A, B, C, D, and G are connected to ground at the same time when Q_2 is turned on. Also a signal turns on the DP decimal-point driver for the interval between clock pulses 2 and 3. When clock pulse 3 occurs, R receives the number 1 (BCD 0001) while M receives 0011, which signals Q_3 to turn on digit 3. This entire process is repeated at least 40 times per second so that the digits appear as if continuously lighted. We call this the common-anode system because within each digit all the anodes of the LEDs are connected together. Some digital displays may use a common-cathode system.

Problems

13-1 In Fig. 13-3, (*a*) what happens if Q_1 and Q_3 turn on together? (*b*) This is prevented by which device in this circuit? (*c*) What happens if Q_1 and Q_3 are both off at the same time? (*d*) What is this condition called? (*e*) Which devices permit this to happen?

13-2 In the parallel-to-serial converter in Fig. 13-5, all T and D flip-flops have been reset so that all M outputs are false. The parallel 8-, 4-, and 1-bit input lines are true (for binary 1101).

(a) Make a chart like that in Fig. 10-16 to show the state of each T (P output) and D (M output) flip-flop for the next eight clock pulses.

(b) On which clock pulse does the number start to appear at the serial output?

(c) Is the binary number repeated at the serial output? (Note: Flip-flops change state only at the beginning of a clock pulse depending on the inputs to the flip-flop just before that clock pulse.)

13-3 Convert these decimal numbers to BCD numbers: 9; 15; 27; 77; 927; 11,973.

14 MEMORY SYSTEMS

Electrical calculation and control systems need to store large quantities of numbers to be used later. Section 10-16 shows that flip-flops can be used for information storage. Like those who devised better memory systems when they ran out of fingers on which to tie string, computer designers invented larger, less expensive, and more compact electronic memories than individual flip-flops. The power of a computer is related to the size of its memory and the speed with which it works; even the small hand-held calculator becomes more versatile when it has larger memory and faster speed. This chapter shows how several types of large memory work and why we need these various types. (But we do not discuss mechanical systems using punched cards or punched paper tape, since their reading circuits are like the optical isolator in Fig. 9-32 except that the card or tape passes between the light source and the phototransistor.)

14-1 SHIFT-REGISTER MEMORY

The shift register in Sec. 10-20 can store a binary number for a very long time when the output is connected back to the input so that the stored number recirculates as shown in Fig. 14-1. Here a true recirculate signal permits data to go from the output of the shift register through AND gate 1 and OR gate 2 back into the shift register. Each clock pulse advances the data through one stage of the shift register. We insert a false recirculate signal at AND gate 3 to allow a new sequence of 1s and 0s to enter from the data input and be remembered by the register. Each digit is stored in sequence; this is called a *sequentially accessed* system. Many systems use four identical shift registers when the data come to this memory on four data lines. This is called *storing the data in parallel* because the 8, 4, 2, and 1 bits of a decimal number now come out of all four registers at once.

The shift register that uses D flip-flop circuits like those in Fig. 10-15b is said to be a *static* shift register because, if the clock pulses stop, the data remain stationary in the register. A *dynamic* shift register uses dynamic

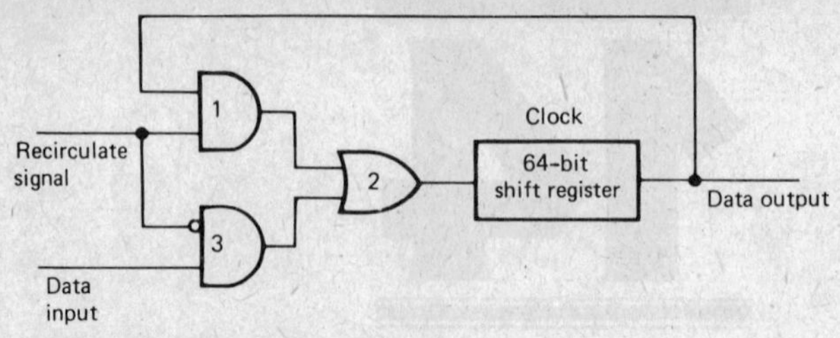

Figure 14-1 Shift-register memory.

MOS gates (Sec. 11-12) so that more stages or circuits can be put on one chip. Here the stored information disappears when the clock stops.

If several numbers are stored in a shift register, we can tell which number is coming out of the register by counting the clock pulses from the time when that certain number was put into the register. If we start to put the second number into the register at clock pulse 32, then that second number comes out 64 pulses later since this is a 64-stage shift register; thus we need a counter to keep track of the data in the shift register. This type of memory is well suited to multiplexed displays (Sec. 13-10) where one digit is displayed at a time as it emerges at the output of the shift register.

14-2 RANDOM-ACCESS MEMORY (RAM)

Using a shift-register memory, the stored data must come out in the same sequence that the data are put in, as on a conveyor; but in the random-access memory (RAM) we can obtain at random any portion of the data we need, without waiting for unneeded data to pass by. However, we must know where the desired data are stored. Each word of data has an address that tells its location in the RAM. A RAM can be made using any of the logic families, but here we discuss a RAM that uses N-channel MOS (NMOS), since this system allows designers to store as many as 4096 bits of data in one IC. (The voltages used for NMOS are the same as those used for TTL in Fig. 11-4.) The RAM also is called a read-write memory since we can both write into and read from this memory. The ROM (read-only memory in Sec. 14-3) cannot be written into, but we can read from any address in the ROM at random; thus the ROM is a special form of random-access memory.

The static RAM uses a flip-flop for each bit (as shown in Fig. 14-2). These flip-flops are arranged in a square pattern (as in Fig. 14-3) so that each flip-flop has a row address and a column address (much like a city map that counts the blocks as you go east and north).

We show a static RAM cell in Fig. 14-2; in Fig. 14-2*a*, Q_1, Q_2, and Q_3 act like resistors; Q_4 and Q_5 are the active transistors of the flip-flop. The simplified symbol for NMOS is the same as is used in the NAND gate in Fig. 11-8*c*, where the only difference in operation is that V_{DD} and V_{GG} are +5

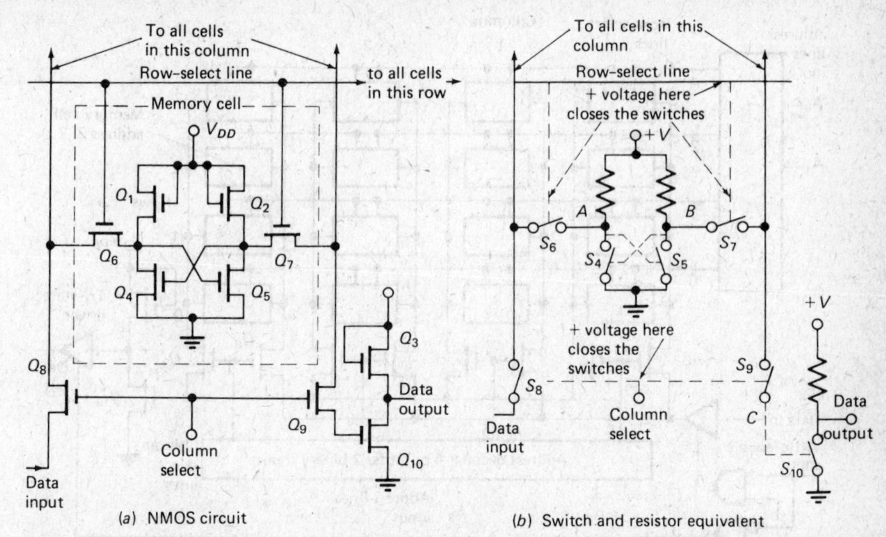

Figure 14-2 Static RAM cell connections. (*a*) NMOS circuit; (*b*) switch and resistor equivalent.

V to ground. (A gate-to-source voltage greater than +2 V will turn on an NMOS device.) We explain the action of this RAM cell in Fig. 14-2*b*, wherein we show switches S_4 to S_{10} instead of Q_4 to Q_{10}.

Assume that this memory cell is in column 3 and row 2 in a RAM that has 4 columns and 4 rows as in Fig. 14-3. To address this particular memory cell 3, 2 we must raise the voltage of column select line 3 to a value of +V; this closes switches S_8 and S_9 in Fig. 14-2*b*. At the left in Fig. 14-3 we also must raise row select line 2 to +V; this closes S_6 and S_7. If the data to be stored in this cell are a 1, then a $+V$ signal enters the data input in Fig. 14-2*b*, passing through S_8 and S_6 so as to set the flip-flop (and close S_5). This process is called *writing* into the memory. If instead a 0 is to be stored here, then the data input is at 0 V; the flip-flop is reset (S_5 is open) and the $+V$ at point B causes S_4 to close. At some later time we wish to see what is stored in memory cell 3,2; so we *read* its contents; to do this we again raise the select lines of column 3 and row 2 to $+V$. If S_5 is set closed (where this means that a 1 is stored here), the voltage at B is 0, which also is 0 V at the gate of Q_{10} or point C in Fig. 14-2*b*. Thus S_{10} is open and the voltage at the data output is $+V$ showing that a 1 is stored in address 3,2.

During those times when we do not read from or write into address 3,2, the column 3 line and row 2 line are kept at 0 V, so that they cannot both go to $+V$ at the same time. (The column 3 line may go to $+V$ when addressing some other cell on that same column; the same is true within row 2.)

Figure 14-3 shows this memory cell 3,2 in its position with other cells on the IC chip. To prepare to write data into this RAM, its address first must be

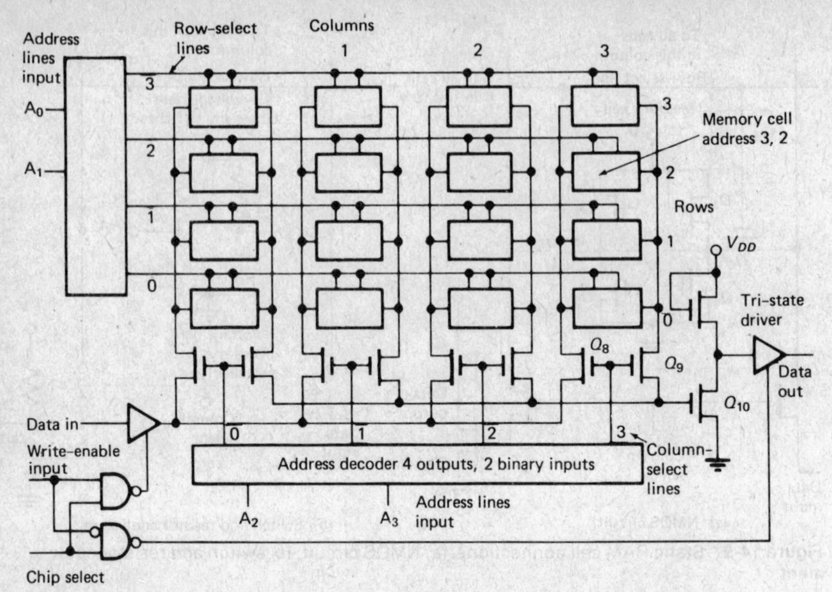

Figure 14-3 A 16-bit (4 × 4) static RAM showing how cell 3,2 is addressed.

selected; to select row 2, we need 1 on the A_1 address input at the upper left, and need a 0 on A_0. (This 10 is decoded to be row 2 by the two-input-to-four-output decoder like that of Fig. 13.6.) To select column 3, we place a 1 on the A_2 and A_3 address line inputs. To write data into this RAM, the write enable (WE) and chip select (CS) inputs must be 1 (or $+V$) in Fig. 14-3; Q_8 and Q_9 turn on and the input data flow into cell 3,2. To read the data, the CS is 1 and the WE is 0; the data flow from 3,2 out through Q_8 and Q_{10}.

Larger memories are possible by adding more memory cells and more address lines. For example, a 1024-bit memory requires 10 address lines, since 1024 equals 2^{10}, which may be arranged in 32 rows and 32 columns of cells. An even larger memory of 1024 words (with eight bits in each word) requires eight 1024-bit chips. One chip is devoted to the 1 bit and is connected to the data bus for 1 bits. (The next chip is connected to the data bus for 2 bits, etc.) With eight lines in the data bus we can address all eight chips at once using an address that lies between 0 and 1023, and can write data in or read data out, at eight bits in parallel, onto the eight data lines. (The same data lines may be used for both incoming data and outgoing data by use of the bidirectional bus driver shown in Fig. 13-4.)

The heat produced within a static RAM limits the number of cells within one IC. For larger and more compact RAM systems the designers use dynamic RAMs. Here the limitations are the same as for dynamic MOS logic[11-12], in that a two-phase clock (ϕ_1 and ϕ_2 in Fig. 11-10) is needed to keep the data alive in the memory. Using this method, a RAM can have 65,000 bits on a chip.

The RAM and shift-register systems lose all their stored data when the power fails; so these are called *volatile* memories. To prevent such accidental loss of data, we use standby battery power sources. These are usually rechargeable nickel-cadmium units that, by their connection to the regular power supply, are kept fully charged and ready to keep the memory alive during a power failure.

14-3 READ-ONLY MEMORY (ROM)

Much of the information used in most systems is repetitive and never changes; this is like our use of the multiplication tables or a list of telephone numbers that do not change. We store such information in a read-only memory since we never have to write into this memory. Initially this information is placed in the ROM by the maker of the IC by use of one of the masks in the IC process.[12-2] (The equipment designer determines what information is needed and then tells the IC manufacturer where the 1s and 0s are to be placed.) This is called a mask-programmed ROM. In this case a program means a pattern of 1s and 0s that represents the desired information.

The ROM (also the PROM and EAROM of Secs. 14-4 and 14-5) is a form of random-access memory, since we address a cell here in the same way that we address a cell in a RAM. An important feature of the ROM, PROM, or EAROM is that the stored information remains indefinitely, even without applied power; thus these are *nonvolatile* memories.

Section 14-4 describes a circuit that allows users of a ROM to insert their own information into it, making a PROM or programmable read-only memory. Figure 14-4 shows a ROM like Fig. 14-2 in that it consists of a row-select line, a column-select line, and a memory cell; here the memory cell is only a

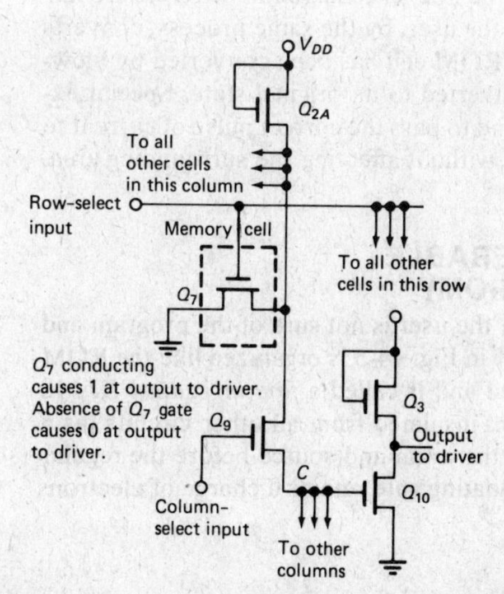

Figure 14-4 ROM that is programmed while being made.

single transistor Q_7. Since there is no writing into this cell, it needs no data input devices; so transistors Q_1, Q_4, Q_5, and Q_8 of Fig. 14-2 are eliminated. At the time the cell is addressed, a 0 (0 volts) occurs at point C in Fig. 14-4; Q_9 is turned on for this column and Q_7 is turned on for this row. This is inverted by Q_{10} so that a 1 appears at the output. If the gate of Q_7 has not been placed in by the manufacturer, the plus voltage at V_{DD} causes a 1 at C when the cell position is addressed (for when Q_7 gate is missing, an empty position remains which cannot be connected to ground). This is inverted by Q_{10} to become a 0 at the output. Here Q_{2A} acts as a pull-up resistor for the whole column instead of for just one cell (Q_2 in Fig. 14-2). The manufacturer can arrange the final mask that makes the gates for all the MOSFETS in the IC so that they either have a gate for Q_7 (for a logic 1) or omit the gate for Q_7 (for a logic 0). These are all induced-channel FETs (Fig. 7-36); so when the gate is omitted, the whole FET is permanently disabled.

Each cell of the ROM is addressed the same way as the RAM cell is addressed in Fig. 14-3.

14-4 PROGRAMMABLE READ-ONLY MEMORY (PROM)

The cost of a custom mask for programming the ROM in Sec. 14-3 is so high that thousands of ROMs using the same program must be sold to pay for the mask. But the PROM may be programmed by the individual user, one at a time in cases where small quantities of a ROM are needed. The PROM is a bipolar circuit since it needs high currents to program it; each memory cell is a bipolar transistor with a fusible connection. The manufacturer supplies a PROM wherein all the cells have a logic 1 level; the user then converts selected cells to logic 0 by electrically overheating those fusible links to open the connections of the 0-level cells. (Some PROMs are furnished having all cells at logic 0 and the user, by the same process, converts selected cells to a logic 1.) Once a PROM cell has been converted by blowing a fusible link, it cannot be reconverted to its original state. Special fixtures are used to select the address and to pass the correct pulse of current to blow the link at the desired address without affecting the surrounding area.

14-5 ELECTRICALLY ALTERABLE READ-ONLY MEMORY (EAROM)

The EAROM is convenient when the user is not sure of the program and may wish to modify it. The EAROM in Fig. 14-5 is organized like the ROM in Fig. 14-4 except that Q_{7A} is added and is called a *floating-gate FET*. In making Q_{7A}, another layer of silicon, insulated from all other circuits (as a floating gate), is deposited between the drain and source before the regular gate is deposited on top of it. This floating gate retains a charge of electrons

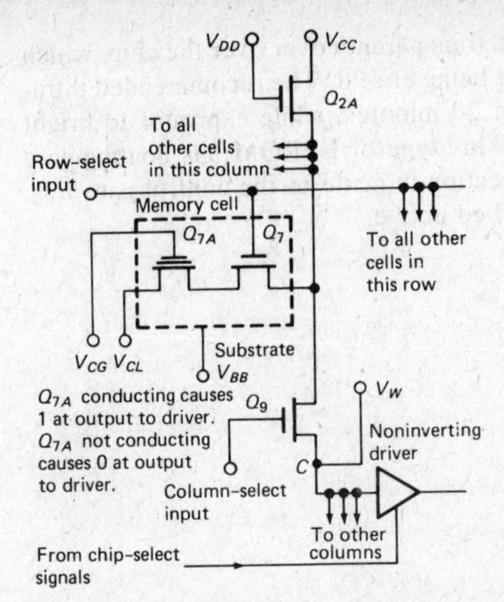

Figure 14-5 EAROM—a ROM that can be erased and programmed after being made.

or holes for up to ten years without being replenished. If this floating gate becomes charged with electrons, Q_{7A} is turned off; but if charged by holes, the floating gate is positive and Q_{7A} is turned on. Some manufacturers use a nitride process (MNOS)[7-27] to make an equivalent device that traps a charge between the substrate and the gate above it.

We can erase the memory of the EAROM if we apply +35 V on the source at V_{CL}, and −40 V on the control gate at V_{CG}, and −5 V on the substrate at V_{BB} (below Q_7 in Fig. 14-5); this injects holes into the floating gate, turns Q_{7A} on, and writes a 0 into the cell. In most EAROMs all cells are erased simultaneously. The output of the memory cells is not inverted by Q_{10} but instead is connected directly to the line driver.

To write a 1 into a particular EAROM cell, we apply +25 V to the control gate V_{CG} and −2 V to the substrate V_{BB}. The desired cell is addressed by raising the row-select line and the column-select line that connect to this cell, and we give to V_W (low in Fig. 14-5, and which is normally open-circuited) a +15-volt 40-millisecond write pulse. This injects electrons into the floating gate of Q_{7A} so that it turns off.

During normal operation V_{CG} and V_{CL} are at 0 V and V_W is open. To read the content of this cell, we raise the proper row and column lines to near V_{DD}. If Q_{7A} has been erased (turned on), then it acts as if connected to 0 volts (V_{CL}) and a logic 0 is read. But if Q_{7A} has been written into (turned off), then there is no connection to 0 volts, and Q_{2A} above raises the voltage to a logic 1.

Another method of erasing the memory is by exposing the chip to high-intensity ultraviolet light (of shorter wavelength than 4000 Å.[23-12] This device is called an erasable programmable read-only memory (EPROM). The

EPROM that uses this method has a transparent cover over the chip, which is covered by opaque tape while not being erased. The recommended ultraviolet source erases the program in 20 minutes, while exposure to bright sunlight requires about one week. This type of EPROM has floating-gate FETs like Q_{7A} except that no connection is made to the control gate V_{CG}. The programming is like that described above.

15 MICROPROCESSORS

While designing a complex system of logic for the automatic control of a machine, control designers have three choices as to how they will build the control: they can assemble many standard logic circuits (often TTL) together on several printed-circuit cards; or they can request from an IC manufacturer a custom-designed LSI[11-1] (large-scale integrated circuit having thousands of devices on one chip) which is tailored to perform the special operation; or they can use a standard LSI called a *microprocessor* (CPU in Fig. 13-1) which is very versatile but which must be programmed to perform the special control operation. The choice depends on the number of systems needed, how soon they are needed, and the price that can be paid for each system. But after the system is built, the designer may wish to change the operation of the machine. If a microprocessor is used, designers must alter the program; if standard TTL circuits are used, they must change the wiring; if a custom LSI is used, the designer can change nothing after the chip is made.

15-1 THE PROGRAM

This chapter shows that a typical microprocessor (such as the Intel 8080 outlined in Fig. 15-1) is a small computer; it is a CPU that requires a program of instructions to tell it what to do; it has many connections to the rest of the system, as is shown in Fig. 13-1.

The program is a set of instructions that tells the microprocessor each step to take toward performing its job; some details of such instructions are given in Sec. 15-3. A program starts as a set of instructions written on paper; then this is transferred to a set of cards with the instructions punched in code on them. These instructions also can be transferred to magnetic tape, paper tape, or directly into a ROM or a RAM, where the instructions are stored in the memory cells. (Thus a program is called *software* because it is coded information, as contrasted to *hardware*, which includes the actual ICs and wir-

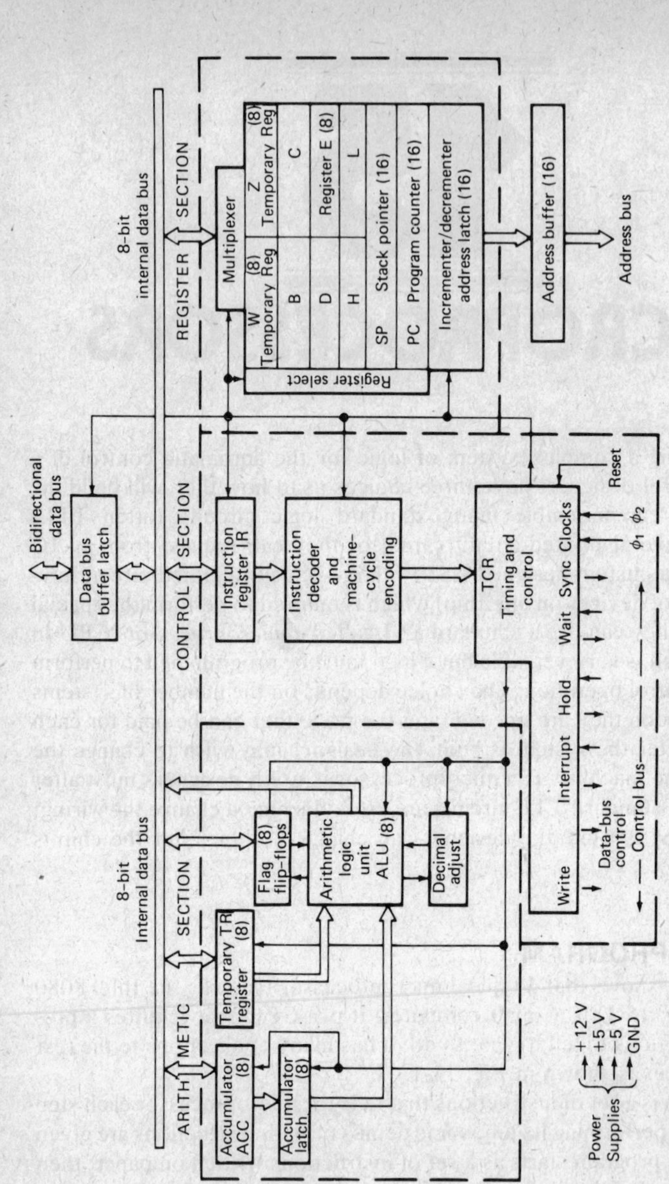

Figure 15-1 Functional block diagram of Intel 8080 CPU.

ing.) The program eventually is stored in IC memory chips which are connected to the CPU through the address bus, data bus, and additional control wires called the control bus. This is also the way that I/O equipment is connected. If the memory is a RAM,[14-2] the program must be loaded into the RAM each time the power is turned on; this can be done by connecting a card reader or tape reader to the buses so as to transfer the program into memory. This requires the help of a loader program permanently built into a ROM within the system. If the program is put into ROM[14-3] or PROM or EAROM,[14-5] then it is loaded only once, either by the IC maker or by the user.

In addition to the program, data also are stored in the memory chips; therefore, the address of each instruction is treated carefully so as not to mix a data word with an instruction word. The CPU also has a type of memory called *registers*, which are used for temporary storage of instructions and data used during the execution of an instruction.

15-2 INSIDE THE CENTRAL PROCESSING UNIT (CPU)

The CPU consists of three major sections of circuits; as shown near the top of Fig. 15-1, these are the arithmetic section, control section, and register section. At the top, the 8-bit internal data bus connects these three sections to the external bidirectional data bus through the data bus buffer/latch. This is a set of eight (one for each bit) three-state bidirectional bus drivers (like Fig. 13-4) with the addition of a latch (another name for a D flip-flop) to temporarily store outgoing data. The address buffer (bottom right in Fig. 15-1) is a set of 16 three-state bus drivers (like Fig. 13-3) that sends address information out of the address bus.

In the arithmetic section of Fig. 15-1 the accumulator (ACC) is an 8-bit register which is the heart of all adding, subtracting, and logic operations. With the help of the arithmetic logic unit (ALU), binary numbers coming in from the data bus can be added to or subtracted from the number already stored in ACC. (Multiplication and division must be programmed as a sequence of additions or subtractions.) The decimal adjust converts a binary number in ACC to a decimal number (using the BCD code) after all the calculations have occurred. The flag flip-flops are a set of five D flip-flops that become set or reset, caused by such things as a negative number, or a *carry* resulting from an addition. These flags inform the programmer of the result of the previous operation.

At the right in Fig. 15-1, the register section contains eight 8-bit registers (such as W or Z or E) for temporary storage of 8-bit data or addresses; to store a 16-bit address, two 8-bit registers are paired side by side. This section also contains three 16-bit registers, including SP and PC. The program counter PC has circuits that let us increase by one the number stored in this register; this is called *incrementing*. The purpose of PC is to keep track of the address in memory that stores the instruction on which the CPU is working. After PC is incremented, it then contains the address of the next instruction that the CPU must perform. Below PC, a number stored in the incrementer/decrementer address latch can be increased or decreased by one; this 16-bit register stores an address (a 16-bit binary number) for a time long enough so that the circuits in the memory chips (RAM or ROM connected to the address bus) can find the proper memory cells to which to send the data on the data bus.

The third 16-bit register, the stack pointer (SP, at right in Fig. 15-1), can increment and decrement also. The SP contains the address in memory which in turn contains the contents of the PC. This is used when the program contains a jump or branch instruction; these instructions occur when some repetitive task is to be performed, such as by the way we multiply or divide. After completion of this repetitive task we wish to return to our original point in the program. (This is like using a separate piece of scratch paper for calculations when completing our income tax form.) The stack pointer finds the way back to the original program.

In the control section (at center of Fig. 15-1) the *instruction register* (IR) stores an instruction that has just been read from memory (using the address contained in the program counter PC), while the CPU performs the instructed task. This instruction is stored while the instruction decoder determines what task that certain instruction requires. The *timing and control* section (TCR) then sends signals to the other parts of the CPU and to the circuits outside the CPU (such as memory chips and I/O devices) to guide their operation.

15-3 HOW THE CPU PROCESSES AN INSTRUCTION

For each type of CPU the manufacturer has defined a set of program instructions which the programmer must use to determine the desired sequence of operations. A program instruction is required for every movement of a number between memory and a register or between registers; arithmetic operation; logic operation such as AND, OR, or compare; and for controlling or selecting other program instructions. Therefore, as users of a CPU, we must know how this CPU works, and the entire effect of each instruction. The processing of a sample instruction can be followed in Figs. 15-1 and 15-2. Let us assume that the CPU has just completed instruction 14 of its program and the program counter PC is incremented to instruction 15. (This is step 1 in the upper left of Fig. 15-2.) In steps 2 and 3 (numbers in circles) the timing and control section (TCR) sends the contents of the PC (which is 15, whose binary form is 0000 0000 0000 1111) to the address latch and driver. This automatically goes out the address bus to all devices that are connected to the bus (step 4). In step 5 the TCR directs the ROM to send the contents of that address through the data bus (step 6) and into the instruction register (IR).

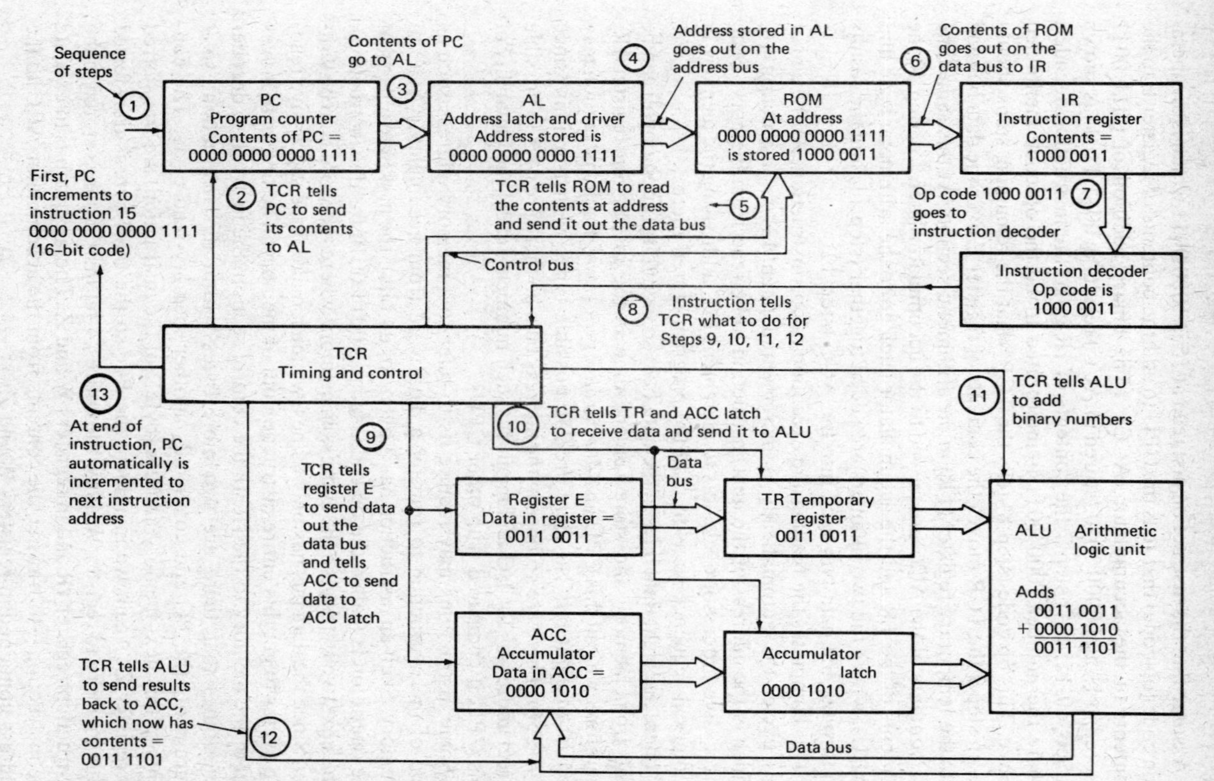

Figure 15-2 Memory instruction 15 tells CPU to add E to ACC.

Assume that the instruction just read at 15 is 1000 0011 which is an operation code (op code) that tells the CPU to add the contents of register E to the contents of the accumulator (ACC). [The binary addition of 0011 0011 (stored in E) and 0000 1010 (stored in ACC) results in 0011 1101 (as shown in Sec. 10-15).] At step 7 the contents of IR go to the instruction decoder, where the number 1000 0011 is interpreted to be the op code mentioned above. This op code (step 8) tells the TCR what the remaining steps should be. In step 9 the TCR moves the contents of register E over the data bus and into the temporary register (TR) in the arithmetic section. At this same time the contents of the ACC are moved to the accumulator latch. At step 10 the contents of the TR and the accumulator latch go to the arithmetic logic unit (ALU), where the two numbers are added together (step 11) and the results go through the data bus back into the ACC (step 12).

This completes the reading and execution of one instruction. At the end of this cycle, PC automatically is incremented (step 13) to instruction 16, which is the address of the next instruction to be read from memory. Each successive processor cycle acts to increment PC, addressing the memory in numerical sequence so as to read the program stored there.

There are eight data lines in the data bus; so eight bits (or one byte) can be read from memory and stored at one time in the instruction register IR; therefore, we call this CPU an *8-bit parallel processor*. Each instruction may consist of eight bits; so there are 256 possible types of instructions (since $2^8 = 256$). There are 16 lines in the address bus; so there are 65,536 possible direct addresses for I/O and memory; such numbers reveal the capability of this CPU if compared with other CPUs.

Some instructions may require us to refer to a memory address such as that of the instruction to transfer a data word from accumulator ACC to memory. Such an instruction has 3 bytes (or 24 bits); the first byte tells what the operation is (called the op code, such as 0011 0010 for this instruction). The next two bytes give the address in memory where the word is to be written. Since the data bus has only 8 lines, we must make three successive reading cycles to get this entire instruction out of memory. The first byte moves out of the memory to the IR. In the control section, the instruction decoder determines that there are two more bytes within this instruction; so it increments the PC and commands another memory-read cycle. The contents of this next memory address (byte 2 of the instruction) are transferred to register Z. Again we increment the PC; so the third byte is transferred from memory to register W. Now the entire 24-bit instruction is stored in the instruction register IR and in registers W and Z. The next step is to execute the instruction—to transfer the contents from the accumulator ACC to the address contained in registers W and Z.

15-4 TIMING IN THE CPU

The data bus is used in three ways; thus it must be time-shared (or multiplexed); this means that at one time the data bus carries an instruction, at

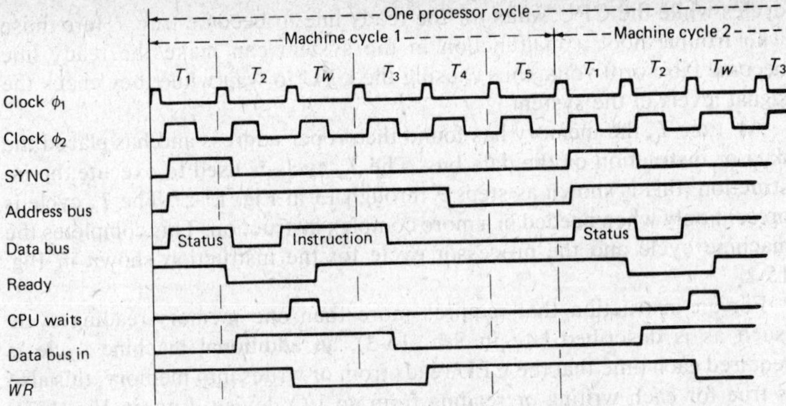

Figure 15-3 Timing signals during one machine cycle and within a processor cycle.

another time it carries data, and at other times it indicates the status of the system. Therefore, the timing and control (TCR) circuit develops an exact time schedule for each CPU operation. An external clock circuit supplies the ϕ_1 and ϕ_2 pulses shown at the top of Fig. 15-3. The time schedule is divided into periods each called a *processor cycle*, which is the time required to read and execute a single instruction. (The length of this period varies according to the complexity of the instruction.) Each processor cycle consists of one to five machine cycles, each of which in turn requires from two to five clock cycles. A clock cycle is measured from the start of one ϕ_1 pulse to the start of the next ϕ_1 pulse.

During the first clock cycle (marked T_1 at the top of Fig. 15-3), the ϕ_2 pulse starts a synchronizing pulse (SYNC) which is sent out of the CPU from the TCR circuits; this pulse tells the entire system that the data bus is about to send status information. The SYNC pulse (and the sending of status information) occurs at the beginning of each machine cycle. The status information tells the system what kind of machine cycle is next to occur; for instance, a 1010 0010 on the data bus tells the memory that it must send back an instruction from that address indicated on the address bus. When the status word on the data bus is 1000 0010, the memory is to send a data byte to the CPU.

A status word of all zeros on the data bus indicates that the memory is to receive a data byte and to write it into that address which appears on the address bus. Other status words tell any I/O equipment when it must send or receive data.

At the second clock pulse T_2, the CPU checks the ready line to see whether the memory chip or the I/O device is ready to send or receive data. If the address circuits within memory or I/O device have not found their proper address, they send a not ready signal to the CPU; the ready line is held false. The CPU waits while the clock continues to run. These clock cycles are shown at T_W in Fig. 15-3; there can be any number of T_W clock cycles while the CPU waits for the ready line to become true. (Here those who troubleshoot a malfunction in the system can make the ready line become false or 0 volts, thus causing the CPU to wait while they check the signal levels in the system.)

At time T_3 the memory has found the proper address and has placed the data or instruction on the data bus. The T_4 cycle is used to execute the instruction (this is shown as steps 9 through 13 in Fig. 15-2). The T_5 cycle is present only when needed in a more complex instruction. This completes the machine cycle and the processor cycle for the instruction shown in Fig. 15-2.

For an instruction that requires more than one memory-reading cycle (such as is described late in Sec. 15-3), an additional machine cycle is required each time that the CPU reads from or writes into memory; this also is true for each writing or reading from an I/O device. Low in Fig. 15-3, DBIN (data bus in) is a signal by which the CPU shows that the data bus is ready to receive information. When the $\overline{WR}$ (not write) signal goes false, this indicates that this segment of time is used in writing in memory or in an I/O device.

In each communication between the CPU and memory or I/O devices, the CPU first signals the device for which it must find an address; the device signals back to CPU when it has done so. The CPU then tells the device when the CPU can receive (or send) data; then the data are sent. There is constant communication back and forth to ensure that each device speaks at the right time; persons who work with computers call this "hand shaking."

15-5 HEXADECIMAL CODE

With microprocessors there are many new words and ideas related to the computer and data-processing industry. When we need more detailed information about a microprocessor, we must be able to read instructions published by the CPU maker. Usually these instructions use the computer-related words just mentioned. CPU makers such as Intel, Motorola, and National Semiconductor use a counting system which is called the hexadecimal code (which means 16). This code saves space when we write long binary numbers (as in Fig. 15-2). In this new code we convert each group of four binary digits into a single hexadecimal character as follows:

Binary	Hexadecimal	Binary	Hexadecimal
0000	0	1000	8
0001	1	1001	9
0010	2	1010	A
0011	3	1011	B
0100	4	1100	C
0101	5	1101	D
0110	6	1110	E
0111	7	1111	F

The op code 1000 0011 (used in the example of Fig. 15-2) is listed as 83 in the CPU maker's instruction book; similarly, the op code 1000 1111 is shown as 8F. The address (used in Fig. 15-2) 0000 0000 0000 1111 now is written as $000F_{16}$ to save space. Here, to prevent confusion with decimal or octal numbers, we add the subscript 16.

15-6 THE CPU USED IN A SYSTEM

There are many ways to properly connect the CPU to the memory and I/O circuits. Figure 15-4 shows a typical system wherein we combine an 8080 CPU (at the top left) with other Intel circuits (such as G and H at lower left) to add more control signals. Here G (the clock generator and driver, or Intel 8224) furnishes the ϕ_1, ϕ_2, ready, and reset signals to the CPU (and at bottom of Fig. 15-1). This reset signal occurs every time that power is turned on, and so it resets to zero many of the flip-flops and also the program counter. The ready signal also comes from this G unit, since the memory circuits used here have no ready output.

The 8316 (the ROM shown as B) and 8111 (the RAMs C and D) Intel units act more slowly than the 8080 CPU; so clock generator G automatically causes ready to be false each time the memory reads or writes, and to remain false during one clock period (at each T_2 time in Fig. 15-3). Thus the CPU waits one clock period to let memory find the required address.

The status strobe signal goes from G into H just after CPU sends a SYNC signal; this slight delay gives time for all eight lines of the data bus to contain the correct status information. The status latch (Intel 8212, shown as H low in Fig. 15-4) is a set of eight D-type flip-flops that temporarily stores the status information (of Sec. 15-4) being sent on the data bus at the time when the status strobe signal occurs. In the control bus gates J (low in Fig. 15-4) this status information combines with signals DBIN and $\overline{\text{WR}}$ to form signals $\overline{\text{MEMR}}$ (not memory read), or MEMW (memory write), or IOR (input/output read), or IOW. The remaining J signal INTA (interrupt acknowledge) is used in systems where an I/O device may have an urgent message for the CPU; so it interrupts the program to send the message.

Above G (at left of Fig. 15-4) we show the data bus of the 8080 CPU directly connected to the memory and I/O devices. However, many systems place an additional set of bidirectional drivers (A) in the circuit because current from the 8080 CPU may not be enough to drive all the circuits on the data bus. Sometimes this same addition is made to the address bus also. Many buffers (amplifiers) may be added but for clarity are not shown here. In this small system we show at the right only two switches E and F (but other I/O devices may be connected, as in Fig. 13-8).

The ROM (at B in Fig. 15-4) stores 2048 eight-bit words. So we connect its eight output lines (O_1 through O_8) to the data bus (D_0 through D_7). To address 2048 words, we need eleven address lines (A_0 through A_{10}). Further, when line A_{11} is false, we select the ROM B by inverting the A_{11} signal and connecting it to the chip select inputs CS_2 and CS_3. When $\overline{\text{MEMR}}$

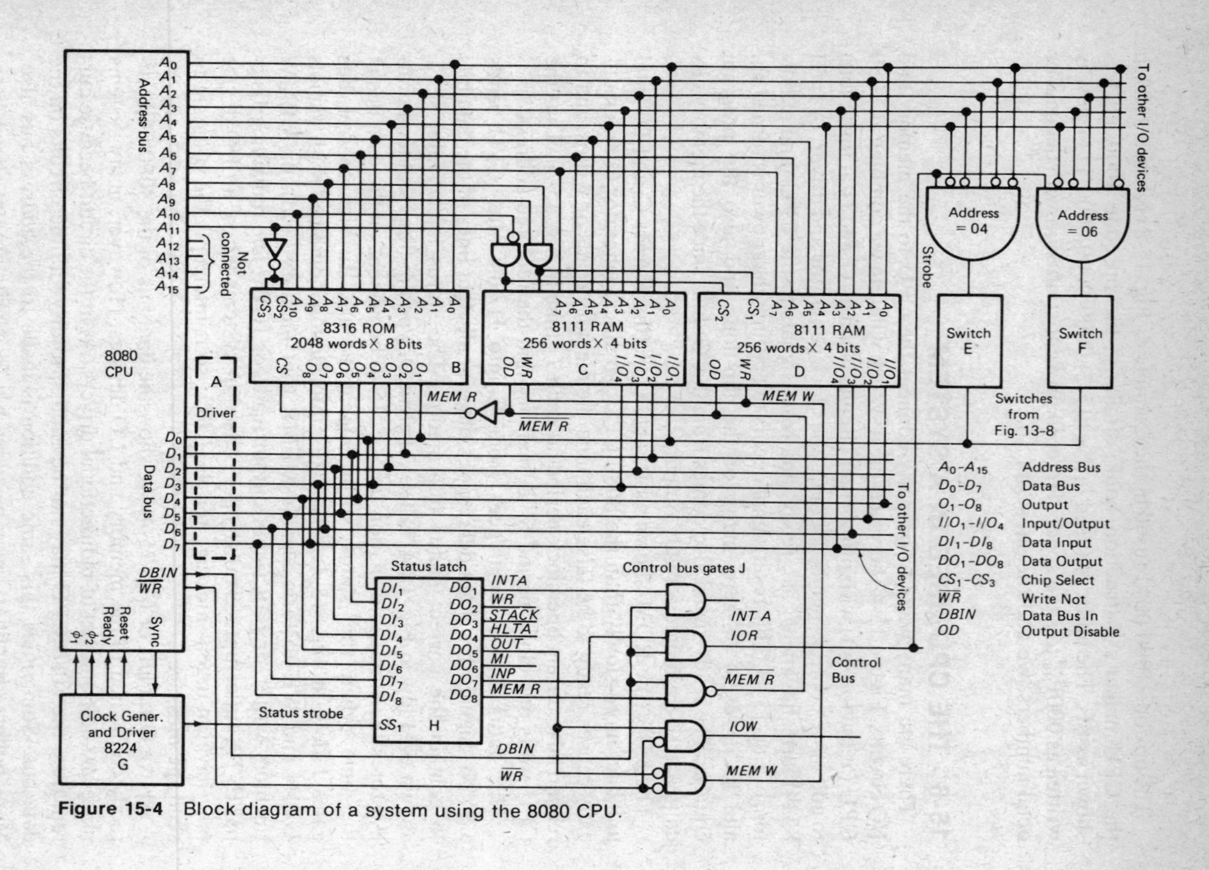

Figure 15-4 Block diagram of a system using the 8080 CPU.

is false, this signal is inverted to become MEMR at the CS_1 input to the ROM which then enables this ROM to read. Thus the addresses contained in ROM B start at 0000_{16} and increase to $07FF_{16}$ (which is 0000 0111 1111 1111).

Each RAM (C or D) stores 256 four-bit words; we must connect C and D in parallel to store eight-bit words. RAM C stores the low-order bits (1, 2, 4, and 8) so the input/output lines of RAM C (I/O_1 through I/O_4) are connected to the data bus (D_0 through D_3). RAM D stores the high-order bits (16, 32, 64, and 128) and its input/output lines are connected to the data bus (D_4 through D_7). We simultaneously write into both RAMs C and D or read from them. These RAMs have address lines A_0 through A_7 (high in Fig. 15-4); to select a RAM address, lines A_8, A_9, and A_{11} must be true and A_{10} must be false. Here the $\overline{\text{MEMR}}$ line is connected directly to the RAM inputs called output disable (OD). When $\overline{\text{MEMR}}$ is false, the RAMs C and D read from the location that is addressed. When MEMW is true, the CPU can write into the location that is addressed. The addresses of the RAMs range from $0B00_{16}$ up to $0BFF_{16}$. With this small system we do not need to use address lines A_{12} through A_{15}.

The I/O devices may have the same addresses as those used for memory in this system. We have separate signals: IO R (I/O device read) and IO W (I/O device write) to tell the I/O devices when to "speak" and when to "listen." The status word that comes from the CPU at the beginning of each machine cycle[15-4] determines whether this is a read cycle or a write cycle and whether the memory or the I/O is involved. Therefore, we can add to the system many more I/O devices such as the A/D converter and multiplexer. (In Fig. 13-8 the line labeled strobe is the same as IOR.)

Other combinations of circuits may be used where many functions shown in Fig. 15-4 are combined into one or more IC packages. In some industrial controllers a single chip contains the entire system as shown but scaled down to lesser requirements. Also more elaborate requirements can be met with additional bus-controlling chips which allow the CPU to communicate with more equipment.

16 PROGRAMMABLE CONTROLLERS

The motors and solenoids of most machine tools are controlled by magnetic contactors, relays, and limit switches. For large complex machines the relay panels require frequent maintenance. Instead, this chapter shows how we can replace relays by solid-state circuits; to replace numerous relays we can use a programmable controller.

16-1 ELEMENTARY OR LADDER DIAGRAM

To show how we may control a machine, such as the automatic conveyor and door of a heating chamber in Fig. 16-1, we use a diagram shown in Fig. 16-2. This elementary diagram shows the connections to the control devices in simplified form for easier understanding. [Some call Fig. 16-2 a ladder diagram because of its shape, having right and left vertical lines (the voltage bus) and horizontal control lines.]

In Fig. 16-1, work trays are moved through the heating chamber by conveyor 0 which is driven at low speed by a motor not shown; by a one-way clutch, conveyor 0 also drives conveyor 1 so as to move the tray slowly to the right. When the tray closes the mechanical limit switch 1LS located just before the door, motor 3 raises the door to the top until stopped by 3LS; then motors 1 and 2 quickly drive the tray onto conveyor 2. The tray opens limit switch 2LS on conveyor 2, which stops conveyors 1 and 2 and starts the door downward; the DOWN limit switch 4LS stops motor 3 when the door is fully closed. [Each limit switch may have a normally-open contact -o⍀o- (open when nothing presses the switch) which is closed by movement of the tray. The limit switch also may have a normally-closed contact -o⊸o- which opens when the tray presses it.]

We may follow this same action in the elementary diagram in Fig. 16-2. (The power connections to the motors, the motor-starter contacts, and other

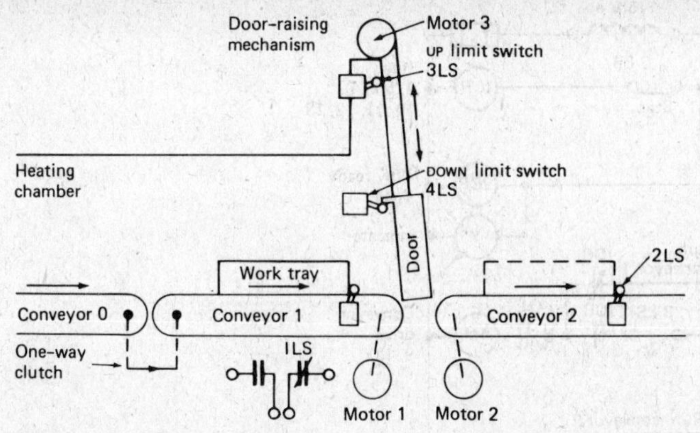

Figure 16-1 Exit door from heating chamber, showing work tray ready to come out.

power-handling devices are not shown in this part of the diagram.) At line 1 (numbered at the upper left in Fig. 16-2) we press the RUN pushbutton 1PB to energize control relay 1CR, which is held closed by a 1CR contact, to provide automatic operation. Also when power is first turned on, or after power is interrupted, 1CR is not energized; so the machine must be started by 1PB. [Pushbuttons 3PB to 6PB may operate individual motors when a malfunction occurs. Numbers at the right of the 1CR coil indicate in which lines the contacts of 1CR are found; underlined numbers indicate normally-closed (n-c) contacts.[8-1]]

In Fig. 16-2, when the moving work tray closes limit switch 1 LS in line 3, this energizes control relay 2CR and closes the 2CR contact in line 11 to 3MF. Coil 3MF is in the motor starter that makes motor 3 raise the door until the UP limit switch 3LS opens line 11. In line 6 the n-o contact of 3LS closes and energizes coil 1M so as to start the conveyor-1 motor. In line 9 contact 1M energizes coil 2M so that the conveyor-2 motor also runs at this time. This moves the tray quickly out of the heating chamber onto conveyor 2 until the tray releases (opens) 1LS and opens limit switch 2LS (and opens the 2CR contact in line 7). In line 6 the n-c contact of 2LS opens the circuit to 1M. Motors 1 and 2 stop and the tray now rests at 2LS. The machine operator may press pushbutton 4PB in line 8 to energize 2M and run the tray to the following work area. As soon as 2LS reopens and 1M is deenergized, the n-c contact of 1M in line 13 energizes coil 3MR; this reverses motor 3 to lower the door until the DOWN limit switch 4LS opens this 3MR circuit.

Contacts 1OL, 2OL, and 3OL are on overload relays within the motor starters; one of these contacts will open if a motor is overloaded. By having an n-c contact of 3MF in series with the 3MR coil in line 13, and also an n-c 3MR contact in the 3MF coil circuit in line 11, this interlocking prevents 3MR and 3MF from trying to run motor 3 in both directions at once.

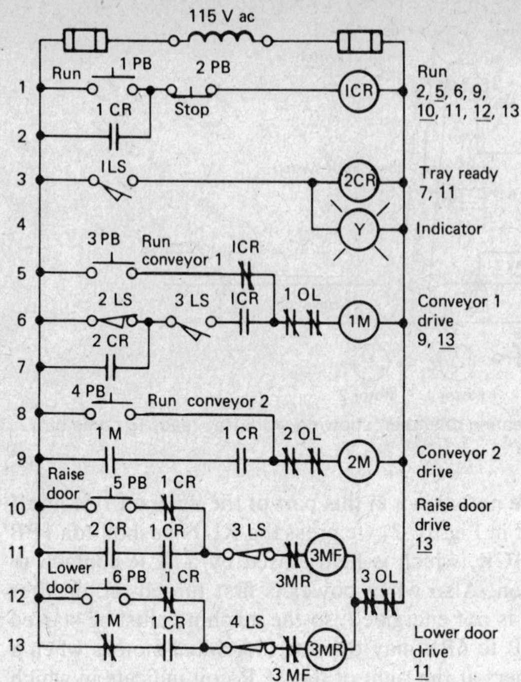

Figure 16-2 Elementary diagram showing connections of control devices and motor starters for Fig. 16-1.

16-2 LOGIC CIRCUITS REPLACE RELAYS AND CONTACTS

In Fig. 16-3 we use logic gates to replace combinations of contacts. The logic AND gate[10-9] acts the same as two or more contacts in series. The logic OR acts like two or more contacts in parallel. For example, in lines 1 and 2 of Fig. 16-2, 1PB is in parallel with contact 1CR; thus the OR gate 1 (high in Fig. 16-3) uses 1PB and 1CR as inputs. But this 1PB and 1CR combined OR gate also is in series with the normally-closed pushbutton 2PB. So the output of OR gate 1 becomes one of the inputs to AND gate 2. Since 2PB is normally closed, a true 2PB signal is inverted (by the small circle) to become the second input to AND gate 2. The output of AND gate 2 is the signal 1CR which is connected back to the input of OR gate 1 and to other gates along the left side of Fig. 16-3.

In Fig. 16-2 just below the 1CR signal we see the limit switch 1LS, which becomes the output 2CR (without going through any gates, since there are no series contacts in line 3 of Fig. 16-2; we use relay 2CR only because the limit switch 1LS does not contain enough n-o contacts.)

In Fig. 16-3 the AND gate 3 acts like 3PB and $\overline{1CR}$ in series on line 5 of Fig. 16-2. Here the normally-closed contact of 1CR is written as a logic

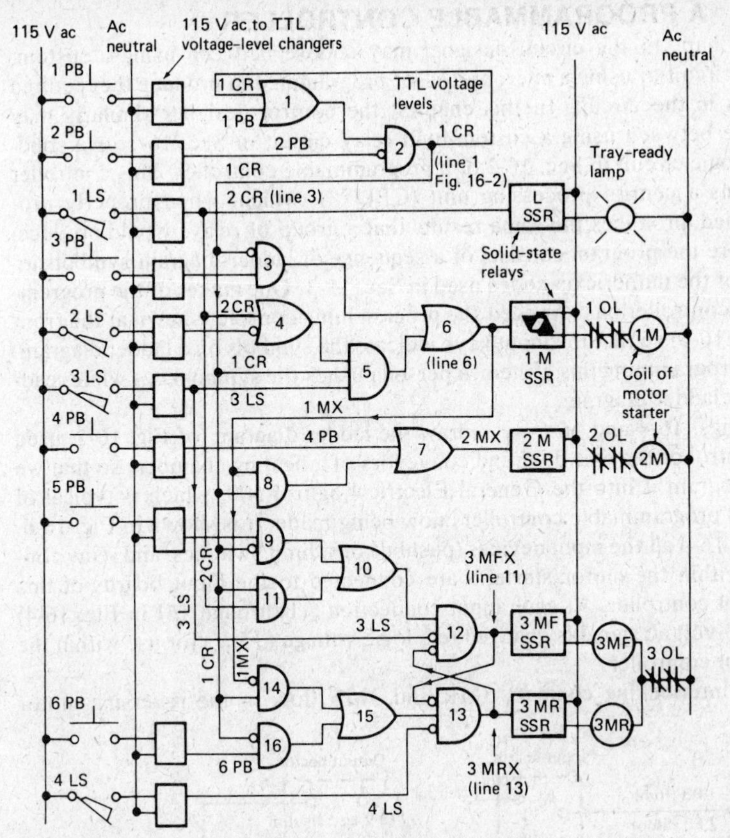

Figure 16-3 Solid-state logic circuits replace the contacts in Fig. 16-2.

NOT 1CR or is $\overline{1CR}$. To obtain this signal we invert the true 1CR signal by a small circle at the input to gate 3 (as we did before with 2PB). The inputs to OR gate 4 are the parallel contact 2CR and the n-c contact of 2LS (in lines 6 and 7 of Fig. 16-2). The output of gate 4 becomes one of the series signals (along with 3LS and 1CR in line 6) that make up AND gate 5. To parallel line 5 and line 6 in Fig. 16-2, we use OR gate 6; the output of this gate is the signal 1MX. Here 1MX from gate 6 energizes the solid-state relay 1MSSR,[9-20] which in turn energizes coil 1M of the starter for motor 1. The solid-state relay used here has a maximum output current of 3 amperes at 115 V ac, which is enough to energize the coil of the motor starter but would not operate an industrial-type motor directly. Each voltage-level changer (at the left side of Fig. 16-3) uses a bridge rectifier and a series resistor to convert the 115 V ac into a dc voltage to operate the LED of an optical isolator.[9-20] The phototransistor of this isolator operates directly at TTL voltage levels.

16-3 A PROGRAMMABLE CONTROLLER

In Chap. 15 the circuit designer may choose between using a custom-made circuit or using a microprocessor programmed to produce the required results in the circuit. In this chapter, the control designer similarly may choose between using a custom-built relay circuit in Sec. 16-1 or a solid-state logic circuit in Sec. 16-2 or a programmable controller. This controller contains a central processing unit (CPU[15-2]), which, when properly programmed, produces the same results that a group of relays would produce. But here the program consists of a sequence of ladder-diagram symbols instead of the numeric op codes used in Sec. 15-3. One maker of the programmable controller has arranged the programming console (shown at the front of Fig. 16-6) so that the input keys indicate the symbols on a ladder diagram. So in programming this system, a person pushes the symbol keys while reading the ladder diagram.

In Figs. 16-4 and 16-5 we redraw the ladder diagram (of Fig. 16-2, used for control of the exit door and conveyors of a heating chamber) so that we can program it into the General Electric Logitrol 500, which is typical of several programmable controllers now being made; it is shown in Fig. 16-6. In Fig. 16-4 all the input devices (pushbuttons, limit switches, and relay contacts within the motor starters) are connected to the input boards of this Logitrol controller. At each input connection (1I through 16I in Fig. 16-4) the 120-volt ac signal is changed to a logic voltage (+5 V) for use within the Logitrol controller.

The interlocking contacts 3MR and 3MF (low in the reversing motor

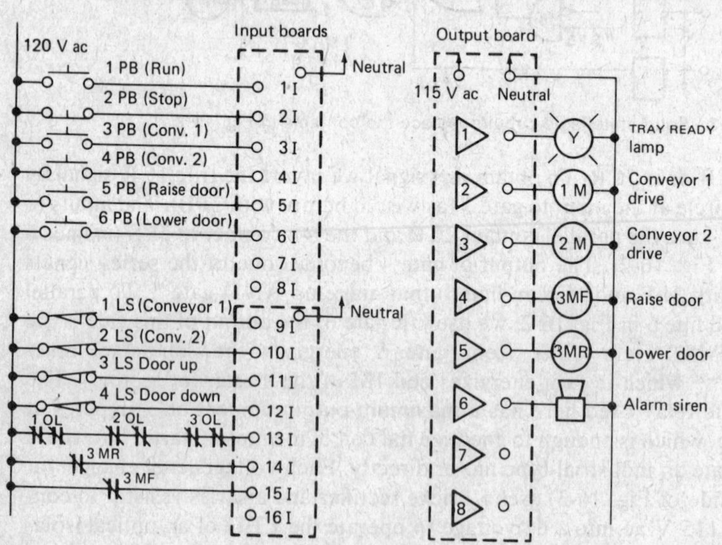

Figure 16-4 Connection of inputs and outputs to programmable controller (General Electric Logitrol).

starter of Fig. 16-2) become inputs 14I and 15I of the controller in Fig. 16-4. This is done so the controller can determine if either the 3MR or 3MF magnetic contactor is being held closed even though its coil is not energized.

Solid-state relays (shown as triangles in the output board at the right in Fig. 16-4) operate the indicator lamp, conveyor-motor starters, and other output devices. [In this Logitrol system we can add more input connections and output connections in groups of eight. Thus if we add an alarm siren (triangle 6 in Fig. 16-4), this requires no additional parts other than the siren itself. Outputs 7 and 8 are not used.]

The modified ladder diagram shown in Fig. 16-5 is entered into the Logitrol program if we push the proper buttons on the programming panel (at the center of Fig. 16-6). Each type of diagram symbol has a corresponding button on the panel: one button for a normally-open relay contact, another button for a n-c limit switch, etc. Thus the ladder diagram never needs to be wired as in a relay panel; instead, it gets programmed. To change the program we need only reprogram a part of the controller; so we need few or no wiring changes. Thus we can improve the circuit if any difficulty occurs during system operation.

At the top of Fig. 16-5, relay 1R corresponds to 1CR in Fig. 16-2. Contacts 1I and 2I close when we push 1PB and 2PB in Fig. 16-4. At the top of Fig. 16-5, notice that the contacts 1I, 2I, 1R are located in certain zones A, C, and B. This helps the programmer to push the buttons on the panel in the correct sequence. After the program is stored in the memory of the Logitrol controller (which is a static RAM[14-2]), the system may be turned on and all the motors then operate in the sequence described in Sec. 16-1.

In Fig. 16-5, relay 2R is operated by the n-c contact 9I; when limit switch 1LS (in Fig. 16-4) is opened by the tray, this causes the n-c contact of 9I to close. At the right of 2R in Fig. 16-5, triangle 1 indicates that relay 2R turns on the solid-state relay 1, which lights the TRAY READY lamp. Also in Fig. 16-5 we must add an auxiliary relay 3R to control the relay 4R (and thus to control solid-state relay triangle 4, which operates motor starter 3MF to open the door). Auxiliary relay 3R is needed because we cannot place contacts in more than five zones A to E, whereas starter coil 3MF is controlled by seven contacts, those of 5PB, 1CR, 1CR, 2CR, 3LS, 3MR, and 3 OL. Relay 6R turns on the solid-state relay 2 for the drive-motor starter of conveyor 1. We add auxiliary relay 5R (like 3R) to provide seven contacts to control 6R (in lines 5, 6, and 7 in Fig. 16-2).

In Fig. 16-5 we need no auxiliary relay for 7R (for solid-state relay 3 to run conveyor 2), since only the four contacts 4PB, 1M, 1CR, and 2OL control this starter. We group together all the overload relays (in 13I in Fig. 16-4) so as to stop the entire system if any overload relay opens. Relay 9R operates solid-state relay 5, to lower the door after the tray has left 1LS and has next opened 2LS. Here we add auxiliary relay 8R to help control 9R; we may realize that each relay corresponds to a tiny section of the controller memory; so it is not costly to add relays (since up to 32

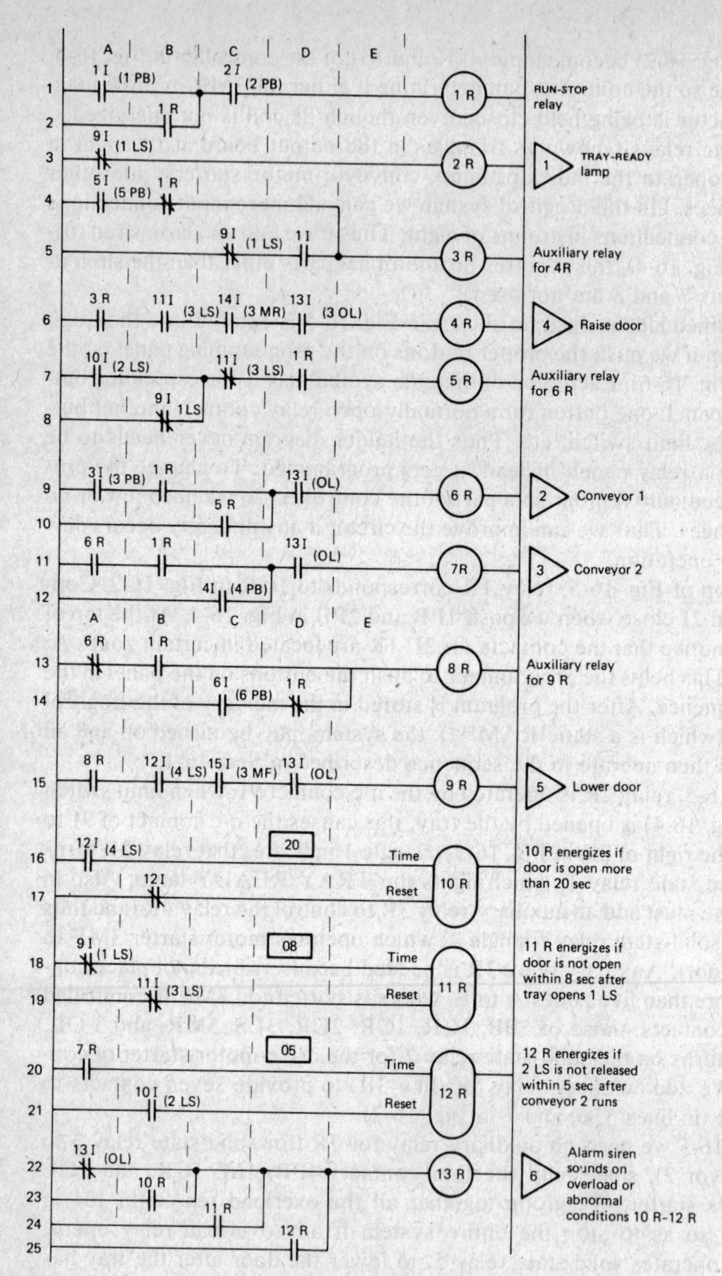

Figure 16-5 Ladder diagram (of Fig. 16-2) modified for GE Logitrol.

relays can be "remembered" in the smallest programmable controller). This new freedom in design lets us add features such as 10R to 13R next discussed.

16-4 TIME-DELAY RELAYS HELP TO DETECT MALFUNCTIONS

Figure 16-5 shows next how time-delay circuits may be included in a solid-state system to further protect the system from damage. Any automatic system may have faulty operation caused by a mechanism failure or inattention of the operator or lack of proper maintenance. Therefore, the designer aims to make the system "fail-safe"; that is, one malfunction must not cause a disaster or a set of other malfunctions. Thus the opening of any overload relay must stop the entire system.

In Fig. 16-5 time-delay relay 10R is programmed to begin timing as soon as the door starts to open. (Relay 10R acts like a motor-driven mechanical timer.) Contact 12I in line 16 closes when 4LS closes (showing that the door has left the fully closed position). If more than 20 seconds elapse before the relay 10R is reset (shown by the number 20 in a rectangle in the D zone on line 16), all n-o contacts of 10R close and the n-c contacts open. Relay 10R is reset (line 17) when the n-c contact 12I closes. Thus if a tray holds the door open or jams inside the chamber, the alarm sounds (contact 10R in line 23 closes the circuit to 13R so that solid-state relay 6 sounds the alarm).

Also, time-delay relay 11R starts timing when a tray opens 1LS (or 9I on line 18). If the door has not opened within 8 sec, the 11R contact closes in line 24 and the alarm sounds. When the door is fully open (opening 3LS), contact 11I closes and this resets 11R. Time-delay relay 12R (low in Fig. 16-5) measures the time after conveyor 2 is started by relay 7R in line 11, until the time when 2LS closes (10I in line 21), thus giving the alarm.

Thus the programmable controller allows us to have these added time-delay circuits at no cost since we have used fewer than 32 relays. It also is possible to have relays that count impulses, so that, for just the cost of a number indicator, we can count the number of trays processed in a day, by counting the number of times conveyor 1 operates.

16-5 HOW THE PROGRAMMABLE CONTROLLER OPERATES

After the program is written into memory and the system is started, the Logitrol controller "solves" each relay circuit in numerical sequence. The controller starts with relay 1R (at top of Fig. 16-5) and tests each contact that controls 1R. If contacts 1I (or 1R) and 2I are closed, the controller operates 1R; it thus has solved the logic equation for the 1R relay circuit, and this is stored in memory. The controller next tests the contacts in the circuit for 2R. If the n-c contact 9I is closed, this operates 2R. The controller continues this testing of each relay circuit in sequence. It does not look at relay 1R again until it has completed the testing of all relay circuits. If a con-

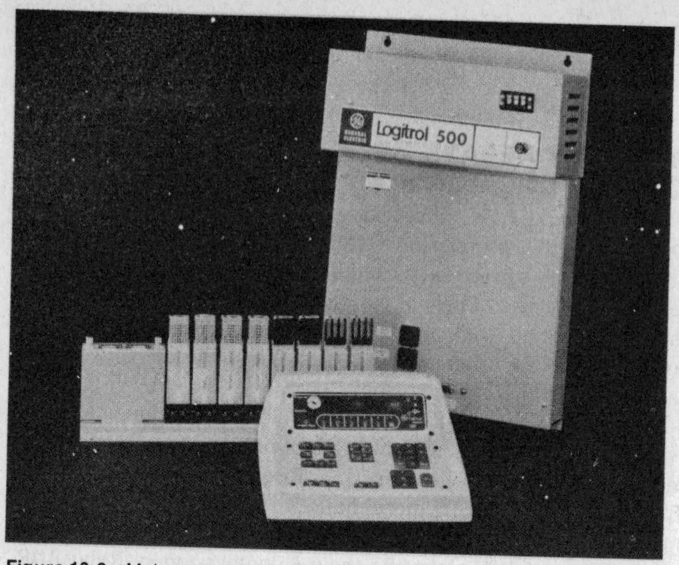

Figure 16-6 Major parts of GE Logitrol programmable controller. (*General Electric Company*.)

tact now has changed in the circuit for 1R, this change is detected by the controller during its next tour of the sequence. It needs about 6 milliseconds to complete one sequence or sweep of the relay circuits; thus the status of each relay is updated each 6 msec. This is like a digital computer that goes through its program completely, then repeats its program to see if any of the input data have changed.

These time-delay relays are counters that are timed by the cycles of line frequency (for 5-sec delay at 60 Hz, the time-delay relay 12R counts 5×60 cycles). The controller tests the 12R circuit once each time it makes a tour of the sequence. When the 12R circuit has counted 300 cycles and the controller has tested that circuit, the controller closes all the n-o contacts (and opens all the n-c contacts) of the 12R relay.

Figure 16-6 shows the major parts of the Logitrol. To the rear is the main panel which contains the CPU, the memory, the power supply, the control-power transformer, and the fuses. The left-hand unit is the input-output rack which contains the solid-state relays, the input voltage-level changers, and small indicator lights to show which circuit is turned on at that moment. In the front of Fig. 16-6 is the programming panel; the operator writes the program into the memory by using this panel; any time the program is modified this panel is again used. The programming panel does not need to be connected to the controller during normal operation of the system; it is needed only for system testing or program writing.

17

GAS TUBES FOR LARGE CURRENTS

As is mentioned in Sec. 1-3, high-vacuum tubes carry small anode currents, generally from 1 to 100 milliamperes (or $^1/_{1000}$ to $^1/_{10}$ A). For industrial circuits, tubes often need to carry large currents, from 1 to 500 amperes (A), even reaching 5000 A for an instant. Such high-current tubes are usually vapor-filled; because they work differently, these tubes are often marked on diagrams by placing a dot inside the tube circle. Some of these gas- or vapor-filled tubes have heated cathodes, and are called *phanotrons* or *thyratrons* (see Chap. 20), which are generally used to carry current in the range from $^1/_{10}$ to 50 A. Another type is called an *ignitron*; for a cathode it contains a pool of mercury (unheated) and is used to carry current much greater than 40 A.

Gradually, the phanotron is being replaced by silicon rectifiers; the thyratron may be replaced by the SCR[9-1]. The ignitron[17-8] still is the favored unit for conducting 300 to 5000 amperes.

17-1 THE PHANOTRON RECTIFIER

The phanotron has only an anode and a heated cathode. When it is being made, a drop of mercury or some gas such as argon or helium is put inside before the tube is sealed. This tube behaves like the diode described in Secs. 2-8 to 2-10. However, owing to the vapor or gas inside it, this tube may carry perhaps a hundred times as much current as a high-vacuum tube of the same size. When it is operating, this gas tube shows its red-hot filament; in addition, when anode current flows, a phanotron lights up with a colored glow, usually blue or purple. Some phanotrons have a metal enclosure, so that the glow is seen only where the anode connection passes through a glass seal.

Two phanotrons may be connected as in Fig. 4-2 to supply loads such as magnetic chucks or dc motor fields. Since these vapor-filled tubes carry so much more current, their heated cathodes must be able to produce more electrons. Therefore, the larger vapor-filled tubes are built with indirectly heated cathodes, as described in Sec. 2-11. While ordinary radio tubes reach operating temperature in 5 to 20 sec, the vapor-filled tubes may need a longer warming time; their life is greatly shortened if they are permitted to carry anode current before the cathodes have reached proper temperature. The large industrial tubes are protected by a time-delay relay which prevents anode current until the cathode has been heated a certain time.

17-2 GREATER ELECTRON FLOW IN A PHANOTRON

Recall that the vacuum tube generally does not use all the electrons that are being emitted from the hot cathode.[2-11] Many extra electrons gather near the cathode, causing the space charge, which tries to prevent other electrons from flowing to the anode. When there is vapor or gas inside the tube, some of the electrons (moving at high speed toward a positive anode) will strike the small particles of gas with enough force to dislodge electrons from them; these extra electrons also are attracted toward the anode. Having lost an electron, each gas particle or atom now retains a positive charge. When gas particles become charged in this way, they act as positive ions; the gas is ionized.

These positively charged particles move toward the cathode and remove or offset most of the negative space charge, so that more electrons are free to travel from the cathode to the anode. Nothing tries to limit the flow of electrons in this tube until the electron flow tries to exceed the amount of electrons being emitted from the cathode. Since such operation quickly damages most cathodes, too much anode-current flow through a vapor-filled tube must be prevented. This current depends on the circuit outside the tube, just as the current through a switch is limited only by the amount of load connected to its contacts.

17-3 ARC DROP; CONSTANT VOLTAGE ACROSS A VAPOR-FILLED TUBE

If we carefully measure (with the proper instrument, such as an electronic voltmeter[31-1]), the voltage between anode and cathode of a high-vacuum tube, this voltage may be any amount, such as 5, 25, 90, or 350 volts (V); it changes when the amount of anode current changes. In contrast, when we measure from anode to cathode of a mercury-vapor-filled tube through which anode current is flowing, the reading is about 10 to 15 V, and this voltage drop changes very little when the amount of anode current changes. Since the voltage drop across the current arc remains unchanged, we say that a gas- or vapor-filled tube has constant arc drop.

When a gas is used inside the tube in place of mercury vapor, the arc drop is near 10 V if the tube has a heated cathode. However, with a cold cathode, a tube filled with neon may have a constant drop of about 75 V so long as its small anode current flows; other gases are used to make tubes having 90, 105, or 150 V drop, and we call these voltage-regulator or glow tubes; for use below 300 V, these mostly have been replaced by Zener diodes for holding a fixed constant voltage.[7-18]

17-4 GLOW AND ARC-DISCHARGE TUBES

Figure 17-1 helps us to see why some gas tubes have cold cathodes and are called glow tubes, while other gas- or vapor-filled tubes (such as phanotrons or thyratrons) have heated cathodes and are called arc-discharge tubes.

If we gradually increase the positive potential of the plate or anode of a gas tube while its cathode is cold, Fig. 17-1 shows that a tiny current (much less than a microampere, as shown at *A*) may flow. (These original electrons do not come from the cathode, but may result from light or cosmic radiation received within the tube.) This current does not increase greatly when the anode voltage is raised to *B*. However, if the anode-to-cathode spacing and the vapor pressure will permit (as in a glow tube designed for this purpose), a voltage *C* may be reached where the amount of anode current increases greatly, so that it must be limited by a resistance in series with the tube. (This additional electron flow is produced at the cold cathode by secondary emission; at *C* in Fig. 17-1, the anode voltage is high enough to attract some of the original electrons so that they ionize gas particles. Now positively charged, these particles rush toward the cathode and dislodge electrons from the cathode surface.) In this process, part of the cathode surface has a visible glow but still is cold.

To maintain or continue this flow of secondary electrons from the cathode, the anode current must be kept at an amount greater than *D* in Fig. 17-1. As this current is increased to *E* (by decreasing the load resistance external to the tube), a larger portion of the cathode surface begins to glow. Operating in this manner, the voltage across the tube remains close to a steady or constant amount, shown at *D*. (To start this tube, the voltage

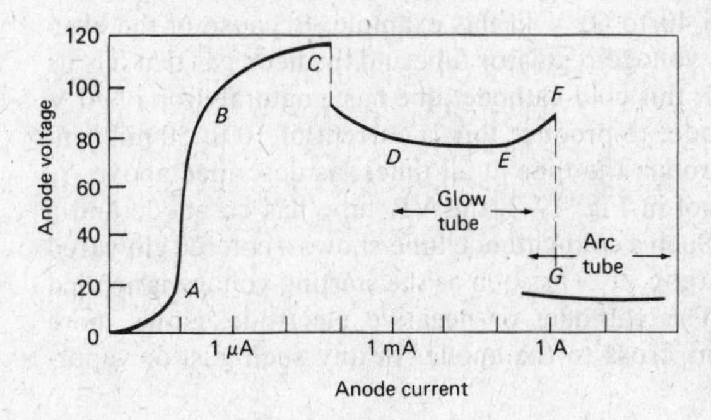

Figure 17-1 Volt-ampere behavior of glow and arc-discharge tubes.

applied at C must be, perhaps, 30 V higher than the steady voltage D. The voltage and current values shown in Fig. 17-1 might represent a 75-V voltage-regulator tube but may not apply to other tube designs.) However, if the anode current is increased beyond the point E, where all the cathode surface is aglow, the voltage across the tube increases, as at F; continued operation at F is abnormal and overloads the glow tube. If this overload is increased, the heat produced at the cathode may cause thermionic emission, so that the voltage across the tube decreases abruptly to the arc drop G.

This glow action is used also in a "numerical readout" or "nixie" tube used in digital instruments or counters. This tube has ten separate cold cathodes, each shaped to form one of the numerals from 0 to 9. When a circuit applies negative potential to a certain one of these cathodes, its glow displays the desired numeral. Since the ten cathodes are sandwiched together in nearly the same plane, the numerals appear at the same position. A series anode resistor permits a glow current in the range between E and F of Fig. 17-1.

Next consider a gas tube whose cathode is heated so that it emits plenty of electrons. This tube does not pass through the stages mentioned above (since its electrode structure and vapor pressure may not permit a glow discharge). When the anode of this tube becomes only 30 or 40 V positive, electrons from the hot cathode are attracted so that they ionize the gas or vapor; at once a large amount of anode current may flow (limited by the external load circuit) and the anode-to-cathode voltage of the tube decreases to the low value of 10 or 15 V shown at G in Fig. 17-1.

17-5 THE VOLTAGE-REGULATOR TUBE

After alternating current has been rectified and filtered, producing a smooth dc voltage supply (as at D in Fig. 4-12), the amount of this voltage still may change, owing to dips or variations in ac supply voltage or to changes in the dc load current passing through the filter. By adding tube 2 and resistor R_1, as shown in Fig. 17-2, a steady dc voltage is obtained between points 4 and 2. Although the input voltage D may change from 130 to 150 V, the output voltage VV remains at 90 V; the difference appears across resistor R_1, varying from 40 to 60 V in this example. Because of the electrode construction of this voltage-regulator tube and the neon gas that fills its enclosure at low pressure, this cold-cathode tube has a natural drop of 90 V between anode and cathode; to produce this, a current of 10 to 50 milliamperes (mA) must flow through the tube at all times, as described above.

As shown by its symbol in Fig. 17-2, the VR tube has an anode and a cathode but no filament. Such a cold-cathode tube shows a colored glow (red for neon gas, purple for argon, etc.) as soon as the starting voltage is applied to the tube terminals. The cathode, or negative electrode, glows more brightly as more electrons cross to the anode. In any such gas- or vapor-

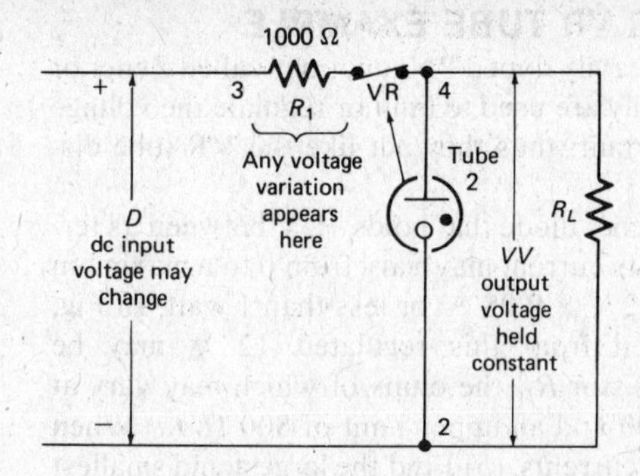

Figure 17-2 Circuit of a voltage-regulator (VR) tube.

filled enclosure, some of the gas particles are already charged (ionized[17-2]); when the starting voltage is applied, these charges move with enough speed to ionize the other particles and supply the needed flow of electrons. Most regulator tubes have large cathode surfaces and small anodes, so that lower voltage is needed to cause electron flow from cathode to anode than in the opposite direction.

To watch the VR tube as it works, the load resistor R_L may be disconnected in Fig. 17-2 for a moment, so that only tube 2 is in the circuit with resistor R_1. If input D is 130 volts (V), this entire voltage is applied across tube 2 until current starts to flow. The natural action of tube 2 is to pass enough current so that only 90 V will remain between its anode and its cathode; this current, flowing also through the 1000 ohms (Ω) of R_1, must be of the right amount to absorb the difference between 130 and 90 V, or 40 V. Since 40 V/1000 Ω = 0.04 A, this 40 mA must flow through resistor R_1 (and tube 2), so that only 90 V remains across tube 2. If D rises to 140 V, tube 2 instantly responds by increasing its current flow to 50 mA; this greater current, flowing through R_1, increases the voltage across R_1 to 50 V; the voltage across tube 2 remains at 90 V, while the 10-V increase is absorbed across R_1.

When the resistor R_L is reconnected in Fig. 17-2, it represents any voltage-divider load connected to the regulated 90-V dc supply; notice how regulator tube 2 responds. If D is 130 V and R_L totals 4500 Ω, the drop across R_1 is still 40 V and the current through R_1 is still 40 mA. However, part of this current now flows through R_L, equal to 90 V/4500 Ω = 20 mA. When this 20-mA load current drawn by R_L is added, the current through R_1 tries to increase and cause greater drop across R_1 to decrease voltage VV. But tube 2 immediately decreases its own current, now drawing only 20 mA, so that the total current through tube 2 and R_L is again 40 mA; VV remains at 90 V. (If voltage-regulator tube 2 is removed from its socket, a jumper between two of its base pins opens the connection at VR in Fig. 17-2; this prevents excess voltage from reaching the load circuits.)

17-6 A ZENER-DIODE OR VR TUBE EXAMPLE

Section 7-18 describes certain heavily doped PN junctions called Zener or breakdown diodes. These commonly are used to limit or regulate the voltage applied to a certain part of the circuit; thus they act like the VR tube discussed above.

The following example uses a Zener diode that holds 12 V between its terminals (anode and cathode) while its current may vary from 0 to a maximum of 80 mA; therefore, its rating is 12 V × 0.08 A, or less than 1 watt. In Fig. 17-3, the changing load supplied from this regulated 12 V may be represented by a variable load resistor R_L, the ohms of which may vary at random between a low limit of 300 and an upper limit of 800 Ω. (*a*) When $D = 21$ V, find the range of Zener currents. (*b*) Find the largest and smallest values of D at which the Zener operates within its rating.

(*a*) The voltage drop across the 150-Ω buffer resistor must be $21 - 12 = 9$ V. Total current $= 9\text{ V}/150\ \Omega = 60\text{ mA} = I_1$.

When $R_L = 300\ \Omega$, $I_3 = 12\text{ V}/300\ \Omega = 40$ mA; therefore,

$$I_2 = 60 - 40 = 20\text{ mA}$$

When $R_L = 800\ \Omega$, $I_3 = 12\text{ V}/800\ \Omega = 15$ mA; therefore,

$$I_2 = 60 - 15 = 45\text{ mA}$$

The range of Zener current is from 20 to 45 mA.

(*b*) When $R_L = 300\ \Omega$, thus using the largest load current I_3, the applied D must have reached its lowest value when the Zener current nears zero. If the load current increases, while operating at this lowest value of D, the Zener no longer conducts; so the voltage across R_L rises; therefore, the largest possible load current must be used in this calculation. Thus $I_2 + I_3 = 40$ mA $= I_1$. Across the 150-Ω resistor is 6 V; so the applied $D_{\min} = 12$ V (across the Zener) + 6 V = 18 V.

When $R_L = 800\ \Omega$, using the least load current (15 mA), D must be at its greatest value when the Zener current also is greatest (80 mA). Thus $80 + 15 = 95\text{ mA} = I_1$. Across the 150-Ω resistor is 95 mA × 150 Ω = 14.25 V. So the applied $D_{\max} = 12\text{ V} + 14.25\text{ V} = 26.25$ V.

17-7 ELECTRON TUBES OR SCRS AS AN AC SWITCH

Although each electron tube acts by itself as a rectifier, a pair of triode tubes (or SCRs) can be connected, as in Fig. 17-4, to pass alternating current and to act as a single-pole ac switch. This connection, wherein the anode of each triode is connected to the cathode of its companion triode, is known as the "back-to-back," or inverse-parallel, connection. As shown in Fig. 17-4, triode *A* passes current during the half cycle marked *A*; line 2 is positive during this half cycle; so electrons pass from line 1 through the load to point 3 and up through *A* to line 2. During those half cycles marked *B*, line 1 is posi-

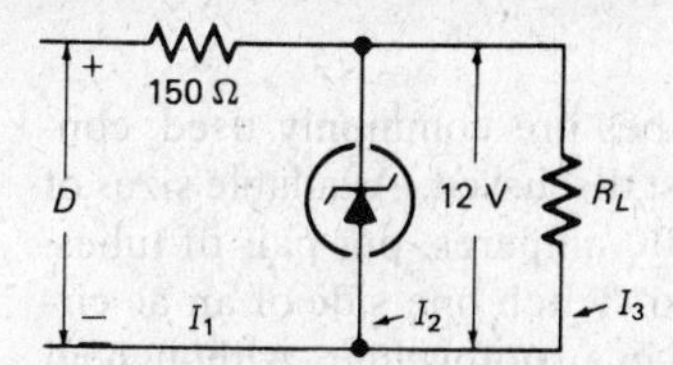

Figure 17-3 A constant-voltage example, using a Zener diode.

tive; so electrons pass from line 2, up through B to point 3, and through the load to line 1. In each case electrons flow in just one triode, cathode to anode; current flows in *either* direction through this combination of triodes. (At the right, Fig. 17-4 shows a pair of SCRs connected back to back, like those in Fig. 9-4.)

Since the SCRs in Fig. 17-4 have gates, no current flows as long as the gates are kept sufficiently negative. When the gate potential of both SCRs is raised, both triodes conduct; so alternating current flows through the load. In this way, two triodes act together like a single-pole ac switch but have the advantages that they are noiseless and have no moving parts.

Thyratron tubes handle about 40 amperes per circuit. Since a thyratron is a gaseous or vapor-filled tube, its grid can prevent current flow but it cannot control the *amount* of current flowing at any instant. (This is similar to the gate control of an SCR, in Sec. 9-1.) Whenever the grid permits the thyratron to "fire" or pass current, the amount of that current is limited only by the external load circuit. This current continues to flow during the rest of the half cycle or until after the anode voltage reverses. For practical pruposes, in an ac circuit we may consider that a thyratron can be grid-controlled (or an SCR can be gate-controlled) so as either to close a circuit or to open it at the start of the next cycle.

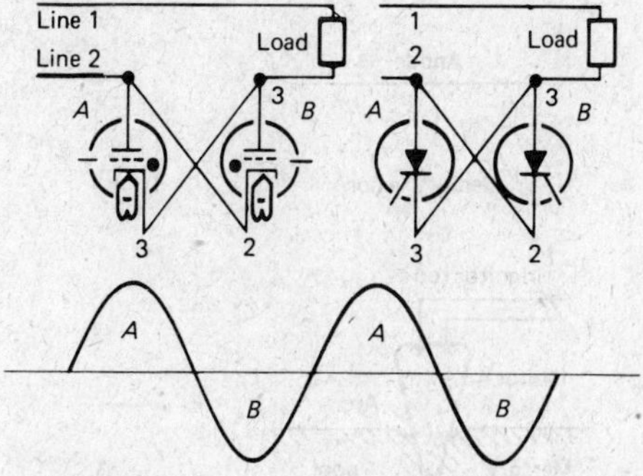

Figure 17-4 Tubes or SCRs connected back to back.

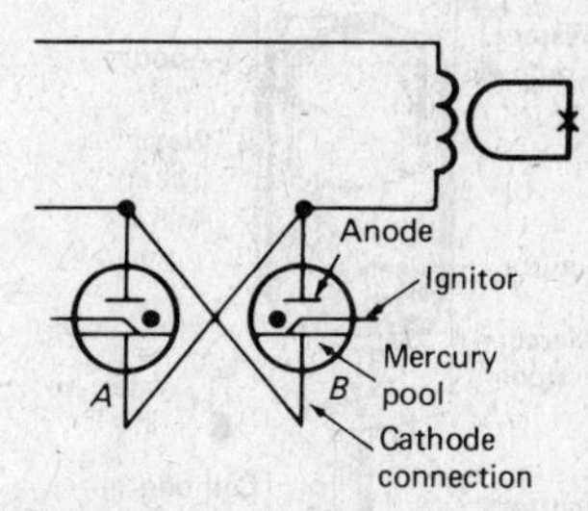

Figure 17-5 Ignitrons, back to back, switching a welder load.

17-8 THE IGNITRON

To control very large ac loads, ignitron tubes are commonly used, connected in pairs like the SCRs or thyratrons just discussed. Available sizes of ignitron will handle currents from 40 to 10,000 amperes, per pair of tubes. Figure 17-5 shows two ignitrons connected to switch one side of an ac circuit feeding a transformer load, such as found in a spot welder. Although ignitrons may handle steady loads of hundreds of amperes, their ability to carry extremely high currents for a short time makes them especially suited to the frequent switching of larger currents. It is common practice to use a pair of ignitrons to pass several thousand amperes for only one or two cycles, repeated on and off a hundred times per minute.

The ignitron is a gaseous tube, but it is not a heated or thermionic tube. As shown by its symbol in Fig. 17-5, it has no filament but uses a pool of liquid mercury as its cathode. If an arc can be started by some means within the ignitron, huge quantities of electrons are driven up out of the surface of the cold mercury pool and are attracted to the single large carbon anode whenever that anode is much more positive than the mercury pool. The ignitron is a rectifier—it produces electrons from only one element, the mercury pool; so its electrons can flow in only one direction, from cathode to anode. So much current may flow in such a tube that a large amount of heat is produced during normal operation. (With a constant arc drop of 15 V, an average load current of 1000 A causes 15,000 W of heat, so that 7.5 kW must be removed from each tube.) To remove this heat, enough water must circulate in the tube water jacket to keep the tube within its safe operating temperature limit. In most circuits the contacts of a thermostat will prevent the flow of current

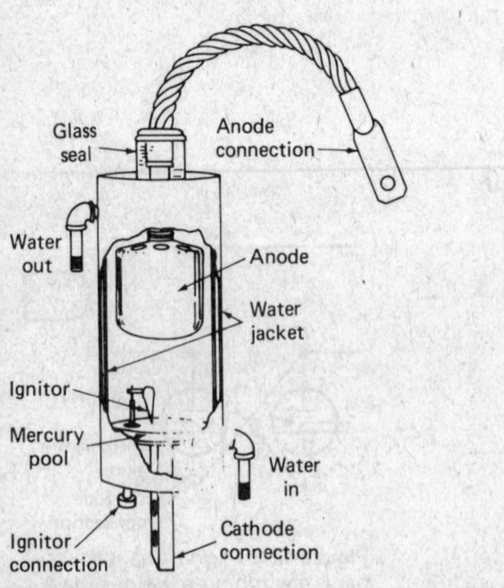

Figure 17-6 Ignitron tube, cut away to show inside.

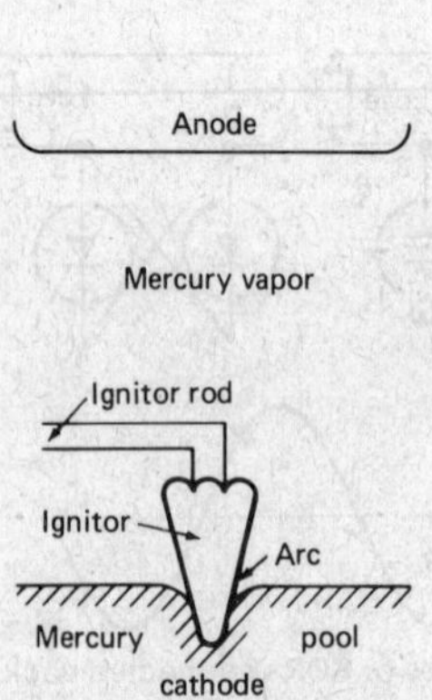

Figure 17-7 Parts that fire an ignitron.

through the ignitrons if the temperature of water or tube becomes too high. The metal water jacket and tube wall are electrically connected to the mercury-pool cathode, as shown in the cutaway view in Fig. 17-6. The large flexible cable at the top connects to the anode of the ignitron, whereas the similar cable of a large SCR connects to its cathode (in Fig. 9-1).

17-9 THE IGNITOR

Until an arc is started inside the ignitron, current cannot flow, for no electrons are freed from the cathode. In contrast, an SCR or thyratron passes current whenever the anode is more positive than the cathode and no restraining gate or grid potential is present.

The ignitor, or starter, is a tapered piece of boron carbide that extends down into the mercury pool but is not wet by it. As shown in Fig. 17-7, the mercury surface is slightly depressed by the ignitor tip. The material of the ignitor is selected because there is considerable resistance (10 to 500 Ω) measured between the ignitor and the mercury pool while they are in direct contact. This being true, a tiny arc is started in the narrow depression next to the ignitor tip, when the tip becomes about 100 V more positive than the pool.

Although only a 100-V drop may be needed for starting this arc, this voltage is applied between parts that are so close together that an extremely high voltage gradient exists, producing an intense electric field, which pulls electrons out of the mercury pool. This is the fourth form of electron emission that has been encountered:

1. Thermionic emission, occurring when the cathode is heated[2-9,2-12,2-16]

2. Photoelectric emission, occurring when certain cathode materials receive light energy

3. Secondary emission, occurring when the anode or grid is hit by other electrons or when the cathode is hit by positive ions[17-4]

4. Field emission, occurring when a very great electric field is present (as in the ignitron, above)

5. Radioactive emission, given off from materials like radium[23-16]

If the load current flowing through the ignitor and into the arc is large enough (20 to 40 A), the top of the ignitor rod becomes much more positive than the mercury pool, and thus it attracts the electrons newly released by the arc. These moving electrons ionize the particles of mercury vapor in the space above them; the positively charged ions are attracted to the cathode with such force that they dislodge huge quantities of electrons from the mercury pool, by secondary emission. These electrons now may pass directly from the mercury pool to the large carbon anode above. Enough electrons can be freed from the pool to carry any required current, which continues to flow until after the anode voltage is reversed at the end of that half cycle. This whole process must be repeated for each half cycle during which the ignitron is to pass current. When anode current has started, the ignitor arc is no longer needed; soon it will be seen that the ignitor current stops when anode current starts.

17-10 SIMPLE IGNITRON CONTROL

A simple arrangement for controlling ignitrons is shown in Fig. 17-8. If we close switches *S* and *T* at the time marked *X* (in half cycle *A*, while line 2 is positive), ignitron *A* instantly passes current, which flows during the rest of half cycle *A*. However, ignitron *B* cannot pass current until half cycle *B* (when line 1 is positive) and after the current of tube *A* stops.

Notice that the circuit through *S* and the ignitor is in parallel with the main cathode-to-anode circuit of tube *A*. When *S* closes, current first flows through the ignitor and *S*, causing the arc that ionizes the mercury vapor in tube *A*. This instantly permits load electrons to flow directly from cathode to anode in tube *A*. The resistance of this main current path from cathode to anode is so much less than that of the circuit through the ignitor resistance and *S* that the current flowing in the ignitor becomes very small. As soon as the current stops flowing in tube *A* and the potential at the anode of ignitron *B* has become more positive than its cathode, tube *B* is then "fired" in the same manner, by electrons flowing first through the ignitor and switch *T*, which instantly makes the mercury vapor in tube *B* able to carry the load electrons directly from cathode to anode. We see that although the load current is carried mainly by the cathode-anode circuit, this flow must be started, or "ignited," every half cycle separately. In Sec. 18-2 this pair of ignitrons is controlled by a single switch for use as an ignitron contactor.

roblems

17-1 True or false? Explain why.

- **(a)** When a tube rectifier supplies current to an inductive load, momentary negative voltages may appear across the load.
- **(b)** There is nearly as much space charge in a phanotron as in a high-vacuum tube.
- **(c)** A colored glow inside a tube indicates that part of the tube is heated.
- **(d)** The voltage drop across a phanotron nearly doubles when it passes twice as much current.
- **(e)** For tubes connected back to back, the voltage across one tube must be exactly equal to the voltage across the other.
- **(f)** A two-tube full-wave rectifier (without filter) furnishes a smooth flow of direct current to a resistance load.

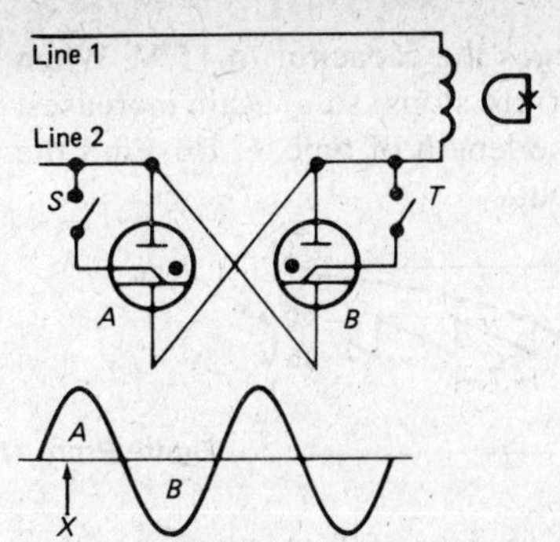

Figure 17-8 A simple method (never used) for firing ignitrons.

(g) Four ignitrons would be needed to close both sides of an ac circuit, like a two-pole contactor.

(h) When two ignitrons are connected in parallel or two thyratrons are connected back to back, only one tube passes current at any instant.

(i) The only requirement for firing an ignitron tube is that its anode and its ignitor be about 100 V positive.

(j) The internal resistance of a vapor-filled tube decreases as the plate current increases.

(k) The amount of glow in a gas-filled tube is constant when the plate current varies.

17-2 Each gas tube in Fig. 17-4 is carrying its rated current of 12.5 amperes (A) average and has an arc drop of 15 volts (V). Assume that the load current has a sine waveshape and that the load resistance is 4.2 ohms (Ω). (*a*) Find the peak voltage between lines and the rms voltage supplied. (*b*) Find the watts received by the load.

17-3 Below, Z is a 12-V Zener diode. If V is 22.5 V, what value of R lets Z operate at 25 mA? With this same value of R and I_3, find the maximum and minimum values of V that will keep Z within its limits of 0 to 40 mA.

Figure Prob. 17-3

17-4 Work Prob. 17-3 if Z is a 15-V Zener diode rated 60 mA. Let $V = 27$ V and $R = 150\ \Omega$. Find minimum and maximum values of load resistance through which the variable I_3 flows.

17-5 When S closes, v_z increases to 20 V, so that Zener diode Z conducts;

instantly the Zener current discharges the capacitor to 15 V. When v_z drops below 15 V, the Zener current stops; so v_z again increases, firing Z again at 20 V. (*a*) Find the length of time T. (*b*) Find the frequency of the pulses at the output.

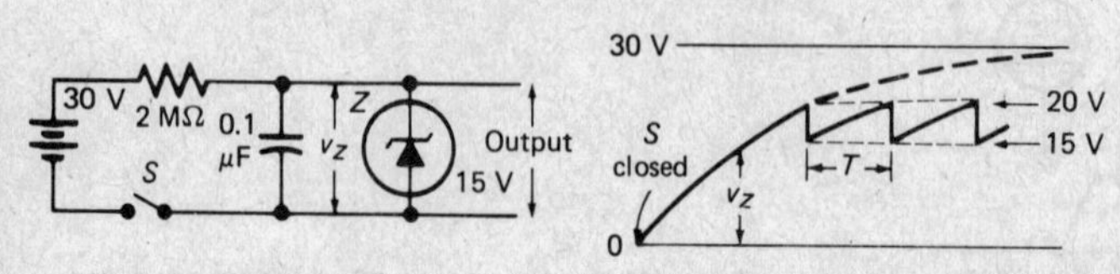

Figure Prob. 17-5

17-6 A dc voltage V is applied across a resistor of R Ω in series with a Zener diode, holding constant 12 V across a load resistor, which also has R Ω. The current through the Zener remains constant 30 mA. Plot the value of V required, for R = 12, 50, 200, and 1200 Ω.

17-7 The drop across tube B is 90 V if its current is between 5 and 60 mA. (*a*) How much current flows while R_L is disconnected? (*b*) With R_L connected, find the three currents. (*c*) With R_L connected, if V drops to 168 V, find the three currents.

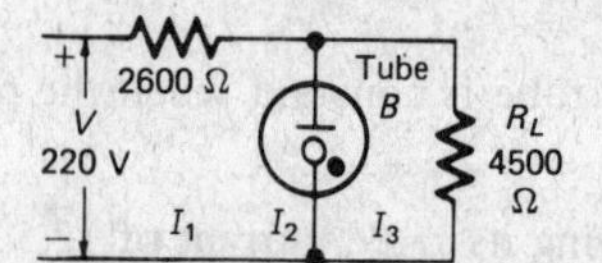

Figure Prob. 17-7

17-8 Find the minimum and maximum values of applied V for which the above circuit can regulate or hold the 300-V output if the current in each tube C and D must be kept between 5 and 40 mA.

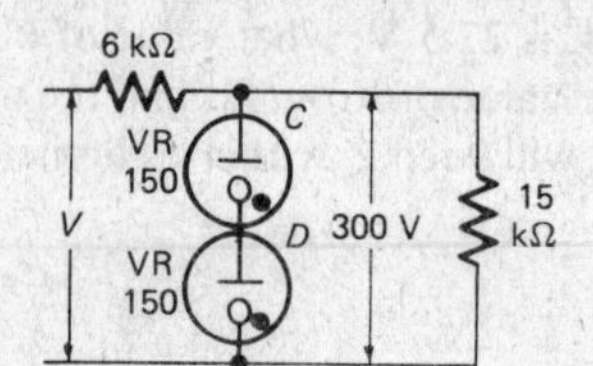

Figure Prob. 17-8

17-9 In a circuit like that of Prob. 17-7, the buffer resistor is rated 2130 ohms (Ω), 10 watts (W). Applied voltage V = 266 volts (V). If the current in this resistor produces exactly this rated heat loss and if the current in the VR tube is 20 milliamperes (mA), find (*a*) the voltage rating of the VR tube, (*b*) the ohms of the load resistor R_L.

18

RESISTANCE-WELDING CONTROL: IGNITRON CONTACTOR

A pair of ignitron tubes,[17-8] arranged so as to start and stop the large flow of current in an ac circuit, is called an ignitron contactor. (A pair of water-cooled SCRs often is used in place of smaller ignitrons as shown in Fig. 18-2*b*; the rating of such SCRs is included in Fig. 18-8.) Such large-current contactors are used most often in the control of resistance-welding machines.

18-1 RESISTANCE WELDING

Two pieces of metal may be welded or fused together by passing large current (1000 to 100,000 amperes) through these pieces while they are being forced together between the electrodes of the welding machine. (But when pieces of metal are being joined or welded together by a bright electric arc, which melts a rod into a pool of metal, the process is called *arc welding*. No arc-welding equipment is described herein.) Figure 18-1 shows how a single phase of the ac supply is received from the power line and transformer so that it passes, at 230 or 460 volts, through a disconnecting device and then through a contactor before reaching the welding machine. Inside the machine, a welding transformer reduces the voltage at the electrode tips to 1 to 10V and supplies the large welding current, while drawing perhaps 50 to 2000 A from the ac supply; the electrode tips are water-cooled and must be kept clean.

To make a weld, the required heat $H = I^2Rt$, or heat equals (current) × (current) × (resistance between the pieces welded) × (time while current flows). Since there must be resistance to current flow between the metal pieces, where most of the weld heat is produced, this process is called *resis-*

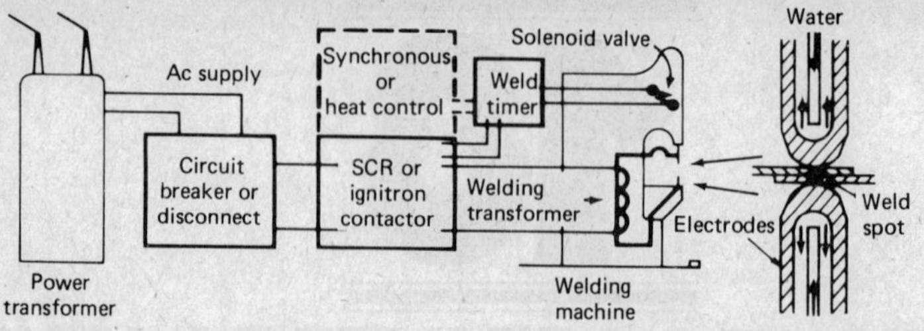

Figure 18-1 Welding machine and its electrical equipment.

tance welding. This resistance depends on the metal that is being welded: steel has high resistance, and welding heat is easily produced; aluminum has low resistance, and the welding heat is harder to obtain. Furthermore, this resistance between the metal pieces decreases when they are forced together by the electrodes with greater pressure. To make a weld, current needs to flow for only part of a second; the contactor must close and open the circuit quickly, and it does this hundreds of times each hour. While magnetic contactors control many such welders, ignitron contactors and other electronic equipments are used where better welds must be made in shorter time with less contactor noise and maintenance.

To make a single spot weld, the pieces of metal are placed in the space between the two electrodes, one of which can move. When the operator presses the button or the foot switch, a solenoid valve applies air pressure so that the electrodes come together and squeeze the metal pieces. Welding current then flows to heat the metal and make the weld. The metal is held under pressure for a moment until the weld hardens; then the electrodes separate so that the metal can be moved before the next weld is started. All these actions of the welding machine are controlled by circuits described in Sec. 18-15 and in Chap. 19. In this complete welding operation or cycle, notice that the ignitron contactor controls only the brief flow of current that produces the weld.

18-2 THE IGNITRON CONTACTOR

An ignitron contactor is shown in Fig. 18-2; it is seen to consist mainly of a pair of large ignitron tubes or a pair of water-cooled SCRs.

Instead of two ignitor circuits controlled by separate switches (as in Fig. 17-8), the ignitors can be connected together through a single control switch *S*, as shown in Fig. 18-3. With *S* closed and line 2 positive, electrons flow from line 1, through the transformer load to point 3, from the mercury pool of tube *A* into its ignitor to 5, through contact *S* and into ignitor 4, to the mercury pool of tube *B*, to point 2 and line 2. This causes the arc between cathode 3 and ignitor 5 and "fires" tube *A*, which immediately passes electrons from cathode 3 to anode 2. Although this ignitor current fires tube *A* in

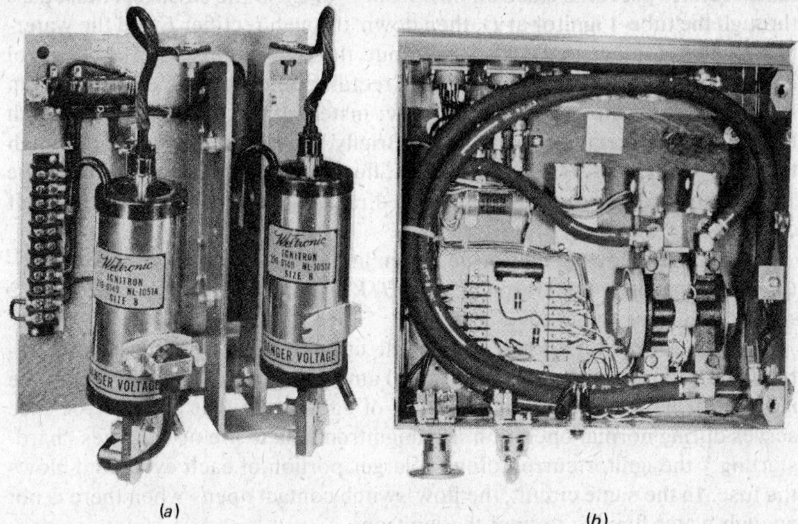

(a) (b)

Figure 18-2 (*a*) An ignitron contactor; (*b*) an SCR contactor.

a normal way, these same electrons flow in reverse direction in tube *B*, or from ignitor 4 to pool 2. Such reverse current definitely damages the ignitor and shortens tube life. To prevent this reverse current, metallic (copper oxide or selenium) rectifiers are added into the circuit, as shown in Fig. 18-4.

Figure 18-4 shows the circuit used in a typical ignitron contactor. The ignitrons, connected back to back, close or open only one side of the ac line. When the control contact is closed (as may be done by a sequence timer, described in Sec. 18-15), both ignitrons pass current; each tube conducts during the half cycle when its own anode is positive. When line *J* (which connects to the anode of tube 1 in Fig. 18-4) is more positive than line *A*, electrons flow from *A* through the welder transformer to *B* and *C*. Here the me-

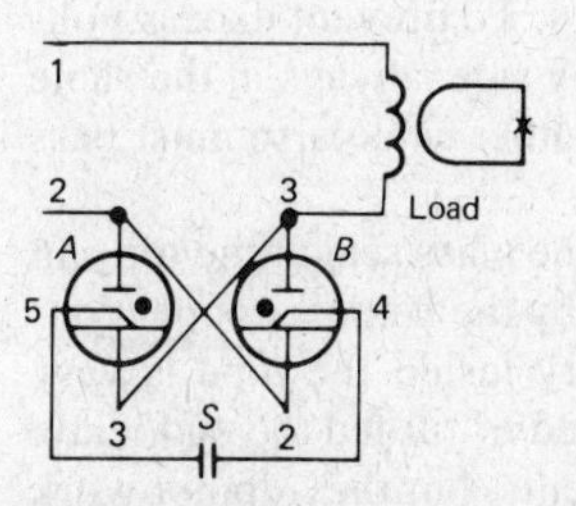

Figure 18-3 One switch *S* may fire both ignitrons.

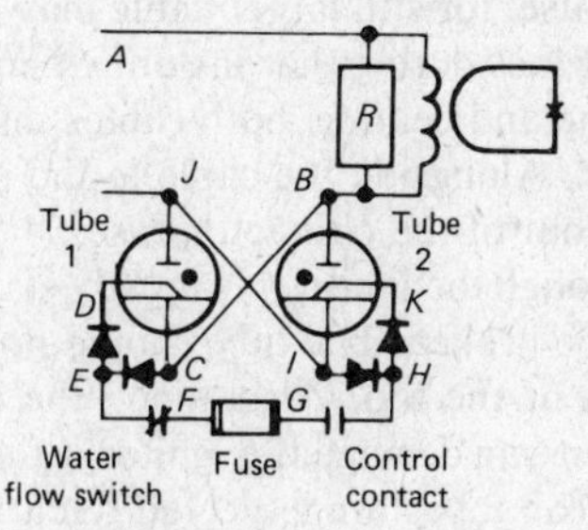

Figure 18-4 Circuit of ignitron contactor.

tallic rectifier prevents electron flow from *C* to *E*; so the electrons must pass through the tube-1 ignitor at *D*, then down through rectifier *E* and the water-flow-switch contact to *F*. They continue through the fuse and the control contact to rectifier *H*. Here the upper rectifier unit prevents electrons from flowing through the tube-2 ignitor at *K*; instead, they pass directly through the other part of rectifier *H* to *I* and *J*. Briefly, the electrons first flow through the path *ABCDEFGHIJ*. This current, flowing through ignitor *D*, fires tube 1 so that electrons now may flow more directly *ABCJ* for the rest of the half cycle.

During the following half cycle, when line *A* is more positive than *J*, ignitor electrons flow first through path *JIKHGFECBA*, which fires tube 2 so that electrons then flow *JIBA*.

The control circuit *EFGH* carries the current of each ignitor in turn. Although this current must reach 25 to 40 amperes (A) momentarily to fire the ignitron, it flows such a small portion of each cycle that a 3- or 6-A fuse serves during normal operation. If an ignitron fails to fire or becomes "hard-starting," the ignitor current flows a larger portion of each cycle and blows the fuse. In the same circuit, the flow-switch contact opens when there is not enough water flowing to cool the ignitrons.

In Fig. 18-4, resistor *R* is connected across the welding transformer, to bypass surge voltages. This resistor is usually a Thyrite[32-7] unit. In a circuit using ignitrons or thyratrons, it is desirable to use such Thyrite resistors across any inductive load, such as a transformer or a motor field; to be effective, the Thyrite must be connected close to the inductive load.

18-3 OPERATING THE IGNITRON CONTACTOR

Since each ignitron contains a pool of mercury, the contactor case must be mounted so that the ignitrons are held straight up and down and without vibration. Their location must not permit the cooling water to freeze within the tubes.

Very large cables may be required between the power supply and the welder, since thousands of amperes may flow during the few cycles while each weld is made. The heating of the cable usually does not determine what size to use, for still larger cable may be needed to prevent excessive voltage drop or loss during that instant when current flows. To prevent excess voltage drop and heating both cables must run side by side, always in the same conduit. Alongside the cable to the ignitrons the other cable also must pass in and out of the contactor case.

Although the ignitron is mostly stainless steel, the glass seal at the top can easily be broken. The tube should not be handled by the flexible copper connection at the top. Also, since the liquid mercury inside the tube is very heavy, it can damage the ignitor if the tube is tipped or turned too suddenly.

Ignitron tubes are expected to carry large currents, but they do not work well on current loads less than 25 to 40 A. When such low loads are possible at any time, a "dummy" load must be connected across the welding transformer. This is a separate resistor that draws additional line current of about 25A whenever welding current flows.

The water-flow switch may be a separate mechanical device within the ignitron contactor. The water that cools the ignitrons flows also through this switch. If the water flow stops, the switch soon opens its electrical contact, shown in Fig. 18-4, which prevents further firing of the ignitrons. A present design of ignitron tube includes a water-switch device on the side of the tube. When the temperature of the wall of the tube rises above a safe value, this thermostat opens an electrical contact that prevents further firing of the ignitrons.

18-4 OSCILLOSCOPE PICTURES OF CIRCUIT OPERATION

This same arrangement of ignitron tubes is also a basic part of more complex controls for resistance welders, as described in Sec. 18-15. In service, the performance of such ignitron tubes with SCRs or thyratrons is best observed by means of an oscilloscope.[31-14] The odd waveshapes seen with the "scope" connected in a typical welder circuit are shown in Fig. 18-6. To understand these better, we must remember the constant arc drop[17-3] of a vapor-filled tube and also see how the power factor of the load affects the tube operation.

When a switch controls a load, the entire circuit voltage appears across the open contacts of the switch. When the switch closes, no voltage remains across the contacts but the circuit voltage appears across the load. Similarly, ignitrons have circuit voltage between anode and cathode as long as no current flows. When these tubes "fire," the circuit voltage disappears from across the tubes and appears across the load—that is, all except the drop of 10 to 20 V that remains across the tube when it passes current; this is the constant arc drop of a mercury-vapor-filled tube.

If oscilloscope leads are connected to anode and cathode of such a tube, the trace of ac line voltage is seen until the tube fires; then the trace drops instantly to within 15V of the zero centerline. Figure 18-5 shows such a voltage trace measured across the tubes in an ignitron contactor. The control switch closes at J and opens at K. Here a resistance load (noninductive) is assumed; so the current is shown in phase with the voltage. [When the alternating current through a load is *in phase* with the ac voltage applied across this load (as when the load has resistance, such as lamps or heaters, but has no inductance), the load is said to have unity, or 1.0, power factor. More often the load is inductive (such as the winding and magnetic iron core of a welding transformer), so that the current wave lags behind the voltage wave; this load is said to have a *lagging power factor*. Power factor usually is

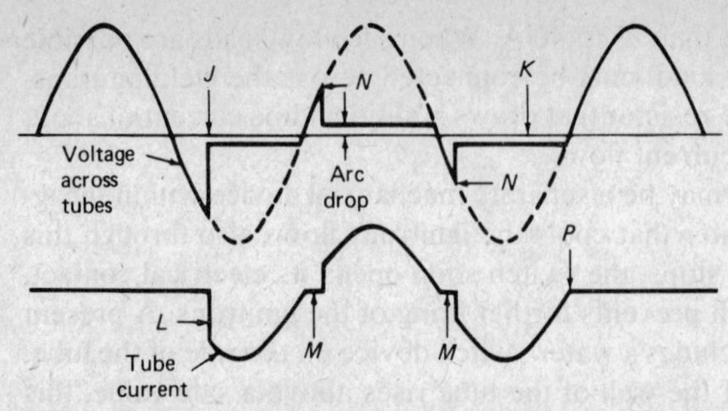

Figure 18-5 Waveshapes of voltage and current—ignitrons with resistance load.

expressed as a number (such as 1.0 or 0.7, or 70 percent) that is the cosine of the phase angle by which the current wave lags (or leads) the voltage wave.]

In Fig. 18-5 (for resistance load) notice the current at *L*, increasing suddenly to its normal value on the sine wave. Also, no current flows at *M*, because an ignitron cannot pass current until the voltage wave rises high enough (at *N*) to force enough ignitor current to cause the arc at the ignitor tip. At least 100 V may be required before the ignitron fires. Also, although the control switch opens at *K*, the tube does not stop its current flow until *P*, where its anode voltage reverses.

18-5 OPERATION WITH WELDER LOAD

For comparison with Fig. 18-5, the curves in Fig. 18-6 show how the ignitron contactor behaves when it passes current to a welder transformer, which is a lagging-power-factor load and is highly inductive. When current flows, it lags behind the voltage by the amount *R*. When the control switch closes at *Q*, the current does not increase suddenly at *S*, for the welder inductance (acting like a flywheel) prevents any sudden current change. Instead, the current increases gradually, like a sine wave. As soon as this current starts, the voltage across the tubes immediately decreases to the 15-V arc drop. Although the circuit voltage reverses at *T*, tube-2 current does not stop, nor does tube 1 start at this point. Instead, tube 2 continues to pass current later than *T*, for the energy stored in the inductance of the welder transformer forces this current to flow until *U*.

Meanwhile, as long as tube 2 continues to pass current, the anode-to-cathode voltage of both tubes is only 15 V, which is not enough to fire tube 1. When the tube-2 current stops at *U* (since no energy remains in the welder transformer to cause further current flow), suddenly the entire voltage *V* becomes available across tube 1. Most of this voltage *V* quickly forces current through tube-1 ignitor and fires tube 1. This all occurs within a few microseconds—so fast that the voltage trace on the oscilloscope may not

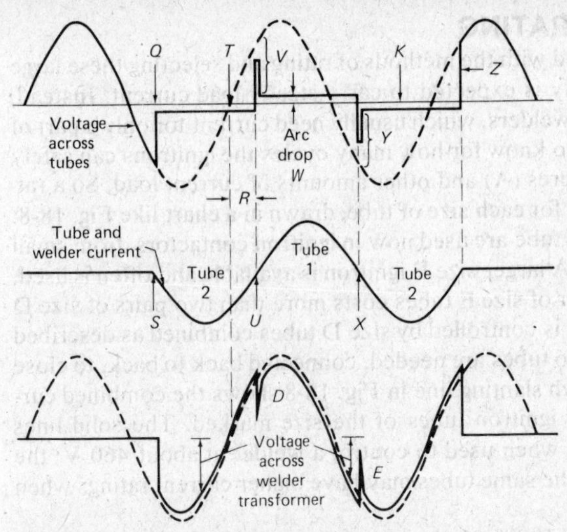

Figure 18-6 Waveshapes of ignitron contactor with welder load.

reach the line voltage curve at V but returns to the arc-drop voltage at W. Tube 1 now carries all the current, until, at point X, the current dies out and voltage Y is then able to restart tube 2. At K, the control switch is opened, but tube 2 continues to pass current until the end of its half cycle. As this current stops, voltage Z appears across tube 1, but it cannot restart tube 1, for the ignitor circuit has been opened by the control contact.

During every instant that tube current flows, voltage is applied to the welder transformer. If the oscilloscope leads are connected across the welder-transformer primary, a trace appears similar to the lower curve in Fig. 18-6. The "slivers" of voltage D and E are not received by the welder transformer; these are the voltage peaks that are applied across the ignitor circuits at the instant when each ignitron tube is being fired. As is shown again in Fig. 18-7, the peak at D fires tube 1. As long as both ignitrons fire or conduct normally, peaks such as D or E are small, narrow and uniform in size. However, if the oscilloscope shows larger erratic peaks, as at F in Fig. 18-7, this indicates that ignitron tube 1 has become "hard-starting" and should be replaced.

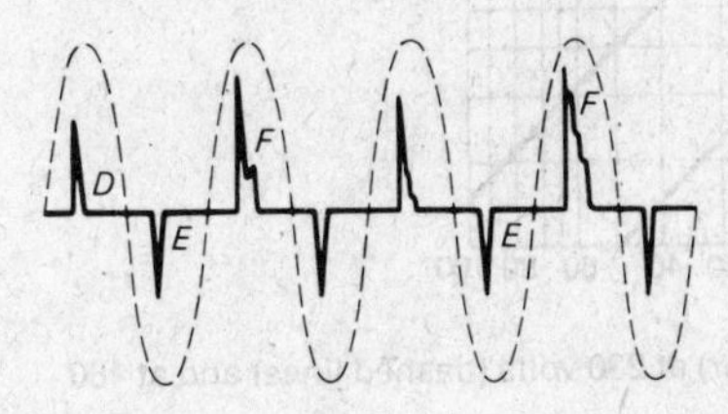

Figure 18-7 Ignitor-current peaks, showing a "hard-starting" ignitron.

18-6 IGNITRON RATING

We must be concerned with the methods of rating and selecting these large tubes. An ignitron rarely is expected to carry steady load current. Instead, ignitrons are used with welders, which usually need current for only a part of each second. We want to know for how many cycles the ignitrons can safely carry 600 or 1500 amperes (A) and other amounts of current load. So a rating curve or line is used for each size of tube, drawn in a chart like Fig. 18-8.

Four sizes of ignitron tube are used now in ignitron contactors, from small size A to large size D. (A larger size E ignitron is available and often is used. However, since one pair of size E tubes costs more than two pairs of size D tubes, a large load often is controlled by size D tubes combined as described in Sec. 18-14.) Since two tubes are needed, connected back to back, to close one line to a welder, each slanting line in Fig. 18-8 shows the combined current rating of a *pair* of ignitron tubes of the size marked. The solid lines show the ampere rating when used to control a welder at about 460 V; the dashed lines show that the same tubes may have higher current ratings when operated at 230 V.

For comparison, Fig. 18-8 includes a rating curve for a pair of back-to-back SCRs (C501X), as shown in Fig. 18-2 and used in Chap. 19.

At the sides of Fig. 18-8, the numbers show "amperes during weld." Here a logarithmic scale is used (like that on a slide rule), showing current values from 100 to 10,000 A. (On rating curves supplied by tube manufac-

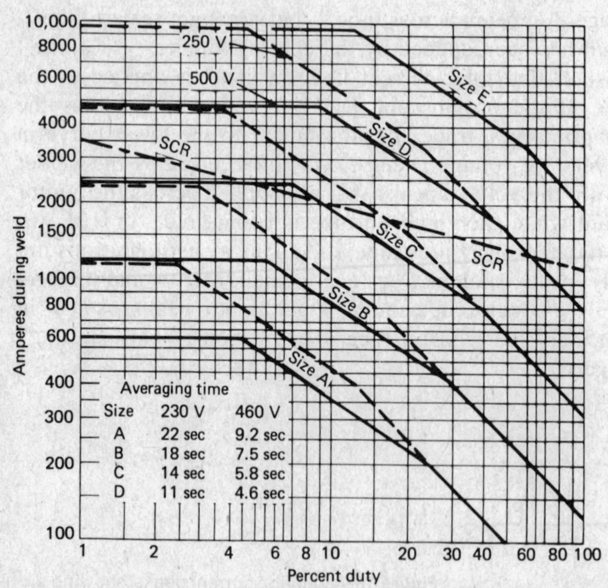

Figure 18-8 Rating curves of ignitron tubes (a pair) at 230 volts (dashed lines) and at 460 volts (solid lines).

turers, this same scale may be called "demand current—amperes rms." "Demand current" shows that this is the current demanded by the welder while the weld is being made and is therefore the same as "amperes during weld." "Amperes rms" means "root-mean-squared amperes," which is another name for *effective current*, such as is shown by an ac ammeter, in contrast to "peak current" indicated by the height of the ac wave shown by an oscilloscope.[4-7])

Along the bottom of Fig. 18-8, numbers from 1 to 100 indicate the "percent duty," discussed in Sec. 18-8. To explain this quickly, tubes that pass current for 10 out of every 100 cycles are working at one-tenth duty, or 10 percent duty. Working 30 cycles during each 60-cycle second is working half the time, or 50 percent duty. Tubes working steadily, without resting, are working at 100 percent duty, and such continuous ratings are shown at the right side of the chart. In Fig. 18-8, the 40 percent duty line and the size C line cross at about 800 A. This shows that 800 amperes is the load that may be carried by two size C tubes back to back at 40 percent duty, and is not the load carried by one tube alone.

18-7 RATINGS OF IGNITRON CONTACTORS FOR WELDERS

Since ignitron contactors are used for welders in the same way that magnetic contactors are used, it is customary to think of size C tubes to replace a 600-A contactor or to use size D tubes as a 1200-A contactor. These are not actual ratings but are used for convenience.

While ignitron contactors are rated only in amperes, they may be selected to handle a certain kVA load (since kVA is merely amperes × volts/1000). However, the kVA rating of the welding transformer must not be used directly, because the tubes must often carry loads two to four times this transformer rated kVA. As a rough guide for general welding service, size A, B, C, and D tubes may be used for 230-V welders rated 20, 50, 125, and 300 kVA, respectively; the corresponding ratings at 460 V are 40, 100, 250, and 675 kVA.

18-8 PERCENT DUTY

This term applies to the question, "What part of the time do the tubes work?" Similarly, what is a man's "percent duty" if he works 8 hours a day, 5 days a week? Within each day, he is on duty 8 hours out of 24; that is, his percent duty is $^{8}/_{24} \times 100$, or $33^{1}/_{3}$ percent. During a whole week his percent duty is

$$\frac{\text{Total hours worked during 1 week}}{\text{All the hours there are in 1 week}} \times 100 = \frac{40\text{ hr}}{168\text{ hr}} \times 100 = 24\text{ percent}$$

In the same way, if an ignitron contactor passes current into a welder for 8 cycles, followed by 16 cycles off, when no current passes, the ignitrons are working 8 out of 24 cycles, or at about 33 percent duty.

If a 460-V welder takes 600 A for a weld lasting 8 cycles and makes five welds every 2 sec, the total time for each welding operation must be

$$\frac{2\text{ sec}}{5\text{ welds}} = \frac{120\text{ cycles}}{5} = 24\text{ cycles}$$

Since current flows for 8 cycles during each 24 cycles, the tubes operate at about 33 percent duty. In Fig. 18-8, the 600-A line crosses the 33 percent duty line at a point that is above the slanting size B line but is below the size C line. This load is therefore too much for size B ignitrons, but size C tubes will carry it easily.

18-9 AVERAGING TIME

To find the right value of percent duty to use above, all figuring must be done within a certain number of seconds, called the *averaging time*. In Fig. 18-8 notice that for each size of tube the averaging time in seconds is given; it is less at 460 V than it is at 230 V. To show the reason for this averaging time, a similar time may apply to a 10-horsepower motor that can carry 10-hp load all day. That motor probably can also carry 20-hp load for 1 minute during each 4 min if it carries no load during the other 3 min. The heat produced by current passing through a motor or a cable increases as the square of the current, so that doubling the load current increases the heat four times. Working 1 min in 4, it is operating at 25 percent duty. If that motor tries to carry 20-hp load for 1 hour and then rests at no load for 3 hours, the duty is still 25 percent, but the motor probably roasts and fails during the first hour. The motor cannot carry this double load for 25 percent of the hour, but it can carry the overload for 25 percent of some shorter time, such as 15 min. This 15 min is called the averaging time of the motor, since this is the longest time during which it is safe to average the periods of overload and no load. The overload produces extra heat, which is stored in the metal body of the motor until this heat can be removed during the no-load period. But if the overload lasts too long, the motor temperature is raised too high by the stored heat.

The curves near the right-hand side of Fig. 18-8 show that the heat produced by current passing through an ignitron tube increases only in direct proportion to the current. Most ignitrons can carry twice as much current at 50 percent duty as they can carry continuously. Since this differs from the ability of a motor, recall that the resistance of a motor winding or a cable is nearly constant; in contrast, the arc drop of a gaseous tube carrying little current is the same number of volts as when it is carrying full or overload current. Since arc-drop voltage V is constant and $V = IR$ (or voltage equals current multiplied by resistance), then the internal resistance of the tube must be decreasing as the current increases. In this way a vapor-filled tube does not behave like ordinary current conductors, but the heating of the tube increases only in direct proportion to the load current. As a result, all single vapor-filled tubes may be rated in average amperes instead of amperes rms. But at duty cycles below 50 percent, heating is not the only limiting factor, as is shown by the left-hand portion of Fig. 18-8.

Similar to a motor, the ignitrons may be operated at overloads followed by periods of no load. But the averaging time of ignitron tubes is very short—a matter of merely seconds, not minutes or hours. These tubes contain no mass of metal comparable with a motor or cable of equal current rating; so an ignitron reaches damaging temperatures in less than a minute of overload operation. Ignitrons selected for 50 percent duty may carry their larger current for 1 out of 2 sec, but not for 1 out of 2 min, for this exceeds the published averaging time of the tube.

18-10 COMPLETE CALCULATIONS OF PERCENT DUTY

Including the averaging time, the right value of percent duty can now be calculated for use with the tube-rating curves of Fig. 18-8. The percent duty of the load must be figured on the most severe conditions that can occur during this short averaging time. Easy examples are first offered.

If tubes pass current for 1 sec and then pass no current for 2 sec, they are said to be 1 sec ON, 2 sec OFF. On a 230-V line, suppose size B ignitrons are 1 sec ON and 1 sec OFF, repeating this during a total of 20 sec, and then resting 40 sec before starting all over again. To find the percent duty, the first step is to find the averaging time for these size B tubes at 230 V. Figure 18-8 shows it is 18 sec. Next find the heaviest load condition during any 18 sec; it is during the 20 sec when the tubes are working. Since the 18-sec averaging time is finished before the start of the 40-sec rest time, none of this rest time can be included. During the 18-sec averaging time, these tubes are on a total of 9 sec and off a total of 9 sec. The duty is $^9/_{18} \times 100 = 50$ percent.

If size B ignitrons at 460 V pass current steadily for 5 sec ON and then are OFF for 45 sec, it is a mistake to say that these tubes work 5 sec during 50 sec and that this is 10 percent duty. Instead, since the averaging time from Fig. 18-8 is 7.5 sec, we must forget all time except the 7.5 sec during which the heaviest load occurs. During these 7.5 sec the tubes are on for 5 sec. The correct duty is therefore $^5/_{7.5} \times 100 =$ about 67 percent.

18-11 FORMULA FOR PERCENT DUTY

The formula or general rule is

$$\text{Percent duty} = \frac{\text{total of all ON time, within averaging time}}{\text{total averaging time in cycles}} \times 100$$

For example, a 460-volt welder puts eight spot welds on one steel frame in

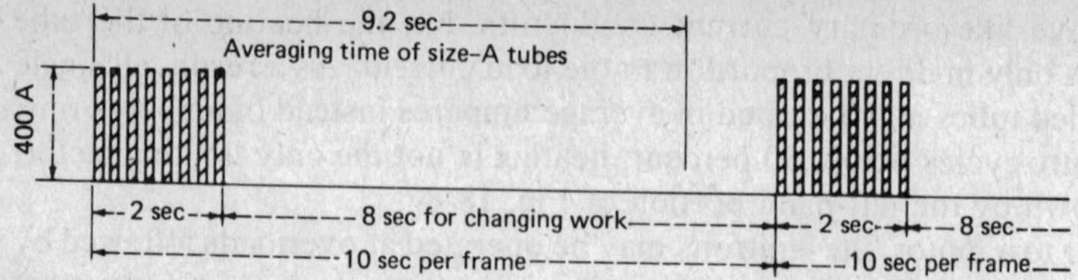

Figure 18-9 Picture of welder operation, to find percent duty.

2 sec and makes six of these frames in a minute. Each spot weld draws 400 amperes for 5 cycles of time. Size A tubes are used. What is the percent duty, and are these tubes overloaded?

It is best to draw a picture to show a duty like this, as shown in Fig. 18-9. Since six frames are made in 1 min, there is a total of 60 sec/6 = 10 sec for welding one frame. The spot welds are made during 2 sec; so this leaves 8 sec for the operator to change work. Figure 18-8 shows 9.2 sec averaging time for size A tubes at 460 V. Figure 18-9 shows that only one frame is welded during any 9.2 sec. So within 9.2 sec there are only the eight spot welds of 5 cycles each, to make one frame. Using the formula above,

$$\text{Percent duty} = \frac{5 \text{ cycles} \times 8 \text{ (spots)}}{60 \text{ cycles} \times 9.2 \text{ (sec)}} \times 100 = \frac{40}{522} \times 100 = \text{about } 7\%$$

In Fig. 18-8, following up the 7 percent duty line, note that size A tubes are rated to carry 430-A load. Since the current drawn by the welder is only 400 A, these size A ignitrons are not overloaded.

18-12 OVERLOADED IGNITRONS

Perhaps the above duty is not the true worst-load condition. It may be that the welder above is expected to make 360 frames an hour, and the ignitron tubes have been selected to give this production, averaged over an hour. Since 360 frames per hour is 6 frames per minute, this is exactly the speed shown in Fig. 18-9; at that speed size A tubes are big enough. But it is well known that in order to produce 360 frames an hour, the operator must weld

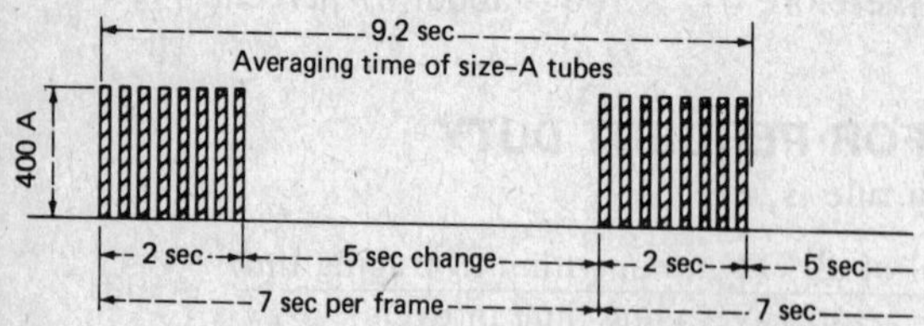

Figure 18-10 Welder operation overloading the ignitrons.

8 or 9 frames per minute for part of the time to make up for occasional lost time or for moving stock. This faster operation never bothers the welder transformer or other parts that can carry overloads for many minutes. However, see what happens to the tubes. Figure 18-10 shows this same welder producing nearly 9 frames per minute, requiring only 7 sec per frame. The operator takes only 5 sec to change work. Within the 9.2-sec averaging time, two frames now are being welded instead of one. The percent duty becomes twice as great as before, or nearly 15 percent. At 15 percent duty on Fig. 18-8, the size A tubes are shown to be rated about 280 A. Used at 400 A, they are being overloaded and should be replaced by size B tubes to prevent damage and to obtain normal tube life. Ignitrons should be selected large enough to handle the load at the greatest speed that the welder will reach during any minute or less.

18-13 CORRECT TUBE AVERAGING TIME

In the above examples the size of ignitron was mentioned; so the averaging time was also fixed. Where the load conditions have been measured and the right size of tube is yet to be found, try one or more sizes. For example, suppose that a larger 460-V welder is making welds at the speed shown in Fig. 18-10 but the measured current during weld is 1600 A. Figure 18-8 quickly shows that size A or size B tubes are far too small. If size D ignitrons are tried first, with 4.6 sec averaging time, the duty is (5 cycles $\times$ 8) / (60 cycles $\times$ 4.6) = 40 / 276 = about 14.5 percent. At this duty in Fig. 18-8, the load of 1600 A is well under the size D curve, but it appears to be just above the curve for the size C tubes, so that size C tubes seem to be too small. But the 14.5 percent duty does not apply to size C tubes. Figure again, using the right averaging time (5.8 sec) for size C tubes, and the duty equals (5 cycles $\times$ 8) / (60 cycles $\times$ 5.8) = 40 / 348 = 11.5 percent. At this lower percent duty, Fig. 18-8 shows that 1600-A load is under the curve for size C tubes. Size C tubes may be used.

18-14 IGNITRON CONTROLS FOR LARGER LOADS

If a new welding machine will require, say, 6000 A from a 460-V supply feeder, Fig. 18-8 shows this current to be greater than size D tubes can carry even at very low duty. Size E tubes[18-6] may be used. Nothing is gained by connecting in parallel several pairs of size D tubes and firing them all at the same time. Ignitrons do not divide the total current in the manner of high-vacuum tubes; whichever ignitron is first to fire will carry the whole load, sharing none of it with another tube in parallel. (When one ignitron fires, the voltage across both ignitrons decreases to the arc drop, which is too small to fire the second tube. Ignitrons sometimes may divide large current loads if reactors are added in their anode circuits.[22-8])

For the 6000-A load above, we may supply two separate welding transformers (whose secondaries are not joined through their contact on the same metal workpiece); each transformer is controlled by its pair of size D ignitrons carrying 3000 A (at less than 18 percent duty, from Fig. 18-8).

Another heavy welding load, such as 2000 A for 3.0 sec at 460 V, may be handled differently. Here size D tubes have 4.6 sec averaging time, and they would be working at 3.0 sec/4.6 sec, or 65 percent duty. But at 2000 A, Fig. 18-8 shows that size D tubes must not work above 35 percent duty. Here two pairs of size D tubes may be used if arranged so that each pair carries the 2000 A for half of the weld time. Timing relays are used so as to fire each pair of tubes in turn. Now each pair works 1.5 sec/4.6 sec, or at 33 percent duty, which is within the rating of size D tubes.

18-15 COMPLETE CONTROLS FOR RESISTANCE WELDING: SEQUENCE TIMER

The welding machine sketched in Fig. 18-1 receives its ac supply through an ignitron contactor; this pair of ignitrons may be controlled by other SCR- or tube-operated circuits. In addition to the welding controls described below, similar controls using solid-state devices are described in Chap. 19.

To change gradually the amount of welding heat by merely turning a small dial, a pair of phase-controlled thyratrons may be added in a *heat-control* equipment. To get better welds by accurate synchronous control, other tube-operated accessory panels may be added to the ignitron contactor, as indicated in Fig. 18-1, or a single larger synchronous-control equipment may be used, mounting the ignitron tubes inside.

Most of these welder equipments aim to control only the flow of alternating current to the welding transformer. But to operate the electrodes of the welding machine and to "tell" the above control equipment when to pass current into the weld, a sequence timer is used.

To control a spot welder, a sequence timer may measure four lengths of time (perhaps from 2 to 80 cycles each) in a certain order or sequence, as is shown in Fig. 18-11. After the foot switch is closed, the *squeeze time* permits the electrodes to build up the right pressure on the work. The *weld time* is the length of time during which the welding current flows. After the welding current stops, the electrodes continue to press against the metal pieces during the *hold time*, while the weld hardens. Then the electrodes separate; if the operator still holds the foot switch closed, the electrodes will reclose after a period called the *off time*, which gives time to move the work to a new position between the electrodes.

18-16 SYNCHRONOUS TIMING

Although the relay contacts of a sequence weld timer may control the welding current for times as short as 2 or 3 cycles, greater accuracy is

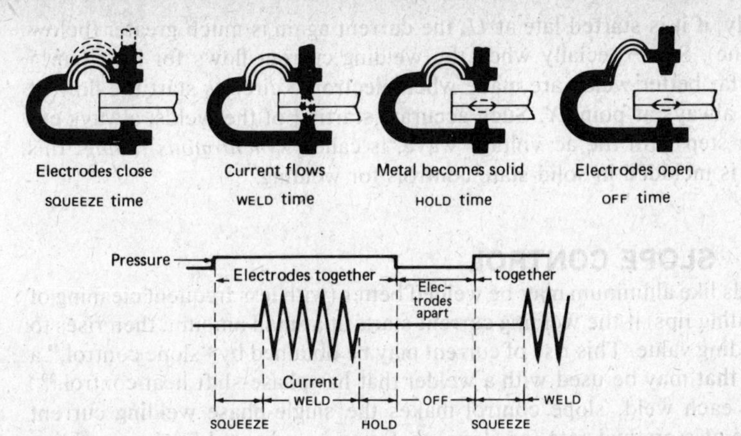

Figure 18-11 Sequence of a spot-welding machine.

needed for welding certain metals and for producing the same amount of heat in each spot weld.

To get these results, an ac welder must be controlled by electronic circuits that can start the flow of welding current always at the same point in the 60-hertz voltage wave. Figure 18-12 shows this voltage wave; it pictures the current that flows if the weld is started at points W, X, or U. Since a welding transformer is a lagging-power-factor[18-4] load, the welder tries to draw current that lags (starting at X) behind the voltage; if the welding current begins to flow at X, its waveshape remains the same, one cycle after another, and gives the best ac weld. However, if the ac welding circuit is closed at W (perhaps only $^1/_{1000}$ sec earlier than X), the amount of current rises much higher than before; for 3 or 4 cycles this current is "off balance" before it returns to normal. This short-time disturbance is called a *transient current*.

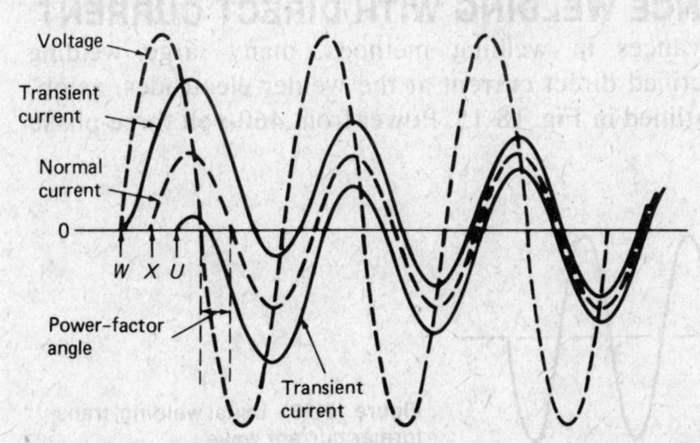

Figure 18-12 Transient currents (starting before or after the power-factor angle).

Similarly, if it is started late at U, the current again is much greater (below the 0 line). So, expecially when the welding current flows for less than 5 cycles, far better welds are made when electronic circuits start the flow of current always at point X. Such accurate starting of the welds, always exactly in step with the ac voltage wave, is called *synchronous timing*; this feature is included in solid-state controls for welding.

18-17 SLOPE CONTROL

Metals like aluminum may be welded better (with less frequent cleaning of the welding tips) if the welding current starts at a small amount, then rises to full welding value. This rise of current may be obtained by "slope control," a feature that may be used with a welder that has phase-shift heat control.[20-8] During each weld, slope control makes the single-phase welding current increase at a gradual rate (or slope) that may be adjusted for best welding results. (The addition of slope control prevents the flash often seen when heavy pieces are being spot-welded; therefore, the electrode pressure may be decreased. Since this increases resistance R between the pieces,[18-1] the line current or kVA needed for a heavy weld may be decreased perhaps 50 percent. Moreover, the small current during the first cycle softens or corrects the fit of the parts being welded, thus producing more consistent welds.)

Figure 18-13 shows first the current wave during an ordinary 4-cycle weld. Here, at R in the first half cycle, the current increases too fast, perhaps causing a flash before the electrode tips have made contact equally over all parts of the weld surface. With slope control added, Fig. 18-14 shows the small first-cycle current at S; then the current increases gradually to the full amount to complete the weld, at T. For each new weld spot, as the welding current starts, the slope control provides this gradual current rise, acting as a fast automatic adjuster in the heat-control circuit.

18-18 RESISTANCE WELDING WITH DIRECT CURRENT

Among recent advances in welding methods, many large welding machines now use rectified direct current at the welder electrodes, as obtained from circuits outlined in Fig. 18-15. Power from 460-volt three-phase

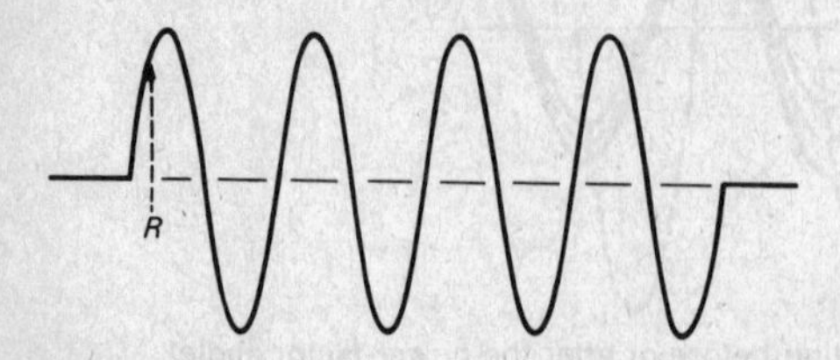

Figure 18-13 Usual welding-transformer current wave.

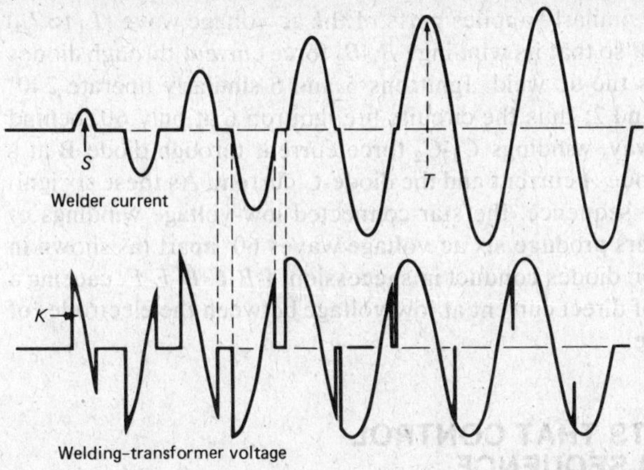

Figure 18-14 Welding-transformer current and voltage waves, using slope control.

lines is controlled through three ignitron contactors, one for each of welding transformers A, B, and C. The center taps of the 20-V secondary windings of these transformers are joined so as to produce six-phase output voltages (similar to Fig. 22-5), which are rectified by large banks of parallel-connected water-cooled silicon diodes A to F. These provide thousands of amperes of direct current, passing from one welder electrode to the other. If roller electrodes are used, as in a seam welder, this method produces continuous welds at speeds not limited by the cyclic alternations as in previous ac machines; the dc output current does not drop to zero value, but has six minor ripples per ac cycle. Spot welding also is improved by this long flow of current in one direction. Meanwhile, the load current is well divided among the three power lines; the required line current is decreased because the load power factor is improved. By means of phase control[20-8] of the firing of the ignitrons, the heat at the weld is varied smoothly, as is desired during the weld program.

The six ignitron tubes appear low in Fig. 18-15. Working between ac lines L_1 and L_2, ignitron 1 is fired by SCR_4 at its left; a half cycle later, ignitron 2 is fired by SCR_5. At the left, transformer T_7 (energized from the L_1-L_2 phase) charges C_7 during the half cycle before SCR_4 is to be fired. When T_3S triggers the gate of SCR_4, C_7 discharges and forces a large sharp pulse of electrons to flow from C_7, cathode to ignitor of ignitron 1, through a pulse-shaping inductance X, and from SCR_4 cathode to its anode, to C_7. All six ignitor-firing circuits are alike.

The firing of ignitrons 1 and 2 applies parts of the ac voltage wave (L_1 to L_2) across transformer A, so that its center-tapped low-voltage windings A_1-A_2 (at lower right in Fig. 18-15) force current alternately through diodes A and D and across the dc weld. One-third cycle later (or at 120°), the firing of ignitrons 3 and 4 similarly applies parts of the ac voltage wave (L_2 to L_3) across transformer B so that its windings B_1-B_2 force current through diodes C and F and across the dc weld. Ignitrons 5 and 6 similarly operate 240° behind ignitrons 1 and 2; thus the circuits fire ignitron 6 at only 60° behind ignitron 1. In this way, windings C_1-C_2 force current through diode B at a time between the diode-A current and the diode-C current. As these six ignitrons fire in correct sequence, the star-connected low-voltage windings of the three transformers produce six ac voltage waves 60° apart (as shown in Fig. 22-6); the silicon diodes conduct in succession A-B-C-D-E-F, causing a nearly steady flow of direct current at low voltage between the electrodes of the welding machine.

18-19 CIRCUITS THAT CONTROL THE IGNITRON SEQUENCE

The upper portion of Fig. 18-15 receives 120 V ac (between points 1 and 2) from the same phase as lines L_1 to L_2; this portion shows the solid-state circuitry whereby unijunction transistor UJT_1 (at upper right) is fired once in each ac cycle, at the desired point as set by the weld-heat adjuster P_1 (and as is detailed below); at this instant, transistor Q_1 energizes pulse transformer T_1 primary. In the central section below, a T_1 secondary winding triggers SCR_2 (provided that Q_3 is conducting, turned on during the weld time by circuits not shown); the SCR_2 anode current energizes T_3 primary. One secondary T_3S fires SCR_4 and ignitron 1. Two nearby T_3S windings send pulses that, by circuits not shown, delay the firing of ignitron 3 until 120° later than ignitron 1, and delay ignitron 6 until 60° later than ignitron 1.

The above may be described in more detail. At the start of each cycle, as top point 1 in Fig. 18-15 becomes more positive than point 2, the Zener diode Z_1 limits point 3 to +27 V; capacitor C_2 is charged toward this constant +27 V by electrons flowing through weld-heat adjuster P_1. By action like that described in Sec. 9-6, the increasing voltage across C_2 raises the gate of UJT_1 so that (at a certain desired angle of delay within the positive half cycle) C_2 suddenly discharges through UJT_1 and R_2; as the voltage across R_2 raises the base of Q_1, this transistor suddenly conducts through T_1P. A pulse produced by nearby T_1S fires SCR_1, so that the SCR_1 anode potential drops near to cathode at point 2; in this way the +27 V is removed from top point 3 so that UJT_1 cannot fire again within that cycle. As point 1 becomes negative during the following half cycle, SCR_1 is turned off.

The central portion of Fig. 18-15 works on dc voltages; bridge rectifier D_2 receives ac voltage from points 1 and 2; filtered by C_3, this holds upper line 4 at 160 V above line 7. Until SCR_2 is fired, no voltage is applied between points 5 and 6. At the instant in each cycle when the firing of UJT_1 makes transformer T_1 fire SCR_2, electrons flow from line 7 up through SCR_2 and

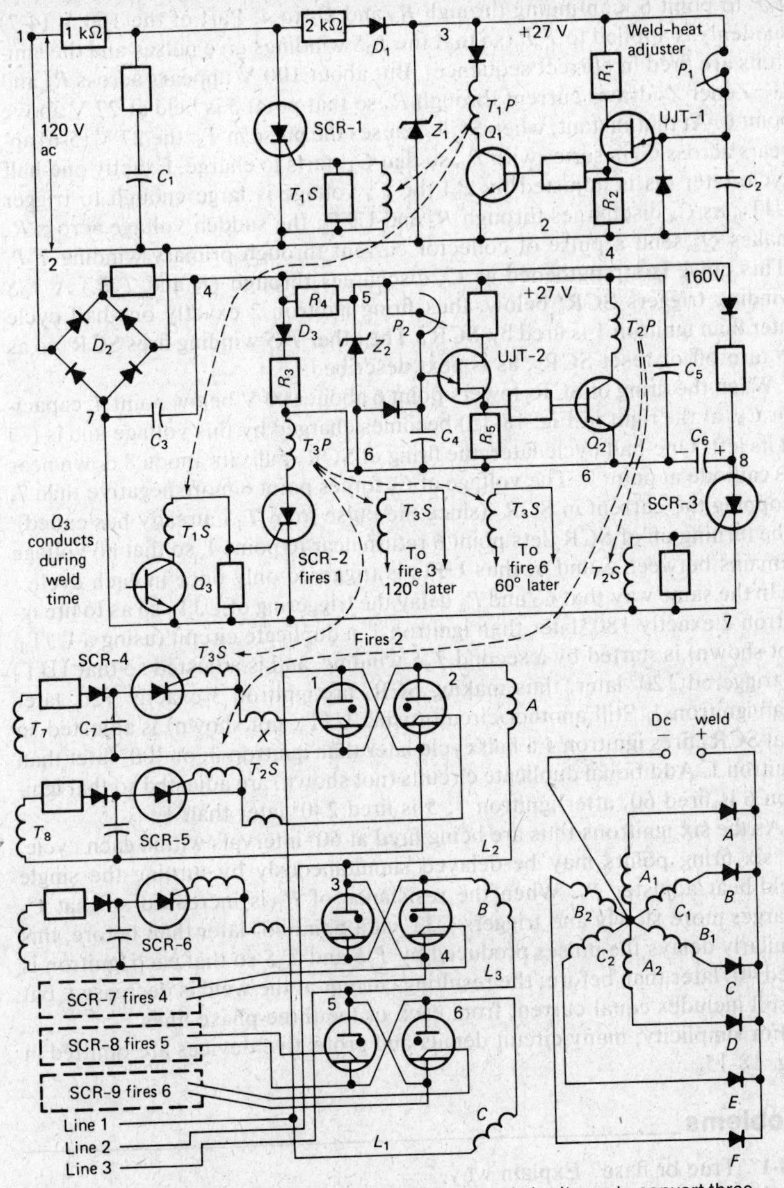

Figure 18-15 Circuit of a large welding control, using six ignitrons to convert three-phase ac to variable dc.

T_3P to point 6, continuing through R_3 and D_3 to 4. Part of the 160 V (4-7) suddenly is applied to T_3P (so that the T_3S windings give pulses and the ignitrons are fired in correct sequence). But about 100 V appears across R_3 and D_3; Zener Z_2 draws current through R_4 so that point 5 is held at 27 V above point 6. At that instant, when SCR_2 causes the pulse in T_3, the 27 V (5-6) appears across C_4 in series with P_2, so that C_4 starts to charge. Exactly one-half cycle later (as is adjusted by P_2) the C_4 voltage is large enough to trigger UJT_2; as C_4 discharges through R_5 and UJT_2, the sudden voltage across R_5 makes Q_2 send a pulse of collector current through primary winding T_2P. (This pulse is strengthened as C_5 discharges through Q_2 and T_2P.) A T_2S winding triggers SCR_5 below, thus firing ignitron 2 exactly one-half cycle later than ignitron 1 is fired by SCR_4. The other T_2S winding fires SCR_3 so as to turn off or reset SCR_2, as is next described.

When the firing of SCR_2 lowers point 6 about 100 V below point 4, capacitor C_6 (at the right in Fig. 18-15) becomes charged by this voltage and is (−) at its left. One-half cycle later, the firing of SCR_3 pulls its anode 8 down near its cathode at point 7. The voltage of C_6 forces point 6 more negative than 7, stopping the current in SCR_2 (since the pulse from T_1S already has ended). The turning off of SCR_2 lets point 6 return near to point 4, so that no voltage remains between 5 and 6; thus UJT_2 is triggered only once in each cycle.

In the same way that C_4 and P_2 delay the triggering of UJT_2 so as to fire ignitron 2 exactly 180° later than ignitron 1, a duplicate circuit (using a UJT_3, not shown) is started by a second T_2S winding, and is adjusted so that UJT_3 is triggered 120° later, thus making SCR_6 fire ignitron 3 exactly 120° later than ignitron 1. Still another circuit (using UJT_4, not shown) is adjusted so that SCR_7 fires ignitron 4 a half cycle later than ignitron 3, or 300° later than ignitron 1. Additional duplicate circuits (not shown) are adjusted so that ignitron 6 is fired 60° after ignitron 1; 5 is fired 240° later than 1.

As the six ignitrons thus are being fired at 60° intervals within each cycle, all six firing points may be delayed simultaneously by turning the single weld-heat adjuster P_1. When the resistance of P_1 is increased so that C_2 charges more slowly and triggers UJT_1 at a point 40° later than before, this similarly delays the pulses produced by T_2S and T_3S so that each ignitron is fired 40° later than before; the resulting current at the weld is decreased, but it still includes equal current from each of the three-phase lines.

For simplicity, many circuit details and protective devices are omitted in Fig. 18-15.

Problems

18-1 True or flase? Explain why.

(a) Full line voltage may exist between the metal shells of the two tubes of an ignitron contactor.

(b) An ignitron rated 300 amperes (A) can operate well on a load current of 10 A.

(c) The curves of Fig. 18-5 apply to the most common use of an ignitron contactor.

(d) The average number of welds per hour determines the size of ignitrons needed.

(e) If an ignitron conducts continuously for 35 sec, followed by 35 sec OFF, it is operating at 100 percent duty.

(f) If the fuse blows in Fig. 18-4, an ignitron is hard-starting or a disk rectifier may be short-circuited.

(g) To produce a given amount of heat in a weld of constant resistance, if the welding current is doubled, it needs to flow for half as long a time.

(h) A hard-starting ignitron cannot be detected until it refuses to pass current for all of a half cycle.

(i) If the average amount of current through an ignitron is doubled, its cooling water must remove four times as much heat.

(j) Ignitrons that are fired by thyratrons or SCRs give more accurate control of welding than big ignitrons alone can give.

(k) Greater accuracy of firing is needed in making a 1-cycle weld than is needed in making a 6-cycle weld.

(l) No point in a tube circuit may be below ground potential.

(m) To provide 100 percent heat or continuous current to a 0.5-power-factor welder, the ignitrons are fired at 60° delay.

(n) All circuits in Chap. 18 that set the length of weld time depend on the *RC* time constant.

(o) Ac and dc cannot be used in the same circuit.

(p) A good half-cycle weld can be made only with electronic control.

(q) By the use of slope control, the pressure at the welding tips may be decreased.

(r) A time-delay relay is needed to protect the tubes in all controls for resistance welding.

(s) When phase-delay control is used, a high transient current may occur in the welder circuit when an ignitron fires too soon, but not when it fires too late.

(t) Slope control is not possible with ignitrons unless they are fired by phase-delay devices such as thyratrons or SCRs.

(u) Any welding control is synchronous if it accurately counts the number of cycles while welding current flows.

(v) When an ignitron contactor, without phase-shift heat control, is fired at 100° by a sequence-timer contact, there will be a large transient current.

(w) Using phase-delay heat control, the welder current is discontinuous within each cycle if the SCRs or thyratrons fire the ignitrons at later than the power-factor angle.

18-2 A 200-kVA 230-volt single-phase 60-hertz welder draws 250 percent of rated current for 40 cycles and repeats this operation 10 times per minute (equally spaced). (*a*) Sketch this operating cycle. (*b*) Select the size of ignitrons required. (*c*) Calculate the resulting percent duty.

18-3 To make one weld in each 30 sec, alternating current from a 230-V supply flows steadily for 2 sec. For ignitron sizes B, C, and D, find the percent duty and the permissible current during the weld.

18-4 Using size C tubes at 230 V 60 Hz, a machine makes 12 welds in succession; during each weld, 1000 A flows for 20 cycles, with 50 cycles off between welds. (*a*) Calculate whether this duty is within the tube rating. (*b*) If the time between welds is shortened from 50 to 30 cycles and 10 sec is needed for changing work after each group of 12 welds, find the new percent duty.

18-5 An ignitron contactor with size B tubes operates at 460 V. Its welder operates at a steady rate of 7.5 welds per minute, equally spaced. For each weld, a current of 700 A flows for $^5/_6$ sec. (*a*) Find the percent duty and whether or not the tubes are overloaded. (*b*) The welder is now changed to operate from 230-V power; it requires the *same kVA* as before, still at 7.5 welds per minute and $^5/_6$ sec per weld. Show calculations for the size of tubes needed.

18-6 To supply a large steady load at 460 V, two ignitron contactors are used, each containing a pair of size D tubes. The entire load current passes through each contactor for half of the time. (*a*) Find the maximum permissible load current. (*b*) For how many seconds may this current flow in one contactor before it must be switched to the other contactor? (*c*) Explain whether or not the load current can be divided between the two contactors so that each pair of tubes handles half the current continuously.

18-7 A 230-V welder, using size C ignitrons, makes 480 welds per hour at equally spaced time intervals. Current flows for 0.5 sec during each weld. (*a*) Find the largest permissible current. (*b*) Still at 480 per hour, these welds are now made in groups of 10, with only 2 sec off between welds. Find the permissible current.

18-8 Size D ignitrons are used at 460 V to weld five assemblies per minute. Each assembly requires four welds in succession; each weld requires current for $^1/_4$ sec, with $^3/_4$ sec off between welds. (*a*) Find the largest current permissible. (*b*) The machine is rebuilt so that, to weld each assembly, only $^1/_2$ sec off separates the first and second welds; also $^1/_2$ sec separates the third and fourth welds. However, 4 sec of no current flow separates the second and third welds. Each weld requires current for $^1/_4$ sec. Find the permissible current. (*c*) Substitute size C ignitrons and determine the permissible current for each case above.

18-9 A large welding machine, using size D tubes at 460 V, makes its welds at uniform time intervals. (*a*) If each weld uses current for 2 sec, find the percent duty and the permissible current when production is 300 welds per hour. (*b*) If this production is doubled, find the new permissible current. (*c*) If this machine operates at 230 V instead, find the permissible currents for 300 and for 600 welds per hour.

18-10 Explain why the heat produced in an ignitron varies directly with the current through it, whereas the heat produced at the weld varies as the square of the current.

18-11 From a 460-V 60-Hz supply, current flows steadily through an ignitron contactor for 1.5 sec, to make one weld in each 7 sec. For ignitron sizes B, C, and D, find the percent duty and the permissible current.

18-12 From a 230-V 60-Hz supply, current flows steadily through an ignitron contactor for 2.5 sec per weld, to make 6 welds per min, equally spaced. For sizes B, C, and D, find the percent duty and the permissible current.

18-13 A 460-V welder makes 15 welds per minute (equally spaced). For each weld, current flows for 1.25 sec. (*a*) Find percent duty and permissible current in the 460-V circuit if the two ignitrons are size C. (*b*) Repeat for size D. (*c*) If the size C tubes are used instead at 21.6 percent duty, and each weld still requires current for 1.25 sec, find the maximum number of welds in 1 min (equally spaced).

18-14 Work Prob. 18-9 substituting size C tubes.

18-15 Each metal piece is welded at three spots; each spot is made by 60-Hz current flowing for 0.5 sec. Current stops for 0.5 sec between welds 1 and 2, and for 0.5 sec between welds 2 and 3. Size B ignitrons are used, at 460 V. Find the percent duty and permissible current during weld, when these pieces are welded at a uniform rate of (*a*) 6 pieces per minute, (*b*) 10 pieces per minute, and (*c*) 15 pieces per minute.

18-16 The pieces described in Prob. 18-15 are to be welded at a uniform rate of 10 pieces per minute. Find the percent duty and the permissible amperes during weld for (*a*) size A tubes operating at 230 V, (*b*) size C tubes operating at 230 V, (*c*) size C tubes operating at 460 V, (*d*) size D tubes operating at 230 V.

18-17 In Fig. 18-11, if the shortest time for each of the four time delays is 2 cycles (of a 60-Hz power supply), what is the greatest number of welds per minute?

19

RESISTANCE-WELDING WITH SOLID-STATE CIRCUITS

To show how transistors and other solid-state devices now are used in industrial circuits, two types of resistance welding control are described in this chapter.

19-1 WELTRONIC BINARY SOLID-STATE CONTROL

This equipment controls a spot welder during its sequence of squeeze, weld, hold, and off times,[18-15] and includes synchronous firing and gradual heat control of two SCRs, back to back. Built in large quantity, each equipment includes about 50 identical transistors and 120 PN diodes, assembled on printed-circuit plug-in boards, as shown in Fig. 19-1. The length of each time, individually adjustable in 1-cycle steps between 1 and 100 cycles, is controlled by digital decade counters shown high in Fig. 19-3, and like those described in Secs. 10-4 to 10-7.

Parts of this welding equipment, such as the COUNTER and LOGIC plug-in boards, are described in the following sections and in Fig. 19-3. These connect also to Fig. 19-2, which includes the control relays, dc power supplies, and the firing control of the pair of large 1200-ampere (A) SCRs. At the bottom, lines $L1$ and $L2$ connect the main ac welding power [such as 460 volts (V), 60 hertz (Hz or cps)] to the back-to-back SCRs and the welding transformer. At the upper left in Fig. 19-2, control power at lower voltage is supplied through transformer $T1$, energized from lines $L1$ and $L2$. Here $T1$ secondary voltages are rectified to produce 24 V dc, also regulated supplies of +12 V dc and −12 Vdc, for use throughout the equipment. (These circuits are like Fig. 4-12, and use Zener diode $Z1$ or $Z2$ as in Fig.

Figure 19-1 Weltronic binary solid-state welding control. (*a*) Case open to show SCRs, (*b*) view inside binary timer. (Weltronic Co.)

7-26.) From *T*1 a 24-V ac wave passes along line 6 to transistor *Q*21 so as always to be ready to act as a *clock pulse* to drive the decade counters.

Most transistors are numbered as in the Weltronic diagrams. Transistors *Q*1 to *Q*4 and those above *Q*32 are shown in Fig. 19-2, while *Q*21 to *Q*31 appear in Fig. 19-3. Many circuits and features of this complete welding control are omitted. Most transistors are 2N1304 type NPN units; each is used in a common-emitter circuit. Each is turned completely on by a positive potential applied to its base; a negative base potential turns the transistor entirely off. (In these switching circuits, each transistor either is driven into saturation or it operates below cutoff.[5-7])

The length of squeeze time is set by turning the squeeze-selector contact to the desired number of cycles, as shown by the dials at the top of Fig.

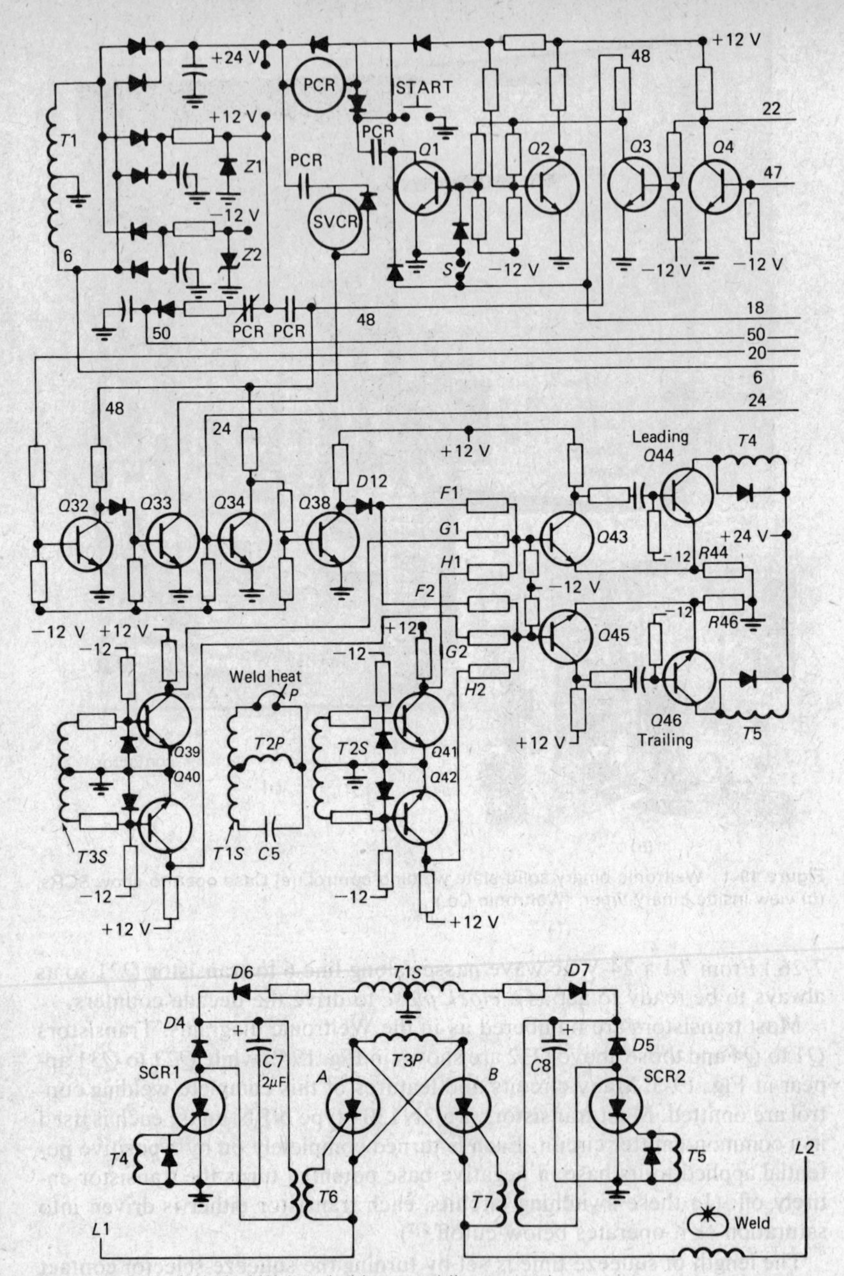

Figure 19-2 Left half of Weltronic binary welding control.

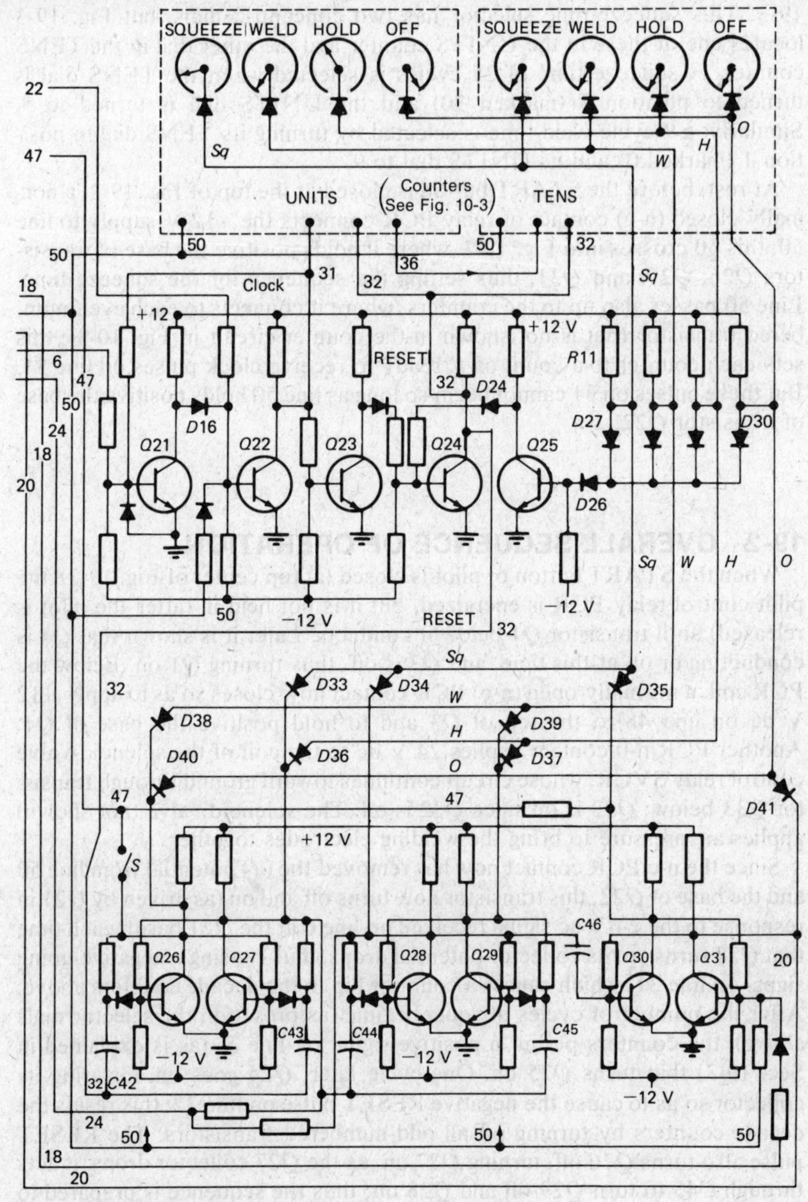

Figure 19-3 Right half of Weltronic binary welding control.

19-3. This squeeze-time selector has two concentric dials, but Fig. 19-3 locates one of these in the UNITS counter and the other dial in the TENS counter. A squeeze time of 25 cycles is selected when the TENS dial is turned to position 3 (marked 20) and the UNITS dial is turned to 5. Similarly, a 9-cycle weld time is selected by turning its TENS dial to position 1 (marked 0) and its UNITS dial to 9.

At rest, before the START button is closed at the top of Fig. 19-2, a normally-closed (n-c) contact of relay PCR connects the +12-V supply to line 50; this 50 crosses into Fig. 19-3, where it holds positive the base of transistors $Q26$, $Q29$, and $Q31$, thus setting the sequence for the squeeze time. Line 50 passes also up to the counters, where it connects to each even-numbered transistor (but is not shown in the counter circuit in Fig. 10-3); this sets each counter to a count of 1, ready to receive clock pulses on line 31. But these pulses on 31 cannot begin so long as line 50 holds positive the base of transistor $Q22$.

19-2 OVERALL SEQUENCE OF OPERATION

When the START button or pilot is closed (at top center of Fig. 19-2), the pilot control relay PCR is energized, but it is not held in (after the pilot is released) until transistor $Q1$ below it conducts. Later it is shown that $Q4$ is conducting or on at this time, and $Q3$ is off, thus turning $Q1$ on. Below the PCR coil, a normally-open (n-o) PCR contact now closes so as to apply +12 V dc on line 48 to the top of $Q3$ and to hold positive the base of $Q1$. Another PCR n-0 contact applies 24 V dc to the coil of the solenoid-valve control relay SVCR, whose circuit continues toward ground through transistor $Q33$ below; $Q33$ is on since $Q32$ is off. The solenoid valve (not shown) applies air pressure to bring the welding electrodes together.

Since the n-c PCR contact now has removed the (+) potential from line 50 and the base of $Q22$, this transistor now turns off and on (as driven by $Q21$ in response to the 24-V ac signal received on line 6 at the $Q21$ base); each time that $Q22$ turns on, its collector potential drops, thus causing a negative-going signal on line 31, which causes a count or flip in the decade counters above. After the number of cycles of squeeze time (as preset on the selector dials above), the counters permit a positive signal on line S_q (as is explained in Sec. 19-3) that turns $Q25$ on. One cycle later, $Q24$ goes on, lowering its collector so as to cause the negative RESET pulse on line 32; this resets the decade counters by turning off all odd-numbered transistors. The RESET pulse also turns $Q26$ off, turning $Q27$ on; as the $Q27$ collector drops, it acts through $C45$ to turn $Q29$ off and $Q28$ on; thus the sequence is prepared to measure weld time, as described in Sec. 19-4.

When the RESET pulse turns $Q27$ on at the start of weld time, the falling $Q27$ collector (acting along line 24) instantly removes positive voltage from the base of $Q34$; as $Q34$ turns off and $Q38$ turns on, this starts the circuit action (low in Fig. 19-2) that fires SCRs *A* and *B* so that they conduct ac power to make the weld, as described in Sec. 19-5. (The first cycle of welding current is caused by the RESET pulse; thereafter, the first clock pulse on 31 at the counters causes the *second* cycle of welding current.) The counting of weld time continues until the counters permit a positive signal on line *W* that again turns *Q*25 on. One cycle later, as the *Q*24 RESET pulse turns *Q*27 off, this turns on *Q*34 so that the welder SCRs do not conduct; the welding current stops.

Now the continuing clock pulses on line 31 are counted during the preset length of hold time, until the counters permit a signal on line *H* that again turns *Q*25 on. One cycle later, the *Q*24 RESET pulse turns *Q*26 off; as *Q*27 goes on, its falling collector acts through *C*44 to turn *Q*28 off. As the *Q*28 collector rises, it turns *Q*29 on and also pulls up through *C*46 to raise the base of *Q*30, turning it on. As the *Q*30 collector falls toward ground, it lowers line 47 at the base of *Q*4 in Fig. 19-2. So, at the end of hold time, *Q*4 goes off, turning *Q*3 on and *Q*1 off; this drops out the PCR relay (if START is released and if switch *S* is set for a nonrepeat weld, so that no off time is used). As *Q*4 is off, its +12 collector voltage is applied along line 22 to the base of *Q*22, keeping it on so as to inhibit or prevent further clock pulses on line 31. Also, since the lowered collector of *Q*30 turns *Q*31 off, the *Q*31 collector applies 12+ V on line 20 to the base of *Q*32. As *Q*32 goes on, it turns *Q*33 off so as to drop out SVCR, allowing the welder electrodes to separate.

If switch *S* is set for REPEAT weld, one *S* contact is open below *Q*2; a second *S* contact is closed, so that the base of *Q*4 is connected by line 47 directly to the collector of *Q*26. Since *Q*26 is turned off at the end of hold time, the +12 V at its collector is applied through *S* to the *Q*4 base; thus *Q*4 is held on during off time, and the clock pulses on line 31 continue to operate the counters. After the preset value of off time, the counters permit a positive signal on line *O* that again turns *Q*25 on. One cycle later, the *Q*24 RESET pulse turns *Q*27 off; as this turns *Q*26 back on, its positive voltage through *S* is removed from the base of *Q*4. Thus, at the end of off time *Q*4 goes off and turns *Q*3 on; this turns off *Q*1 and *Q*2 (but this does not drop out PCR if the START or pilot button remains closed). As *Q*2 goes off, its rising collector makes line 18 positive (since the *S* contact is open to release this point from ground); thus line 18 turns *Q*31 on. The RESET pulse on line 32 acts through *C*43 to turn *Q*27 off. As *Q*26 goes on (and *Q*29 and *Q*31 also are on) the sequence now has been reset for squeeze time, and a new complete welding cycle can begin.

When *Q*31 turns on at the end of off time, this turns *Q*30 off; this raises line 47 so that *Q*4 goes back on, *Q*3 off, and *Q*1 on, so as again to form a holding circuit around the START button. But if this button is open at the end of off time, the turning off of *Q*1 drops out PCR, whose n-c contact applies +12 V to line 50 so as to reset all circuits ready for another operation.

19-3 COINCIDENCE CONTROL OF Q25

Near the counters in Fig. 19-3, the base of transistor *Q*25 connects through diodes *D*26 and *D*27 to line *Sq*. During squeeze time, this *Sq* line is released from below so that it can become more positive (since diodes *D*33, *D*34, and *D*35 are reverse-biased, as is explained in Sec. 19-4). If the *Sq* line up to the counters also is released (as when certain counter transistors turn off at the end of a count), electrons can flow from ground, emitter to base of *Q*25 and through *D*26, *D*27, and *R*11 to +12 V, thus turning *Q*25 on; here the potential of line *Sq* may be several volts positive. But inside the counter, line *Sq* connects to the collector of a transistor. For example, Fig. 10-3 shows (at the lower left, where the squeeze-time selector is set for a 2-cycle count) that the *Sq* line connects through an upper selector-switch contact to *V*, which is also the collector of *Q*2. During the count of 1 (at the RESET pulse on 32), *Q*2 is on; so its collector *V* is near ground potential; this lets the selector-switch diode *D*11 conduct, thereby holding line *Sq* at such low potential that *Q*25 is held off. (Here lines *V* and *Sq* may be 0.2 to 1.2 V positive; but there is about 0.7-V drop across each diode *D*26 and *D*27, so that the *Q*25 base is near −0.2 V, holding *Q*25 off.) But at the count of 2, the clock pulse on 31 turns *Q*2 off and *Q*1 on; now *Q*2 collector V rises to much higher potential than line *Sq* and this reverse-biases *D*11. Since *D*11 no longer conducts (nor clamps *Sq* to ground), the potential of line *Sq* is free to rise, thereby letting *Q*25 turn on. (Here line *Sq* rises to perhaps +2 V; when the 0.7-V drops across *D*26 and across *D*27 are subtracted, the *Q*25 base receives +0.4 V, driving it into saturation.)

Thus, while the counter circuits at the top of Fig. 19-3 are making a count of squeeze time, line *Sq* is clamped so near to ground that *Q*25 is off. When the count has reached that value where all the diodes touching the *Sq* line become reverse-biased (which is called *coincidence*), this turns *Q*25 on. [If the selector is set for a 12-cycle squeeze time, the TENS selector is set at its second position (marked 10), like the UNITS squeeze selector shown in Fig. 10-3; now line *Sq* is held near ground both by *Q*2 and by the second transistor in the TENS counter; when the count has reverse-biased both *D*11 and the corresponding diode in the TENS counter, the *Sq* line can turn *Q*25 on.]

At the *Q*25 base, four diodes *D*27 to *D*30 act together as an OR gate, as is described in Sec. 10-10; if S_q OR *W* OR *H* OR *O* is (+), *Q*25 conducts.

19-4 THE PROGRAM OF SQUEEZE, WELD, HOLD, OFF

Low in Fig. 19-3, transistors *Q*26 to *Q*31 determine which of the four times is being counted at any instant. Before the START button energizes relay PCR (as stated in Sec. 19-2), the +12 V of line 50 holds on *Q*26, *Q*29, and *Q*31; this is the condition for squeeze time. Thus *Q*27, *Q*28, and *Q*30 are off, so that their collectors are at +12 V. These three collectors connect above to diodes *D*33, *D*34, and *D*35, each of which then connects to the *Sq* line. [These diodes form an AND gate;[10-9] if the collector inputs from *Q*27 AND *Q*28 AND *Q*30 are (+), this lets output line *Sq* be (+).] These three diodes now are reverse-biased, so that the *Sq* line is released during the squeeze time and can rise to turn *Q*25 on at the end of the count. Meanwhile, the other lines, *W*, *H*, and *O*, are being clamped to ground through other diodes to *Q*26, *Q*29, or *Q*31, which are on.

To end the squeeze time, as *Sq* rises and turns *Q*25 on, the lowered *Q*25 collector reverse-biases *D*24, so that *Q*24 no longer is held on by *Q*25. In the following half cycle, as the ac wave on line 6 turns *Q*21 on (*Q*22 off and *Q*23 on), this lowers the *Q*23 collector and the *Q*24 base; this turn-off of *Q*24 raises the RESET line 32 so that it applies +12 V that charges those capacitors touched by line 32, including *C*42 below *Q*26. As ac line 6 reverses and turns *Q*21 back off, this turns *Q*24 on so as to produce the negative-going RESET pulse on line 32; this turns off each odd-numbered transistor in the counters, and also acts through *C*42 to turn *Q*26 off. This turns *Q*27 on; as the *Q*27 collector potential falls, it acts through *C*45 to turn *Q*29 off, so that *Q*28 goes on. The sequence control (*Q*26 to *Q*31) thus has been set to measure the weld time. (At the instant when *Q*27 turns on, its collector lowers the potential of line 24 that leads to *Q*34 in Fig. 19-2; this causes the flow of ac that makes the weld, as is described in Sec. 19-5.) Also, as *Q*27 lowers its collector, diode *D*33 conducts, holding line *Sq* near ground, so that the squeeze-time selector no longer affects *Q*25.

Since *Q*26 and *Q*29 are off during weld time, their collectors rise to +12 V so as to reverse-bias *D*28 and *D*39; this releases the *W* line from below so that *W* can rise and turn *Q*25 on as soon as the counters reach the value for which the weld-time dials are set. (If these dials are set for a 1-cycle weld, as shown low in Fig. 10-3, the *W* line is not clamped to ground through any switch contact in the counter; so *Q*25 still conducts when the pulse on 32 resets *Q*26 at the start of weld time. Thus *Q*24 produces a second RESET pulse 1 cycle later so as to change from weld time to hold time.) This RESET pulse acts through *C*43 to turn off *Q*27, whose rising collector acts along line 24 to turn on *Q*34 to prevent further flow of ac to the weld.

As *Q*27 goes off to start the hold time, *Q*29 remains off. Thus their collectors reverse-bias *D*36 and *D*37 so as to release line *H*; after the time preset on the hold-time selector, the counters let *H* rise, turning *Q*25 on. One cycle later, the RESET pulse turns *Q*26 off, so that *Q*27 goes on, thus turning *Q*28 off. As the *Q*28 collector rises, it turns on *Q*29 and *Q*30, so that *Q*31 goes off. As is described in Sec. 19-2, this drops out SVCR to separate the welder electrodes. If switch *S* is set for REPEAT welding and the START button remains closed, the off time begins. Now *Q*26, *Q*29, and *Q*31 are off; their collectors reverse-bias *D*40 and *D*41, releasing line *O*. After the off time, the counters let *O* rise, turning *Q*25 on; 1 cycle later, the RESET pulse on 32 turns *Q*27 off; *Q*26 goes on, acting along 47 to turn off *Q*4, *Q*2, and *Q*1 in Fig. 19-2. As is described in Sec. 19-2, the rising collector of *Q*2 acts through line 18 to turn $Q31$ on; the $Q31$ collector lowers line 20 to turn $Q32$ off, so that $Q33$ energizes SVCR. Since $Q26$, $Q29$, and $Q31$ now are on, the sequence control again is ready to measure squeeze time and to start a new welding operation.

19-5 CHECKING THE AC CIRCUITS DURING WELD TIME

At the start of weld time, Sec. 19-4 shows that $Q27$ turns on, thus lowering the potential of line 24 that leads to the base of $Q34$ near the center of Fig. 19-2. As this turns $Q34$ off, $Q38$ is turned on for the duration of weld time. As $Q38$ conducts, its collector drops to ground and reverse-biases $D12$; this removes the positive input at $F1$ that has been holding $Q43$ on (and also removes input $F2$ mentioned below).

At the base of $Q43$ (near the center of Fig. 19-2), three resistors receive the inputs $F1$, $G1$, and $H1$; all three of these inputs must fall near to ground before $Q43$ can turn off and thus turn $Q44$ on. This sends a pulse through transformer $T4$ so as to fire SCR1 and the large SCR A (bottom of Fig. 19-2), which conducts the first or leading half cycle of the ac welding-transformer current. In the following or trailing half cycle, all three of the inputs $F2$, $G2$, and $H2$ must drop near to ground before $Q45$ can turn off and thus turn $Q46$ on, which sends a pulse through $T5$ so as to fire SCR2 and the large SCR B.

These G and H inputs occur during each ac cycle and at all times. As is detailed below, the input $G1$ assures that the large SCR A will receive its firing pulse only during that half cycle when the SCR A anode is positive; this synchronizes the control circuits with the ac power supply. Also, input $H1$ occurs only at a preset point within each positive half wave of ac, thus providing phase-shift heat control (as in Sec. 20-8).

The G inputs to $Q43$ or $Q45$ are received from the collector potentials of $Q39$ and $Q40$ at the left, whose bases are driven by the ac voltages of the secondary winding of transformer $T3$; the primary $T3$ winding is connected between the anodes of SCRs A and B, near the bottom of Fig. 19-2. Here $T3$ receives the entire ac voltage between lines $L1$ and $L2$, so long as neither SCR A nor SCR B is conducting; when either SCR fires, $T3$ receives almost zero voltage, since nearly all the ac line voltage is applied across the welder load at such times.

When the ac line voltage becomes (+) at the anode of SCR A, transformer $T3$ drives positive the base of $Q39$ for the rest of that half cycle; as $Q39$ conducts, it removes the (+) input $G1$. But $Q40$ does not conduct or remove the $G2$ input until that half cycle when the anode of SCR B is positive. Moreover, $T3$ cannot furnish the base current to turn $Q40$ on, so long as SCR A continues to conduct. (With such an inductive welder load, SCR A may continue to conduct far into the trailing half cycle, within which the SCR B is waiting to fire. See Fig. 9-14. Thus the (+) input $G2$ is not removed from

*Q*45 until a positive voltage appears at the anode of SCR *B*. The removal of the *G* inputs shows that the ac voltage is correct and available for firing the large SCRs.

The *H* inputs to *Q*43 or *Q*45 are received from *Q*41 and *Q*42, whose bases are driven by the ac secondary voltage of transformer *T*2. To the left, the primary *T*2 winding operates in an *RC* phase-shifting network consisting of capacitor *C*5 and adjustable resistance *P*; thus the *T*2*S* voltage lags behind the secondary voltage of *T*1, and does not turn *Q*41 on until at a desired point *after* the ac wave (of anode voltage of SCR *A*) has risen into its positive half cycle. By the turning of weld-heat adjuster *P*, the turn-on of *Q*41 occurs later within the half cycle, thus delaying the firing of SCR *A* and decreasing the heat at the weld.

One sees that *F*1, *G*1, and *H*1 are the inputs to an AND circuit;[10-9] all three inputs must be 0 before *Q*43 can go on, making its output 0.

19-6 FIRING THE SCRS TO MAKE THE WELD

As shown above, the (+) inputs *G*1 and *H*1 are removed from *Q*43 at the desired point within each positive half cycle of the ac supply; a half cycle later, the inputs *G*2 and *H*2 are removed from *Q*45. But during weld time, the turn-on of *Q*38 removes also the (+) inputs *F*1 and *F*2. Therefore, within each positive half cycle of the weld, the removal of input *H*1 lets the *Q*43 base drop toward −12 V; as *Q*43 turns off, it turns *Q*44 on. Electrons flow from ground through *R*44, *Q*44, and the pulse transformer *T*4 to +24 V. (Because of the 15-ohm *R*44, the transistors *Q*43 and *Q*44 act as a Schmitt trigger[6-8] so as to send a sharp current pulse into *T*4.) The *T*4 secondary winding is at the lower left in Fig. 19-2, where its pulse fires SCR1 (which fires SCR *A*, explained below).

A half cycle later, the removal of input *H*2 lets *Q*45 turn off, thus turning *Q*46 on; the current pulse of *T*5 now fires SCR2 and the trailing SCR *B*.

These 1200-ampere SCRs *A* and *B* are water-cooled; each requires a strong fast pulse of gate current, such as that provided by the sudden discharge of a capacitor. For this purpose, the 2-μF capacitors *C*7 and *C*8 are used, low in Fig. 19-2. During those half cycles when the anode of SCR *A* is negative, the *T*1*S* winding above it is (+) at its left, and (through *D*6) charges *C*7 (+) on top. In the following half cycle, if the *T*4 pulse fires SCR1, this completes a path for *C*7 to discharge through transformer *T*6 below; electrons flow from ground up through SCR1, up through the *T*6 primary to the top of *C*7. As *C*7 discharges rapidly, *T*6 forces a pulse of current through the gate of SCR *A*, which conducts during the leading half cycle until its load current drops to zero after the end of that half cycle. (Energy stored in the inductance of *T*6 may force a discharge current through *D*4.) A half cycle later, the pulse from *T*5 fires SCR2 so as to discharge *C*8 through *T*7, thus firing SCR *B*.

19-7 RING COUNTER USING PUTs

Whereas the preceding counting circuits use transistors connected in binary flip-flops, a later design of welding equipment uses PUTs (programmable unijunction transistors) which operate in ring counters. Before this welder control is studied in Sec. 19-8, a simple ring counter is shown in Fig. 19-4, having the four PUTs *U*1 to *U*4.

Each PUT (such as the General Electric 2N6027) is a small PNPN switching device having three terminals, called the anode, anode gate, and cathode. Its symbol shows that it more nearly resembles the SCR than the UJT. It is *programmable* inasmuch as its internal resistances may be chosen to let its operation fit into a desired circuit program. For use in the ring counter, it acts as an anode-fired SCR; it fires, conducting full anode current, if its anode gate becomes more *negative* than its anode. This anode current continues until the anode voltage momentarily is removed.

The circuit in Fig. 19-4 is a *ring* counter, since the four PUTs conduct in turn as in a ring; as *U*1 turns off, it fires *U*2; as *U*4 turns off, it completes the ring by again firing *U*1.

This ring counter is turned on or off by transistor *Q*1. To hold the counter off, line *A* (at the left) is at +18 volts, equal to the top supply line; *Q*1 is on, thereby lowering its collector near to ground; the 0.7-V drop across diode *D*2 forces line 1 below ground, removing all anode voltage from the PUTs. Notice also that capacitor *C*1 (below *Q*1) has +18 V at each end (since no current is flowing in *R*1 and *R*6 thus *C*1 has no charge). The pulses to be counted occur on clock line *C*. Each time that *C* becomes (+) and acts through capacitor *C*5 and diode *D*1 to turn *Q*1 on, note that *Q*1 conducts very briefly, since *C*5 discharges quickly through *R*5, again lowering the *Q*1 base.

To turn the ring counter on, line *A* is lowered and held near ground. As this turns *Q*1 off, line 1 rises and applies +18 V to all PUT anodes. Also, as line *A* lowers one terminal of *C*1, it charges quickly toward this new voltage;

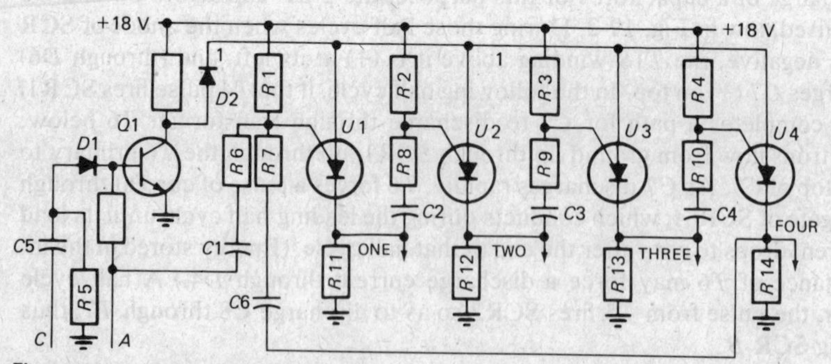

Figure 19-4 Ring counter using PUTs.

these electrons flow from $C1$ up through $R6$ and $R1$ to +18 V. This sudden voltage drop across $R1$ drives the anode gate of $U1$ below its anode, thus firing or turning $U1$ on. (In the equipment described in Sec. 19-8, the turn-on A pulse and the firing of $U1$ both occur at the first pulse being counted; the $U1$ cathode terminal marked ONE rises to +18 V and may be used as an external signal at the count of ONE.) This rise of the $U1$ cathode also removes any charge from $C2$. (Such discharge of $C2$ through $R8$ and $R2$ *raises* the anode gate of $U2$ and does not fire it.)

When the clock pulse drives line C positive (at the left in Fig. 19-4), $Q1$ turns on briefly; this lowers line 1 so that $U1$ quickly is turned off. Since anode current in $R11$ stops, the bottom of $C2$ drops to ground; $C2$ draws charging current through $R8$ and $R2$, lowering the $U2$ anode gate. Before $C2$ completes this charging action, $Q1$ again is off and restores +18 V to the PUT anodes; thus $U2$ is fired. (Charge is removed from $C3$. This also is the output signal of TWO.)

When the next clock pulse turns $Q1$ on and turns $U2$ off, current stops in $R12$, thus lowering the bottom of $C3$; as $C3$ charges through $R3$, this fires $U3$. (As the $U3$ cathode rises to +18 V, this count of THREE is used at "coincidence" in Sec. 19-12.) Another clock pulse then resets $U3$, so that $C4$ charges through $R4$, thus firing $U4$. As the $U4$ cathode rises, it removes charge from $C6$ (below $U1$), and also gives an external count of FOUR.

As the next clock pulse makes $Q1$ reset $U4$, thus lowering the bottom of $C6$ to ground, $C6$ charges through $R7$ and $R1$, and fires $U1$ for a second time. So the four PUTs continue to count in a ring until line A is raised and holds $Q1$ on, thus turning all PUTs off.

19-8 WELTRONIC PUT WELDER CONTROL

Solid-state control of a spot or gun welder is provided by the PUT and ring-counter circuits shown in Figs. 19-5 and 19-6; these include the circuit described in Sec. 19-7. This equipment gives the same weld results as do the circuits of Figs. 19-2 and 19-3.

The upper ring counter in Fig. 19-5 counts the UNITS (of cycles of ac), to determine the length of the squeeze, weld, hold, or off time. (A duplicate ring that counts the TENS of cycles is omitted, as are many other useful features of this equipment. Circuits that produce the dc supplies of +18 and −1.4 V are not shown; they resemble those at the upper left in Fig. 19-2.) The lower ring counter ($U21$ to $U24$) controls the sequence of operation of the welder.

Here is a quick outline of operation, to be followed by detailed sections. When the pilot or START button is closed (at the lower left in Fig. 19-6), transistor $Q5$ turns on or conducts, lowering line A and turning $Q1$ and $Q2$ off in Fig. 19-5; $Q1$ starts the UNITS ring counter while $Q2$ fires $U21$, which conducts during the squeeze time. The +18 V now at the $U21$ cathode acts along line G to energize the solenoid valve (as is described in Sec. 19-11), and along line H so as to latch around the START button.

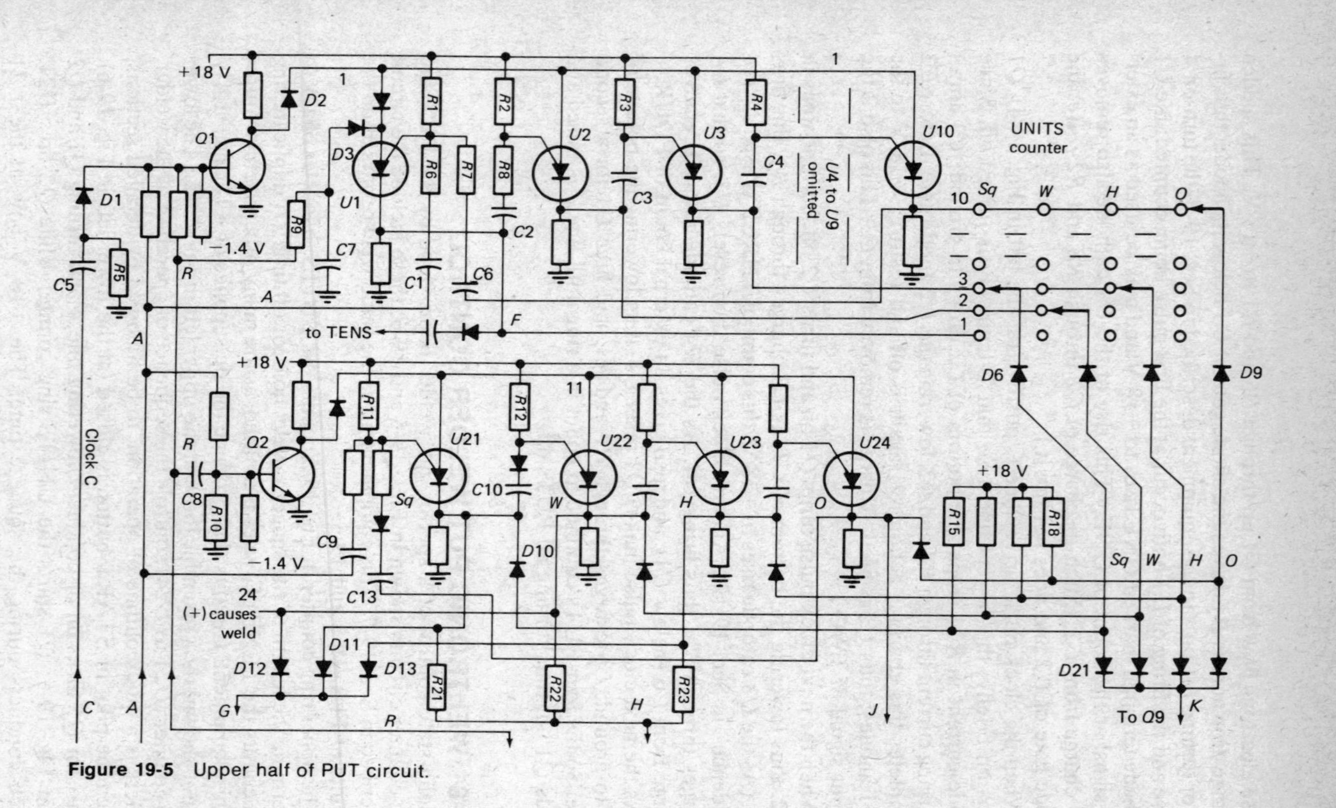

Figure 19-5 Upper half of PUT circuit.

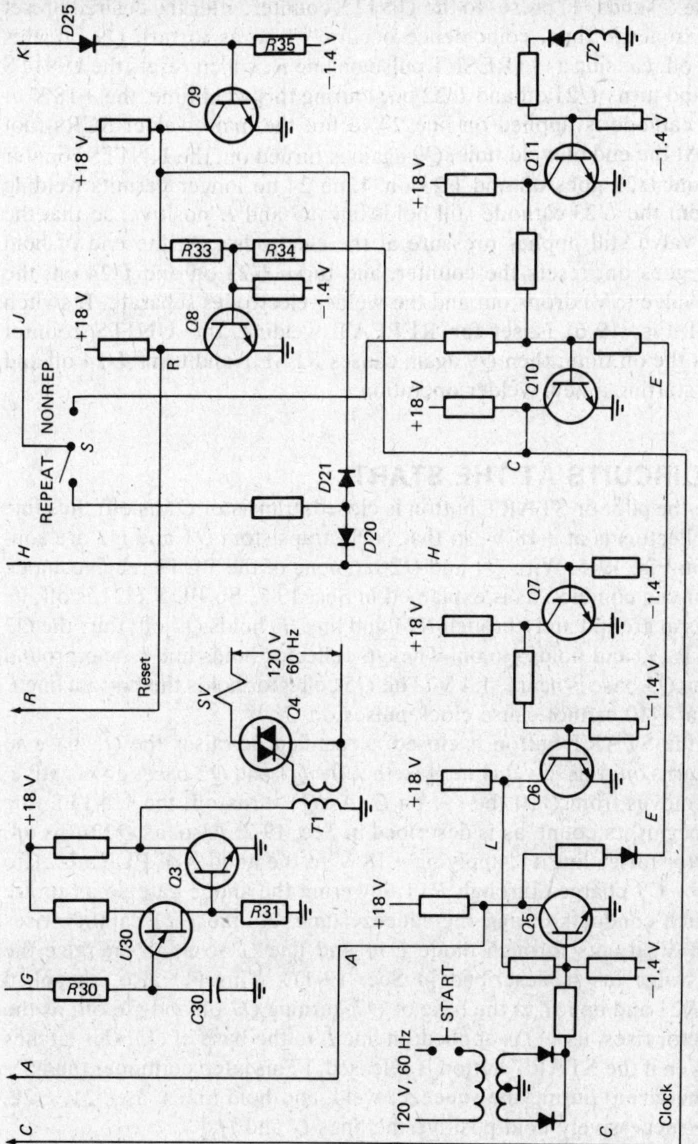

Figure 19-6 Lower half of Weltronic PUT welding control.

Clock line C sends (+) pulses to the UNITS counter; after the desired preset length of squeeze time, coincidence occurs,[19-12] so as to turn $Q9$ on; this turns $Q8$ off, causing a (+) RESET pulse on line R, which resets the UNITS counter and turns $U21$ off and $U22$ on. During this weld time, the +18 V at the $U22$ cathode is applied on line 24 to fire the main welder SCRs (not shown). At the end of weld time, $Q9$ again is turned on; the UNITS counter is reset and $U22$ goes off and $V23$ on. Line 24 no longer permits welding current, but the $U23$ cathode still holds lines G and H positive, so that the solenoid valve still applies pressure at the electrodes. At the end of hold time, $Q9$ goes on, resets the counter, and turns $U23$ off and $U24$ on; the solenoid valve (SV) drops out and the welder electrodes separate. If switch S (top of Fig. 19-6) is set for REPEAT welding, the UNITS counter measures the off time; then $Q9$ again causes RESET and turns $U24$ off and $U21$ on, starting a new welder operation.

19-9 CIRCUITS AT THE START

Before the pilot or START button is closed, transistor $Q5$ is off; thus line A ($Q5$ collector) is at +18 V, so that NPN transistors $Q1$ and $Q2$ are conducting, in Fig. 19-5. With $Q1$ and $Q2$ on, none of the PUTs receive anode voltage or can conduct, as is explained in Sec. 19-7. So PUT $U21$ is off; its cathode is at ground and (through $R21$ and line H) holds $Q7$ off; thus the $Q7$ collector is (+) and holds $Q6$ on. The $Q6$ collector holds line L near ground so that the $Q5$ base is near −1.4 V. The $Q5$ collector holds the bottom line E (+) so that $Q10$ cannot cause clock pulses on C.

When the START button is closed, a rectified dc raises the $Q5$ base so that $Q5$ turns on; this lowers line A so that the $Q1$ and $Q2$ bases go negative; it also removes from $Q10$ the (+) on E. As $Q1$ turns off, the UNITS ring counter begins its count, as is described in Sec. 19-7. Also, as $Q2$ turns off, its collector raises line 11, applying +18 V to the anodes of PUTs $U21$ to $U24$. Now $C9$ charges through $R11$, lowering the anode gate so as to fire $U21$, which conducts during the squeeze time. As the $U21$ cathode rises near +18 V, it acts through diode $D11$ and line G so as to energize the solenoid valve (as is described in Sec. 19-11). This (+) also is applied through $R21$ and line H to the base of $Q7$, turning $Q7$ on and $Q6$ off; as the $Q6$ collector rises, its (+) is applied on line L to the base of $Q5$; this latches $Q5$ on, even if the START button is released. [This latch continues (and SV also is energized) during the squeeze, weld, and hold times, as $U21$, $U22$, and $U23$ successively hold positive the lines G and H.]

19-10 THE RING COUNTERS

At the top of Fig. 19-5, the UNITS counter shows only four PUTs; the circuits for $U4$ through $U9$ are omitted, since each is a duplicate of the $U3$

circuit. The cathode of each PUT is connected to its number position on the time-selector switches at the right.

During a count longer than 10 cycles, PUTs *U*1 to *U*10 fire in turn without causing coincidence,[19-12] since they wait for a diode in the TENS counter to become reverse-biased also. At the count of 10, the cathode of *U*10 (in the UNITS counter) rises to +18 V and removes charge from *C*6, below *U*1. As *U*10 turns off at the count of 11, its cathode falls to ground, letting *C*6 charge through *R*7 and *R*1, again firing *U*1. As the *U*1 cathode rises, this (+) is fed down on line *F* into the TENS counter (not shown) so that a brief pulse shifts the counter into the next range, such as between 10 and 20.

19-11 SOLENOID VALVE ENERGIZED THROUGH A TRIAC

As *U*21 conducts and starts the squeeze time, its cathode applies +18 V (through *D*11 and line *G*) to the circuit of unijunction transistor *U*30 high in Fig. 19-6; this energizes the solenoid valve SV, which closes the welder electrodes onto the metal. This UJT acts as a relaxation oscillator (like that described in Sec. 24-7). With (+) applied through resistor *R*30, capacitor *C*30 charges until it triggers *U*30; *C*30 quickly discharges through *U*30 and *R*31 so that *Q*3 turns on. The resistance of *R*30 lets *C*30 charge and discharge about 1000 times per second; thus *Q*3 applies to transformer *T*1 a voltage that changes at near 1000 hertz (Hz or cps). The *T*1 secondary voltage fires the triac *Q*4 during both half cycles of this 1000-Hz supply,[9-15] thus connecting full-wave ac at 60 Hz to the coil of the solenoid valve; SV closes the welder tips. SV remains energized during the weld and hold times also, since *D*11, *D*12, or *D*13 conducts while either *U*21, *U*22, or *U*23 is firing. Transformer *T*1 is needed so as to isolate the control circuits from any ground potential that exists in the 60-Hz supply to the SV coil.

During the weld time, *U*22 applies its +18-V cathode potential on line 24 so that the 1200-ampere SCRs are fired and welding current can flow; this action is like the use of (+) on line 24 in Fig. 19-2, as is described in Sec. 19-6.

19-12 CLOCK PULSE; COINCIDENCE; RESET

At the lower right in Fig. 19-6, transformer *T*2 always applies a 24-V 60-Hz wave to the base of *Q*11; during its (+) half cycle, *Q*11 turns on and *Q*10 off. The *Q*10 collector rises, giving the clock pulse on line *C*; this turns *Q*1 on momentarily once each cycle, and steps the count ahead.[19-7] This *C* voltage also is applied to the base of *Q*8; but *Q*8 steadily is being held on, so long as *Q*9 is off, as next explained.

Let the selector be set for 3 cycles of squeeze time (shown at the upper right in Fig. 19-5, where the arrow contact in the *Sq* column touches at 3). Until this desired count is reached, *U*3 is off. The base of *Q*9 is being held negative, as electrons flow from −1.4 V and *R*35 (at the *Q*9 base) up through diode *D*25 to *K*, *D*21, and *D*6 to the arrow contact and to ground potential at the *U*3 cathode. (The voltage drop across the diodes holds the *Q*9 base below ground.) At a count of 3, *U*3 turns on and raises its cathode potential; this reverse-biases *D*6 so that the *Sq* line can rise. But this *Sq* line connects also through diode *D*10 to the cathode of *U*21; only during the squeeze time does *U*21 conduct and thus reverse-bias *D*10.

At the end of squeeze time, coincidence occurs, as both *D*6 (UNITS) and *D*10 (sequence) are reverse-biased, thus releasing line *Sq* from ground. Electrons now may flow from the *Q*9 base and through *D*25 to *K*, *D*21, and *R*15 to +18 V. As *Q*9 goes on, its collector removes (+) from the *Q*8 base; *Q*8 now may be turned off when *Q*10 conducts and lowers line *C* (as when the ac voltage wave from *T*2 enters its negative half cycle). This turn-off of *Q*8 produces the (+) RESET voltage on line *R*. This (+) on line *R* turns *Q*1 on for an entire half cycle (which is much longer than the turn-on caused by clock *C*). This long *R* pulse gives time for *C*4 to have completed its charging before the +18 V is restored on line 1 to the *U*4 anode. [This occurs after *U*3 is turned off (and if set for a count of 3).] Thus *U*4 is not fired, and all counter PUTs are reset off. [At the start of RESET, the (+) of *R* acts through *R*9 and *D*3 to give anode voltage to *U*1 to ensure that *U*1 is on at the start of the next count.]

This RESET pulse reaches transistor *Q*2 also, but only as a short pulse, because of the short time constant of *R*10 and *C*8. As *Q*2 goes on momentarily, the dip at the anode of *U*21 turns off this squeeze-time PUT; the lowered *U*21 cathode causes *C*10 to charge through *R*12, so that *U*22 fires and the weld time starts. Thus, following each coincidence that turns *Q*9 on, the *R* pulse resets the time counters and also transfers the sequence ring counter to its next position.

19-13 OFF TIME AND REPEAT WELDING

High in Fig. 19-6, switch *S* is set to the right to obtain NONREPEAT welding. At the end of hold time, *U*24 conducts, applying its +18-volt cathode through line *J* and switch *S* to the base of *Q*10, to stop the clock pulses on line *C*. Since *U*21, *U*22, and *U*23 now are off, line *H* drops below ground, thus turning *Q*7 off and *Q*6 on; this removes the latch *L* around the START button. Line *G* also removes (+) from *U*30 so that the 1000-Hz oscillations stop, and triac *Q*4 removes voltage from the solenoid valve; this lets the welder electrodes separate. When both the START button and latch *L* remove (+) from the *Q*5 base, *Q*5 goes off, and its collector raises line *E* and clamps *Q*10 on. The rising line *A* turns on *Q*1 and *Q*2; since this removes anode voltage from all PUTs, the whole circuit is reset, ready for another operation when the START button again is closed.

When switch S is set to the left for REPEAT welding, the end of hold time finds $U24$ conducting as before; but the (+) at the $U24$ cathode now acts along line J and through S and $D20$ to hold $Q7$ on. (The open S contact leaves $Q10$ free to produce clock pulses on C.) At the end of the off time, $Q9$ goes on at coincidence; the lowered $Q9$ collector lets $D21$ conduct so that the (+) of line J is removed from the base of $Q7$. [The (+) also is removed from $R33$, but $Q8$ is held on through $R34$ by line C.] As $Q7$ goes off and $Q6$ on, the latch of L is removed from $Q5$. If the START button is open at this instant, $Q5$ turns off, letting line A rise and stop the counters; all PUTs are off, waiting for the START button to begin a new weld cycle.

But if the START button still is closed during the half cycle when $Q6$ removes the L latch, $Q5$ remains on. A half cycle after coincidence, the ac voltage of $T2$ turns $Q11$ off; as $Q10$ goes on, line C falls, letting $Q8$ turn off, causing a RESET pulse on R. As this turns $U24$ off, the charging current of $C13$ passes through $R11$ so that $U21$ again is fired, starting another squeeze time. The (+) at the $U21$ cathode acts through $R21$ and line H to turn $Q7$ back on. Thus the latch L is removed for only a half cycle, always at the end of the off time.

Problems

19-1 True or false? Explain why.

(a) When transistors are used throughout a sequence timer, these all must be NPN or all PNP.

(b) The same kind of transformer winding and same type of diode can be used to produce a dc supply of −12 V (Fig. 19-2) as are needed to produce a +12-V supply.

(c) In a welding control, the voltages in the transistor circuits are about as large as the voltages in the thyratron or ignitron circuits.

(d) In Fig. 19-3, the weld time depends on an RC time constant.

(e) In Fig. 19-2 the percent weld heat depends on an RC time constant.

(f) To control $Q25$ in Fig. 19-3, the four diodes $D27$ to $D30$ form an AND gate that keeps $Q25$ off.

(g) A transformer cannot transmit a signal between two parts of a circuit that operates from dc supply.

(h) In Fig. 19-5 the diodes $D11$ to $D13$ to line G form an AND gate to $U30$.

(i) There is an upper limit to the number of PUTs that can be used in a ring counter.

(j) In Fig. 19-5, $C6$ serves the UNITS counter in the same way as $C13$ serves the sequence ring.

20

THYRATRON TUBES AND PHASE CONTROL

Hot-cathode tubes containing mercury vapor or gas[13-1] are used *as phanotron* rectifiers. Such a tube can be controlled by adding a grid; this grid-controlled tube is the *thyratron*+ it corresponds to the solid-state SCR of Chap. 9.

20-1 THYRATRON ACTION

The thyratron's action differs from that of the high-vacuum radio tube mainly because of the gas or vapor inside the thyratron. Either tube can prevent the start of current flow if its control grid is sufficiently negative. The difference between the tubes appears when the anode current has started to flow. In the high-vacuum type, the flow of electrons from the heated cathode (limited by the space charge[2-13]) can be increased gradually or decreased by changing the potential of the grid. But in the thyratron, when the grid permits a few electrons to start toward the anode, these electrons strike gas particles and ionize them[17-2]. Now positively charged, these particles move toward the cathode and remove the space charge, so that many more electrons become free to rush to the anode. Many of these positive charges land on the grid, so that its negative potential is obscured; the grid potential no longer has effect; so the tube now conducts full current. The vapor-filled thyratron is rated to carry larger values of current compared with the same size of a high-vacuum tube.

When the thyratron is "fired," it immediately passes all the anode current that its external load circuit will permit. It has a trigger action (similar to a mousetrap, and cannot be reset or turned off merely by working the trigger); it is turned off or reset by removing its anode voltage.

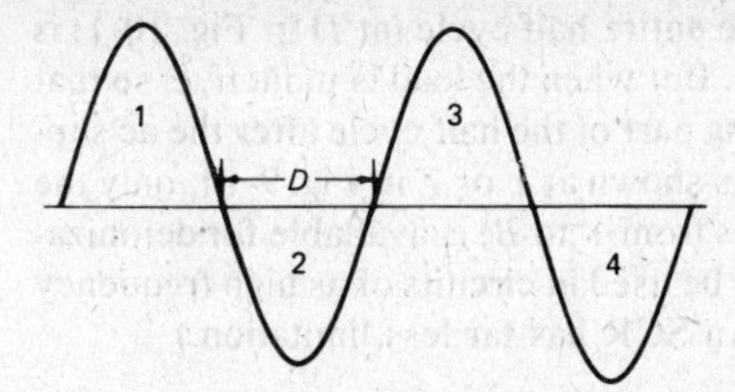

Figure 20-1 The grid of a thyratron regains control during interval *D*.

20-2 ACTION ON AC SUPPLY

Most thyratrons are used in circuits that apply ac voltage across the tube, anode to cathode. When the anode of the thyratron becomes positive, as during half cycle 1 in Fig. 20-1, this tube may be fired whenever its grid also becomes positive or rises above the critical grid voltage (as described further in Sec. 20-4). When the thyratron is permitted to start current flow at any point in half cycle 1, its grid is unable to stop current flow during that entire half cycle. In half cycle 2 the anode voltage becomes negative and repels electrons, thus stopping the tube current just as effectively as if the anode circuit were opened for the same length of time. Therefore, during interval *D* in Fig. 20-1, the tube has enough time to return to its original condition; with anode current temporarily stopped, the gas particles lose their ionization or charge. If the grid is again negative by the time that anode voltage returns at the beginning of half cycle 3, the grid retains its control over the electrons and can prevent the thyratron from starting to pass current. When a thyratron operates on 60-hertz ac power, its grid is given 60 chances each second to permit or to prevent current flow through the tube.

20-3 DEIONIZATION TIME

When the anode current of a thyratron stops (because anode voltage is removed or reversed), some small time is needed before the electric charges disappear from the gas particles. The time required to remove these charges or to deionize the gas is called the *deionization time* of the tube. [The time required for a grid signal to fire a thyratron, called its *ionization time*, may be only 10 microseconds (μsec).] If positive anode voltage returns to the thyratron during deionization time, it will again pass current (disregarding its own grid), touched off by the few particles that have not yet lost their electric charges. Since the deionization time is usually 100 to 1000 μsec (1/10,000 to $^1/_{1000}$ sec), this explains why many thyratrons cannot be used to control circuits at higher frequency, such as 500 Hz ac. (Special thyratrons filled with hydrogen gas can deionize much more quickly and are used for rapid high-current pulses, such as those needed in inverters.[24-6])

When the load is resistive, so that anode current stops at once when the ac supply voltage becomes negative, the entire half cycle (at D in Fig. 10-1) is available for deionizing the thyratron. But when the load is inductive, so that anode current continues to flow during part of the half cycle after the ac supply voltage has become negative, as is shown at Y or Z in Fig. 9-14, only the remaining portion of the half cycle (as from Y to B) is available for deionization. Thus a certain thyratron cannot be used in circuits of as high frequency when its load circuit is inductive. (An SCR has far less limitation.)

20-4 CRITICAL GRID VOLTAGE

Figure 20-2 shows the critical value of grid potential that permits one kind of thyratron suddenly to fire or pass current. For example. the slanting line shows that with grid potential of −4 volts (V), the tube passes no current when anode voltage is 300 but it passes total current when the anode voltage increases to 400. Or holding 400 V steadily at the anode, this thyratron does not fire when its grid potential is −5 V, but it fires suddenly when the grid potential is raised to −4 V.

To see more clearly just what value of grid voltage permits this thyratron to fire when operating with ac supply, this critical-grid-voltage curve in Fig. 20-2 is drawn again at the left in Fig. 20-3, but the grid voltage is plotted at a scale more nearly the same as the anode voltage. If we now draw a half sine wave of ac to represent the changing anode voltage of the thyratron, a new critical-voltage curve is gotten in Fig. 20-3 to correspond to this ac anode voltage. (This potential, which the thyratron grid must have so as to prevent

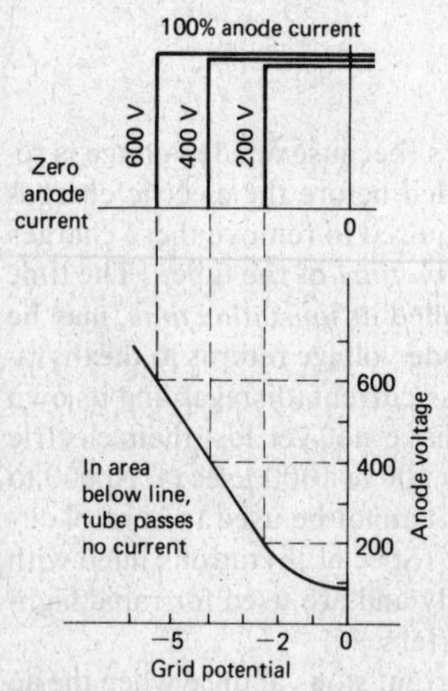

Figure 20-2 Tripping point or critical grid potential of a thyratron.

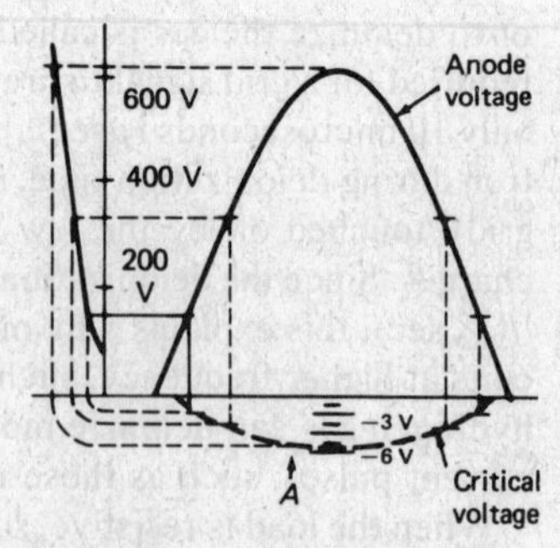

Figure 20-3 Critical grid voltage of a thyratron with ac supply.

the flow of anode current, is called the *critical voltage* of the tube. For most thyratrons, this critical voltage is so close to zero that it is omitted in most diagrams; in later chapters it is assumed that the thyratron may fire or pass current only when its grid potential becomes zero or slightly more positive than the cathode potential.) Figure 20-3 shows that a grid potential of only −3 or −4 V will prevent the thyratron from firing near the start of the half cycle. A grid bias of −5 V prevents this tube from firing until point *A* is reached, and then the thyratron passes current for the rest of that half cycle. At −6 V, the grid prevents any firing.

20-5 EFFECT OF THYRATRON TEMPERATURE

Figure 20-2 shows a single slanting line, indicating the grid potential that lets a thyratron fire; if this thyratron is of a mercury-vapor type, then this slanting line is correct only when the coolest part of the tube enclosure is at perhaps 40°C. (This is called the *condensed mercury temperature* and is measured on the tube glass just above its supporting base. A thyratron may be damaged if cooling air strikes it from above, for mercury then may condense at the top of the tube and drop onto the grid structure.) If the tube temperature rises another 20 or 40°, the slanting line of Fig. 20-2 must move to the left; we must now apply 1 to 2 V more negative grid potential to keep the tube from firing. [Higher temperature greatly increases the pressure of the mercury vapor, so that the tube is more easily fired at a certain grid potential. At such higher temperature, mercury-vapor thyratrons can withstand less peak reverse voltage; this increases the possibility of arc-back (failure to rectify).] The firing characteristic curves of such a tube lie on either side of the slanting line in Fig. 20-2, forming an area within which it is uncertain whether the tube will fire or not (depending on its temperature and including any variation between tubes of the same type). This causes a similar uncertain region near the critical-voltage curve in Fig. 20-3. Therefore, to provide definite control of thyratrons in industrial circuits, the grid usually is kept at a potential 10 to 40 V below the critical region until the tube is to be fired; then the grid is raised quickly to 10 to 40 V above the critical region.

Such temperature effects are less noticeable in thyratrons that contain inert gas such as argon or xenon. However, these tubes contain only a certain amount of gas; during operation, the metal parts within the tube may absorb, or "clean up," much of the gas, causing shorter tube life. Some thyratrons contain both mercury and a gas so as to obtain longer life and faster warmup.

20-6 GRID CONSTRUCTION

While the grid of a high-vacuum tube may be merely a wire mesh, which can prevent most electrons from reaching the anode, the thyratron grid must prevent *all* electron flow; if some electrons escape toward the anode, they

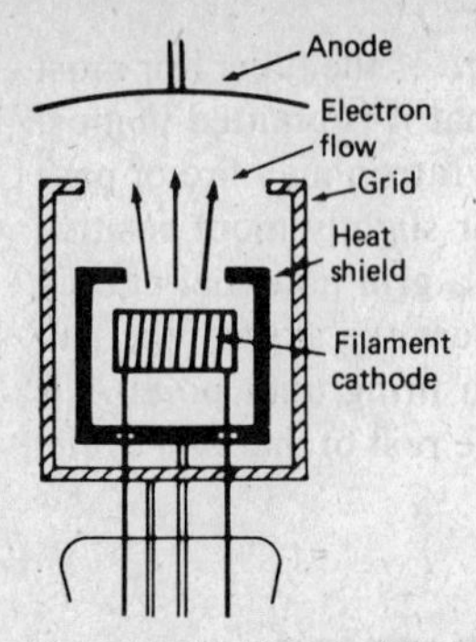

Figure 20-4 Parts inside a single-grid thyratron.

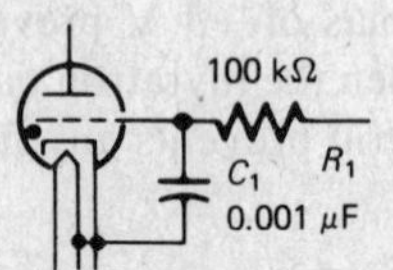

Figure 20-5 Use of a triode thyratron.

may ionize the gas particles so that the grid can no longer prevent the main flow of anode current. Therefore, the thyratron grid is usually a metal cylinder large enough to surround the cathode, as shown in Fig. 20-4; when this large grid surface is sufficiently negative, all electrons are repelled and cannot reach the anode. This grid surface helps also to contain the cathode heat and to shield the cathode from unwanted stray-field effects.

If the grid becomes much more positive than the cathode, the large grid structure permits a large flow of grid current that can damage the tube unless a limiting resistor is used, as shown as $R1$ in Fig. 20-5. Here the dot inside the tube circle shows that the tube contains gas or vapor.

Since the grid cylinder is close to the anode, any sudden rise in anode potential can cause a similar rise at the grid (because of "interelectrode capacitance"—the action of the anode and grid as the metal plates of a capacitor); this can cause false or unwanted firing of the tube. (A flicker of grid voltage lasting less then 1/10,000 sec can easily make the thyratron pass anode current for a half cycle.) To offset this effect, a small capacitor [0.0001 to 0.005 microfarad (μF)] is added between grid and cathode, shown as $C1$ in Fig. 20-5. Thus protected, the single-grid thyratron is widely used.

If the grid must be kept more negative than the cathode in order to prevent the tube from firing, as is shown in Fig. 20-2, this kind of tube is called a *negative-control* thyratron. If the opening in the grid top (Fig. 20-4) is enlarged, the anode can more strongly attract the cathode electrons; a more negative grid potential now is needed to prevent firing. If the grid potential becomes zero (being the same as the cathode potential), such a tube probably fires.

20-7 THE SHIELD-GRID THYRATRON

By adding a second grid, we produce a tetrode thyratron, which has less grid current and is more sensitive to its grid signal; this feature is provided in small thyratrons such as the type 2050.

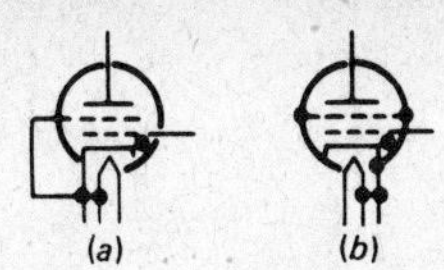

Figure 20-6 Symbols of a shield-grid thyratron.

The shield grid is usually connected to a base pin; outside the tube, the shield grid is often connected to the tube cathode. (This added grid should not be confused with the screen grid of a high-vacuum tube, whose operation is similar only with respect to decreasing the interaction between anode and control grid.) So connected, this thyratron may have nearly the same operation as is shown in Fig. 20-2. Therefore, when the shield grid is connected to the cathode, this extra grid may be omitted from circuit discussion. However, if the shield grid is connected to a point in the circuit that is a few volts more positive than the cathode, this has the same effect as moving the slanting line of Fig. 20-2 to the left; now a more negative control-grid potential is needed to prevent the tube from firing. Similarly, if the shield grid is made more negative than the cathode of the thyratron, then the control grid must be made less negative to let the tube fire; if the shield grid is 5 or 10 V negative, this tube requires a positive grid potential to make it fire.

Symbols of shield-grid tubes appear in Fig. 20-6: (*a*) is used for tubes with glass envelopes; (*b*) applies to large all-metal thyratrons, in which the shield grid is connected to or becomes the metal outer shell of the tube, which is connected to the cathode.

20-8 GRADUAL CONTROL OF A THYRATRON

Very large currents can be turned on and off by using SCRs, thyratrons, or ignitrons, but the amount of current through such SCRs or vapor-filled tubes is limited only by the external load circuit. The SCR gate, the thyratron grid, and the ignitron ignitor can turn on or fire these devices when desired but cannot control or limit the amount of current flowing, once the SCR or tube has fired.

For gradual control of the average current through an SCR, as described in Sec. 9-5, the phase-control circuit of Fig. 9-8 produces a pulse of gate current to fire the SCR. This pulse occurs early or late within each half cycle of the ac supply, as varied by an *RC* timing circuit and a UJT or a transformer. But similar gradual control of a thyratron is more simple; no current pulse is needed, since the thyratron is fired merely by the voltage applied between its grid and cathode. Complete waves of grid voltage may be used instead of the current pulses needed for the SCR. Methods that change or limit the *average* anode current are known as phase-delay controls. When this is used for gradual control of a resistance welder (Fig. 18-1), it is called *phase-shift heat control*.

A thyratron tube often is used for firing an ignitron, as shown in Fig.

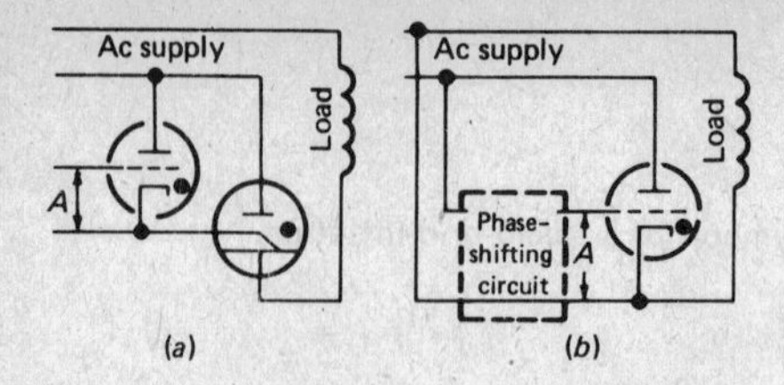

Figure 20-7 Ignitron fired by a thyratron whose grid voltage may be phase-shifted.

20-7*a*. Since the thyratron is connected in series with the ignitor or starter, the ignitron cannot fire until the thyratron first passes current into the ignitor. So we now may study the thyratron alone.

20-9 SHIFTING THE THYRATRON-GRID PHASE

If ac supply voltage (reduced through a transformer) is connected between grid and cathode of the thyratron, this tube may be fired at the start of the ac half cycle. If the transformer connections are interchanged (so that the grid-voltage wave is negative while the anode is positive), the tube never fires. But if a "phase-shifting circuit" is used, as shown in Fig. 20-7*b*, this circuit can make the ac grid-voltage curve lag, so that it does not cross the zero line or become positive until after the anode voltage has become positive. If the grid crosses the zero line (in an upward or positive direction) one-fourth cycle later than the anode voltage, we say that the grid voltage lags the anode voltage by 90°

If now the phase-shifting circuit of Fig. 20-7 is adjusted so that the grid-voltage wave lags the anode voltage by a small angle Z, as shown in Fig. 20-8*a* the tube fires as soon as the grid voltage rises above the zero line, as shown at *G*. Once the tube has fired, it makes no difference what the grid potential is during the rest of the half cycle. In Fig. 20-8*a* the tube conducts for

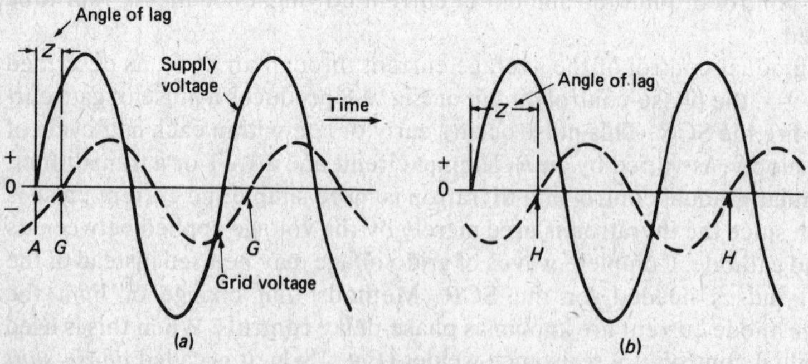

Figure 20-8 Waveshapes of anode voltage and grid voltage for delayed firing.

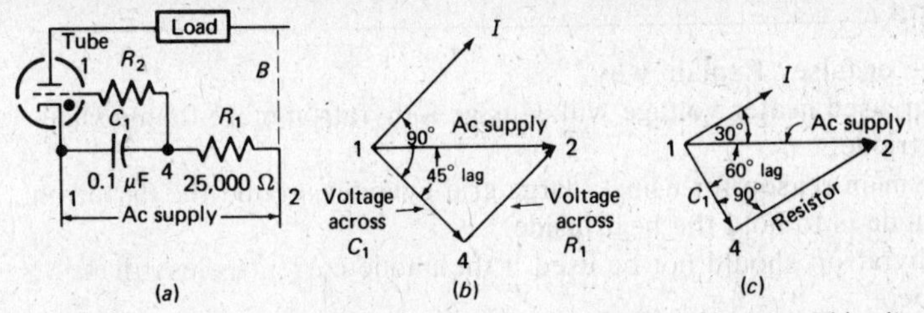

Figure 20-9 Using resistors with capacitors for phase-shifting the grid voltage.

about three-fourths of its half cycle, or 135°. In Fig. 20-8*b* the grid voltage lags by a greater angle, so that the tube fires later in the half cycle, as shown at *H*; anode current flows for a smaller portion of the half cycle. In this way, a thyratron is made to control the *average* amount of voltage applied to its load.

20-10 GRID-VOLTAGE WAVES THAT LAG

Inside the phase-shifting rectangle in Fig. 20-7*b*, a resistor usually is combined with a capacitor or an inductance so as to produce a grid voltage *A* that lags behind the ac anode voltage. As an example, in Fig. 20-9 resistor R_1 and capacitor C_1 are in series across an ac voltage that is in phase with the tube-1 anode voltage (and may be the anode voltage if the dashed line at *B* is used); C_1 is connected between the tube-1 cathode and through R_2 to the grid. (Resistor R_2 limits the amount of grid current when the grid potential becomes positive.)

In this resistor-capacitor circuit the current *I* leads the voltage 1-2 as shown in Fig. 20-9*b* The 0.1-microfarad capacitor has 26,500 ohms [at 60 hertz, $1{,}000{,}000/(377 \times 0.2) = 26{,}500$]. Since the reactance of C_1 nearly equals the 25,000 Ω of R_1, the current *I* causes about the same amount of voltage drop across either R_1 or C_1. The phasor triangle in Fig. 20-9*b* shows that the voltage 4-2 (across R_1) is in phase with current *I* and is about equal to voltage 1-4 (across C_1); current *I* leads voltage 1-2 by about 45°. The voltage across C_1 is used as the tube-1 grid voltage; it lags 90° behind current *I* and about 45° behind the anode voltage. This ac grid voltage delays the firing of tube 1, as shown in Fig. 20-8*a*.

If R_1 in Fig. 20-9 is increased to 50,000 Ω, the result is shown in Fig. 20-9*c*—more voltage across this resistor, less current *I*, less voltage across C_1. Current *I* leads the voltage 1-2 by about 30°, so the grid voltage 1-4 lags about 60°. By this increase of R_1 (or by using a larger capacitor for C_1), the grid voltage lags further behind the anode voltage and fires tube 1 later, thus decreasing the average voltage across the load.

Problems

20-1 True or false? Explain why.

(a) Decreased heater voltage will damage a thyratron more than a vacuum triode.

(b) The main reason for using a large grid cylinder around the thyratron cathode is to hold the heat inside.

(c) A thyratron should not be used if the anode current is less than $^1/_{10}$ ampere.

(d) The grid has the same ability to start a thyratron that it has for starting a vacuum tube.

(e) Shield grid is another name for a screen grid.

(f) In a tube containing mercury or gas, anode current flows only as long as the grid remains above the critical grid potential.

(g) The critical-voltage curve is made more positive by making the shield grid more positive.

(h) A thyratron has twice as much voltage drop (anode to cathode) when passing twice as much anode current.

(i) Most tetrode thyratrons may be fired by a more positive impulse at either the shield grid or the control grid.

(j) Two thyratrons may be enclosed in one shell, keeping individual grid control.

(k) A 25-V ac voltage may be connected directly between grid and cathode of a thyratron without damage.

(l) While conducting, a thyratron has about ten times as much voltage drop as an SCR.

(m) If the amount of anode current of a thyratron could be controlled each instant by the grid potential, there would be no need for phase control.

(n) The glow seen in a vapor-filled tube is brighter as the tube is fired earlier in its half cycle.

(o) Any grid voltage that becomes more positive while the tube anode is positive (on ac supply) may be used to phase-control this tube.

(p) The height to the peak of a voltage wave changes when it is phase-delayed.

(q) A grid-voltage wave that leads the anode voltage is useful for phase delay.

(r) When two identical thyratrons are back to back in series with a load, if each is fired at 90°, a dc voltmeter across the load reads near zero.

20-2 If the deionization time of a thyratron is 1000 microseconds (μsec), find the maximum frequency of the applied power which permits grid control of a resistive load. Find the maximum deionization time that a thyratron may have for operation with 3000-hertz (Hz or cps) power supply.

20-3 If the tube of Fig. 20-6 is operated with its shield grid connected directly to its anode instead of by its usual connection, how does this affect (*a*) the life of the tube, (*b*) the control-grid potential needed to prevent anode current?

20-4 Find the highest frequency of plate voltage that can be used for a thyratron and yet retain grid control within each cycle if the plate load is resistive and the deionization time of the tube is (*a*) 1500 μsec, (*b*) 300 μsec. (*c*) Repeat (*a*) and (*b*) if the load is inductive so that plate current flows for 40° after the plate supply voltage has become negative.

20-5 This negative-control tube will fire whenever its control grid is at a potential less negative than one-twentieth of the anode potential. At what angle does it fire when battery $B = 0$ and (*a*) $A = 12$ V? (*b*) $A = 25$ V? (*c*) If B now is made 4 V, explain whether the tube fires earlier or later than in (*a*) or (*b*).

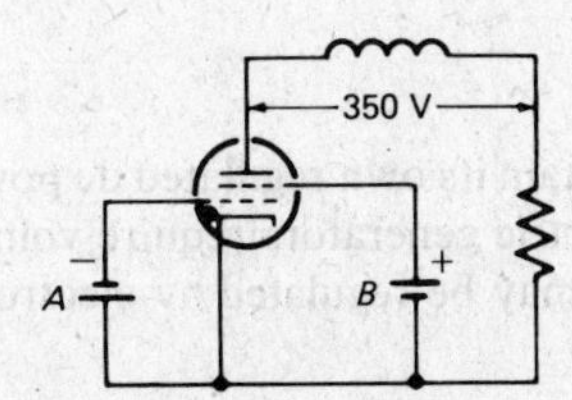

Figure Prob. 20-5

21 REGULATORS OF VOLTAGE AND MOTOR SPEED

Whereas most electronic equipment may contain its own regulated dc power supply (as in Sec. 21-2), many industrial electric generators require voltage regulators; likewise the speed of dc motors may be regulated by electronic controls.

21-1 A VOLTAGE COMPENSATOR

To give to a load a more constant supply of ac voltage [60 hertz (Hz) or cycles per second], Fig. 21-1 shows how a triac[9-15] may be used in series with the load; if the ac voltage *A*-to-*B* increases, the triac is phase-delayed so as to reduce to normal the rms or effective voltage across the load.

The ac supply voltage *A*-to-*B* is applied to a diode bridge rectifier[4-5] whose dc output raises top line 1 about 100 volts (V) above bottom line 2 during most of each half cycle. This rectified voltage is not filtered, but lets points 1 and 4 drop near to 0 V between half cycles. The right-hand half of Fig. 21-1 resembles Fig. 9-10; the phase control by pedestal and ramp (as described in Sec. 9-7) is a part of Fig. 21-1.

While the ac voltage *A*-*B* is at its low value of 110 V, rheostat *P* is adjusted clockwise until the triac is fired early (at the start of each half cycle) so that nearly the entire ac voltage wave is applied across the load. In causing this action, the pedestal voltage at point 5 is so high that capacitor C_1 charges rapidly through diode *D* at the start of each half cycle, quickly raising point 6 to the tripping voltage V_E of the UJT. This unijunction transistor conducts, so that C_1 suddenly discharges through the UJT and the primary winding of transformer *T*; the *T* secondary (at the left) supplies a pulse of gate current that fires the triac early.

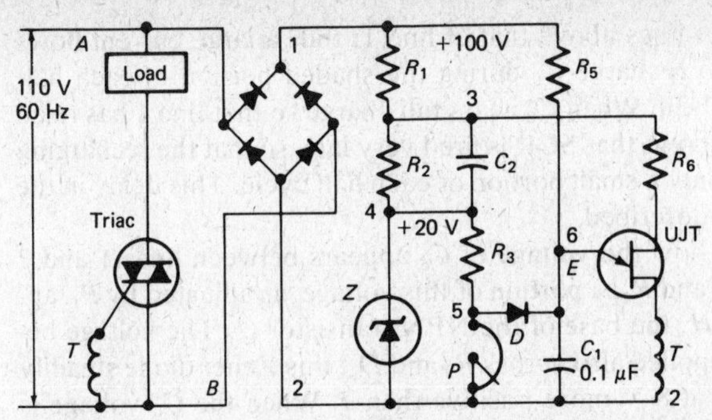

Figure 21-1 Voltage compensator; a UJT phase-controls a triac.

With only 110 V at the load and +100 V at line 1, about 5 V appears across R_2 and large capacitor C_2 (whose time constant is about 0.1 sec). This C_2 voltage, added to the 20 V across Zener diode Z, applies a total of about 25 V between points 3 and 2, and this is the interbase voltage V_{BB} of the UJT. As described in Sec. 8-6, a given UJT fires when V_E rises to a certain fixed fraction of V_{BB}.

If the size of the ac voltage increases (A to B in Fig. 21-1), the potential of line 1 rises above +100 V, thus increasing the voltage across C_2; this raises point 3 and V_{BB} of the UJT, so that its V_E also rises to a higher level. Capacitor C_1 needs more time to charge to this higher level of tripping point V_E, so the UJT fires later in each half cycle. (This additional slower charging of C_1 is produced by electron flow through large resistor R_5, since diode D has become reverse-biased.) With such phase delay, the triac applies only a part of each half wave of ac voltage to the load, so that the effective value of this partial wave remains near 110 V.

At the end of each half cycle, the ac supply voltage is near zero long enough to reset the triac and to discharge C_1 but not C_2. Thus the firing of the UJT (and the triac) is regulated by the rate of charge of C_1 within each separate half cycle.

21-2 A SOLID-STATE DC VOLTAGE REGULATOR

The circuit in Fig. 21-2 converts the 60-Hz supply (from a 115-V outlet) into 10 amperes of dc at a closely regulated output of 120 V. This voltage regulator is designed to furnish the dc supply at terminals 1 and 2 so as to recharge the large capacitor C_6 after some of its stored energy is used while making a weld.

At the left in Fig. 21-2, diodes D_1 to D_4 form a single-phase bridge rectifier so that the potential at A rises to a 160-V peak during each half of the ac cycle. If load capacitor C_6 at the right has been discharged partially so that the potential at line 1 has decreased to 100 V, the SCR is fired very soon after the potential at A rises above that of line 1; thus a large current flows through SCR so as to recharge C_6 during the shaded portion of each half cycle shown in Fig. 21-3a. When C_6 nears full charge so that line 1 has risen to 118 V, Fig. 21-3b shows that SCR is fired very late, so that the recharging current flows during only a small portion of each half cycle. This delay in the firing of SCR is next described.

Figure 21-2 shows how the voltage of C_6 appears between lines 1 and 2 and across R_5, P_1, R_6, and R_7; a portion of this voltage, as adjusted by P_1, appears between J and H, the base of the NPN transistor Q. The voltage between line 1 and J is applied also across R_9 and D_6; this Zener diode steadily holds emitter E of Q at 8 V more positive than J. When the C_6 voltage is lower than desired, less than 8 V appears between H and J, so that the base of Q is more negative than emitter E. With this reverse bias Q cannot conduct; therefore, no collector current flows through R_8 and R_2. In this case, C_2 quickly is charged through R_2 so as to raise the potential of G near to F very early in each half cycle. (At the start of each half cycle, when A rises higher than line 1, current flows through R_1 and quickly charges C_1; Zener diode D_5 limits this C_1 voltage to 18 V. Near the end of each half cycle, as A drops below line 1, C_1 discharges through the circuit of R_3 UJT, and R_4. Thus the potential at F falls near to line 1 before the start of each half cycle, as shown in Fig. 21-3.) Current flows through the emitter of UJT; therefore, as explained in Sec. 8-6, C_2 discharges through UJT and R_4, so that the gate of SCR receives a positive pulse that fires SCR early in each half cycle.

When the output voltage to C_6 nears the desired 120 volts (V), this higher potential on line 1 increases the H-to-J voltage to more than 8 V; as H

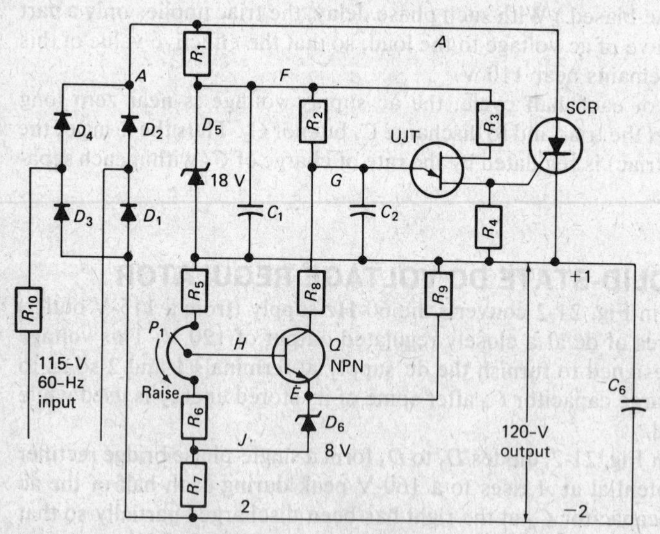

Figure 21-2 A solid-state dc voltage regulator.

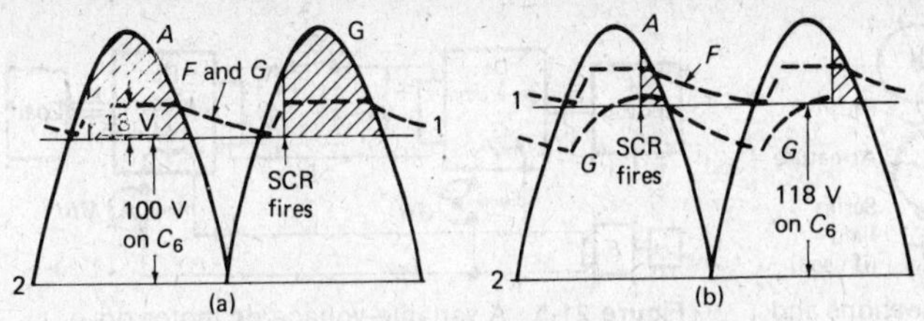

Figure 21-3 Firing of SCR in Fig. 21-2 when load C_6 voltage is (*a*) low and (*b*) high.

becomes more positive than E, collector current flows in transistor Q and through R_8 and R_2. This current through R_2 lowers the potential at G far below that at F; thus the top of C_2 becomes negative during the interval between half cycles. When F again rises, the small charge on C_2 makes G rise more slowly; thus a major part of each half cycle passes before G rises high enough to let UJT fire SCR.

When C_6 is fully charged to the voltage level selected by P_1, greater collector current from Q causes so much voltage drop across R_2 that G never rises high enough to trigger UJT or fire SCR.

The circuits studied thus far are used to control equipments that have little or no movement. Electric motors and generators also are controlled by SCRs or tubes; such circuits are often used to give gradual and accurate control of the motor speed or of the output voltage of the generator.

21-3 THE DC SHUNT MOTOR

For use with electron devices, the dc motor has electrical parts as shown in Fig. 21-4. The part that moves or rotates is the armature, whose current-carrying windings are connected to a part of the armature called a commutator, made of many copper bars shaped into a cylinder. The smooth, curved surface of the commutator slides beneath carbon brushes; through these brushes the direct current flows into or out of the armature. The dc motor has one or more field windings in its frame; a series field winding uses the same current as the armature, but the shunt field has a smaller flow of current separate from the armature.

To increase the speed of the dc motor, the voltage across the armature must be increased or the voltage across the shunt field must be decreased. A field rheostat (*FR* in Fig. 21-4) is often used for speed control; however, when the armature voltage is reduced by rheostat T, a change in motor-driven load also causes a change in speed. (A greater load increases the armature current and causes greater voltage drop across the resistance of T; this reduces the voltage across the armature; so the speed decreases.) This effect of load on speed is avoided if the armature is connected directly to a dc supply whose voltage can be carefully controlled.

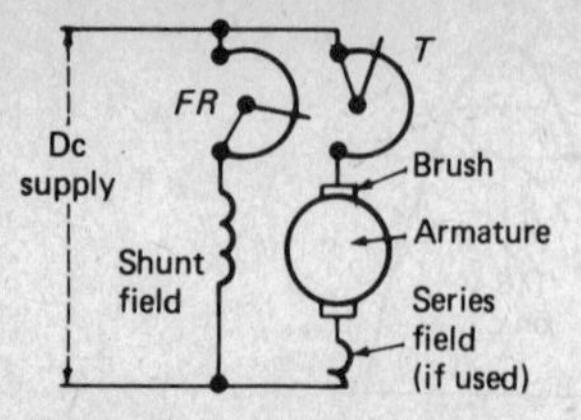

Figure 21-4 Connections and parts of a dc shunt motor.

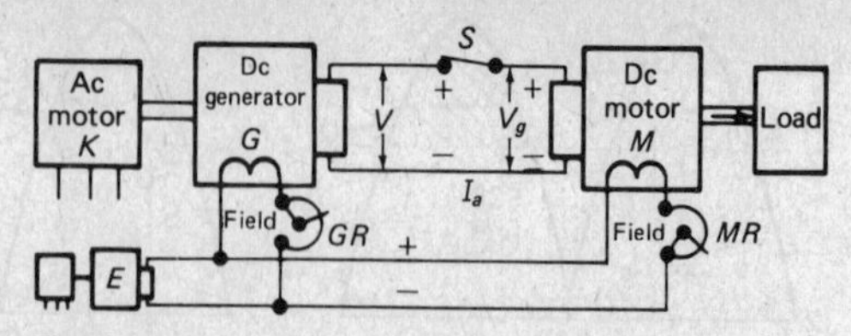

Figure 21-5 A variable-voltage dc motor drive.

Often the dc motor receives its armature current from a separate dc generator, as shown in Fig. 21-5. Although this generator G is driven at constant speed, its output voltage may be varied by control of the generator field; turning field rheostat GR clockwise increases the generator-field current, raising the output voltage V that generator G supplies to the armature of the dc motor M, thereby increasing the motor-M speed. At the same time, motor M receives its field current from the smaller generator E; if the motor-field rheostat MR is turned clockwise, decreasing the motor-field current, the motor-M speed rises. This then is a variable-voltage dc drive, wherein the motor speed may be varied by a change in either the motor-armature voltage or the motor-field voltage.

Basic dc motor equations may be useful here. In Fig. 21-5, the closing of switch S applies the generator voltage V across the motor armature; if motor M is not turning, a large armature current I_a flows, limited only by the armature resistance, so that $I_a = V/R_a$. This current flows through the armature windings in the presence of the magnetic flux ϕ produced by the field current. Therefore, the motor produces a torque $T = 7.04K\phi I_a$ (where K is a constant for a given motor); this torque is applied to the armature so that the motor speed rises.

Suppose that motor M drives a large flywheel as a load, as shown in Fig. 21-5; when brought up to speed, this flywheel stores great energy. While S is closed, a voltmeter measures voltage V, applied across the M armature. If S now is opened, disconnecting V, the voltmeter still shows the presence of a voltage V_g, which is generated by the rotating motor armature as its windings yet are being driven to cut through the field flux ϕ, using the energy previously stored in the flywheel. Although slightly smaller than V, this V_g is an emf that is produced by the turning M armature, whether or not S is closed. Since, by nature, the polarity of V_g always opposes the applied V, this V_g is called a *back voltage* or *counter emf;* $V_g = K\phi N$ (where $N = \text{rpm}$).

Now motor current $I_a = (V - V_g)/R_a$. Thus an increase in motor speed raises V_g, so that I_a decreases; less torque becomes available to drive the motor. This equation is written again as $I_aR_a = V - K\phi N$, from which comes tl motor-speed equation

$$N = \frac{V - I_a R_a}{K\phi}$$

This equation shows that, even when the applied voltage V and the field flux are held constant, the motor speed decreases when the shaft must produce greater torque to drive an increased load; this greater T requires greater I_a, thus increasing $I_a R_a$ in the above equation.

To raise the motor speed, V may be increased (by armature control) or flux ϕ may be decreased (by field control that decreases the field voltage and current).

21-4 ARMATURE CONTROL AND FIELD CONTROL OF MOTOR SPEED

The speed of a dc motor is controlled through a wide range by changing both the armature voltage and the field voltage, as mentioned above. When the armature is connected across the largest voltage that the motor is designed to receive continuously (called its rated voltage) and the field current is also at its largest or rated amount, the fully loaded motor runs at a medium speed, called its base speed. Figure 21-6 shows the usual way of operating a dc motor below or above its base speed; in this example, the base speed is 1750 rpm. At point A the armature voltage and the field voltage are both at their largest amounts (250 V), and this is at base speed. To reduce the speed, the field flux ϕ remains at full value in the equation for N above, but the armature voltage V is reduced (as by lowering the voltage supplied by the dc generator). To make the motor run faster than base speed, the armature voltage is kept at 250 V but the field flux ϕ (and field current) is reduced by turning the field rheostat to increase its resistance. If the field current is decreased too far, the motor speed rises above a safe amount (as above point B in Fig. 21-6).

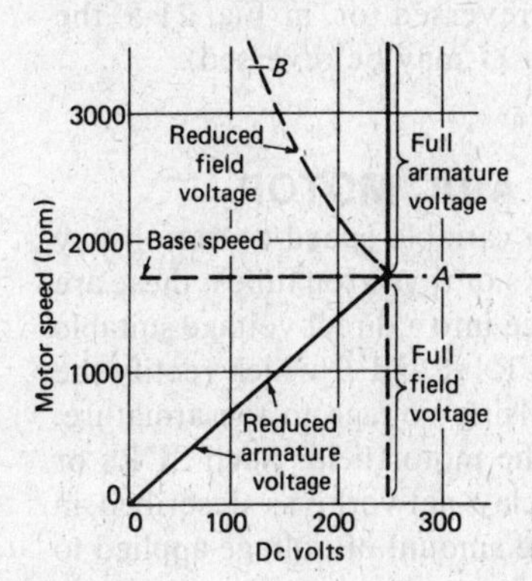

Figure 21-6 Dc motor operation above and below base speed.

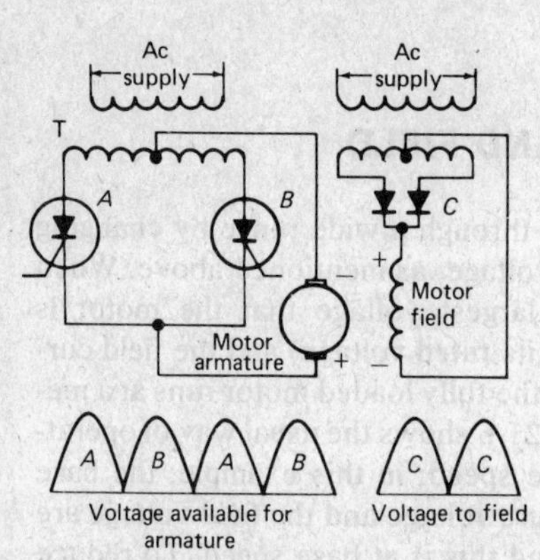

Figure 21-7 Dc motor operation from SCRs and diodes.

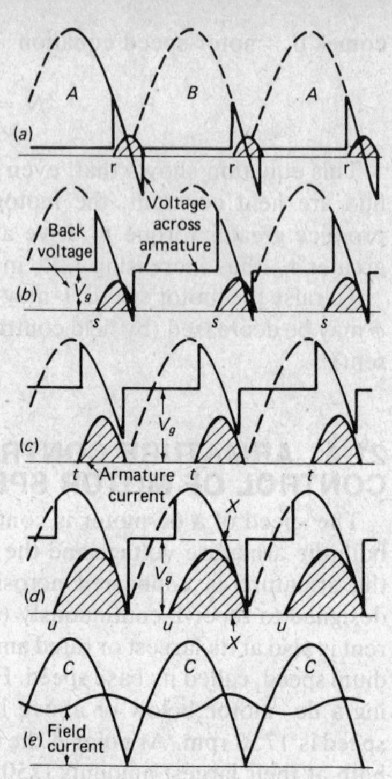

Figure 21-8 Motor current and voltage in Fig. 21-7, varied by firing of SCRs.

The dc motor usually is started having full field voltage, but with reduced armature voltage, so as to decrease the inrush or starting current.

To reverse the direction in which a dc motor turns, the connections to either the motor field or the armature may be reversed (or, in Fig. 21-5, the polarity of the voltage produced by generator *G* may be reversed).

21-5 ELECTRONIC CONTROL OF A DC MOTOR

Instead of operating from a dc generator, a variable-speed dc motor may receive power from an ac feeder by using SCRs or thyratron tubes; these are arranged so as to change the alternating voltage into a direct voltage suitable for the dc motor. Figure 21-7 shows such SCRs *A* and *B* which rectify the output of transformer *T* so as to apply a pulsing voltage to the armature, while diodes *C* supply a similar voltage to the motor field. Such SCRs or thyratrons may be controlled by a phase-delay network, as described in Secs. 9-5 and 15-10, so as to vary the average amount of voltage applied to the motor armature and thereby to change its speed. Such phase control may also provide smoother starting.

In Fig. 21-8*a*, the phase control delays the firing of SCRs *A* and *B* until late in each half cycle, at points *r*. Current flows only during the small shaded portions; so the motor remains at low speed. To increase the motor speed, the SCRs are fired earlier in each half cycle, at points *s*, as shown in Fig. 21-8*b*. Notice that the motor now produces its counter emf (shown at V_g in Fig. 21-8); the height of this back voltage is an indication of motor speed. To run the motor at full speed (at base speed, with full field current), the SCRs are fired earlier, at *t*; if the load increases at the motor shaft (tending to slow the motor), the SCRs must be fired earlier, at *u* in Fig. 21-8*d*, and current flows through the SCRs and armature for a larger portion of each half cycle. [The current waveshapes in Fig. 21-8 show that the motor armature is inductive in nature; the current does not change as abruptly as does the voltage. If this were a pure resistance load, the armature current would stop (at *X* in Fig. 21-8*d*) when the sine wave of applied voltage becomes less than the back voltage V_g of the motor. Instead, inductive energy causes the SCR to continue to conduct, to the right of *X*, so that this more negative portion of the sine wave may oppose and reduce the current to zero.[9-10] Calculation of the average value of SCR current is discussed in Sec. 9-13, when the SCR connects voltage to a motor armature that may have inductance.]

Meanwhile, the motor operates with full field current; as shown in Fig. 21-8*e*, this current is nearly constant during each cycle, for the large inductance of the field winding prevents much change in current.

Although in Fig. 21-7 only two SCRs are used to supply the armature current, larger motors may require so much current that three, four, or six SCRs are needed in this rectifier circuit. In contrast, small dc motors may receive armature current from a single SCR that supplies only a half-wave pulse during each ac cycle, as described in Sec. 27-1.

When a medium-size dc motor, receiving its armature current through SCRs, must reverse its direction of turning, a reversing magnetic contactor often is used for this purpose, instead of a second set of SCRs.

21-6 CONTROL OF SMALL MOTORS

In place of SCRs as used above, solid-state diodes are used in the Variac speed control of motors below 2 hp. (A product of General Radio Company, the Variac is an autotransformer whose ac output voltage is varied by turning a knob.) Figure 21-9 shows how a bridge rectifier *D* is used to supply constant direct current for the shunt field, while another bridge *E* gives to the armature the rectified wave of the ac voltage received from the Variac. A choke or inductance *L* decreases the ripple in the armature current. When the Variac slider *S* is near *R*, a small voltage is applied to the armature to start the motor or to run it at low speed. As *S* is moved to the right, the armature voltage is increased so that the motor speed rises.

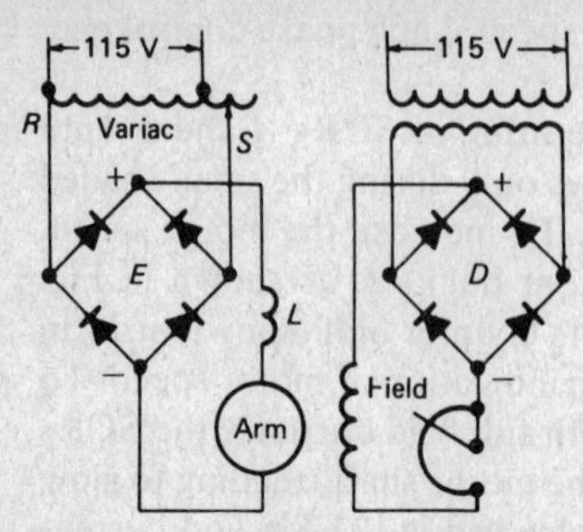

Figure 21-9 Variac speed control of dc motor.

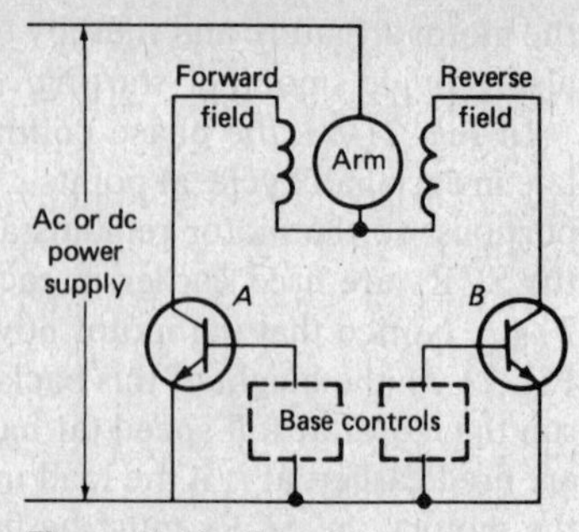

Figure 21-10 Transistors may control dc split-field motor.

To produce a smaller shaft output, two transistors *A* and *B* may control a motor that has only a series field, split into two parts as shown in Fig. 21-10. When other control circuits lower the base of *B* but raise the base of *A*, electrons flow through *A*, the left-hand part of the series field, and the armature; this current turns the motor in a forward direction. Its speed increases when greater collector current is permitted by the base current of *A*. If the transistor *B* base is raised instead, electrons flow through *B* and the right-hand series field, thus turning the motor in a reverse direction.

For a similar purpose, a small two-winding induction motor is described and used in Sec. 25-4. Its speed and direction are controlled by transistor Q_5 in Fig. 25-3.

21-7 SPEED-REGULATOR ACTION

Before describing systems or circuits that automatically regulate or hold the motor speed at a desired value, we may recall how you control motor speed by hand. When you turn a dial (such as *FR* in Fig. 21-4 or slider *S* in Fig. 21-9) to change the speed, you have in mind a certain desired speed or standard; you will adjust the dial until you observe that this desired speed is obtained. Somehow the motor must "tell" you how fast it is turning; you may read its speed on a scale or may judge its speed by its noise. When this indication of speed matches or becomes equal to the desired standard you have in mind, you stop turning the dial. (This example shows the elements of a closed-loop regulator or servomechanism, studied in Chap. 28.) Here your brain is an error-detecting device; when you detect any error or difference between the speed you want (which is called the standard or reference speed) and the actual motor speed (which you observe by the speed-scale reading or the sound that the motor feeds back to you), you turn the dial which, assisted by outside power, brings the motor closer to the desired speed until you no longer detect any error.

To replace you by an automatic speed regulator, the following actions are needed: (1) The regulator must be "told" what speed is desired by feeding into it a reference signal or voltage that represents the desired speed; (2) the actual motor speed must feed back to the regulator a similar signal or voltage, which exactly equals the reference voltage only when the actual speed equals the desired speed; (3) the regulator must detect any small error or difference between the reference voltage and the feedback voltage and must amplify this observed difference into a larger voltage that is strong enough to turn on the power needed to produce the required speed correction.

21-8 FULL-WAVE MOTOR-SPEED REGULATION BY ONE SCR

The speed of a 3-hp shunt-wound dc motor may be regulated by the circuit of Fig. 21-11. The ac power is supplied to a bridge rectifier so that both half waves (not filtered) raise top line 1 about 105 V dc above line 2 and supply steady shunt-field current. The SCR is fired in each half cycle, at a point or phase angle adjusted by R_1, thereby setting the motor speed; the SCR and SUS are reset when each half wave of voltage drops to zero.

Before ac voltage is applied to start the motor, R_1 is turned counterclockwise to insert its resistance. With voltage applied, C_1 charges slowly within each half cycle (by electrons flowing from C_1 terminal 4 through R_1, D_1, and the motor armature to line 1). Near the end of each half cycle, when C_1 has charged to about 10 V, terminal 4 reaches the breakover or tripping voltage of the SUS (silicon unilateral switch of Sec. 9-18); as SUS suddenly conducts, C_1 discharges through SUS and the SCR gate, so that SCR fires late and applies low voltage to start the motor from rest. As the motor rotates, its counter emf lowers the line-3 potential below line 1 and decreases the voltage available for charging C_1. As the speed selector R_1 is turned clockwise (for less resistance), C_1 charges more rapidly and reaches the SUS 10-V breakdown point earlier in the ac half cycle; SCR fires earlier and applies larger average voltage, raising the motor speed.

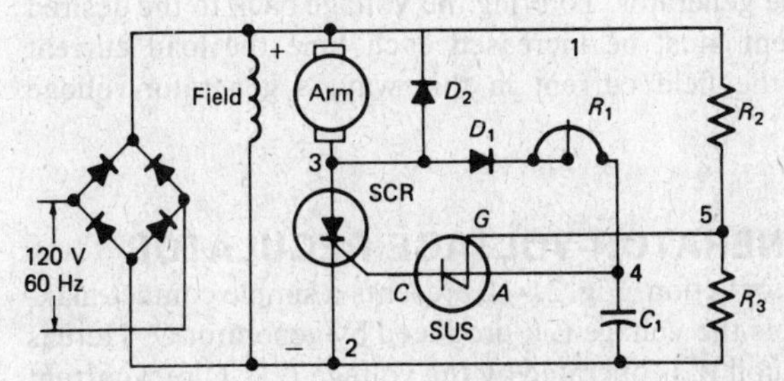

Figure 21-11 One SCR fires twice each cycle, to regulate motor speed.

While the motor is running at a fixed speed as set by R_1, its speed may decrease because of greater load torque at its shaft. But as the armature counter emf decreases, letting point 3 rise, the larger 3-to-2 voltage charges C_1 to trigger SUS sooner; the earlier firing of SCR applies greater armature voltage to return the motor speed to its desired value. Thus the speed is regulated to offset changes in load.

When the voltage at line 1 drops to zero between half cycles, the energy stored in the motor winding produces a voltage [(+) at line 3] that would force current to flow through SCR to prevent its being reset. Therefore, diode D_2 is added so that this decreasing armature current can circulate through D_2, letting SCR reset, ready to be fired in the next half cycle.

The SUS acts as though it contains a 10-V Zener diode (whose voltage sets the breakover point); also a PNP transistor whose base connects to the SUS gate G. At the end of each half cycle, as line 1 and point 5 decrease toward zero potential, this negative-going gate turns on the internal PNP transistor, letting C_1 discharge completely through SUS and the SCR gate-cathode circuit, to be ready to be charged again in the next half cycle.

Further motor controls are described in Chap. 27.

21-9 THE DC OR AC GENERATOR

A dc generator is much like the motor described in Sec. 21-3. However, instead of using electric power and driving a load, the generator may produce electric power if it is driven by some engine or motor. When the generator is being driven at the required speed, it produces no voltage or electric power unless direct current flows in its field winding. When there is field current and the generator forces current through a load, much greater power is required from the driving engine. The produced voltage increases when the generator is driven faster and also increases when the field current is increased.

An ac generator acts in the same way; direct current must flow in its field winding, and the amount of this field current controls the amount of ac voltage produced. Even if it is driven at constant speed and with steady field current, the produced voltage or output voltage may change when greater load current is taken from the generator. To bring the voltage back to the desired amount, the field current must be increased each time the load current increases. To control the field current in this way, a generator-voltage regulator is used.

21-10 BASIC GENERATOR-VOLTAGE REGULATOR

To show basic regulator action, Fig. 21-12 presents a simple contact-making regulator that controls the voltage GV produced by generator G. Here is a sensitive relay whose coil W is operated by the voltage GV. Direct current flows through the generator-field winding and the regulator contact; this con-

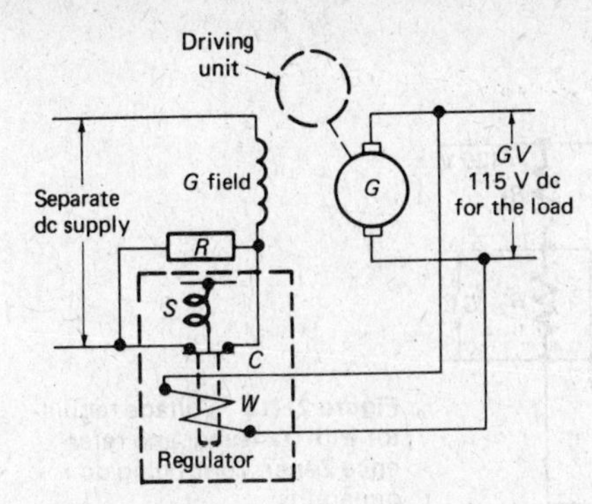

Figure 21-12 Simple voltage regulator uses spring *S* as reference.

tact *C* is held closed by the spring *S*. When the generator produces more than 115 volts, this voltage forces enough current to flow through the regulator coil *W* so that its downward pull (on its metal core) is greater than the upward pull of the spring *S*; the metal core moves downward, opening contact *C*. The resistance *R* is now in circuit and decreases the amount of field current; this decreases the voltage *GV* to perhaps 113 V. At this lower voltage, less current is forced through the regulator coil *W*; since its downward pull is not so great as the upward pull of spring *S*, contact *C* closes. This short-circuits *R* and increases the field current and the voltage *GV*. The contact *C* opens and closes often, to keep the *GV* voltage close to the desired 115 V. If the load current suddenly increases, causing the *GV* voltage to drop, contact *C* stays closed until the amount of field current increases to the greater amount needed; the *GV* voltage returns to normal before contact *C* opens again.

Notice that the strength of the spring *S* is the standard or reference that sets the amount of *GV* voltage produced by *G*; to raise this *GV* voltage to, say, 120 V, spring *S* must be tightened (or a stronger spring must be used) so that contact *C* does not open until a greater current flows in coil *W*, forced by 120 V. In any regulator, there must be such a standard or reference; if the produced voltage is greater than this standard, the regulator reduces the voltage. The regulator tries to hold whatever voltage the standard "tells" it to hold.[21-7]

While moving-contact regulators are used with earlier generators, electronic circuits may regulate the voltage and speed with greater accuracy. Note how a transistor may be used in this way.

21-11 TRANSISTOR RESPONSE TO GENERATOR VOLTAGE

To keep a simple circuit, Fig. 21-13 includes a generator *G* that is so small that its dc field current can pass directly through a transistor *Q*. (Later[21-14]

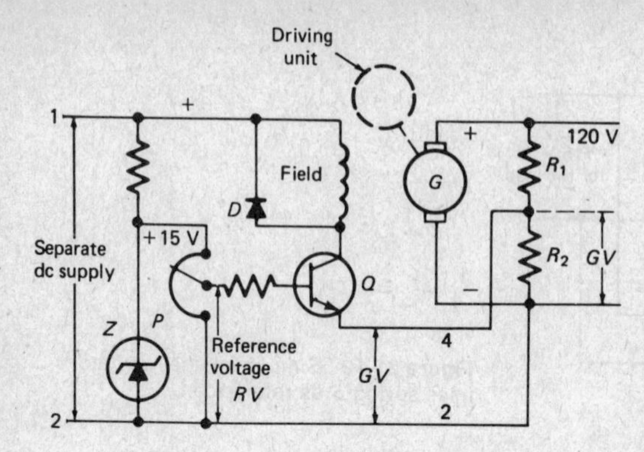

Figure 21-13 Voltage regulator with transistor and reference Zener, controlling dc generator.

other circuits will be added to permit use with larger generators.) When the base current of Q permits, electrons flow from bottom terminal 2 through R_2, emitter to collector of Q, and through the generator-field winding to terminal 1. Such a circuit has no spring like the regulator of Fig. 21-12; to provide a similar standard or reference, Fig. 21-13 uses the constant voltage across Zener diode Z. The slider of P (connected across this Zener) is turned to select the amount of voltage that generator G should produce. Across G, the voltage-divider R_1-R_2 feeds back the voltage GV as a 12-V portion of generator G's total of 120 V, a ratio of 10:1. (The Q current through R_2 causes negligible voltage drop.)

If P is set so that the reference voltage RV is about 13 V, so that RV is larger than GV, the base of NPN transistor Q now is more positive than its emitter, so that enough collector current flows through the field to make G generate about 120 V. If G now must supply greater load, so that its increased armature current causes its output voltage to decrease to 110 V, the portion across R_2 decreases to 11 V, thus lowering the Q emitter (which has the same effect as raising the Q base); Q passes greater current through the field, so that the G output voltage returns to nearly 120 V.

If load current suddenly is removed so that the G voltage rises to 130 V, the 13 V at GV may equal or exceed the reference RV, so that the Q base current is nearly zero; Q collector current may stop, and the decreasing current of the inductive field winding may circulate through diode D, until its reduced value returns the G voltage near to 120 V. As GV returns near to 12 V, field current again is supplied through Q. Thus GV continually is being compared with the reference RV; any error or difference between GV and RV makes Q change its current through the field (supplied from an external supply of dc power) so as to reduce this error toward zero.

Figure 21-14 shows that Q also may regulate the voltage of an ac generator. The only difference is that the generator's ac voltage at A is first rectified by diodes and smoothed by capacitor C. The resulting dc voltage GV

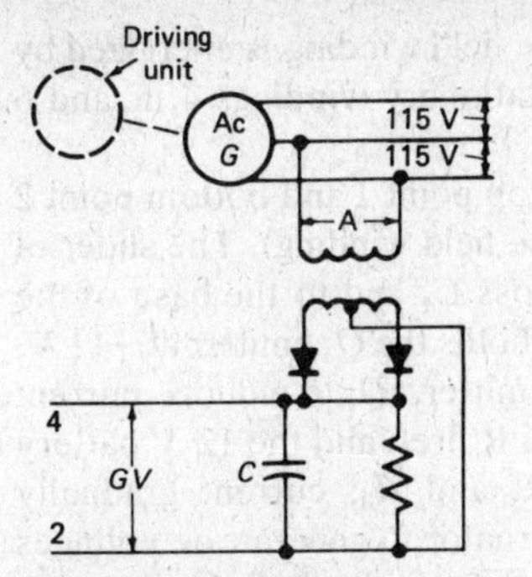

Figure 21-14 Regulator of Fig. 21-13, controlling ac generator.

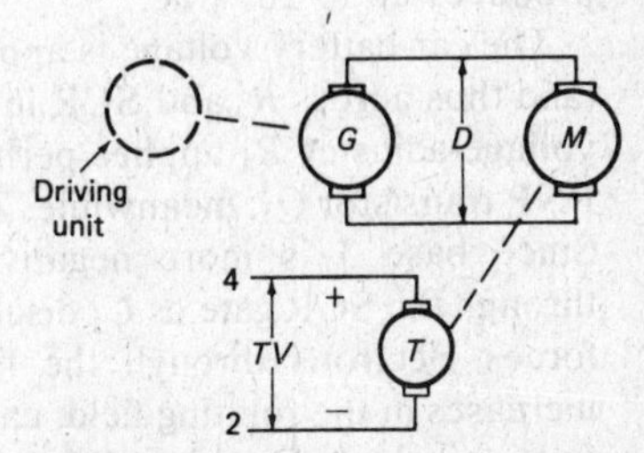

Figure 21-15 Using voltage regulator of Fig. 12-14 for speed control of motor *M*.

(4-to-2) is compared with *RV* as before; *Q* then corrects the field current to make generator *G* produce the desired ac voltage.

21-12 A SPEED REGULATOR

A similar transistor circuit can regulate the speed of a dc motor, such as *M* in Fig. 21-15. (This also is like the variable-voltage dc drive shown in Fig. 21-5.) As before, greater current in *Q* and the generator-*G* field raises the voltage *D* (produced by *G*) and therefore increases the speed of motor *M* (whose constant field is not shown). Although this voltage *D* sometimes is used as a signal to show the motor speed, a more accurate speed signal is produced by a tachometer generator *T*, driven by motor *M*. In Fig. 21-15, voltage *TV* increases at the same rate as the speed of *M* increases, and is fed back in place of *GV* in Fig. 21-13.

This transistor-controlled circuit still is a voltage regulator; if the tachometer voltage *TV* becomes too small, as compared with the reference voltage *RV*, *Q* controls generator *G* until the *TV* voltage rises to the correct amount. Since this *TV* voltage cannot rise unless the speed of motor *M* also rises, the circuit of Fig. 21-15 also controls motor speed, merely as a "by-product" of holding the correct voltage at *TV*. If the *P* slider is turned (counterclockwise) to select a smaller reference voltage *RV*, the speed of *M* decreases until *TV* is again the correct amount: *P* adjusts the speed.

21-13 CAR-ALTERNATOR VOLTAGE REGULATOR

The voltage produced by a three-phase alternator (or ac generator in an automobile) may be regulated in the circuit of Fig. 21-16, to control the charging of the 12-V battery. At the top, switch *S* is closed when the ignition switch closes; the car engine now rotates the field winding, connected through slip rings in the SCR circuit. When the field winding is energized by pulses of current through SCR, each of the stationary windings 4, 5, and 6 produces up to 20 V ac.

The car-battery voltage is applied between top point 1 and bottom point 2 (and thus across R_3 and SCR in series with the field winding). The slider of voltage-adjuster R_1 applies perhaps 10 V across C_1 and to the base of the PNP transistor Q_1; meanwhile, Zener diode Z holds the Q_1 emitter at +11 V. Since base 3 is more negative than the emitter, Q_1 conducts current through the SCR gate as C_1 discharges. The SCR fires, and the 12-V battery forces electrons through the field, the SCR, and R_3; current gradually increases in the rotating field, causing the alternator to generate ac voltages at terminals 4, 5, and 6. When the peaks of these voltage waves become greater than the opposing 12 V of the car battery, pulses of electrons flow through diodes A to F (of the three-phase full-wave rectifier, as described below and in Sec. 22-5) and into the negative battery terminal so as to charge it and increase its voltage.

When terminal 4 becomes negative during each cycle of the ac voltage generated, it forces negative the SCR anode 4 so that the SCR current stops; SCR is fired again when anode 4 returns positive, so long as the battery voltage is low. When the charging current has increased the battery voltage (between 1 and 2) so that the portion 3-to-2 (as selected by R_1) becomes equal to the Zener's 11 V, current stops in Q_1 so that SCR is not fired. Field current decreases, lowering the ac voltage of windings 4, 5, and 6 so as to decrease or stop the battery-charging current. If R_1 is turned clockwise toward its lower end, the battery must be charged to greater voltage before Q_1 stops firing SCR.

As is shown also in Sec. 22-5 and Fig. 22-9, when alternator terminal 4 becomes most positive and terminal 5 most negative, electrons flow from 5 through diode E to the (−) side of the battery; from battery (+) the electrons

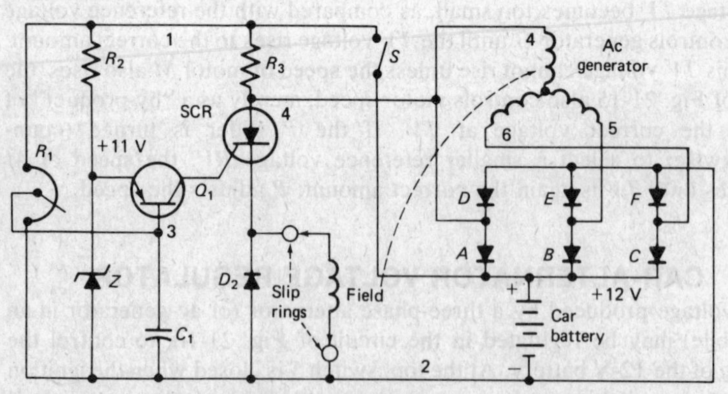

Figure 21-16 Car-alternator voltage regulator.

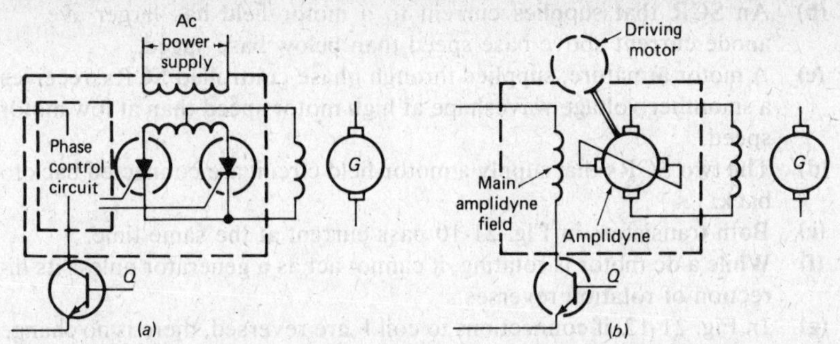

Figure 21-17 Transistor *Q* controls large generator (*a*) by phase-controlled SCRs and (*b*) by an amplidyne amplifier.

continue through diode *A* to 4. One-third cycle later, electrons leave alternator terminal 6 through diode *F*, the battery, and diode *B* to 5. Still later, as terminal 4 becomes most negative, electrons flow from 4 through diode *D*, the battery and diode *C* to terminal 6.

21-14 A TRANSISTOR MAY CONTROL LARGE FIELD CURRENT

Still using the voltage-regulating circuits already shown, the transistor *Q* may control much larger generator-field current if we add an "amplifier" between *Q* and the large field winding. Two kinds of amplifier often used in such regulators are shown within the dashed rectangles in Fig. 21-17; either of these rectangles may be controlled by transistor *Q*. In Fig. 21-17*a*, the amplifier consists of two SCRs, which rectify and control the large field current; these SCRs are phase-controlled by any one of several methods already explained;[9-5] in this way the small increase in *Q* collector current causes a large increase in the generator-field current.

In Fig. 21-17*b*, the amplifier is not electronic but consists of a special dc generator, such as an amplidyne,[32-1] which is driven at constant speed by a separate motor. The main-control-field current of this amplidyne passes directly through *Q*; an increase of 10 milliamperes in *Q* may cause more than 20 amperes increase in the direct current that the amplidyne supplies to the field of generator *G*.

Since some recent transistors can conduct 3A continuously, such a power transistor may be used at *Q* in Fig. 21-13, decreasing the need for the complex equipment in Fig. 21-17.

Problems

21-1 True or false? Explain why.

(a) In Fig. 21-2, SCR and diodes D_1 to D_4 are connected like those in Fig. 9-5.

(b) An SCR that supplies current to a motor field has larger ave. anode current above base speed than below base speed.
(c) A motor armature, supplied through phase-controlled SCRs, receives a smoother voltage waveshape at high motor speed than at low motor speed.
(d) The two SCRs that supply a motor-field circuit are connected back to back.
(e) Both transistors in Fig. 21-10 pass current at the same time.
(f) While a dc motor is rotating, it cannot act as a generator unless its direction of rotation reverses.
(g) In Fig. 21-12, if connections to coil V are reversed, there is no change in operation.
(h) A speed regulator is usually a voltage regulator.
(i) A voltage regulator is influenced by only one voltage.
(j) A rotating dc motor acts like a resistor, where armature resistance = applied V/I_a.
(k) In Fig. 21-15, if a sudden removal of shaft load causes the speed of motor M to rise, transistor Q of Fig. 21-13 decreases the G-field current.
(l) In Fig. 21-16, Q_1 compares part of a regulated quantity (across C_1) with a reference quantity (across Z).
(m) The SCR and D_2 in Fig. 21-16 perform like S and D in Fig. 9-15.

22

LARGE-CURRENT POLYPHASE RECTIFIERS

Most of the circuits discussed thus far use or control an amount of current small enough to be obtained from two wires or from a single phase of the ac power supply. Rectifiers using one, two, or four diodes are discussed in Chap. 4. When more electric power is needed for driving motors larger than 1 or 2 horsepower (hp) and to produce more than 1 or 2 kilowatts (kW) of rectified dc, current is used from all three wires of the three-phase ac power supply. Such rectifiers use three, four, or six diodes; the smoother waveshape of their dc output is often important.

22-1 POLYPHASE RECTIFIERS

This chapter describes five different rectifier circuits, any one of which may operate from a three-phase power supply; yet they are called two-, three-, four-, or six-phase rectifiers, depending upon the way they operate. Since most polyphase rectifiers must furnish large current output, they may use gas- or vapor-filled tubes, as described in Chap. 17, or now use solid-state rectifier units, described in Secs. 4-6, 5-1, and 9-1.

While three-phase power is supplied over three wires, a single phase of power can be taken from any two of these same wires. In Fig. 22-1, wires 1 and 3 supply single-phase power to *A*, which is the primary or input winding of a transformer whose secondary or output winding is *AA*. (Notice that winding *AA* is shown in line with *A*, both being vertical.) The solid sine wave at the right shows how this single-phase voltage of *AA* changes within a small part of a second.

At the same time, wires 3 and 2 furnish single-phase power to *B*; in line with primary winding *B* is its secondary winding *BB*. The voltage of *BB* has

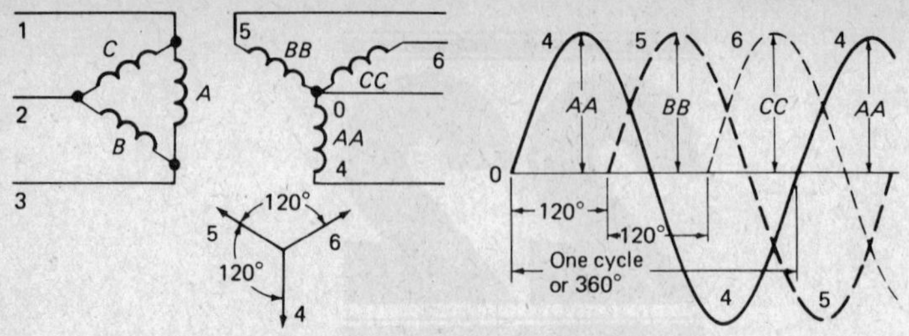

Figure 22-1 Voltages from a three-phase power supply.

the same size as voltage *AA* and may be shown by a sine wave of the same height, changing at the same rate or frequency. But this *BB* voltage (shown dashed in Fig. 22-1) lags 120° behind the *AA* voltage; the sine wave of *BB* rises above 0 later than (to the right of) the *AA* wave, by an amount of time equal to one-third cycle, or 120°.

Between wires 2 and 1 is a third phase that supplies voltage to transformer windings *C* and *CC*; this voltage (equal in size to *AA* or *BB* and shown dotted) lags 120° behind the voltage of *BB*. These phase relations are shown also by the phasor diagram in Fig. 22-1, where the phasors are turning counterclockwise at one revolution per cycle.

In the above manner the three-phase power supply is studied or seen as three separate single-phase voltages that are 120° apart in time. In Fig. 22-1 the primary windings A, B, and C of the three transformers are Δ-(or delta) connected, while their secondary windings are Y-(wye or star) connected. The 0 connection at the center of the Y is called the neutral; it becomes a fourth wire in this three-phase system. The voltage supplied by winding *AA* (or *BB* or *CC*) between one terminal and neutral is called the secondary voltage per leg. (When transformers supply 480 V between lines 5 and 4, then 277 V is supplied by leg *AA*, from 0 to 4.)

22-2 A THREE-DIODE (THREE-PHASE HALF-WAVE) RECTIFIER

Three transformer secondary windings are shown again in Fig. 22-2; each is connected to the anode of a diode rectifier or a tube. (Where diodes are shown in these rectifier circuits, vapor-filled tubes previously were used. So in circuit explanations, a mention of diode *B* refers equally to a tube *B*.) Here *AA*, *BB*, and *CC* supply the three sine waves of voltage 120° apart, as observed above. During that part of the solid wave when point 4 is more positive than the neutral 0, electrons flow from 0 through the load and through diode *A* to point 4. If diodes *B* and *C* were not also in the circuit, current would flow through diode *A* during the entire half cycles that are shaded in

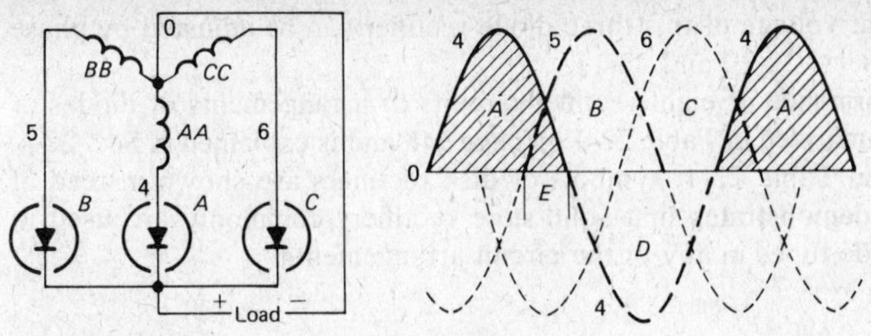

Figure 22-2 Three-phase half-wave rectifier.

Fig. 22-2; the rectifier action of diode A prevents current from flowing during the negative half cycle D.

The dashed wave of voltage is applied by winding BB to the anode of diode B and to the 0 end of the load. When point 5 is more positive than 0, electrons flow from 0, through the load and diode B. Similarly, the dotted wave of CC voltage forces electrons through the load and diode C.

In the region above E in Fig. 22-2, it appears that current flows in diode B during part of the time when current flows also in diode A. While solid-state diodes will share this load, the vapor-filled tubes (if used) generally do not share load and do not work in parallel; the load current flows through only one tube at any time. So, as is shown in Fig. 22-3, tube A carries all the load current until, at F, the tube-A anode-4 voltage becomes less than the rising wave of anode-5 voltage; then the whole load current passes instead through tube B until G, after which tube C carries the current until H, where tube A again takes its turn. Each tube carries the load current for one-third of each cycle; current flows in tube B for 120° and not for 180° (as would occur in a single-phase rectifier). Each tube in its turn applies across the load the upper or more positive portion of its anode-voltage wave. Since only 10 to 15 volts (arc drop)[17-3] appear across the tube that is conducting, the voltage across the load consists of the total combined shaded area in Fig. 22-3. When various rectifier circuits are compared, the voltage or arc drop while conducting often is assumed to be zero; this is more nearly true with solid-state diodes.

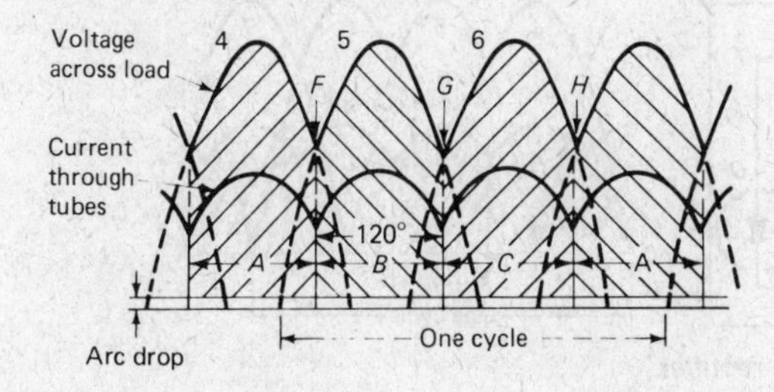

Figure 22-3 Voltage and current waveshapes from three-diode rectifier of Fig. 22-2.

The output voltage of this three-diode rectifier can be adjusted by phase control, in Secs. 22-10 and 22-11.

The performance of eight rectifier circuits or arrangements of diodes or tubes is summarized in Table 22-1 on page 348 and is explained in Sec. 22-6. At the left in Table 22-1, symbols of disk rectifiers are shown instead of tubes; this demonstrates that solid-state rectifiers commonly are used in place of diode tubes in any of the circuit arrangements.

22-3 A FOUR-DIODE (FOUR-PHASE HALF-WAVE) RECTIFIER

A larger rectifier may use four diodes instead of three; to make this possible, there are special transformers that convert the three-phase supply into two-phase power, as shown in Fig. 22-4. [These are known as Scott-connected transformers. Such four-diode rectifiers may be used to supply power to variable-speed dc motors (5 to 15 hp).] Transformer T_1, receiving single-phase power from lines 1 and 3, supplies biphase half-wave output from its T_1S windings for the anodes of rectifier diodes A and C (like the circuit of Fig. 4-4b). The primary T_2P of the second transformer (connected between line 2 and the center of T_1P) causes secondary voltages T_2S that are at right angles, or at 90°, from the T_1S voltages.

While T_1S terminal 4 is near the top of its positive half wave of voltage, electrons flow from neutral 0 through the load and diode A. As transformer terminals 5, 6, and 7 become more positive in turn, the load current transfers from diode A to diodes B, C, and D in succession. At the right in Fig. 22-4, it is seen that each diode carries the total current for one-quarter cycle, or 90°. The voltage applied across the load includes four peaks or ripples during each cycle of the ac voltage.

22-4 A SIX-DIODE (SIX-PHASE HALF-WAVE) RECTIFIER

As single-phase power (when applied through a center-tapped anode transformer) may supply a two-diode biphase half-wave rectifier, three-

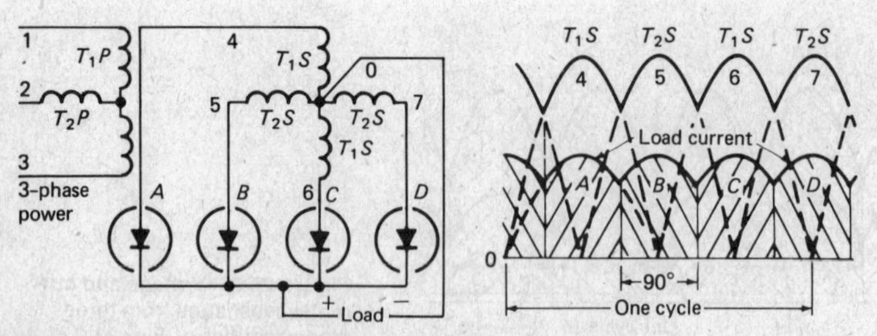

Figure 22-4 Four-diode half-wave rectifier.

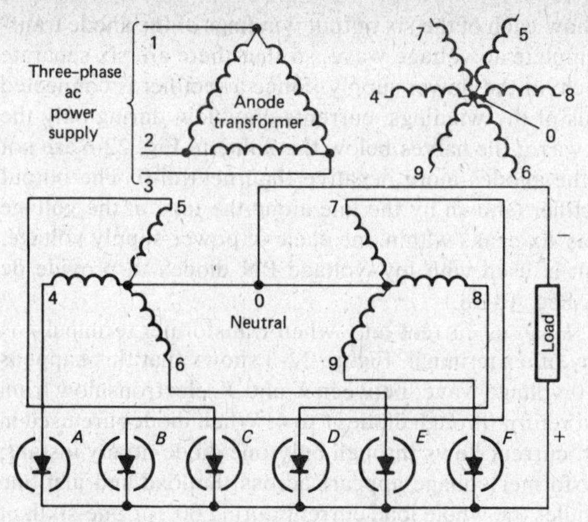

Figure 22-5 Six-phase half-wave rectifier.

phase power (applied through three such transformer windings) may supply a six-phase half-wave rectifier using six diodes, as shown in Fig. 22-5. The anode transformer has three secondary windings (4-8, 5-9, 6-7), each of which has a center tap; the three center taps are connected together at a neutral, 0, and they are also connected to the negative side of the dc load. This forms the six-ended "snowflake" shape shown in the upper part of Fig. 22-5. Without changing any connection, these secondary windings are shown again in two groups, making them look like six separate windings, each having one end connected to 0. The other ends of these windings connect to the six anodes. All six cathodes are connected together and to the positive side of the dc load.

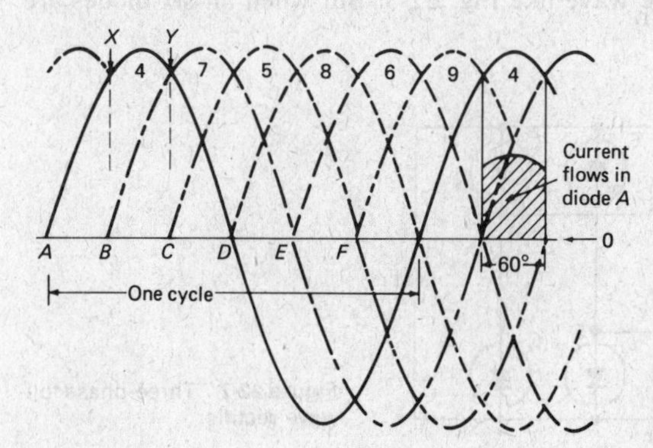

Figure 22-6 Transformer voltages supplied to six-phase rectifier of Fig. 22-5.

Figure 22-6 shows how each of the six output windings of the anode transformer produces a complete ac voltage wave, so that there are six separate waves during each cycle of the power supply. Since a rectifier is connected to each of the six ends of the windings, currents may flow during only the upper half of each ac wave; the halves below the 0 line in Fig. 22-6 are not used, for they make the anodes more negative than neutral 0. The output waveshape of this rectifier (shown by the line along the tops of the voltage waves in Fig. 22-6) has six peaks within one cycle of power-supply voltage. (This six-phase circuit is used with low-voltage PN diodes to provide dc power to a welder, in Sec. 18-18.)

In Fig. 22-5, diode *A* passes current only when transformer terminal 4 is more positive than any other terminal. Figure 22-6 shows that this happens near the top of the 4–0 voltage wave; between *X* and *Y*, electrons flow from 0 through the load and return through diode *A* to 4. When diodes are used in the six-phase rectifier, current flows through only one diode at any instant; the whole 4-to-0 transformer voltage appears across the load and just one diode. Each diode handles the whole load current during 60°, or one-sixth of each cycle.

22-5 A SIX-DIODE (THREE-PHASE FULL-WAVE) RECTIFIER

This popular rectifier cirucit often operates directly from the three-phase power lines, without any anode transformer; if 440-V three-phase power is supplied to the rectifier diodes, the resulting rectified output is suitable for driving 550-V dc motors. However, when anode transformers are used to permit operation at other amounts of voltage, Fig. 22-7 shows that only three connections 4, 5, and 6 are made to the secondary windings. Since the neutral 0 is not connected to the load, this six-diode arrangement is a bridge circuit (see Fig. 4-5*c*). Current may flow alternately in both directions in each winding; so transformers of standard design may be used.

Alone, diodes *A*, *B*, and *C* will operate like the three-diode rectifier of Sec. 22-2, producing a voltage wave like Fig. 22-3. But when all six diodes are

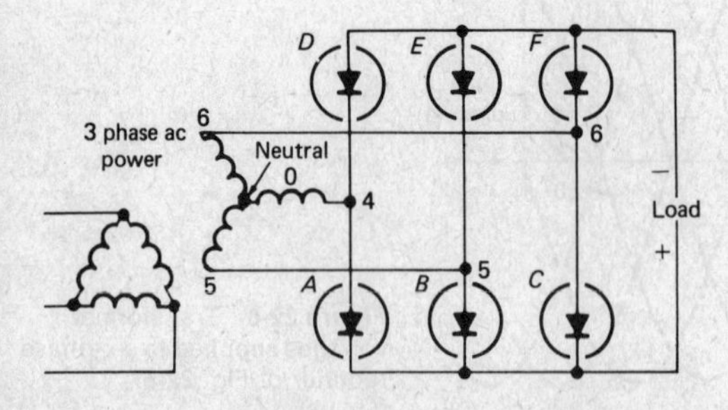

Figure 22-7 Three-phase full-wave rectifier.

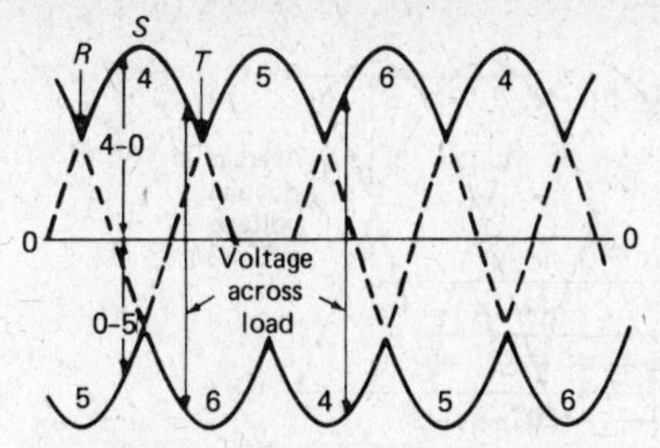

Figure 22-8 Voltage waves, line to neutral, from transformer in Fig. 22-7.

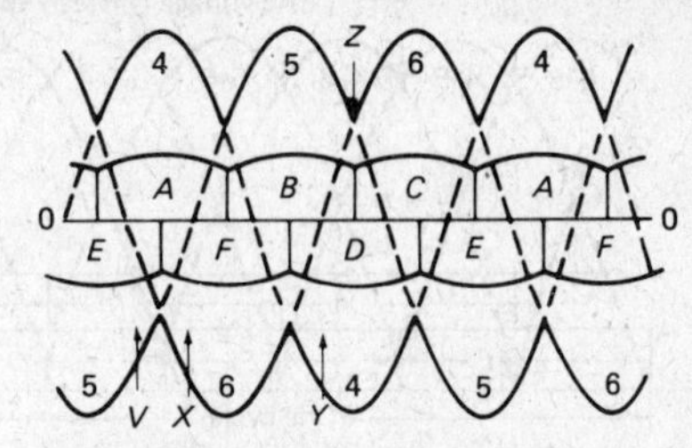

Figure 22-9 Load current flows in two diodes in series, in the sequence shown.

used in Fig. 22-7, and just before point 4 reaches its highest potential (as at *V* in Fig. 22-9), transformer terminal 5 is at a potential lower than 6 or 4 or 0. Since 5 is connected to the cathode of diode *E*, the anode of diode *E* becomes more positive than its own cathode; so diode *E* can conduct. Here electrons start from negative terminal 5 and pass upward through *E*, through the load to the cathodes, then upward through diode *A* to positive terminal 4. Here load current flows through diodes *A* and *E*, in series.

When terminal 6 drops below 5 (at *X* in Fig. 22-9), diode *F* has the most negative cathode and can conduct; load current flows through diodes *A* and *F* in series. Later, at *Y*, where the negative potential of anode 4 prevents diode *A* from conducting, this same potential lowers the cathode of diode *D* so that electrons may flow upward through diode *D* to the load and through diode *B*, whose anode (at terminal 5) is most positive at this time. At *Z*, when wave 6 rises above wave 5, current transfers from diode *B* to diode *C*; the total load current now passes through diodes *C* and *D* in series.

So long as the potential at transformer terminal 4, 5, or 6 is more positive than the neutral 0, diode *A*, *B*, or *C* connects this positive potential to the load so that it receives the voltage shown between the 0 line and the solid upper curve in Fig. 22-8. At the same time, as the potential of either terminal 4, 5, or 6 drops furthest below neutral 0, either diode *D*, *E*, or *F* connects this negative potential to the load so that it receives also the voltage between the 0 line and the solid lower curve. The total voltage to the load, as measured between the upper and lower lines, is seen to have an average size that is twice as great as the load voltage supplied by the three-diode rectifier of Fig. 22-2.

Next this dc output or load voltage (the total distance between the top and bottom curves in Fig. 22-8) may be plotted so as to form a new curve in Fig. 22-10 whose values rise above a straight reference line. This output voltage curve has six peaks, or ripples, during each full cycle of the ac power supply, although only three ac voltage waves come from terminals 4, 5, and 6. Point *S* shows the same instant in Figs. 22-8 and 22-10; *R* and *T* show other identical instants. Since the height of this curve combines the voltages measured

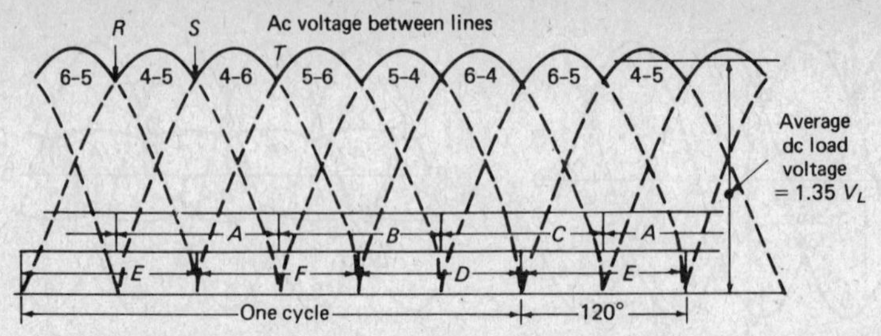

Figure 22-10 Output-voltage wave of three-phase full-wave six-diode rectifier.

from each transformer terminal to neutral, Fig. 22-10 shows the rectified waves of the voltage supplied between lines 4 to 5, or 5 to 6, or 6 to 4. The total load current flows in each diode during two consecutive voltage peaks in Fig. 22-10; each diode conducts during 120°, or one-third of each cycle.

Since the six-diode rectifier of Sec. 22-5 supplies an output voltage that contains six peaks or ripples per cycle (each peak being 60° wide), the average or dc value of this voltage is 1.35 times the applied ac voltage per leg, or $V_{dc} = 1.35\ V_{rms/leg}$. This is shown in Fig. 22-11*c*. The diodes are assumed to have 0 voltage drop. In Fig. 22-10, V is the ac *line* voltage; so $V_{dc} = 1.35\ V_{line}$.

In Fig. 22-8, the average voltage above the 0—0 line is 1.17 times V per leg (from line to neutral). The V_{avg} below the 0—0 line also is 1.17V_{leg} so the total output voltage is 2.34V_{leg}. For a three-phase system, line voltage is 1.732 times leg voltage; so $V_{dc} = 2.34V_{leg} / 1.732V_{leg} = 1.35V_{line}$.

22-6 RECTIFIER PERFORMANCE

Preceding examples show that a polyphase rectifier (without phase control) supplies to the load a voltage wave that never decreases to zero at any instant. For the three-diode rectifier, at points F or G in Fig. 22-3, the load voltage is half of its maximum value. Having less variation during the cycle (than the single-phase rectifiers described in Chap. 4), the ripple factor[4-9] here is only 0.17; the output voltage from three diodes has 17 percent ripple, as compared with the 48 percent ripple when the rectifier has two diodes.

In a two-diode single-phase rectifier, current flows in each diode for a half cycle, or 180°; Sec. 4-7 shows that the dc output voltage or $V_{dc} = V_{avg} = 0.636V_{max}$, while the ac applied input voltage $V_{ac} = V_{rms} = 0.707V_{max}$. Therefore, $V_{dc}/V_{ac} = 0.636/0.707 = 0.9$; as would be indicated by voltmeters, the dc voltage output is 0.9 as large as the ac input voltage V; this is shown in Fig. 22-11*a*. In the three-diode rectifier, however, since current flows in each diode for one-third cycle, or 120°, the load receives only the top 120° of each sine wave of voltage. As shown in

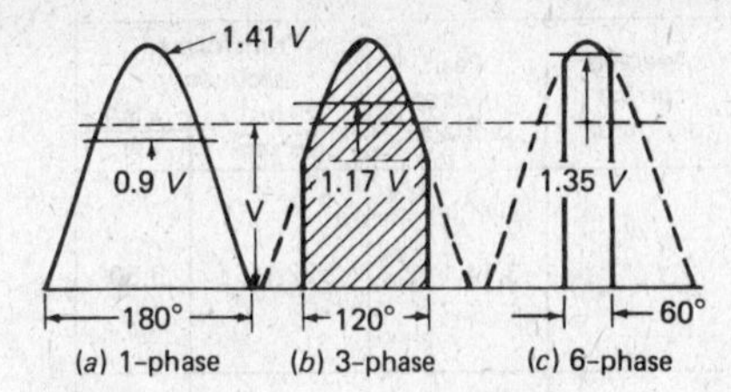

Figure 22-11 Dc output voltage increases as more diodes in turn carry the load.

Fig. 22-11*b*, the average voltage during any such 120° is greater than the average during the entire 180°. For 120°, $V_{dc} = 1.17V$, where V is the ac voltage per leg of the transformer secondary. This value is obtained by finding the mean height of the shaded area in Fig. 22-11; this refers also to the portion between F and G in Fig. 22-3, and its max height is $\sqrt{2}$ (line to neutral). Since this curve is repeated three times within each cycle, only one-third cycle, or 120°, need be considered. The shaded area is

$$\int_{30^\circ}^{150^\circ} \sqrt{2}\, V \sin \omega t\, d(\omega t)$$

and $$V_{dc} = \frac{1}{2\pi/3} \int_{-\pi/3}^{\pi/3} \sqrt{2}\, V \cos \omega t\, d(\omega t) = 1.17V$$

Or as is shown for a three-diode rectifier in Table 22-1, the required transformer secondary voltage per leg is 1/1.17, or 0.855, of the dc output voltage.

Similarly, for the six-phase rectifier of Sec. 22-4, where each diode conducts during only the top 60° of its voltage wave, Fig. 22-11*c* shows that the average height (V_{dc}) of this 60° section is $1.35V_{leg}$; the required V_{rms} per leg is 1/1.35, or 0.74, of V_{dc}.

When comparing rectifier circuits, the kVA rating or size of the required anode transformer also must be considered. To produce a given amount of watts or kilowatts output (where $\text{kW} = V_{dc} \times I_{avg}$ of the load/1000), Table 22-1 indicates (by the ratio of kVA to kW) that a half-wave rectifier circuit requires a larger transformer kVA rating than a full-wave or bridge circuit requires. To supply the two-diode rectifier (the biphase half-wave rectifier of Fig. 4-2 or Fig. 4-5*b*), each leg or half of the transformer secondary carries current only half of the time, since each diode permits current to flow in only one direction through each leg. Similarly, in Fig. 22-2, current flows through each of the three secondary legs in only one direction. However, in bridge or full-wave circuits, such as in Fig. 22-7, several diodes combine to permit current to flow alternately in both directions in each winding of the transformer; since fewer secondary windings now are needed, the required kVA size or rating of the whole transformer is thus decreased.

The kVA rating of the anode transformer depends on the heating or rms value of current that flows in each secondary winding. Using the current

	Rectifier circuit	Average current per diode	Peak reverse voltage	Transformer secondary V rms per leg	$\frac{\text{kVA}}{\text{kW}}$
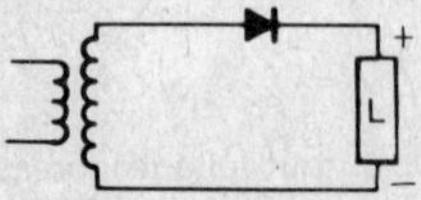	1-phase half-wave	I_{dc}*	3.14 V_{dc}*	2.22 V_{dc}*	3.50
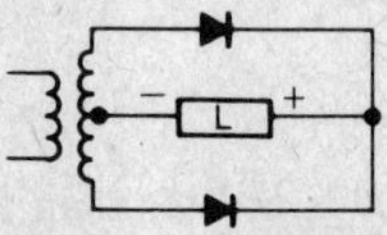	Diametric. Bi-phase half-wave (1-phase supply)	$\frac{I_{dc}}{2}$	3.14 V_{dc}	1.11 V_{dc}	1.57
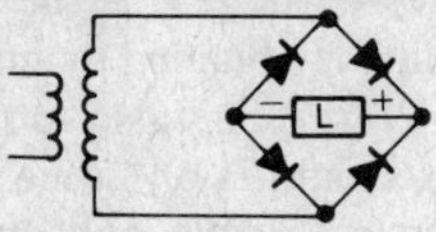	1-phase full-wave bridge	$\frac{I_{dc}}{2}$	1.57 V_{dc}	1.11 V_{dc}	1.11
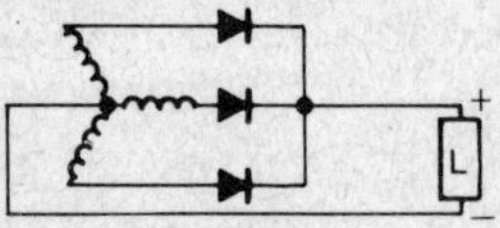	3-phase half-wave	$\frac{I_{dc}}{3}$	2.09 V_{dc}	0.855 V_{dc}	1.48
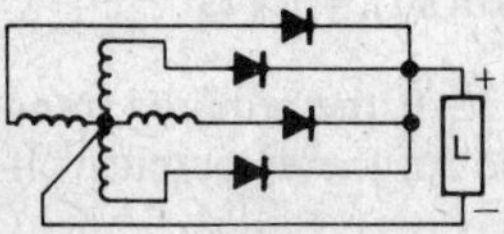	4-phase half-wave (2-phase supply)	$\frac{I_{dc}}{4}$	2.22 V_{dc}	0.785 V_{dc}	1.57
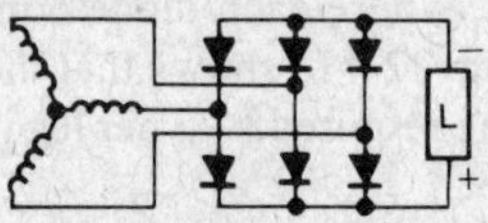	3-phase full-wave	$\frac{I_{dc}}{3}$	1.05 V_{dc}	0.428 V_{dc}	1.05
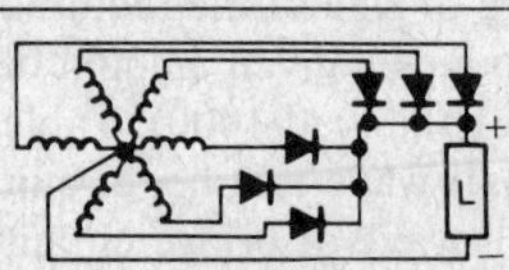	6-phase half-wave (3-phase supply)	$\frac{I_{dc}}{6}$	2.09 V_{dc}	0.740 V_{dc}	1.82
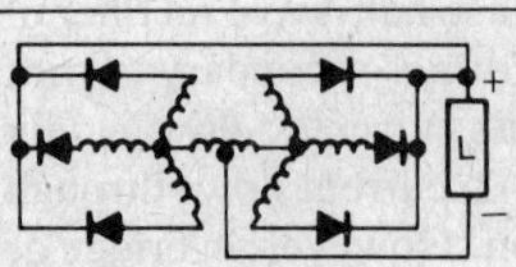	3-phase double-Y	$\frac{I_{dc}}{6}$	2.09 V_{dc}	0.855 V_{dc}	1.48

* I_{dc} is the average current of the dc load and V_{dc} is the average output voltage that the rectifier applies to this dc load; here the load is assumed to be highly inductive.

TABLE 22-1

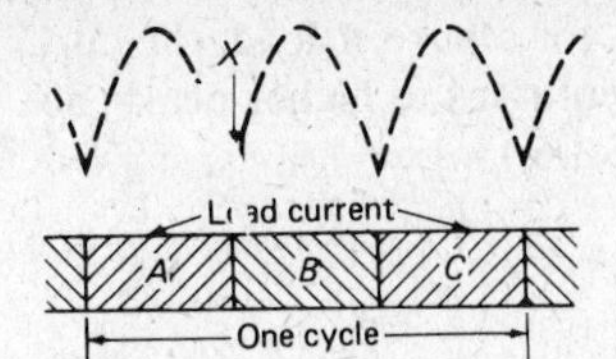

Figure 22-12 Steady load current, supplied through each diode in turn.

wave of inductive load as shown in Fig. 22-12, each diode or each transformer secondary winding carries the entire load current I_{dc} for one-third of each cycle or for $2\pi/3$ radians. Therefore, the rms value of current in one diode is

$$I = \left[\frac{1}{2\pi}\left(\frac{2\pi}{3} I_{dc}^2\right)\right]^{1/2} = \frac{I_{dc}}{\sqrt{3}}$$

The volt-ampere input to one secondary $= VI_{dc}/\sqrt{3}$; so the total voltampere rating of three secondaries is $\sqrt{3}\,VI_{dc}$. However, the resulting dc output of this three-diode rectifier is only $V_{dc}I_{dc} = 1.17VI_{dc}$. The ratio of this dc output to the total transformer volt-amperes is known as the *secondary utilization factor*, which, in this case, is $1.17VI_{dc}/1.732VI_{dc} = 0.675$. The inverse of this ratio is shown in Table 22-1 as kVA / kW, and is 1.48.

22-7 DIODE LOAD AND CURRENT RATING

A rectifier diode is designed and rated to carry a certain amount of average current continuously (see the SCR, Sec. 9-2); the maximum current a tube can conduct safely at any instant is limited by the electron emission from its cathode.

In Fig. 22-3, the load is assumed to be pure resistance R; therefore, the wave of current, flowing through R and each diode in turn, has the same variation or shape as the voltage. However, when the load includes also a large inductance L, this smooths out or removes the variation until the load direct current becomes steady at a value equal to the average height, I_{avg} or I_{dc}, of the varying current wave. Such a steady current is shown in Fig. 22-12; if, for example, this load current is 18 amperes (A), diode A then carries 18 A for one-third of each cycle. Throughout the whole cycle, the average value of the current in one tube is only 6 A; since such tubes are rated in amperes average, three tubes rated at 6 A can handle this 18-A load. Since 18 A at 350 V equals 6.3 kW, or enough to drive a $7^1/_2$-hp motor, these three diodes can serve as the rectifier to operate the $7^1/_2$-hp dc motor from a three-phase ac supply. (Here the average load current I_{dc} is also the maximum current that each diode must carry. So for each diode alone, its I_{max} of 18 A is seen to be $3 \times I_{avg}$ of the diode; as is shown for this three-diode rectifier in Table

22-1, for inductive load, $I_{avg} = {}^1/_3 I_{dc}$. However, for a pure R load, the current wave in Fig. 22-3 shows that the load current rises to higher peaks, so that the ratio I_{max}/I_{avg} reaches a higher value of 3.6.)

22-8 EFFECT OF INDUCTANCE

The top part of Fig. 22-13 shows again the 18-A load current I_{dc} as it flows in diode A for 120°, then seems to decrease instantly from I_{dc} to zero. Similarly, current in diode B needs to rise instantly from zero to I_{dc}. Such sudden changes in current are prevented by any inductance L in each diode circuit, which is present mainly in the leakage reactance of each transformer secondary winding. When these effects of inductance are included, the lower part of Fig. 22-13 shows the diode-A current decreasing more gradually, between t_1 and t_2. In the same interval, the diode-B current increases so that the sum of these two currents equals I_{dc} of the load. Thus two tubes (or diodes) share the current; this is made possible because, during this interval, the voltage at tube-A anode is kept at the same value as the tube-B anode voltage. As tube-A current i_A decreases, a voltage is produced equal to $-L di_A / dt$ that adds to or raises the voltage at tube-A anode. Meanwhile, the increasing current in tube B produces a similar voltage, $-L di_B / dt$, that lowers the voltage at tube-B anode. Thus, during the time between t_1 and t_2 the voltage at both tube anodes is halfway between the waves of the two phases, as shown at X in Figs. 22-12 and 22-13. The shaded area shows the decrease or loss of voltage at the load.

If the transformer reactance is increased, this overlap of the tube currents exists for a longer time. By adding reactors or an interphase transformer (as in Sec. 22-12), the load I_{dc} can be divided between two tubes at all times.

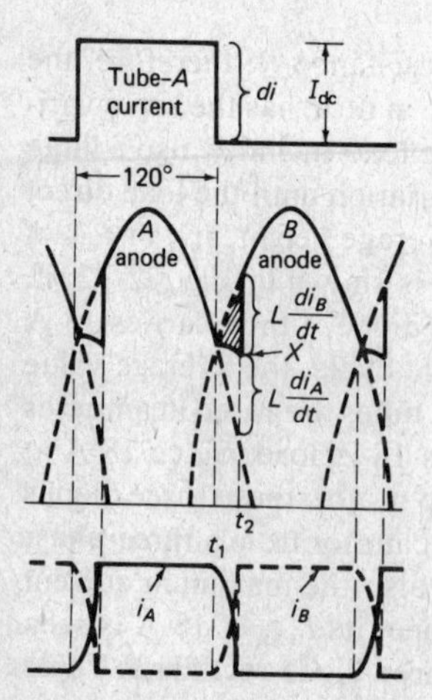

Figure 22-13 Current overlap caused by circuit inductance.

Thus the action detailed in Sec. 22-12 is merely an intentional extension of the effect of the overlap that may exist in any polyphase rectifier circuit.

22-9 PRV IN POLYPHASE RECTIFIERS

As is shown in Sec. 4-10, each tube or diode in a rectifier circuit must withstand high reverse voltages during part of the cycle when that diode is not conducting. However, Table 22-1 shows that for the same dc output voltage, each diode is exposed to greater peak reverse voltage (PRV) when it is used in a half-wave type of rectifier. Therefore, the full-wave circuit of Fig. 22-7 often is preferred for high-voltage rectifiers so as not to exceed the permissible reverse-voltage rating of the diodes.

For any bridge rectifier, PRV $= \sqrt{2}\,V_{\text{line}}$. But PRV $= \sqrt{2}\,V_{\text{leg}}$ for any half-wave rectifier having an even number of legs and diodes, as shown in Fig. 22-14. Here we see that diode D applies line-to-neutral voltage or leg voltage V_1 across the load while conducting. But in the following half cycle, while V_1 drives the diode D anode to a max negative value, voltage V_2 drives the diode D cathode to a max positive value, for there is negligible voltage drop across diode E while it is conducting. Therefore, the max reverse voltage across diode D, or PRV $= \sqrt{2}(V_1 + V_2) = 2.828\,V$.

For the three-phase half-wave rectifier of Fig. 22-15, the anode of diode A is driven negative by V_3 at the time when diode B conducts and raises the diode A cathode to the positive potential of V_4. However, since V_4 lags only 120° behind V_3, the max difference between these two curves occurs at $4\pi/3$ rad, which is the point where $d(V_4 - V_3)/d(wt) = 0$. Here PRV across diode $A = \sqrt{2}\ 2\pi/3 - \sin 4\pi/3) = 2.45\,V_{\text{leg}}$.

22-10 PHASE-SHIFTING A POLYPHASE RECTIFIER

Thyratron tubes or SCRs may be used in place of the diodes shown in the preceding rectifier circuits or to replace the semiconductor rectifiers in-

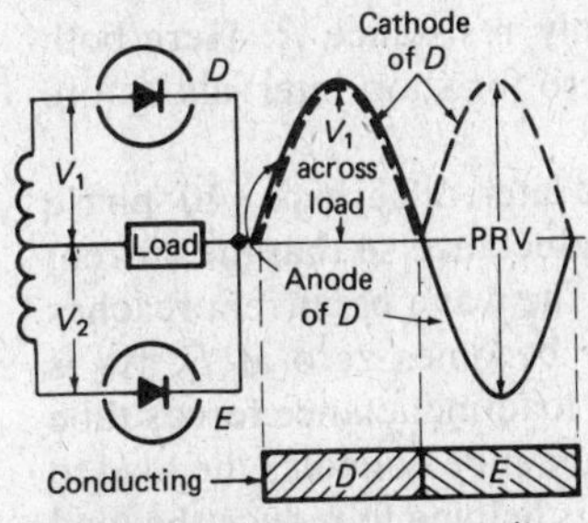

Figure 22-14 Peak reverse voltage in rectifier having even number of diodes.

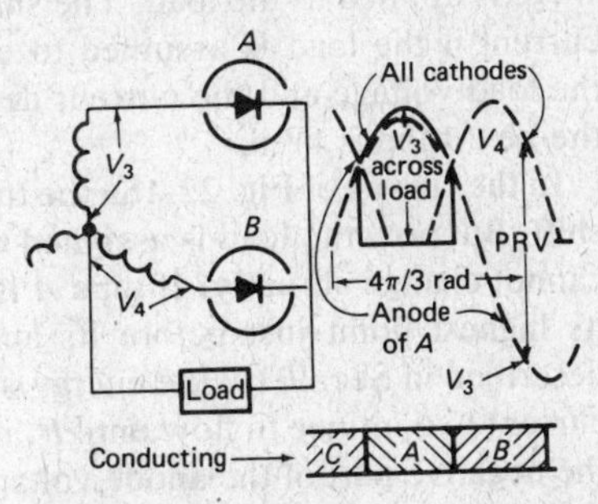

Figure 22-15 Peak reverse voltage in three-diode rectifier.

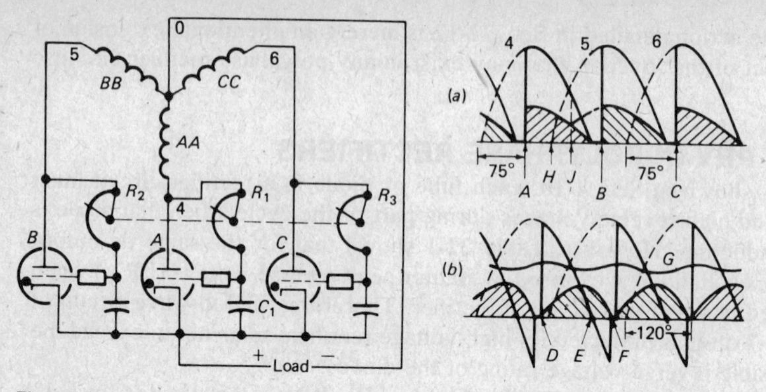

Figure 22-16 Phase-shift control of three-tube rectifier (*a*) with resistance load and (*b*) with inductive load.

dicated in Table 22-1. By grid or gate control of such units, the output voltage and current of the rectifier may be varied or regulated.

The three-diode rectifier of Fig. 22-2 is shown with tubes in Fig. 22-16; here, if the grids of thyratrons *A*, *B*, and *C* never keep them from firing, the circuit operates exactly as is described in Sec. 22-2.

In Fig. 22-16 the three thyratrons have identical phase-shifting circuits for control of their grid potentials. Capacitor C_1 and variable resistor R_1 are connected between anode and cathode of tube *A*, similar to the circuit shown in Fig. 20-9. When the resistance of R_1 is increased (turned clockwise), tube *A* is fired later in its half cycle, as is explained in Sec. 20-10. In Fig. 22-16, the dashed line connecting R_2 to R_1 and R_3 indicates that these three resistors are gang-operated by hand, so that all three tubes are phase-shifted the same amount.

In the curves of Fig. 22-16*a*, the tubes are fired at *A*, *B*, and *C*; the firing of each tube is delayed 75° behind the start of its own wave of anode voltage (or we say it is phase-shifted 75°). Only the solid part of the anode voltage wave is applied to the load. The shaded portions show the resulting flow of current if the load is assumed to consist of only resistance *R*. Here both the load voltage and the current decrease to zero for short intervals before the next tube is fired.

In the curves of Fig. 22-16*b* the tubes are fired later, at perhaps 120° phase shift. But now the load is assumed to include inductance so that the current cannot change abruptly. If tube *A* is fired at *D*, the wave of current reaches its highest point just before its anode voltage becomes zero at *E*. As is described in Sec. 9-10, the energy stored in the load inductance forces tube current to continue to flow until *F*; meanwhile, the tube connects the load to the negative part of the anode voltage wave, thus helping to reduce the load current to zero before the next tube fires. If the tubes were fired earlier, perhaps at 90°, the current waves through the separate tubes would overlap so that the current would not reach zero. If the tubes are fired at 30°, the current wave is larger and is fairly steady, as shown at *G*. [In the three-tube rectifier, the load current is not increased when tube grids are shifted less than 30°. Even if the grid of tube *B* is made positive at *H* (in Fig. 22-16), tube *A* still carries the load current, at least until *J*. Not until the 30° point *J* does the tube-*B* anode voltage rise high enough to permit the load current to transfer from tube *A* to tube *B*.]

Any method that controls a three-tube rectifier (as just described) may also be used to phase-shift the six-diode full-wave rectifier of Fig. 22-7. Only diodes *A*, *B*, and *C* need be replaced by thyratrons (or SCRs). Since no current passes through diodes *D*, *E*, or *F* unless it passes also through thyratrons *A*, *B*, or *C*, the control of only three grids is necessary; the phase-shift control of thyratrons *A*, *B*, and *C* may be the same as the control of tubes *A*, *B*, and *C* in Fig. 22-16. However, phase control of this circuit by three SCRs is described below.

22-11 PHASE CONTROL OF SCRs IN A THREE-PHASE BRIDGE

A three-phase full-wave rectifier like that in Fig. 22-7 is shown at the right in Fig. 22-17, except that the lower three diodes are replaced by SCRs *A*, *B*, and *C*. The left-hand side of Fig. 22-17 is like Fig. 9-9, but now point 1 receives voltage through R_1 and the three diodes D_1, D_2, and D_3. When ac line 4 becomes positive so that current flows in D_1, point 1 rises to 20 volts (V) above point 2, and is limited by Zener diode Z. Capacitor C_1 starts to charge toward 20 V at a rate adjusted by R_3. After the desired delay in the cycle (between 30 and 150°) the C_1 voltage has risen high enough to trigger unijunction transistor UJT_1;[8-7] this lets C_1 discharge quickly through UJT_1 and R_4. The sudden voltage across R_4 produces a pulse of current through the gate of each SCR *A*, *B*, and *C*, but fires only *A*, which has the most positive anode at this moment; electrons may flow from line 5 through diode *E* to the load and return through SCR *A* to line 4.

Since an SCR has only 1-V drop (anode to cathode) while conducting, the firing of SCR *A* brings point 2 to almost the same potential as line 4, and thus removes the voltage between points 1 and 2; this turns off or resets UJT_1. Current continues through SCR *A* and the load until its anode 4 goes negative (or until SCR *B* is fired). Meanwhile, when line 5 becomes positive (120° behind line 4,) current through D_2 lets point 1 rise to 20 V; C_1 charges (at the same rate as before, since R_3 is the same), so that UJT_1 fires again, but this time the voltage pulse across R_4 fires SCR *B*. Similarly, when line 6 becomes positive (240° behind line 4), current through D_3 again starts the R_3-C_1 timing action so that the UJT_1 pulse fires SCR *C*.

To apply greatest voltage across the load, the resistance of R_3 is set at a low value so that each SCR is fired 30° after its anode becomes positive. When R_3 is increased so that each SCR fires 45° later, we may use the curves

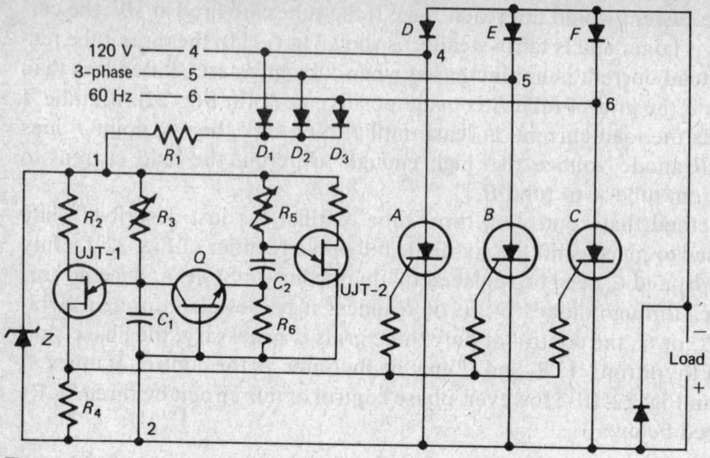

Figure 22-17 Phase control of SCRs in a three-phase bridge.

in Fig. 22-16*a* to see that SCR *A* is fired 75° after its anode becomes positive. Further increase of R_3 may fire each SCR at 120° behind its anode voltage; this is shown in Fig. 22-16*b*, wherein SCR *A* fires at *D*. But the firing of SCR *A* must not be delayed as much as 150° behind its anode 4 (as at *J* in Fig. 22-16*a*), for here the anode-5 voltage of SCR *B* rises above that of anode 4; here a pulse from UJT_1 fires SCR *B* early instead of firing SCR *A* late. Therefore, the circuit of Fig. 22-17 cannot delay the firing of the SCRs within the last 30° of the wave of ac voltage. The load voltage may be varied between 150 and 40 V dc, or may be dropped abruptly to zero.

To prevent the unwanted firing of SCR *A* as late as *J* (150° behind anode voltage 4), the center of Fig. 22-17 includes UJT_2 and transistor *Q*; normally, these do not affect the previous UJT_1 circuit, since *Q* does not conduct. But R_5 is set so that C_2 charges (through R_5 and R_6) so as to trigger UJT_2 about 145° later than the rising wave of anode voltage. As C_2 discharges, electrons flow from C_2 through *Q* (emitter to base) and from the lower terminal of UJT_2 through its gate and to C_2. This base current forces *Q* into saturation so that C_1 quickly is discharged through *Q* and thus cannot trigger UJT_1. Thus, when R_3 is increased so much as to delay the firing of the SCRs later than 145°, the *Q* current prevents any SCR from firing; the load receives zero voltage.

22-12 SIX-TUBE RECTIFIER WITH INTERPHASE TRANSFORMER

This rectifier (shown in Fig. 22-18 and called a three-phase double-*Y* half-wave rectifier) has the same circuit as Fig. 22-5, except that an interphase

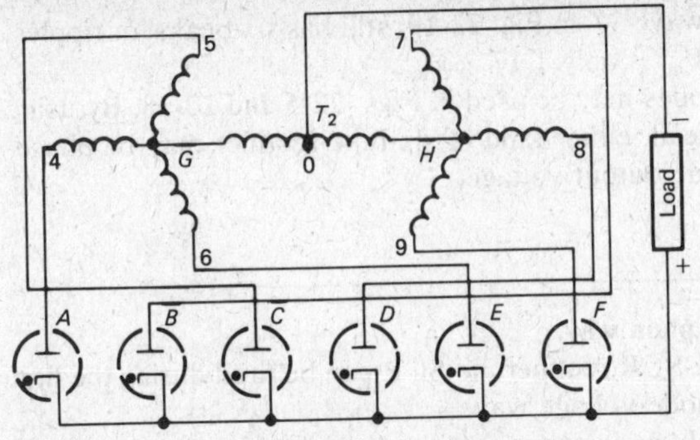

Figure 22-18 Six-tube rectifier with interphase transformer T_2.

transformer T_2 is added between neutral 0 and the center taps G and H. This transformer T_2 has large inductance; to show its effect, Fig. 22-19 includes an enlarged picture of the rectified voltage near the peaks. At point Y (which is the same as Y in Fig. 22-6), when the current through tube A decreases (to let the tube-B current increase), the current through the T_2 leg G-to-0 also must decrease. The inductance of T_2 reacts to this decreasing current by producing a voltage (shown at R in Fig. 22-19) that prevents voltage 4–0 from decreasing so fast; instead, the potential of tube-A anode is made to follow the curved line from Y to S. This sudden voltage R in the G-to-0 leg makes a similar voltage L appear across the 0-to-H leg of T_2; this voltage L (in Fig. 22-19) prevents voltage 7–0 from rising so fast. Instead, the potential of tube-B anode is also made to follow the curved line Y to S. Since the anode voltages of tube A and tube B are now equal, both of these tubes may pass current at the same time. Not until S does the tube-A current stop; this tube-A current shifts to tube C. Meanwhile, tube B continues to pass its half of the load current until T, where it is shifted to tube D.

Thus, when the interphase transformer is added, the load current is made to divide between two tubes. Each tube needs to carry only half as much peak current as it would carry in the six-phase circuit of Fig. 22-5, but it must carry this current for one-third instead of one-sixth cycle. The output

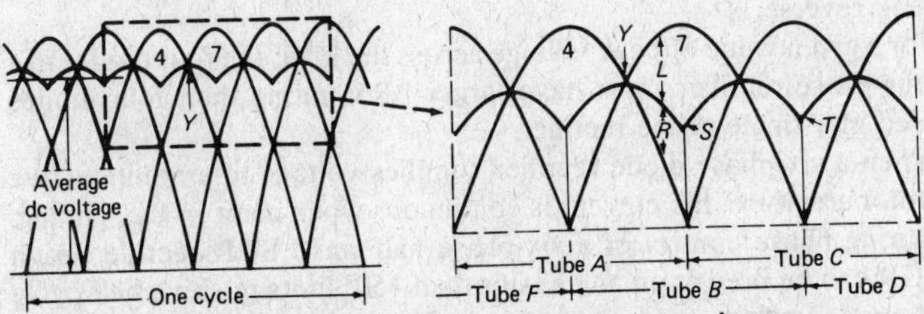

Figure 22-19 Waveshapes of rectifier with interphase transformer.

voltage of this rectifier (wave ST in Fig. 22-19) still has six peaks, or ripples, during each cycle; this V_{dc} is only $1.17 \times V_{leg}$.

Vapor-filled or PN diodes may be used in Figs. 22-5 and 22-18. By using SCRs or thyratrons instead, either kind of six-tube rectifier may be phase-shifted to give variable dc output voltage.

Problems

22-1 True or false? Explain why.

(a) In a normal three-SCR rectifier, no SCR can be fired during the first 30° of its own anode-voltage wave.

(b) The output of only a six-phase rectifier has six rippies per cycle.

(c) If a four-SCR rectifier receives power from a three-phase supply, the load is not equally divided between the four SCRs.

(d) A half-wave rectifier does not use the anode transformer efficiently.

(e) In Fig. 22-17, phase delay of each SCR is caused by varying an RC time constant.

(f) For the same V_{dc}, diodes in half-wave rectifiers need less PRV rating than in full-wave rectifiers.

(g) In a bridge rectifier, current flows in both directions in an anode-transformer secondary winding.

(h) In any rectifier circuit that uses four diodes, each diode conducts for 90°.

(i) If diodes B, D, and F are removed from the six-diode rectifier of Fig. 22-5, the output waveshape becomes the same as in Fig. 22-3.

(j) For a rectifier output of 150 kW at 500 V, each diode may be of a size rated 50 A avg (1) when connected three-phase full-wave, (2) when connected six-phase half-wave.

(k) If an interphase transformer is added into a six-diode half-wave rectifier, the output voltage is decreased about 13 percent.

(l) In Fig. 22-7, current does not flow through diodes B and E at the same instant.

(m) Using a large number of phases, V_{leg} may be as low as $0.71\ V_{dc}$.

(n) If one diode fails in a three-diode rectifier supplying a highly inductive load, each of the other diodes may conduct for 180°.

(o) No rectifier with 75-V output can use diodes rated at only 100 V peak reverse.

(p) For a given value of peak voltage across the load, the four diodes in a four-phase rectifier must have larger PRV rating than four diodes used in a single-phase rectifier.

(q) When a six-phase diode rectifier supplies voltage to a noninductive motor armature, the current is continuous when cemf = V_{rms} per leg.

(r) During phase control of a six-phase half-wave SCR rectifier, each SCR can be fired at an angle later than 150° in its positive half cycle of anode voltage.

22-2 If six diodes, each rated 16 amperes (A) average, are used in a half-wave rectifier to furnish 96 A to a steady inductive load: (*a*) Find the rms amperes in each diode. (*b*) Repeat when three such diodes furnish 48 A to the load.

22-3 Three SCRs form a three-phase half-wave rectifier. Internal drop is zero. (*a*) Draw the output-voltage waveshape for one complete cycle when the turn-on gate current of each SCR occurs 30° after the point where its anode voltage rises above the 0 line. (*b*) What is V_{dc} for this condition, in terms of V_{leg}? (*c*) Repeat for delayed firing at 90°, assuming that the load is inductive so that the current is not interrupted.

22-4 Six stacks of PN diode rectifiers are connected as a three-phase full-wave rectifier, operating from 220-V 60-Hz supply. Each diode has 0.3-Ω internal resistance and a peak reverse rating of 20 V; its continuous rating is 2 A average. Do not parallel diodes, but use the minimum safe number in series. (*a*) Find the voltage and continuous power output of the complete rectifier. (*b*) Calculate whether these identical stacks can be used safely when reconnected as a six-phase half-wave rectifier receiving 220 V line to neutral.

22-5 Each of six tubes is rated 12.5 A average, 50 A instantaneous, and 1000 V peak reverse. Assume zero tube drop. Using the greatest ac voltage that does not cause the tube ratings to be exceeded, find the dc voltage and output kilowatts when these tubes are connected as (*a*) a six-phase half-wave rectifier; (*b*) a three-phase full-wave rectifier; (*c*) a four-tube half-wave rectifier.

22-6 Diodes (having zero drop) are connected to form a three-phase full-wave rectifier that supplies an inductive load of 18 kW at 400 V dc. Find (*a*) the required PRV and average current rating of each diode and (*b*) the ac voltage supplied to the rectifier.

22-7 Each SCR or thyratron in a six-phase half-wave rectifier is fired at 90° in its own anode voltage wave. Internal drop = 0. The transformer furnishes 150 V per leg. Find (*a*) V_{dc} across the load and (*b*) PRV. (*c*) If a minimum of 25 V is needed to fire each tube, find the earliest and latest angle at which each tube can be fired, in this circuit.

22-8 The noninductive armature of a dc motor has $R_a = 5$ ohms (Ω) and generates 200 volts (V) at 1000 rpm; it is supplied from a four-phase half-wave rectifier using four SCRs having zero drop. The anode transformer gives 250 V leg to neutral. The shunt field strength is constant. (*a*) Find the maximum motor speed while the armature current is continuous. At 1500 rpm, find (*b*) the angle at which each SCR starts to conduct, and (c) the average armature current.

22-9 A new car uses a three-phase generator that has four output terminals and 20 V leg to neutral. This generator is connected to a rectifier consisting of silicon diodes, each rated 12 A average and 50 V PRV. The dc load is highly inductive. Find the dc output voltage and largest load current if the rectifier consists of (*a*) three diodes, (*b*) six diodes connected full wave. (*c*) If now a six-phase generator is substituted, find its generated voltage, leg to neutral, so that the same six diodes will receive no greater PRV than before; then find the dc output voltage and largest load current.

22-10 Three diodes operate with a transformer (276 V leg to neutral) to supply rectified voltage to a noninductive motor armature, whose $R_a = 4\ \Omega$. Diode drop is zero. Find average armature current (*a*) when cemf = 180 V, (*b*) when cemf = 250 V.

22-11 Eight diodes (with zero drop) are used in a four-phase full-wave rectifier supplying current to a highly inductive load. The anode transformer gives 200 V, leg to neutral, 60 Hz (cps). Each diode is rated 10 A average, 50 A instantaneous. Find (*a*) V_{dc} across the load, (*b*) the largest permissible I_{dc} in the load, (*c*) PRV at each diode, and (*d*) the load resistance that permits the flow of I_{dc} of *b*.

23 HIGH FREQUENCIES AND SHORTER WAVELENGTHS

All the circuits studied this far use dc, or they use ac at a power-supply frequency, such as 60 Hz (or 60 cycles per second). Many electronic circuits in industry operate at much higher frequencies; most transistors and electron tubes may be made to produce ac that changes direction millions of times each second. Today radio, TV, induction heating, fluorescent lights, and x-rays exist because electron devices can make such very high frequencies or oscillations. The success of these fields of electronics is due to the high frequencies themselves; if we could produce such high-frequency ac by other devices besides transistors or electron tubes, there still could be radio, x-rays, etc. (Early radio used no electron tubes, but produced the needed high frequency by arc gaps. X-rays produced by electron tubes[23-15] give about the same result as radium, the rare material made by nature.) Since various kinds of electron devices can help to produce these very high frequencies so easily or can respond to them, the results are included in the study of electronics.

As we read about electronics, we find words or names such as microwaves, megacycles, ultraviolet, x-ray diffraction, artificial fever, FM, UHF, shortwave radio, television, ultrasonics, infrared, and angstroms. Although many of these apply to the field of communications and broadcasting, electronics in industry makes similar use of these ideas and terms. Therefore, this chapter reviews some of the knowledge usually obtained in the study of physics. Also, since electronics is used in problems of sound, heat, and light, we must know the nature of these things.

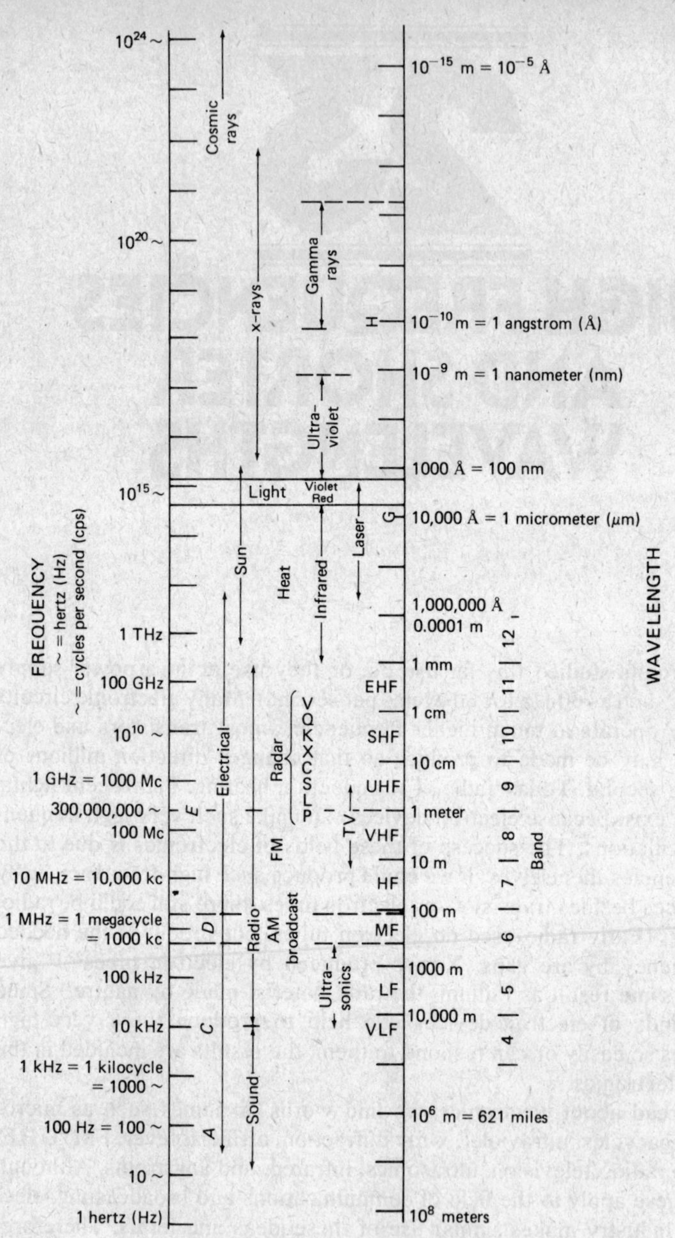

Figure 23-1 Spectrum of frequencies and wavelengths.

23-1 THE FREQUENCY SPECTRUM

To understand many aspects of electronics, we must learn how electricity behaves at higher frequencies. Besides flowing as electric current in a wire or through a transistor or tube, electricity sends an impulse or a signal through space perhaps for thousands of miles. Electricity that reverses a million times per second can cause results far beyond what the same electricity can do at 60 cycles per second. This effect that electricity produces out in space is called *electromagnetic radiation*.

This electric signal through space (which produces radio, induction heating, or artificial fever) is exactly the same thing as a beam of light or x-rays or heat from the sun, except that the frequency is different. Any light that can be seen (whether it is sunlight or comes from a lamp) is really a radiation or movement of energy through space; it is vibrating about a million billion times per second. A human eye responds to this kind of energy signal, and it is called *light*. If this same kind of energy passes through space but vibrates only one-tenth as rapidly as the light ray, the eye cannot see it but one can feel it—it is now the kind of energy signal that is called *heat*. Vibrating at these frequencies of light and heat, we do not say that this energy is electrical; yet it was proved 60 years ago that the only difference between a ray of light and a radio electrical beam is in its frequency, or rate of vibration. Since it is known that all these kinds of radiation (light, heat, radio, ultraviolet, x-ray, etc.) differ only in frequency or wavelength, we can show and study them better by putting them on a chart; the entire range of these known frequencies is called the *frequency spectrum*. Such a chart is shown in Fig. 23-1. Even a 60-hertz (or 60 cycles per second) alternating current may produce a radiation of energy through space (which also is called its *magnetic field*); such a radiation is shown at the left-hand or low-frequency end of Fig. 23-1, at the point marked *A*. (Tracing from left to right, the frequency increases and the wavelength decreases.)

Between *A* and *C* on this chart is a part marked "Sound." A sound that we hear is not a radiation of electricity through space; instead, sound is the effect on our ears caused by a vibration passing through the air. [If an electric doorbell is placed inside an airtight glass tank, the sound of the bell may be heard by a person outside the tank as long as enough air is left inside the tank; the air carries the sound vibrations from the bell to the wall of the tank. However, when the air is pumped out of the tank (producing a vacuum), the bell is no longer heard, although it is still seen to be moving or vibrating.] However, this sound vibration has a frequency of about 30 to 10,000 Hz; sound is included in Fig. 23-1 (even though it is not an electromagnetic radiation) to complete the picture of those things that are recognized or known by their frequency or rate of vibration.

23-2 FIGURES ON THE SPECTRUM CHART

To be able to include the frequencies of these known kinds of electromagnetic radiation, the chart of Fig. 23-1 must reach from 1 Hz to 10^{24} Hz. To make this possible (and still be able to show useful figures at each part of the chart), a logarithmic scale is used. With such a scale, each time we move a single division to the right on the top scale, the number of cycles has increased 10 times (thus the 1000-cycle mark is two divisions from the 10-cycle mark).

Above 1000 cycles (and through part of the radio range), the frequency is given in kilocycles (kc) or kilohertz (kHz). Each kilocycle is 1000 cycles (as shown in the following table); so the point marked 100 kc is also 100,000 cycles. Similarly, a million cycles is called a megacycle or 1 MHz; so 10 MHz is the same as 10 million cycles or 10,000 kHz. (At point *E* in Fig. 23-1, the frequency of 300,000,000 cycles per second is also called 300 MHz). At still higher frequencies, instead of using "millions of megacycles" or gigahertz, etc., we often use values of wavelength[23-10]. However, these huge numbers of cycles may also be shown as 10^{15} or 10^{20}, etc. (In the figure 10^{15}, the ^{15} shows the number of zeros in the whole number. 10^{15} is the same as 1,000,000,000,000,000. Similarly, $10^6 = 1$ million = 1,000,000; $10^{10} = 10$ billion.) To show the size of these numbers in the upper right-hand part of Fig. 23-1, we may realize that if the entire national debt of the United States is \$8,000 billion or \$8,000,000,000,000, it is merely $\$8 \times 10^{12}$. So the number of cycles per second in a light beam is greater than the number of pennies in the national debt.

While these figures at the top of Fig. 23-1 are increasing, there are other figures, at the lower side of the chart, that are decreasing. At point *E*, notice that a frequency of 300,000,000 cycles per second (or 300 MHz) is on a line with a 1-meter wavelength.

Prefix	Symbol	Meaning	Example
pico	p	micro-micro, or 10^{-12}	picofarad, or $\mu\mu$F
nano	n	milli-micro, or 10^{-9}	nanosecond
micro	μ	$\frac{1}{1,000,000}$, or 0.000001, or 10^{-6}	microwatt, microfarad
milli	m	$\frac{1}{1000}$, or 0.001, or 10^{-3}	milliampere, millimeter
centi	c	$\frac{1}{100}$, or 0.01	centimeter
hecto	h	100	hectowatt
kilo	k	1000, or 10^3	kilowatt, kilocycle
mega	M	1,000,000 or 10^6	megacycle, megohm
giga	G	1,000,000,000, or 10^9	gigahertz, or kilomegacycle
tera	T	1,000,000,000,000, or 10^{12}	

23-3 FREQUENCY AND WAVELENGTH

When we watch waves of water move past the end of a pier, the waves may be 10 ft apart (from one tip or crest to the next crest); if one wave passes during each second of time, the waves are traveling 10 ft/sec. This wave movement is a kind of vibration in the water; the wavelength of this vibration is 10 ft, while its frequency is 1 wave per second. If now conditions change so that the waves are only 5 ft apart (but traveling at the same speed of 10 ft / sec), twice as many waves must pass during each second. The wavelength is now 5 ft; the frequency is 2 per second. As the wavelength decreases, the frequency increases (as long as the speed is unchanged).

Similarly, a sound travels through the air at, roughly, 1000 ft / sec. If this sound is a low note that vibrates 100 times per second, then 100 waves (or air-pressure crests) pass our ear each second. As these waves radiate or move in a straight line through the air, the distance between them must be 10 ft. (Wavelength = 10 ft. Frequency = 100 per second.) If the sound changes to a higher note, of 1000 vibrations per second, it still travels at the same speed of 1000 ft / sec; however, the wavelength (or distance between air-pressure crests) is now only 1 ft.

For any other part of Fig. 23-1 except "sound" or "ultrasonics," the speed at which the electromagnetic radiations travel is the speed of light or the speed of electricity. This speed is about 186,000 miles each second; this is also 300,000,000 meters/sec (for each meter is about 40 in. long). At point *E*, where a radio beam changes at the rate of 300,000,000 cycles per second, the distance between crests of these radio waves is 1 meter. Moving one scale division to the left of *E*, to where the frequency is decreased to 30,000,000 cycles or 30 Mc, the wavelength is increased to 10 meters. [The radio wavelength (in meters) is always equal to 300,000/kilocycles. So a station broadcasting at 1000 kc has a wavelength of 300 meters. A television station using a 5-meter wave has a frequency of 60 MHz.]

At the lower frequencies (to the left of *D*, the AM broadcast range in Fig. 23-1), the wavelength is seldom mentioned; however, to the right of *E* we find radar or other units using "centimeter waves"; a 3000-Mc or 3-GHz signal has 10-cm waves. Farther to the right, heat and light wavelengths are often described in nanometers or in angstroms, as explained in Sec. 23-10.

23-4 SOUND

Most ac motors or transformers have a humming noise, a low note such as a person might hum. Operating from 60-Hz supply, this hum is a vibration of 120 cps. (The transformer hum is caused by pulses of ac power within the iron core; one power pulse occurs during each half cycle of current flow; so the sound has a frequency twice that of the ac supply.) As shown in Fig. 23-1, the range of most sounds is between 20 and 10,000 cycles per second;

there are air vibrations below 20 or above 20,000, but the ear cannot respond to them. (The human ear responds best to sound at about 1000 cycles per second, with less response to higher or lower frequencies. Only a young ear hears well above 10,000 cps.) To know this range of sound frequencies, recall that middle C on a piano is at a frequency of 256 cycles; one octave higher is 512 cycles. Raising the note or pitch by one octave doubles the frequency. If you can whistle through a range of two octaves, the top note is a vibration four times the frequency of the lowest note.

While the highest main note of a piano is about 4000 cycles/sec and that of a violin is 3000, most musical sounds contain overtones or frequencies above 4000; these higher frequencies make a piano note sound different from a flute or a violin note. If these frequencies above 4000 cps are not included in a recording or a broadcast, the result does not sound the same as the instrument itself. Therefore, a range of 6000 cycles is needed for each "channel" through which radio or sound entertainment is sent. High-fidelity, or "hi-fi," equipment uses the wider range of all frequencies heard by the human ear.

23-5 ULTRASONICS

As a sound rises above 10,000 to 20,000 cps it is very shrill; gradually it fades and cannot be heard. The vibration is still there, but it is above the range of the ear; it is now an ultrasonic (beyond sound) vibration [*Ultrasonic* refers to a rate of vibration more frequent than 10 kc (the greatest frequency at which sound usually is heard); *supersonic* refers to a velocity or speed faster than about 740 miles per hour (the speed at which a sound travels through air).] Some insects and animals produce or hear such "noises," which man never hears. One type of police whistle is heard by a dog far away but cannot be heard by a man near or far. A bat flies in the dark without striking a wall or even a wire inside a room; the bat makes ultrasonic "noise," at about 50,000 cps, and then listens for the echo reflected from the wall or the wire. If the bat's mouth or ears are covered, it strikes the wall. Making more than 20 of these "noises" each second, the bat acts like a radar (whose electronic circuit sends out pulses of high-frequency waves, then measures the time of their reflected return).

In industry, ultrasonic vibrations (produced by electronic circuits and vibrating crystals) may mix together liquids that usually stay apart. Such waves also measure distances through water or locate defects in thick metal castings. These results come from the physical wave motion or rapid change of pressure within the liquid or solid, vibrating at high frequency. Transistor or electron-tube oscillators may produce electromagnetic waves at such frequencies, but this electrical vibration must be changed into a mechanical vibration or movement within the liquid; this is done by connecting the electrical terminals to two surfaces of a piezoelectric crystal or transducer[28-5] such as a piece of plastic or barium titanate. Such materials change shape as voltage is applied across them; they may be molded into shapes that act as a lens to focus their ultrasonic vibrations so as to give higher-intensity effects in the desired direction. When such waves bounce back from unseen objects, the distance to the object is measured by the time required before the reflected waves return.

Intricate metallic parts are cleaned by placing them in liquid that is agitated by an ultrasonic transducer. Also, a small transducer may agitate a liquid that contains abrasive particles, driving them at high velocity (but small distance) so as to cut hard metals or to act as a dentist's tool.

These ultrasonic waves are like sound, moving through water or metal at speeds less than 1 mile per second. Their frequencies are the same as those used for some kinds of radio; however, at this same frequency, the radio waves are electromagnetic and travel 186,000 times faster through space.

23-6 RADIO, TELEVISION, RADAR

So much is written about these means of communication, discussion of them here is needless, except for a few names. Radio and TV equipment use mostly circuits of transistor or vacuum-tube oscillators (see Chap. 24) to produce and to receive high-frequency signals. Figure 23-1 shows how these services use the frequency range above 10 kHz to wavelengths of 1 mm or less. This range is split into the eight divisions marked with initial letters for "very low frequency," "low frequency," "medium frequency," "high frequency," "very high frequency," "ultrahigh frequency," "superhigh frequency," and "extremely high frequency." By international agreement these radio frequencies now are called by band number—VLF is band number 4, SHF is band number 10; bands 11 and 12 show further radio investigation at yet higher frequencies. ("Band N" extends from 0.3×10^N to 3×10^N cycles per second.)

The entire AM broadcasting range (550 to 1700 kHz) for most radio entertainment is at D in the medium-frequency division. "Short-wave," FM, and TV broadcasts occur in the HF and VHF divisions. Radar and military defense make great use of the UHF, SHF, and EHF divisions, which were almost unused 40 years ago. Near its center, Fig. 23-1 shows eight frequency bands used for radar. Near 10 cm, such radar pulses use S band for communication, sent to and reflected from an object so as to display its distance and direction. [These centimeter waves, like light waves, can be focused into narrow beams; in contrast, radio waves near the AM broadcast range spread in all directions, so that their direction is not easily controlled. Notice how the shortest radio waves are closer (in the spectrum) to light waves; they behave quite like beams of light, traveling in straight lines and permitting radio "shadows." Therefore, a TV antenna is placed high to receive these high-frequency waves; it receives programs from stations whose towers are not hidden beyond the horizon by the curvature of the earth. By being reflected back from a Telstar satellite, such direct-line TV programs are sent from or to remote points on the earth's surface.]

Since a radio program consists of sound, the information or signal broadcast through space must include sound frequencies. Such sound [at less than 6000 Hz (or cps)] is carried along on a radio wave that vibrates at least 100 times as fast. The radio wave is merely the carrier; by itself, it produces no sound at the radio receiver, for its radio frequency (RF) is far above the human-ear range. However, the program is carried by changing the shape of the RF waves at a slower rate [called the *audio frequency* (AF), 50 to 6000 times per sec second]; this "slow," or AF, change operates the receiver speaker—the RF wave merely carries the AF signal there.

When the audio signal is loaded onto the RF carrier wave, we say that the carrier is modulated by the signal; the radio oscillators may be controlled in different ways to produce this modulation. If the sound signal affects the RF wave so as to change the size or strength of this carrier wave (but does not change the radio frequency), this is the earlier method used in radio and is called *amplitude modulation* (AM). However, if the size of RF wave is kept unchanged but the sound signal makes the frequency of the RF wave change so as to carry the program, this is called *frequency modulation* (FM). Using FM requires not only a different form of transmitter circuit (still using oscillators) but also different receiver circuits. Many FM broadcasts use frequencies in the VHF division; many more program channels (each 6000 to 200,000 cycles wide) can be used here than in the crowded broadcasting range.

23-7 INDUSTRIAL ELECTRIC HEATING OF MATERIALS

Frequencies in these same ranges (as used by sound, ultrasonics, and radio) are used also in the industrial field of electric heating. The heating of materials by electricity is faster and cleaner and is more accurately controlled than heating in fuel-fired furnaces. When all factors are included, electric heating usually is more economical.

When dc or ac voltage is connected directly across a piece of metal or other conducting material, current flows and generates heat at a rate equal to I^2R, where I is the current (amperes) and R is the resistance (ohms) of the material. Such metallic heaters may be part of a resistance-type furnace. Electric power is used also in arc furnaces and in infrared ovens; such furnace heat must penetrate the material from the outside.

In contrast, heat may be produced inside a conducting material by *induction heating*; similarly, a nonconducting material may be heated internally by *dielectric heating*. These two processes require the use of high-frequency oscillators.

Any conducting material may be heated merely by being placed close to an ac circuit. Figure 23-2 shows how this alternating current may be passed through a work coil that surrounds (but does not need to touch) the workpiece of metal that is to be heated. The flow of current produces a magnetic field or flux that surrounds each turn of the work coil; this flux passes also through air or through any metal that is within or near the coil. Each reversal or alternation of the current causes the flux to change also. The change of flux causes or induces a voltage within the workpiece; this voltage forces large eddy currents to flow through the metal. As these induced currents pass through the resistance of the workpiece, they generate heat.

23-8 INDUCTION HEATING OF CONDUCTING MATERIALS

In Fig. 23-2 the work coil acts as the primary winding of a transformer, while the workpiece being heated acts as a single-turn secondary winding that is short-circuited, so that current is forced to circulate within it. Cooling water often is circulated within the work coil.

To melt metal or to heat large pieces uniformly throughout, a frequency below 10,000 cycles per second (Hz), or 10 kHz, is used, obtained from a motor-alternator set. When current in the work coil reverses at less than 3000 Hz, the resulting flux may pass through all parts of the metal block; heat is generated deep within the block as well as nearer the surface. Thus a solid block of copper or brass, 3 in. across by 10 in. long, may be heated quite uniformly to 1500°F in 1 min; this is called "through heating." With such methods, heat is produced in steel 50 times faster than heat can be transferred into the metal within a hot furnace, and the resulting temperature is more uniform throughout.

Most of the produced heat is caused by eddy currents, which exist equally in nonmagnetic and magnetic materials. In magnetic materials, additional heat is caused by hysteresis losses, but this magnetic effect disappears above 1350°F (the Curie point). Since higher temperatures are used in most induction heating, nonmagnetic materials are heated as effectively as steel is heated, and the same frequency may be used for all conducting materials.

For heating smaller pieces of material or for heat treatment (surface hardening) of metals, higher frequencies are used so as to obtain greater "skin effect"; this effect is shown in Fig. 23-2. The flux produced by the work-coil

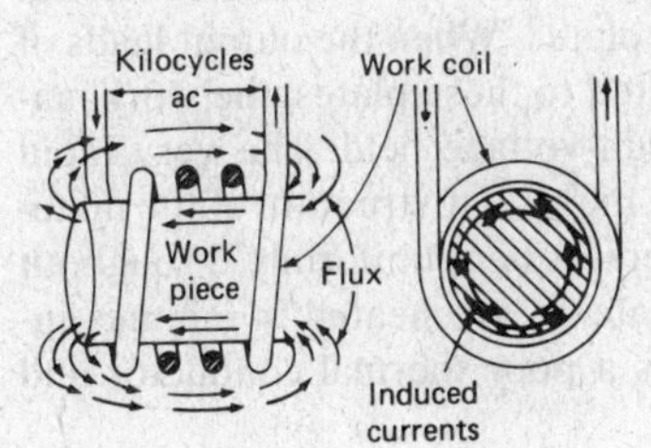

Figure 23-2 Induction heating of conducting materials.

current is strongest near the inside surface of the coil. The resulting currents induced in the workpiece tend to concentrate near the surface of the material, but this effect is less noticeable in pieces of small cross section or at frequencies below 1000 hertz (Hz). For the past 50 years power at 2000 to 5000 Hz (obtained from motor-alternator sets) has been used to heat engine crankshafts for hardening their bearing surfaces. Owing to the skin effect, the induced currents heat only the outer $^1/_{20}$ in. of the bearing surface to above 1500°F. This hot surface is immediately quenched in cool liquid to cause the desired hardness; meanwhile the metal below the surface is not greatly heated, and so it remains softer and tougher, to give desired strength.

Although heat may be generated near the surface, much of this heat soon is conducted to the cooler portion within the workpiece or is radiated from the hot surface. Therefore, it is necessary to bring the surface to high temperature within very few seconds and quench it before much heat travels inward or is lost; in this way the electrical cost of hardening is decreased. Also, the main part of the piece holds its shape, eliminating the straightening that often becomes necessary if the whole piece is heated.

The frequency required by induction heating depends less on the type of conducting material to be heated but is determined by the size and shape of the workpiece and the desired depth of heat penetration. If at 2000 Hz this depth cannot be kept less than 0.08 in., frequencies of 10 and 100 kHz may be needed to limit the penetration to depths of 0.04 and 0.02 in. While this depth decreases somewhat in proportion to $\sqrt{f}$, the amount of power that can be transferred from the work coil to the workpiece increases in proportion to $\sqrt{f}$. By limiting the penetration depth with higher frequency, the high temperature is obtained faster and with less total energy input. Most metal hardening requires input power of 5 to 50 kW/sq in. of surface heated. Whereas the surface of rods larger than $^1/_2$-in. diameter is hardened with less than 10,000 Hz and 15 kW/sq in., the surface hardening of smaller rods requires higher power and frequencies to 100 kHz or more.

23-9 DIELECTRIC HEATING OF NONCONDUCTING MATERIALS

To heat materials that do not conduct electricity, power is required at frequencies above 1000 kHz or 1 megahertz (MHz). But now, since current cannot pass through the material, high voltage is applied across the material by placing it between several parallel metal plates. When the output leads of an HF or VHF power oscillator are connected to these plates, the work material is stressed by the presence of this high-voltage field. The very rapid reversal of this field distorts and agitates the molecular structure of the material, so that internal molecular friction generates heat uniformly throughout all parts of the material. Thick layers of material are heated in minutes instead of hours, even though the material is a poor thermal conductor and prevents much travel of heat through itself.

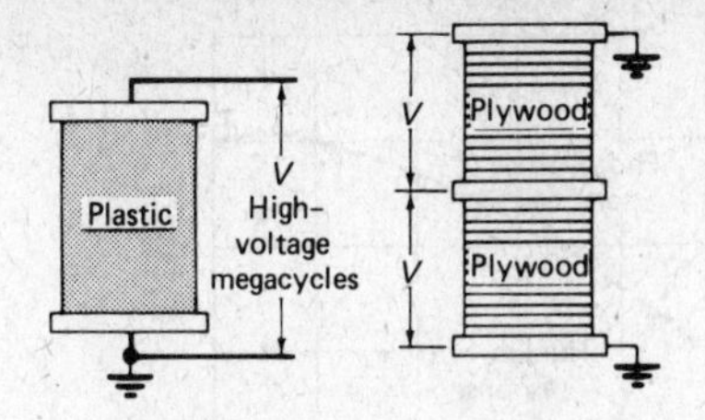

Figure 23-3 High-frequency dielectric heating of nonconducting materials.

Figure 23-3 shows how this arrangement resembles a capacitor, in that the work material becomes the dielectric or insulating material between the high-voltage plates of the capacitor. And just as induction heating depends on the square of the current (I^2) induced within the workpiece, dielectric heating depends on the square of the voltage (V^2) applied across the material. From 2000 to 5000 volts is used per inch of thickness of material and at frequencies such as 3.4, 6.8, 13.7, and 27.4 MHz.

One use of dielectric heating is for drying glue between the wood layers in the manufacture of plywood. Ordinary drying of bulk materials in this way may not be economical, but bulk foods may be sterilized while sealed in their final containers.

Frozen foods are rapidly thawed in a dielectric heater, or "electronic oven," which then proceeds to cook the food uniformly in a few minutes.

Plastic fabrics are "sewed" by being pressed together momentarily between high-frequency plates. Many articles are made by molding or shaping plastic material within large presses. Since such material flows into shape only at the higher temperatures produced within the press, much greater production is obtained from each press if the plastic material is preheated. A biscuit-size "preform" of plastic is placed in a dielectric heater for a minute before the press receives it and molds it into the desired shape. About 2 kW will heat a 1-lb preform to 300°F in 1 min.

High frequencies are needed in producing the special materials used in P or N semiconductors.

A similar VHF or band-8 oscillator may be used for heating the human body; it produces artificial fever when desired for medical treatment. The heat is produced inside the blood vessels when VHF electricity flows in wires several inches away from the body.

23-10 LIGHT AND COLOR

Near the center of Fig. 23-1 is the band of frequencies that can be seen by the human eye; this visible radiation is called *light*. The frequency of light is fifty times greater than the highest radio frequency now used; a light wave is shorter than one-millionth of a meter; so there are about 50,000 light waves to the inch.

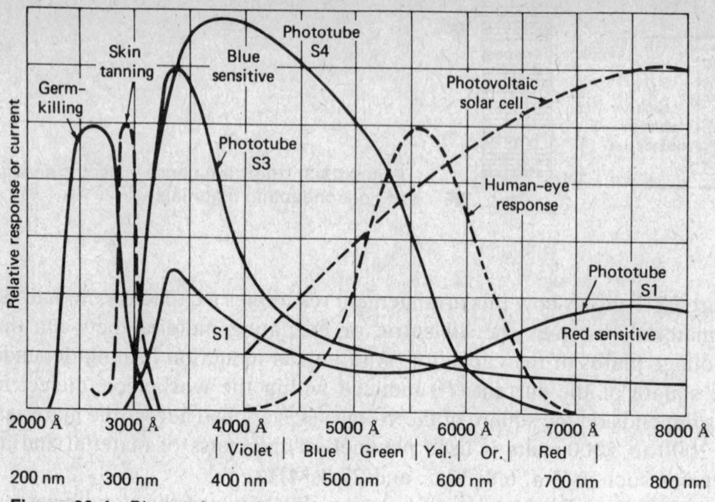

Figure 23-4 Phototube and eye response to color wavelengths.

Each color of light has its own wavelength and frequency. The rainbow colors red to violet are named in order as the wavelength decreases. When charts are used to show colors or heat by wavelength, often the wavelength increases from left to right as in Figs. 23-4 and 23-5. A different unit of wavelength is shown at the bottom of Fig. 23-4; here violet is marked at 4000 Å (angstroms) and also 400 nm (nanometers). At *H* (high in Fig. 23-1) a line is marked 10^{-10} meter = 1 angstrom; from the table in Sec. 23-2, one nanometer = 10^{-9} meter or a billionth of a meter. Thus 1 Å is a ten-billionth of a meter; 100,000 Å is 10^{-6} meter or a millionth of a meter, which is a micrometer (μ) as shown at *G* (near the visible range of Fig. 23-1). Wavelengths of light may be given in angstroms or in nanometers.

Figure 23-4 shows that a violet-colored light may have wavelengths between 3800 and 4300 Å; a green-light wavelength is longer, or between 4900 and 5600 Å. Notice the curve marked "Human-eye response"; the shape of this curve shows that a human eye usually responds best to a green or a yellow light. If a blue light, a yellow light, and a red light are adjusted so that each sends the same amount (radiant energy) of light over the same distance to the eye, the yellow light looks much brighter than the other two. Also, just as there are "sounds" of too high frequency to be heard by the human ear, so there are "colors" of too high or too low wavelength to be seen by the human eye. The average eye cannot see or respond to wavelengths below 4000 or above 7000 Å (therefore, the "visible range" is also 400 to 700 nanometers). As ultrasonic vibrations can be heard by a dog or a bat,[23-5] color wavelengths beyond the human-eye range can be "seen" by some kinds of phototube or solar cell. People who are colorblind may not be able to see a red color; to them there is no light of this color, for it looks gray or black. Notice that their eyes fail to respond to a wavelength of 6500 Å, in the same way that most eyes cannot respond to 7500 or 8000 Å.

When light rays of all wavelengths between 4000 and 7500 Å are mixed together in the right amounts, the result is white light or outdoor daylight. Similarly, a mixture of all frequencies of sound is called "white noise."

23-11 INFRARED, OR HEAT, RAYS

Years ago when men learned that heat rays were like light rays, except that they were longer in wavelength, they did not know about x-rays or other rays shown near the right-hand end of Fig. 23-1. To them, the low frequencies of sound were well known; from this starting point, light rays seemed far out in the spectrum. When the rays produced by a hot (but not red-hot or white-hot) metal were found to have wavelengths longer than the familiar red rays, so that their place in the spectrum was between those of light and sound, it was natural that these heat rays should be called *infrared* rays (meaning "inside" or "nearer than" the red rays). Similarly, when they found other rays shorter than the visible violet rays, which therefore were placed beyond the violet on the spectrum, these new rays were called *ultraviolet* (meaning "beyond" or "farther than" the violet rays). These two names are still used.

Anything that is hot enough to be seen in a dark room is giving out rays of visible light; at the same time, it is also giving out much greater amounts of heat rays, which are not seen but which can be felt and measured; these invisible rays are infrared rays and have wavelengths from 7500 to 100,000 Å and higher. To show infrared or heat wavelengths, a chart may use microns (or micrometers) instead of angstroms, as in Fig. 23-5. This

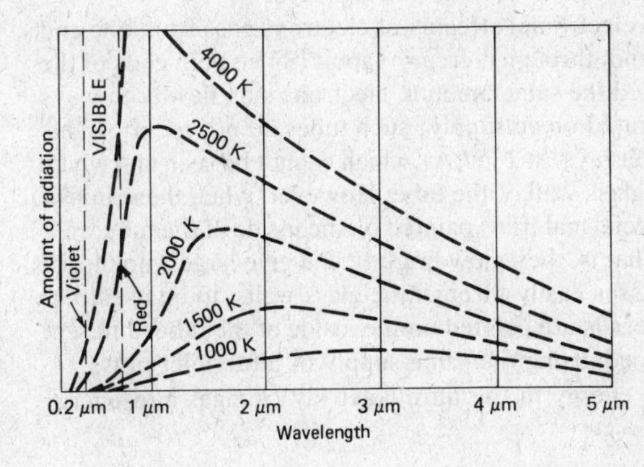

Figure 23-5 Radiation from an object at high temperatures.

chart shows how an object (such as a piece of metal, black when cold) produces more rays of shorter wavelength as its temperature rises. The lowest curve of Fig. 23-5, showing the radiation produced when the metal or "blackbody" has a temperature of 1000 K, has its peak or highest value at a wavelength of 3 microns (μ). When the temperature rises to 1500 K, there is much greater total radiation (shown by the area or space under the curve), and the peak is now at 2 μ. (The temperature in degrees Kelvin is equal to degrees Celsius + 273°. The zero on the Kelvin scale is at absolute zero, or −273°C. Temperatures like 2000 or 4000 K are used when speaking of objects that are so hot that they produce visible light; the color of that light is called the *color temperature*. The tungsten filament of an electric lamp works at 2500 to 2870 K. Fluorescent lights often are listed by color temperature, such as 5000°. No part of the tube operates at such high temperature, but the glow produced by the fluorescent material has the same wavelengths as though it had been radiated from a metal at this high temperature.

23-12 ULTRAVIOLET RAYS

Of those wavelengths near the visible violet, the most useful region is between 2000 and 4000 Å, shown at the left in Fig. 23-4. The sunlight we receive outdoors includes wavelengths to 2800 A, as well as the visible and infrared regions. (However, most of this ultraviolet sunlight cannot pass through window glass.) The invisible wavelengths near 2900 Å cause the burning and tanning of the skin, whether this light comes from the sun or from a lamp.

Most of the lamps that produce large amounts of ultraviolet rays are electronic; electrons flowing through mercury vapor produce such rays. When the outside of the lamp is made of special glass or quartz, these rays may pass through into the outside air. Some of these mercury lamps give out rays close to 2500 Å, which can kill germs. Only under a doctor's care can the human body safely be exposed to such germicidal rays.

Fluorescent lamps are electronic; streams of electrons pass from one end of the lamp to the other end, through mercury vapor. (Since both ends of the fluorescent tube are heated the same amount, electrons may flow both ways through such a tube operated on ac supply; such tubes do not rectify.) This action produces ultraviolet rays (at 2857 Å), which cannot be seen and which cannot pass through the glass wall of the tube. However, when these invisible rays strike against special materials painted on the inside of the tube wall, the materials fluoresce; that is, they glow brightly and give large amounts of visible light; this light passes easily through the glass walls, to be used outside. When different materials are painted on the inside of the tube, different colors of light are produced, using the same supply of ultraviolet rays.

Notice above that the energy in the ultraviolet ray changes into energy having a longer wave length; the resulting generated or emitted oscillation has a frequency enough lower than ultraviolet so that the new radiation is in the visible range. This action resembles the formation of a laser beam as is next described.

23-13 THE LASER AND ITS COHERENT LIGHT

Until recent years, all sources of artificial light produced waves that spread throughout a band of frequencies within the visible sepctrum. (Even though electric lights may operate from a single-frequency power supply, the radiation from an incandescent or a fluorescent light produces a radiation band that contains many and much higher frequencies.) But scientists have been seeking a source that can produce light having only a single frequency, which is called *coherent* light. In 1960, the laser was produced; this is a complex electrical-optical circuit that generates coherent light; the name *laser* is formed by the initials of light amplification by stimulated emission of radiation. To explain this name and the operation of a laser, we use facts learned from the branch of physics called quantum mechanics. Here it states that if we apply an external energy source or effect (such as the sudden flashing of a vapor-filled lamp) so as to raise the level of energy that an atom contains, we can raise this energy level through only certain constant amounts or jumps. Certain materials (such as a rod made of synthetic ruby crystal treated with a trace of chromium) may contain several such energy levels, which correspond to lines in the absorption spectrum of that material.

Figure 23-6 shows such a spectrum, having base line 1, a single-line level at 2, and a narrow band of energy levels at 3. As an analogy that shows this atomic action, Fig. 23-6 next pictures a pump that raises tiny balls (atoms) from 1 into the hopper at level 3. Although these hopper-3 atoms may have individual energy levels that vary slightly, they by nature roll down to level 2, where each atom has exactly the same energy. By plating a mirror surface at each end of the ruby rod, internal reflection increases the accumulation of atoms at level 2 until they become more than a critical value (where the number or "population" of atoms at level 2 exceeds the atom population remaining at level 1).

Then further flashes of the lamp stimulate these level-2 atoms, acting as if to open a gate *G*; the strength of the stimulating signal impulse determines how many of the accumulated level-2 atoms are permitted to drop through

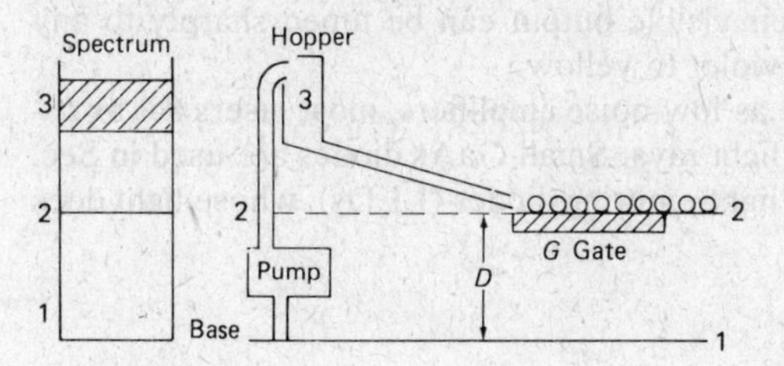

Figure 23-6
A laser produces coherent light.

the constant distance D to level 1. The energy released by these falling atoms determines the strength and the wavelength of the radiation now being emitted out of one end of the ruby rod (whose mirror surface purposely is made less than completely reflective). Each such atom releases almost exactly the same amount of energy. Scientist Planck showed that this quantum of energy is equal to a constant times the resulting frequency of oscillation, which must be constant (and therefore coherent). Continuing flashes of the vapor lamp (called optical pumping) make the ruby laser give spurts of oscillation at high frequency, producing a wavelength of exactly 6943 angstroms, which Fig. 23-4 shows to be in the red end of the visible spectrum. These coherent light rays are so nearly parallel that their beam diverges or expands less than 2 miles during a 249,000-mile trip to the moon.

Since these light waves have the same frequency (and also are in step with each other), this beam of coherent light is hundreds of times more effective than ordinary light waves; its single frequency lets it be focused to a tiny spot and be controlled like a short-wave radio beam. This permits the use of hundreds of separate additional communication channels within the large band of frequencies thus made available. While such laser beams assist greatly in voice signals through space via satellite, each laser beam must struggle through the dust and moisture of our atmosphere; therefore, such beams often are channeled through optical fibers, greatly speeding the operation of circuits such as those used in computers.

Another type of solid laser uses a crystal of yttrium-aluminum-garnet (YAG) that is doped with neodymium; this Nd:YAG laser produces strong invisible emission at 1.06 μm (10,600 Å). In later forms of laser, the ruby rod is replaced by an enclosed column of gas, which is electrically "pumped" and stimulated by a radio-transmitter coil. Such a helium-neon gas laser provides continuous orange light at 6328 Å; likewise an argon ion laser generates blue and green rays. Thus lasers are available to produce dozens of specific wavelengths between 2000 and 300,000 Å.

One type called an injection or semiconductor laser uses a small block of gallium arsenide (GaAs) doped to form a semiconductor PN junction.[7-6] When several amperes of direct current are forced to pass across this junction, it emits nearly coherent light near 8450 Å in a beam out of the small ends of the block. (Because this large current produces great heat, this PN diode must work in a cryostat at near absolute zero.)

Newer liquid and organic-dye lasers give high power output while operating at room temperature; their visible output can be tuned sharply to any frequency in the range from violet to yellow.

Although lasers may serve as low-noise amplifiers, most lasers act as oscillators to provide coherent light rays. Small GaAs diodes are used in Sec. 23-15 as solid-state lamps or light-emitting diodes (LEDs), whose light does not need to be coherent.

23-14 COLOR RESPONSE OF PHOTOTUBES

The human eye receives a different color sensation from green light than it receives from red light. However, lights of different colors reaching a phototube make its cathode produce different amounts of electrons. The phototube current (or solar-cell voltage of Sec. 23-15) is a measure of the *total* light it receives, of all colors; the phototube does not form an image such as the human eye forms. If a fly crawls up a white wall within view of the phototube, the phototube cannot "tell" that the fly is there unless the fly occupies perhaps one-twentieth of the total space viewed by the phototube. The dark fly then causes a decrease in phototube current; this current does not change as the fly moves about within the space viewed.

The ability to sort or detect different colors depends on the kind of phototube used, regardless of the circuit in which it works. From the light-sensitive metal surface of the phototube cathode, more electrons are driven by one color of light than by some other color of light. In Fig. 23-4, the curve S_1 shows the amount of current produced by various colors of light reaching one kind of "red-sensitive" phototube. This phototube responds to all colors of visible light and to many invisible rays. Its large response between 7000 and 10,000 Å lets it work well with hot-filament lamps (like auto headlights) or with daylight. These infrared rays may be invisible to the human eye, yet they are easily changed into a useful signal by this phototube or by a solar cell.

This tube (curve S_1, Fig. 23-4) has similar response to either violet light or orange light; it cannot sort or distinguish between these two colors. However, if you place in front of the phototube a light filter or colored glass that passes orange light but does not pass violet light, then this combination of light filter and phototube passes more current in response to orange light than to violet light; an orange box may energize the relay, while a violet box does not. Of course, when a different kind of phototube is used (such as curve S_3 in Fig. 23-4), the phototube itself passes more current responding to violet light than to orange light; here a color filter may not be needed.

Using curve S_1, can this phototube alone sort a red box from a white box, in daylight? This curve is high in the red region (above 6000 Å); also, the large area under the curve through all the colors (4000 to 7000 Å, which combine to make white light) shows that this phototube has large response to white light. This phototube may pass about the same current for either a red box or a white box. However, if a colored-glass filter prevents red and infrared rays from reaching the phototube (while letting other colors pass through), the phototube receives a large amount of light from a white box, but very little from the red box; so now it can select between them. Notice also that another phototube ("blue-sensitive," shown by curve S_4 in Fig. 23-4) by itself responds well to white and colors between 4000 and 6000 Å, but cannot "see" red.

23-15 SOLAR CELL AND SOLID-STATE LAMP OR LED

In place of the phototube described above, many light-sensitive circuits use a photovoltaic cell, which generates a small voltage in proportion to the intensity of light reaching it; such a cell is used in many photographic light or exposure meters. More recently this light-sensitive device is a form of solar cell like those used to convert the sun's energy into electricity to provide power for satellites; this is a PN silicon diode and is used as photodiode PD in Figs. 8-5 and 8-7. At the right, Fig. 23-4 shows that this solar cell responds well throughout the region of human-eye response, and produces its greatest voltage in the infrared region; thus it works well with an incandescent light source. This solar cell generates as much as 0.4 V and can supply 1.5 milliampere (mA) if needed; it works well also in data-processing equipment, where light beams pass through holes in punched tape so as to actuate counters or computers.

To give faster on-off action than a hot-filament lamp, we use a light-emitting diode (LED) [or solid-state lamp (SSL)] made of gallium arsenide. It acts like a PN diode[5-1] but requires more than 1 V in the forward direction. A continuous current of 1 A may flow; it may be operated in $^{1}/_{100}$-μsec pulses up to 10 or 15 A. All its output is near 9000 Å; so it works well with the solar cell above.

23-16 X-RAYS AND GAMMA RAYS

Near the right-hand end of Fig. 23-1, gamma rays are shown having wavelengths less than 1 Å. These rays come from radium, the rare metal discovered by the Curies. (Radium continually gives off three kinds of rays, named alpha, beta, and gamma; of these, only the gamma rays are electromagnetic.) These rays can pass through the human body and are used in medical treatment. Even tiny pieces of radium are so powerful that they are dangerous; their cost is high.

Since radium was discovered, it has been found that similar rays are produced by high-vacuum tubes that operate at very high voltages. These rays appear in Fig. 23-1 at wavelengths between 100 and 1 Å. Special electron tubes are made to produce these x-rays; as shown in Fig. 23-7, such a tube has a hot-filament cathode and an anode made of very heavy metal. Electrons flow from the cathode to the anode as in any diode tube. However, a large dc voltage is used between cathode and anode of the x-ray tube; the anode is so positive that the electrons rush to it at very high speed. The electrons strike the metal anode with such speed that new rays are made; from the slanting surface of the anode these x-rays seem to bounce sideways and out through the wall of the tube. As the dc voltage (anode-to-cathode of the x-ray tube) is increased, the wavelength of the x-rays decreases. Some tubes now operate at more than a million volts; the x-rays produced have wavelengths less than 1 Å and give results equal to the gamma rays from radium.

Such high-voltage x-rays serve industry by helping to photograph thick

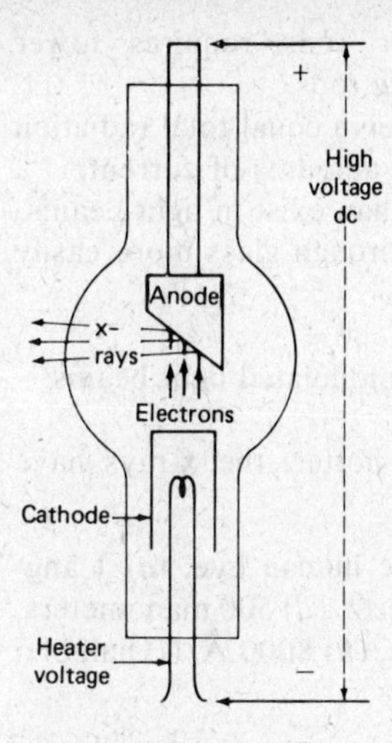

Figure 23-7 Working parts of an x-ray tube.

metal objects, or by measuring and controlling the thickness of hot steel strip while it is being rolled to the desired size. The very short wavelength of these rays also lets them pass between the tiny crystal particles of various metals, making a diffraction picture, which helps to analyze the conditions inside the metal.

The cosmic rays (shorter than gamma or x-rays) play no part in industrial electronics; they seem to come from space outside the earth. Cosmic rays merely complete the chart of known electromagnetic radiations.

Problems

23-1 True or false? Explain why.

(a) The resistance of a material heated by induction is lower than the resistance of materials whose temperature is raised by dielectric heating.

(b) All ultraviolet rays kill germs.

(c) Frequencies of 200 and 800 hertz (Hz or cps) may be carried on one radio frequency at the same time.

(d) A lamp used for infrared heating has a hotter filament than a lamp for lighting.

(e) A phototube that "sees" very short wavelengths can operate a relay faster than a phototube that "sees" only longer wavelengths.

(f) A fluorescent lamp at 3500 K feels warmer than a tungsten lamp at 2800 K.

(g) A beam of light may be modulated to carry speech.

(h) All oscillations at 1000 Hz are sound vibrations.

(i) The induction heating of small-diameter rods requires lower frequency than the induction heating of large rods.

(j) In Fig. 23-4, when phototubes *P* and *R* receive equal total radiation from an incandescent lamp, they pass equal amounts of current.

(k) Shortwave radio uses shorter wavelengths than exist in light beams.

(l) Rays of 1-meter or 1-Å wavelength pass through glass more easily than rays of 1000 Å.

(m) All waves at 25 kHz are called ultrasonic.

(n) Blinking light signals from ship to ship use modulated light beams.

(o) A 100-mHz wave lies in band 8.

(p) If the filament of an x-ray tube is made hotter, the x-rays have shorter wavelengths.

23-2 Which of these can be seen by the average human eye: (*a*) 1 angstrom, (*b*) 10^{-15} hertz, (*c*) one billion megahertz, (*d*) 500 manometers, (*e*) 2500 K, (*f*) 2857 Å, (*g*) 600 micrometers, (*h*) 8000 Å, (*i*) half of a millionth of a meter, (*j*) band 15?

23-3 If the broadcast band includes wavelengths from 200 to 550 meters and each radio station requires a channel 10 kHz wide, find the greatest number of stations that may use this band without any overlapping of wavelengths.

24 OSCILLATORS AND INVERTERS

When ac devices or equipment must be operated from the dc supplied by a battery, fuel cells, or solar cells, we may use an oscillator or inverter to convert this dc into ac for such equipment; this is the reverse of the action of a rectifier. Units that change ac into dc are called *converters* or *rectifiers*; all devices that change dc into ac are *inverters* even though the alternating output may be like a square wave. In electronics, an *inverter* generally means a unit that uses SCRs or vapor-filled tubes; therefore, it may produce large voltage signals or ac output at low frequency [such as 60 or 20,000 hertz or cycles per second (Hz or cps)]; an *oscillator* uses transistors or high-vacuum tubes, so that it may produce alternating current at higher frequency.

Dozens of oscillator circuits are described in textbooks. Here we discuss a few basic circuits to see how an oscillator and inverter work.

24-1 OSCILLATORS

The transistors and high-vacuum tubes studied in amplifier circuits may also be used in oscillator circuits. Some types of radio receiver include an oscillator. An oscillator circuit is self-contained; taking power from dc or low-frequency ac supply, the oscillator produces ac output at a higher frequency, which depends on the sizes of capacitors and inductances used in the oscillator circuit. However, if something outside the oscillator causes a change in the oscillator-circuit capacity or inductance (as when a metal vane passes between the coils in an oscillator circuit), the output frequency of the oscillator changes—its oscillation may stop.

In industry, oscillators have two main uses. First, an oscillator may be an off-on device; a very tiny outside signal or changed condition may stop the oscillator action and thereby operate a relay or a visible signal. In this case, the frequency of the oscillator is not important so long as it is easily stopped by the outside signal.

In the second use, the oscillator supplies its high-frequency output to produce action that cannot happen at lower frequencies. The radio oscillator produces high-frequency waves that travel through space carrying news or music. Similar uses of oscillators are described in Secs. 23-5 to 23-9.

24-2 FROM AN AMPLIFIER TO AN OSCILLATOR

Here we may show that an amplifier may become an oscillator if feedback is added to its circuit. As an example, the common-emitter amplifier circuit of Fig. 5-6 is used again in Fig. 24-1. The input signal (between R_B and base 4 of the NPN transistor Q) is a tiny 60-Hz ac voltage supplied by T_2, which is like a doorbell transformer. When this signal voltage is 0.14 volt (V) peak-to-peak, the collector current of Q swings through a change of 3.2 milliamperes (mA) at 60 Hz; this current passes also through transformer T_1 and output load resistor R_L. [For the reader who wishes to see how this value of 3.2 mA is obtained, Fig. 5-10 gives the collector-characteristic curves for transistor Q. Sections 5-5 and 5-6 explain how the load line is added and used; the combined resistance of T_1 and R_L is assumed to be 4000 ohms (Ω) or 4 kΩ. The 0.14-V input signal (in series with $R_B = 1.75$ kΩ) causes the Q base current I_B to swing from 100 μA (at J in Fig. 5-10) to 20 μA at K. The resulting collector current I_C swings from 4.1 mA at C to 0.9 mA at D, or a change of 3.2 mA.]

When this varying 3.2 mA passes through Q and the primary winding of T_1, its secondary winding generates slightly more than 0.14 V peak-to-peak between its terminals 1 and 2; this is the same amount of voltage as is provided by doorbell transformer T_2. So, in place of T_2, why not try to feed back this 60-Hz voltage from T_1 to act as the input signal? To do this, connect terminals 1 and 2 to the transistor-circuit terminals 3 and 4, and then remove the jumpers from the T_2 terminals 5 and 6. We must be careful to connect base 4 to whichever T_1 terminal (1 or 2) is more positive when the Q collector current is greatest. (Figure 24-2 shows the wave of Q base current I_B which is caused by this feedback ac voltage wave from T_1 terminals 1 and 2. The resulting wave of collector current I_C is in phase with I_B. But when I_C is highest, it causes greatest voltage drop across T_1 and R_L, so that the Q collector voltage V_{CE} is most negative. When I_C swings down to low values, V_{CE} rises near to V_{CC}. Thus Fig. 24-2 shows that the input signal I_B is 180° out of phase from collector voltage V_{CB}; this is a basic requirement for oscillation.) If this is successful, transistor Q will be working as a 60-Hz oscillator, supplying its own input signal so as to vary the Q base current.

24-3 A SIMPLE OSCILLATOR

Such a trial will not be successful until we add a capacitor (C in Fig. 24-1) of just the right size, so that this capacitor has 60-Hz (or 60-cps) resonance

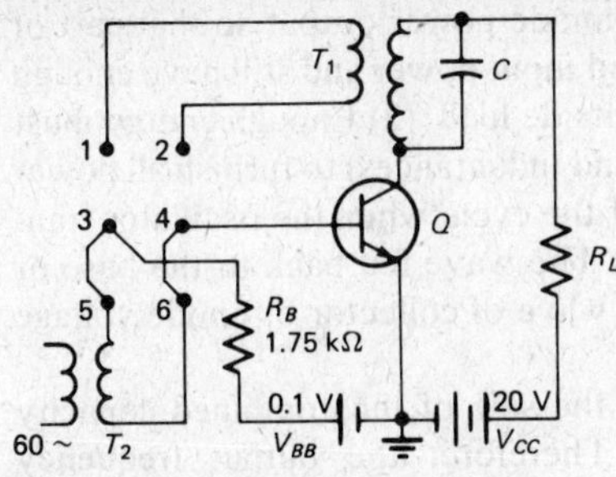

Figure 24-1 A transistor amplifier may become an oscillator.

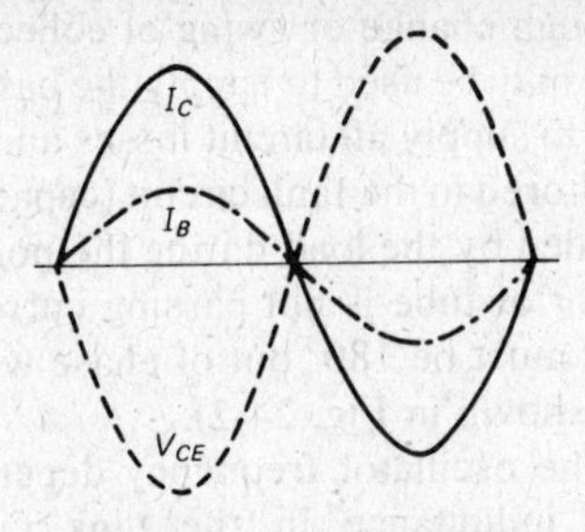

Figure 24-2 Curves of base current versus collector current and voltage.

with the inductance of transformer T_1. (This means that $1/2\pi fC$ must be equal to $2\pi fL$, where $f = 60$ Hz, C is in farads, L is the transformer inductance in henrys.) With C added, the circuit of Fig. 24-1 becomes a simple but uneconomical method of changing direct current into 60-Hz alternating current. However, if we now gradually reduce the size of capacitor C, the transistor circuit will oscillate faster, so that at this increased frequency, C and L are still in resonance.

This is the basic explanation of the transistor oscillator; by proper selection of the amounts of L and C used in its output circuit, Q will oscillate (alternately increase and decrease its collector current) at the desired frequency. This combination of L and C not only fixes the oscillating frequency, but also stores the energy necessary to supply a flow of power into the output or load circuit even when Q is not passing current continuously.

The "tank circuit" of an oscillator consists of the capacitors C and inductances L that determine the output frequency.

A mechanical illustration of such an oscillator is the grandfather clock; its input, or driving force, is the steady pressure given by weights or a wound spring; its output is the swinging of the pendulum. Steady pressure (like direct current) is converted into oscillating motion (like alternating current). The steady pressure may not be enough to start the pendulum from rest, but it keeps the pendulum swinging, because the pressure supplies the losses of the clock's movement. The length of the pendulum sets the rate of oscillation, or the frequency. Once each swing, the pendulum receives only a short "push" from the spring; the energy stored in the pendulum carries it through its complete swing and back to receive the next push.

24-4 MAIN OSCILLATOR FEATURES

A transistor or tube circuit of the feedback type must include certain features before it will oscillate. (1) The circuit must amplify; there must be enough change or swing of collector or anode power output so that part of this may be used to supply the base or grid input power and still have enough left to supply all circuit losses and the outside load. (2) Enough energy must be stored in the tank circuit (capacitors and inductances) to furnish all power needed by the load during the portion of the cycle when the oscillator transistor or tube is not passing current. (3) The wave fed back to the base or grid must be 180° out of phase with the wave of collector or anode voltage (as shown in Fig. 24-2).

The oscillator frequency depends on the size of the combined capacity and inductance in the tank circuit. Therefore, the output frequency $f = {}^1/_{2\pi}\sqrt{LC}$ [where L is in henrys, C is in farads, f is in hertz (cycles per second)]. At resonance,[24-3] $2\pi fL$ must equal ${}^1/_{2\pi fC}$, so

$$f^2 = \frac{1}{(2\pi L)(2\pi C)} \quad \text{or} \quad f = \frac{1}{\sqrt{(2\pi L)(2\pi C)}} = \frac{1}{2\pi\sqrt{LC}}$$

Similarly, for high-frequency work,

$$\text{Frequency, kc} = \frac{1{,}000{,}000}{2\pi\sqrt{\mu\text{H} \times \mu\mu\text{F}}} \quad \text{or} \quad \text{kHz} = \frac{1{,}000{,}000}{2\pi\sqrt{\mu\text{H} \times \text{pF}}}$$

24-5 STANDARD OSCILLATOR TYPES

Several well-known oscillator types are sketched below in the hope that they will invite the reader to study them in more complete texts.

A Colpitts oscillator is shown in Fig. 24-3 in the forms used in many texts. This type is recognized by the tank circuit consisting of two capacitor groups (C_6 and C_7) and a single continuous inductance (L_4 and work coil combined). This inductance is the path by which part of the anode output is fed back to the grid or base. In Fig. 24-3*b* a Colpitts oscillator uses an NPN transistor.

A Hartley oscillator (Fig. 24-4) is like the Colpitts, except that the tank

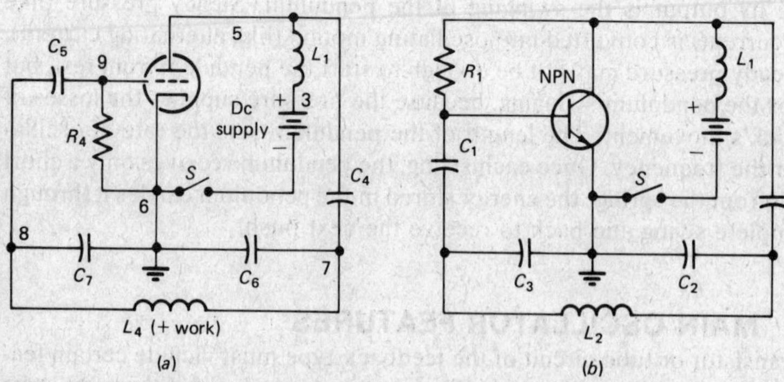

Figure 24-3 Colpitts oscillators.

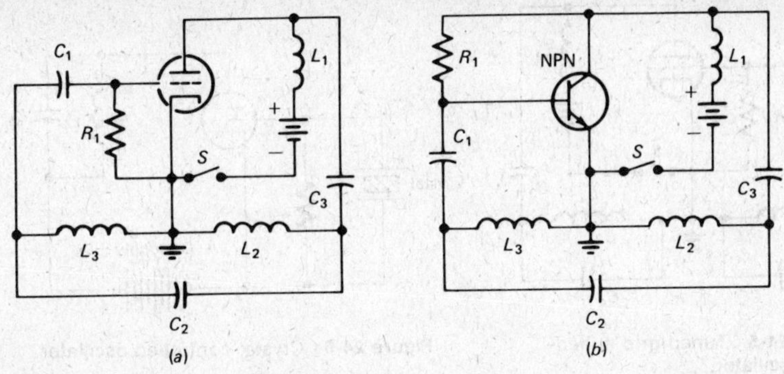

Figure 24-4 Hartley oscillators.

circuit uses a single capacitor C_2 and two inductances L_2 and L_3. During that part of the oscillation when anode or collector current flows, the energy stored in C_2 forces electrons to flow counterclockwise in the loop consisting of C_2, L_2, and L_3; the voltage across L_3 drives the grid or base more positive than ground so that C_1 is charged (−) on top. This charge remains as a negative bias so that anode current flows only in short "spurts," which occur as the L_3 voltage reaches its positive peak; this current is correctly timed to assist or increase the electron flow in the loop and thereby to supply or make up for the energy lost from the loop during the preceding cycle. Similar actions occur in the transistor circuit in Fig. 24-4*b*.

For the dielectric heating of nonmetals,[23-9] the material to be heated is placed between two metal plates, which act as the two sides of capacitor C_2 in Fig. 24-4. The tank circuit feeds part of the anode output back to the base or the grid.

The oscillator circuit of Fig. 24-5 looks like Fig. 24-4, except that there are two capacitors, C_4 and C_5, instead of C_2 alone. In the grid circuit, C_5 and L_5 are chosen so they are resonant[24-3] at the desired output frequency; C_4 and L_4 are similarly chosen so they are resonant at this same output frequency. This is a tuned-grid-tuned-plate oscillator. Here L_4 and L_5 are separate inductances and there is no transformer action between them. Therefore, how does the grid circuit receive the voltage signal from the anode or plate circuit so that the tube will oscillate? The necessary grid signal passes through the tube, directly from anode to grid, because these parts of the tube act like a capacitor. This "interelectrode capacity" lets the rapid changes of anode voltage cause similar voltage changes at the grid; in this way, part of the anode output voltage is fed back to the grid through the tube itself.

The output frequency of most oscillators may change when the load varies. While this frequency drift may have little effect on the results produced by oscillators used in industry, government regulations may

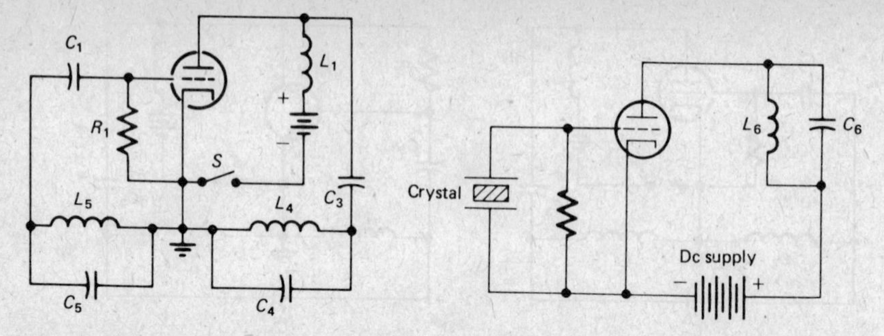

Figure 24-5 Tuned-grid–tuned-plate oscillator.

Figure 24-6 Crystal-controlled oscillator.

require that the output frequency be held more constant. More constant frequency is produced by a *crystal-controlled* oscillator. As is shown in Fig. 24-6, such an oscillator may be quite like Fig. 24-5, for the crystal takes the place of the tuned-grid circuit. This crystal is a thin piece of quartz that has been accurately cut and finished to the desired thickness; this thickness sets the oscillator frequency. The crystal is mounted between two metal surfaces; when low voltage is applied between these two surfaces, the crystal expands or contracts. (If a mechanical force is applied across this crystal, a voltage is produced. This crystal behavior or interaction between voltage and pressure is known as the *piezoelectric effect*.) In the circuit of Fig. 24-6, the tiny changes of grid voltage (fed back between anode and grid within the tube) make the crystal vibrate. Greatest vibration occurs at just one frequency for each crystal; the crystal acts like a capacitor and inductance that are tuned, or resonant, at that one frequency. If L_6 and C_6 are also resonant at this crystal frequency, the circuit oscillates. The crystal vibration decreases sharply if the frequency changes a tiny amount; therefore, such a crystal-controlled oscillator holds the frequency within narrow limits.

24-6 INVERTERS TO SUPPLY LARGE AC POWER

To furnish greater ac power from a dc supply, the inverter commonly uses SCRs or thyratrons, because of their small power loss while conducting large currents. Since the SCR has only 1-V drop at full current, an SCR inverter may operate at 90 percent efficiency, at loads of 1000 kilovolt-amperes (kVA). Most large inverters are separately excited, for they contain no devices to control the rate of SCR firing or to set the frequency of the inverter ac output. Instead, the SCRs are fired by pulses of gate current produced by a separate low-power oscillator or multivibrator. As an example, the two-SCR inverter in Sec. 24-9 may be triggered by gate pulses produced in the UJT circuit of Fig. 24-7 or by the multivibrator of Fig. 24-8 (described in Sec. 24-8).

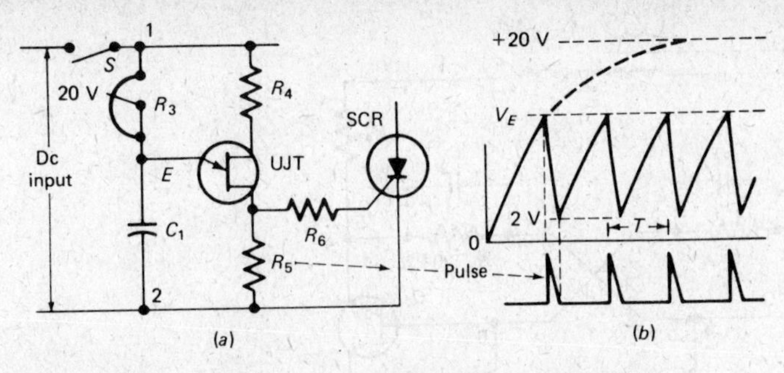

Figure 24-7 A UJT relaxation oscillator triggers SCR inverter.

24-7 A UJT RELAXATION OSCILLATOR TO TRIGGER AN INVERTER

The UJT in Fig. 24-7 works in a circuit like that of Fig. 9-8. When switch S is closed, capacitor C_1 starts to charge toward the +20 V at top point 1, at a speed adjusted by the resistance of R_3; this is shown by the rising wave in Fig. 24-7*b* (and similar to Fig. 3-4). When the increasing C_1 voltage raises emitter E above the UJT trigger value V_E (as described in Sec. 8-7), UJT suddenly conducts, letting C_1 discharge quickly through UJT and R_5; this discharge current produces a pulse of voltage across R_5, which is fed through R_6 to fire SCR.

When the C_1 voltage has decreased to about 2 V, the emitter no longer conducts and UJT is turned off. But C_1 again charges, so that UJT is triggered at regular intervals. Somewhat like the action described in Sec. 9-6, the R_5 voltage pulses may be used to fire alternately either of two SCRs in the inverter circuit of Fig. 24-9. The time between the UJT pulses is shown at T in Fig. 24-7*b*. If the standoff ratio η of UJT is 0.63, Sec. 3-5 shows that T is equal to the time constant of R_3 and C_1; either may be reduced to decrease T and raise the inverter frequency.

Because of its waveshape, this UJT circuit may be used as a sawtooth oscillator. In the oscillograph circuit of Fig. 31-10, thyratron tube 3 acts as such an oscillator.

24-8 A TRANSISTOR MULTIVIBRATOR

In Fig. 24-8, dc power is applied to identical transistors Q_1 and Q_2, which turn each other off and on so as to produce an alternating current through transformer T_3 at the top. The output peaks produced in the T_3 secondary windings A and B may be used as the gate pulses to trigger the two-SCR inverter of Sec. 24-9.

Transistors Q_1 and Q_2 have identical common-emitter circuits and may begin by having equal collector currents. (A small current flows through R_3,

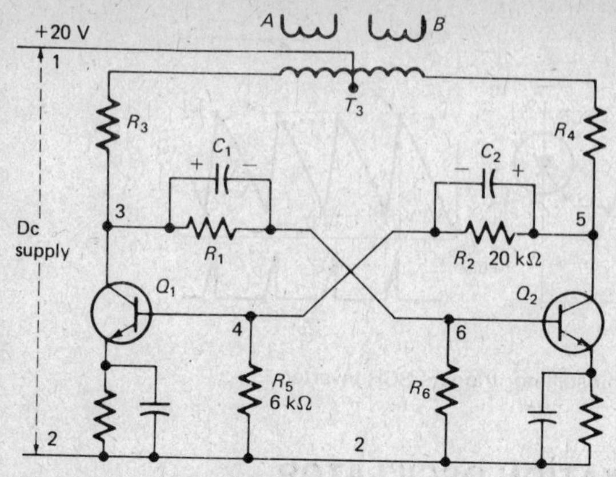

Figure 24-8 A transistor multivibrator.

R_1, and R_6 in series, thus charging C_1. Similar current through R_4, R_2, and R_5 charges C_2.) But this circuit cannot remain in such a stable condition. Any momentary disturbance can slightly increase the Q_1 collector current, thus increasing the voltage drop across R_3. This lowers Q_1 collector 3; acting through C_1 (which cannot change its charge or voltage instantly), this lowers base 6 of Q_2. With less base current, the Q_2 collector current through R_4 decreases, letting collector 5 rise; fed back through C_2, this higher potential raises base 4 of Q_1, so that greater base current turns on Q_1 completely. Such large Q_1 current through R_3 lowers points 3 and 6 so fast that Q_2 is completely off. (With Q_1 in saturation and Q_2 cut off, collector 5 has nearly the +20-V potential of the dc supply; this 5-to-2 voltage is applied across large R_2 and small R_5 in series, so that C_2 is charged to perhaps 15 V.)

But conditions change as C_1 gradually discharges through R_1; soon C_1 no longer can hold base 6 negative; so Q_2 starts to pass current through R_4. This lowers collector 5 and (through C_2) the base of Q_1. Very quickly this positive feedback turns Q_1 off and Q_2 on. Again the circuit waits while C_2 discharges through R_2; the decreasing C_2 voltage lets base 4 rise, so that the Q_1 collector current again increases. Thus Q_1 and Q_2 conduct in turn; the rate at which this alternation occurs may be adjusted to a desired value or frequency by changing the size of C_1 and C_2. The *RC* self-bias circuits below Q_1 and Q_2 help to stabilize this operation, as described in Sec. 6-5.

The abrupt increase of Q_1 electron flow passes left to right through the T_3 primary winding, to its center tap. When Q_2 conducts, its electrons flow right to left to the center tap and reverse the flux in T_3. Thus the secondary winding *A* may furnish a spike of voltage to trigger SCR 1 in Fig. 24-9; as the T_3 flux reverses, winding *B* may trigger SCR 2.

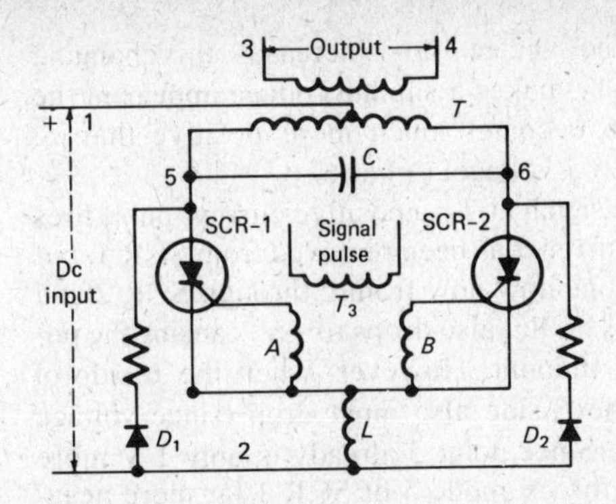

Figure 24-9 Two-SCR inverter, separately excited.

24-9 A TWO-SCR INVERTER

While two controlled rectifiers may be connected in many ways to operate as an inverter, Fig. 24-9 shows a parallel inverter; here the direct current passes through each SCR in turn, when fired by a separate circuit (such as Fig. 24-8) acting through transformer T_3.

Figure 24-9 looks like a center-tap rectifier circuit. [Notice that the SCR cathodes connect through L to the (−) side of the dc input whereas the cathodes of a center-tap rectifier connect to the (+) side of the dc load, as shown in Fig. 4-5*b*.] However, although the anode transformer T and the SCRs are connected as in a center-tap rectifier, no alternating voltage appears at T terminals 3 and 4 unless SCR 1 and SCR 2 make it appear there by inverter action. This can be done if each SCR can be made to fire in turn. From the dc input, electrons flow from point 2 through L and SCR 1 and pass left to right to the midtap 1 of transformer T; if this flow then stops and electrons pass instead through SCR 2 and right to left through T to reach the midtap, it is seen that this flow in T has changed direction. These changes and reversals of current in T, caused by alternate firing of SCR 1 and SCR 2, produce an alternating or square-wave voltage in the T secondary winding, appearing at terminals 3 and 4. (A filter of R, L, and C can convert this output to more nearly a sine wave.)

But recall (from Sec. 9-1) that when an SCR is passing current from a dc supply, its gate cannot regain control to shut it off unless another device is added, such as capacitor C in Fig. 24-9. (Without C, both SCR 1 and SCR 2 may pass direct current at the same time, after the first turn-on current pulse at their gates; such anode currents, flowing steadily through T, produce no voltage at terminals 3 and 4.)

When (+) dc potential is applied to both anodes, neither SCR fires until its gate receives a positive current pulse. Since transformer T_3 drives one gate negative while the other gate receives a positive pulse, only one SCR fires, say SCR 1. As electrons flow from 2 through L, SCR 1, and T to 1, the voltage across SCR 1 drops to 1 volt and the voltage 5-to-1 increases; this changing voltage across one half of T primary makes a similar voltage appear in the other half 1-to-6, so that point 6 becomes much more positive than 5. Capacitor C is charged by this 6-to-5 voltage, (+) at 6.

During the next half cycle of the signal at T_3, a positive current pulse fires SCR 2; at this same time the gate current has been removed from SCR 1, but this cannot turn off SCR 1. Electrons now flow from 2 through SCR 2 and from 6 to 1 of T. The voltage across SCR 2 also drops to 1 V, causing the potential at point 6 to drop a large amount. However, when the 6 side of capacitor C drops in potential, the 5 side also must drop (since voltage across C cannot change instantly). Since point 5 already is only 1 V more positive than point 2, capacitor C forces anode 5 of SCR 1 far more negative than cathode 2; so anode current stops in SCR 1. Capacitor C now changes its charge; electrons flow from 2, through L and SCR 2 and into C. By the time anode 5 again rises above cathode 2, the SCR 1 gate has regained control, so that it prevents SCR 1 from firing. Point 5 now rises to its most positive potential, while 6 remains within 1 V of point 2. Capacitor C becomes charged to this voltage difference: (+) at 5, (−) at 6.

When the current pulse from T_3 again fires SCR 1, point 5 again drops close to point 2; the charge on C now drives the SCR 2 anode more negative than its cathode, so that the SCR 2 current stops. C acts as a *commutating* capacitor, to turn off one SCR when the other SCR fires.

The feedback diodes D_1 and D_2 improve circuit action when the output load is inductive, and permit the use of smaller values of L and C.

24-10 ADJUSTABLE FREQUENCY INVERTER FOR AC MOTOR DRIVE (GENERAL ELECTRIC ST100, FIG. 24-10)

This equipment includes two oscillators, a three-SCR rectifier and a six-SCR three-phase-bridge inverter. This has been introduced in recent industrial processes that require the use of small ac motors whose speed must be gradually adjustable (as from 600 to 3600 rpm) but must remain constant at the set speed. Perhaps two or more motors must be brought up to speed together, acting at all times as if their drive shafts were geared to each other. Such speed control or "electronic gearing" is provided by the system outlined in Fig. 24-11; this diagram does not show some of the needed circuits and protective devices, but merely outlines the basic overall operation. (The circles are omitted from the transistor and SCR symbols, which agrees with advanced circuit practice.)

At the upper left in Fig. 24-11, three-phase power (120 V from line to neutral 0) is converted through SCRs A, B and C into dc that is adjustable from 0 to 130 V. This dc power (between top line 2 and centerline 0) is applied to a three-phase-bridge inverter (SCRs 1 to 6) that furnishes alternating cur-

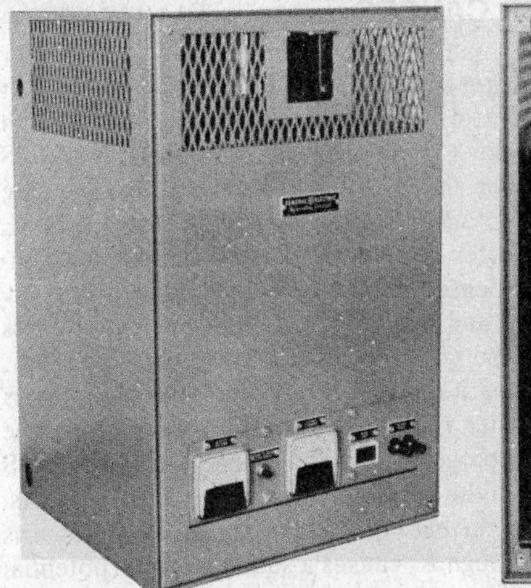

Figure 24-10 Adjustable frequency inverter (General Electric ST100).

rents to the three-phase windings of a motor M (or to several such motors connected in parallel). This motor may be of the synchronous reluctance type that runs in step with the ac voltage applied to its stationary windings (like a squirrel-cage induction motor that has a slotted rotor).

At the left in Fig. 24-11 diodes D_1 send rectified dc through R_1 so that Zener diode Z_1 can hold line 3 at 25 V above 0. (Diodes D_1 also supply dc, which Z_2 holds at 50 V for use in the SCR firing circuits, like that of Q_3 shown at the lower right.) Across the Z_1 voltage, potentiometer P may be turned clockwise to raise the potential at point 4; this controls the voltage-regulator circuits that advance the firing of SCRs A, B, and C so as to increase the dc voltage applied to the inverter (between points 2 and 0). But point 4 also raises the base of transistor Q_1, which increases the frequency of the inverter and the speed of motor M, as explained in Sec. 24-11.

When the inverter applies higher frequency to increase the motor speed, it should raise also the voltage applied to the M windings, to provide better performance of motor M. So the turning of the single dial P raises point 4 and increases both the voltage and the inverter frequency, so as to provide constant volts per hertz. Before motor M starts from rest, a normally-closed contact of a relay CR connects point 4 to the bottom 0 potential, giving 0 dc volts and 0 frequency. When a START button (not shown) picks up CR, point 4 rises slowly as capacitor C_3 becomes charged; thus the voltage and frequency increase gradually to bring M to the desired speed as set by P.

24-11 SUS OSCILLATOR CAUSES INVERTER FREQUENCY

Shown below the voltage regulator in Fig. 24-11, the point-4 potential at the base of NPN transistor Q_1 controls the amount of electron flow through R_3 and Q_1 that is charging capacitor C_4, minus at the bottom. At first SUS acts as an open circuit;[9-18] but when the C_4 voltage reaches a certain value (near 10 V), this triggers SUS into conduction so that it discharges C_4 through R_4 and inductance X_2. After C_4 has discharged, the current continues to flow in X_2 (because of the energy stored in its inductance); this current charges C_4 minus at the top, and this stops the SUS current and lets SUS return to an open circuit. The Q_1 collector current again charges C_4 until SUS again trips, thus causing a repeating cycle, so that Q_1 controls SUS as an oscillator. When adjuster P is turned, raising base 4 of Q_1, the increased Q_1 collector current charges C_4 more quickly, tripping SUS sooner and raising the frequency of the oscillator. Each time SUS conducts, the voltage drop across R_4 lowers the base of PNP transistor Q_2; this turns on Q_2, whose collector current through R_5 causes a sudden drop in potential at point 5.

These negative pulses at 5 (lower center of Fig. 24-11) are applied to a ring-counter circuit, which includes three transistor flip-flops similar to those shown earlier in Fig. 10-3; these flip-flop transistors are so interconnected that they produce output voltages at proper times so as to fire the inverter SCRs 1 to 6 in the desired sequence, as outlined in Sec. 24-13. The oscillator pulses of SUS occur six times as fast as the desired output frequency produced by the inverter; thus SUS gives pulses at 60° intervals within each cycle of inverter frequency. The ring-counter circuit also sets or programs the time when each inverter SCR is turned off by the commutating action of SCR 7 or 8, as is described in Sec. 24-14.

24-12 A FEEDBACK OSCILLATOR FIRES EACH SCR

The output voltage or control signal produced by each ring-counter transistor is fed into an SCR firing circuit like that shown at the lower right in Fig. 24-11; here the control signal is applied at S to control Q_4. When Q_4 is not conducting, the circuit of transistor Q_3 acts as an oscillator that produces a rapid succession or train of gate-current pulses throughout the time when we want the SCR to conduct. These oscillator pulses are produced in the following way. Electrons flow through R_7, emitter to base of Q_3, and through R_8 to the +50 V (obtained through diodes D_1 at upper left). This base current partly turns on Q_3, so that its small collector current flows in the primary winding of transformer T_4; this produces a voltage in each T_4 secondary winding (plus at its top), which increases the Q_3 base current, further increasing the current in T_4P. This regenerative action suddenly turns Q_3 completely on; as the T_4P current continues to rise, the T_4S_2 winding

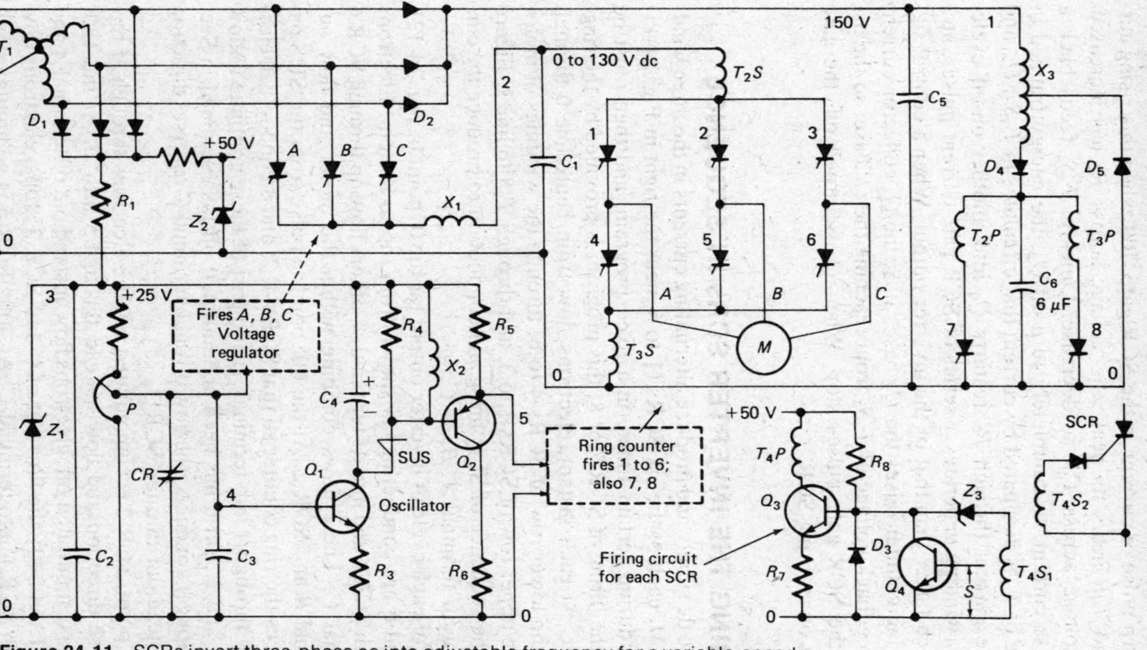

Figure 24-11 SCRs invert three-phase ac into adjustable frequency for a variable-speed motor.

delivers a sharp pulse of current in the SCR gate. But when this rising current in Q_3 and T_4P nears its peak, the voltage across R_7 has increased, causing the voltage across T_4P to decrease. Quickly, T_4S_1 feeds back a decreasing base current, to completely turn off Q_3; the energy trapped in the inductance of T_4 is dissipated by current that circulates in T_4S_1, D_3, and Z_3. Then base current through R_8 restarts Q_3 into another on-off cycle. Thus the T_4S_2 winding generates a series of SCR gate-current pulses, at a frequency much faster than that of the inverter output. When a control signal from the ring counter raises the Q_4 base, at S, the Q_4 collector current prevents the feedback voltage of T_4S_1 from reaching the Q_3 base; so the oscillation and the SCR gate pulses stop. When Q_4 is turned off, the gate pulses start at once, firing SCR.

24-13 FIRING THE INVERTER SCRs IN SEQUENCE

To invert the dc supply and produce alternating currents in the three windings of motor M, each of the six SCRs (1 to 6, near the right in Fig. 24-11) must be fired during certain times, in a fixed program, and then must be turned off by the firing of SCR 7 or 8; this program is provided by the ring-counter circuit. At each instant, electrons flow from centerline 0 through T_3S, through the lower row of SCRs 4 to 6, through the windings of motor M, through the upper row of SCRs 1 to 3, and through T_2S to line 2. Figure 24-12 shows the sequence of SCR firing and conduction to produce the current in each motor terminal A, B, or C.

At the start of each cycle of inverter output (at the 0° point in Fig. 24-12), SCRs 4, 2, and 6 are conducting, as shown from top to bottom. Electrons flow up through SCR 4 and into M terminal A; others flow up through SCR 6 into M terminal C. These flows combine within the motor and flow out through terminal B and SCR 2. At the 60° point, a pulse from the SUS oscillator advances the ring counter so that SCRs 4, 2, and 3 conduct; all electrons now flow through 4 into terminal A, and part of these continue to flow out through B and 2. But 6 has been commutated off (as explained in Sec. 24-14) and no longer conducts; the flow through terminal C reverses direction and passes instead out through SCR 3.

At the 120° point, SCR 2 is commutated off; the electrons through M terminal B reverse direction and flow instead through 5 into B. At the 180° point, SCR 4 is commutated off; electrons flow instead out of terminal A and through SCR 1. At 240°, the flow out of C and SCR 3 stops; electrons flow instead through SCR 6 into terminal C. At 300°, SCR 5 is commutated off. Electrons flow through 6 into terminal C; part of these flow out of terminal A through SCR 1, while the rest flow out of B through SCR 2. At 360°, the electron flow out of A and 1 stops; as flow resumes through SCR 4 into terminal A, the conditions have returned for the start of another inverter cycle.

Figure 24-12 shows that electrons flow into motor terminal A for 180° then out of A for 180°. A similar reversal occurs in terminal B 120° later; the

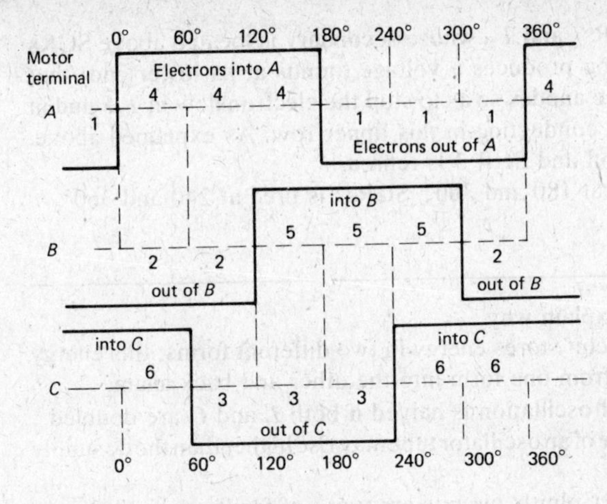

Figure 24-12 Sequence of SCR firing in Fig. 24-11, inverting dc for a variable-speed three-phase motor.

reversal in terminal *C* lags another 120°. These three current waves, although square in shape, act as a three-phase power supply that runs this ac motor at a speed set by the frequency of the inverter output. If more than one synchronous motor is used, each motor runs in step with the inverter output wave; therefore, all motors run at exactly the same speed.

24-14 TURNOFF OR COMMUTATION OF INVERTER SCRs

Since SCRs 1 to 6 in Fig. 24-11 operate in a dc circuit, no inverter SCR can be turned off unless its anode is driven more negative than its cathode. Such turnoff or commutation is performed by circuits at the upper right in Fig. 24-11. Here a large capacitor C_5 is charged through diodes D_2 to nearly 150 volts; in turn, C_5 supplies the current to charge C_6. Because of reactor X_3, C_6 is charged to nearly 300 V, which is retained because of D_4.

Just before the 60° point in the inverter ac output, the ring-counter circuit sends a signal that lets SCR 8 be fired by its gate oscillator; this lets C_6 discharge through SCR 8 and the primary of T_3, whose secondary is located below SCRs 4 to 6. The T_3S winding produces a voltage (plus at its upper end) that raises the three SCR cathodes above their anodes so as to stop the electron flow in T_3S and in both SCRs 4 and 6 that are conducting, in this lower row. Since current is stopped in T_3S, the energy trapped in this transformer makes its primary winding produce a reverse voltage that charges C_6, minus on top; this C_6 voltage holds the anode of SCR 8 negative, so that it is turned off. After SCRs 4 and 6 thus are commutated off, SCR 4 is refired by the ring counter, but 6 remains off.

Just before the 120° point, the ring counter lets SCR 7 be fired; C_6 now discharges through SCR 7 and T_2, whose secondary is located above SCRs 1 to 3. The T_2S winding produces a voltage (minus at its lower end) that drives negative the three anodes so as to stop the electron flow in T_2S and in SCRs 2 and 3 that are conducting in this upper row. As explained above, SCR 7 then is turned off and SCR 3 is refired.

SCR 8 is fired again at 180 and 300°; SCR 7 is fired at 240 and 360°.

Problems

24-1 True or false? Explain why.

(a) An oscillating circuit stores energy in two different forms; this energy rapidly changes from one form into the other and back again.

(b) The frequency of oscillation is halved if both L and C are doubled.

(c) The anode voltage of an oscillator tube may rise higher than the dc supply voltage.

(d) The Hartley and Colpitts circuits are types of feedback oscillator.

(e) A tank circuit may contain only inductance and resistance.

(f) An oscillator is not self-starting if a fixed voltage (such as a battery) is used to bias the tube below cutoff.

(g) All Hartley oscillators operate from batteries.

(h) A tank circuit containing 0.0002 henry (H) and 81.1 picofarads (pF) oscillates at 1250 kilohertz (kHz).

25 TEMPERATURE RECORDERS

Electronic circuits help to make a record chart of slowly changing temperatures, accurate within part of a degree. (This accuracy usually is expressed to a fraction of 1 percent of full-scale range.) Such temperature recorders must respond when the input voltage changes less than $^1/_{10,000}$ volt and must amplify this signal until it can run a motor to drive a recording pen. These amplifier circuits may respond to tiny voltage changes caused when some other circuit becomes slightly unbalanced; since the amplifier makes the motor turn in the right direction to bring the circuit back to a balanced condition, it is called a self-balancing circuit. Similar circuits are used in airplane controls, as in one kind of autopilot. (Another temperature recorder is described in Sec. 12-7.)

25-1 A CHANGE OF 0.0001 VOLT TURNS A MOTOR

One kind of temperature recorder (whose amplifier circuit is described in Sec. 25-2) uses a thermocouple to "tell" how hot the furnace or the metal is. This thermocouple has two pieces of different metals, which are joined at one end; this end, when hot, produces a tiny voltage. This dc voltage changes less than $^1/_{10,000}$ V (or 0.1 mV) for each 10°F change in temperature. Such a thermocouple is included in Fig. 25-1, which shows the main parts of the recorder.

Instead of directly amplifying this 0.1-mV change, most electronic-circuit designers prefer to convert such a dc signal into an alternating or changing signal, for it then can be amplified more easily. So in Fig. 25-1 a converter receives the dc signal from the thermocouple and produces a tiny ac signal at transformer *T*; after passing through several electronic amplifier circuits, this ac signal becomes a current large enough (at *H*) to make a motor turn. This balancing motor is geared so as to move the recording pen (not shown);

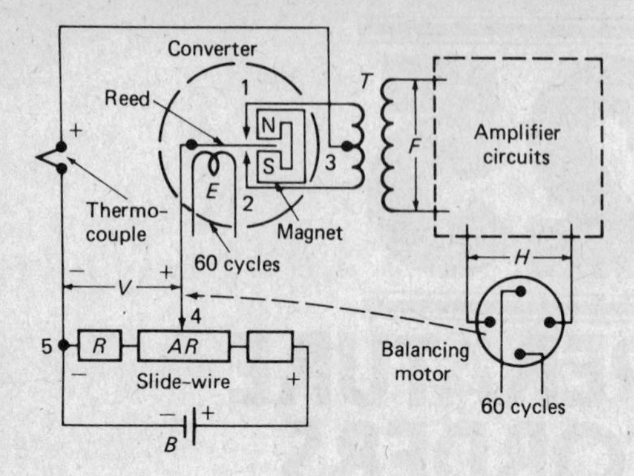

Figure 25-1 Thermocouple voltage is converted and amplified, to turn a motor.

the motor also moves the slider at 4 along a slide-wire, until the voltage V is exactly equal to the voltage produced by the thermocouple.

The converter or chopper contains a steel reed, which is made to move up and down 60 times per second, being driven by a 60-hertz (Hz or cps) coil E. [The steel reed of the converter touches upper contact 1 during each positive half cycle of the ac power supply. (This ac timing wave is shown in curves 1 and 8 of Fig. 25-2.) To see why the reed moves upward, notice that the permanent magnet in Fig. 25-1 has a north upper pole; during the up half cycle, current flows in coil E in that direction which magnetizes the reed so that its right-hand or free end is a south pole, which is therefore attracted upward. A half cycle later, current has reversed in coil E, and now produces a north pole at the free end of the reed; the reed is pulled down by the south or lower pole of the permanent magnet.] For a moment, suppose this reed is held upward so that it closes the circuit to contact 1. Now, as temperature rises, the thermocouple produces a greater voltage (than battery B produces at V); this voltage difference makes electrons flow from 5 through R and slider 4, to contact 1, down through the upper half of T to midpoint 3, back to the thermocouple.

A half cycle later, when the reed touches lower contact 2, the electrons (which had been flowing up into contact 1) flow now into contact 2, upward through transformer T to midtap 3. Notice that as long as the thermocouple voltage is larger than V, the electrons flow through T always *toward* its midtap, and alternately through the upper and lower halves of the primary winding of T. Meanwhile, the secondary winding of T produces a voltage (alternately positive and negative, as shown at curve 2 of Fig. 25-2), which is fed to the amplifier. This makes the motor turn (say clockwise, as explained later) and moves slider 4 toward the right (also moving the pen to show a higher temperature); this increases voltage V until it becomes equal to the thermocouple voltage. When these voltages balance, no voltage remains at T; so the amplifier gives no voltage at H to turn the motor. Although the reed

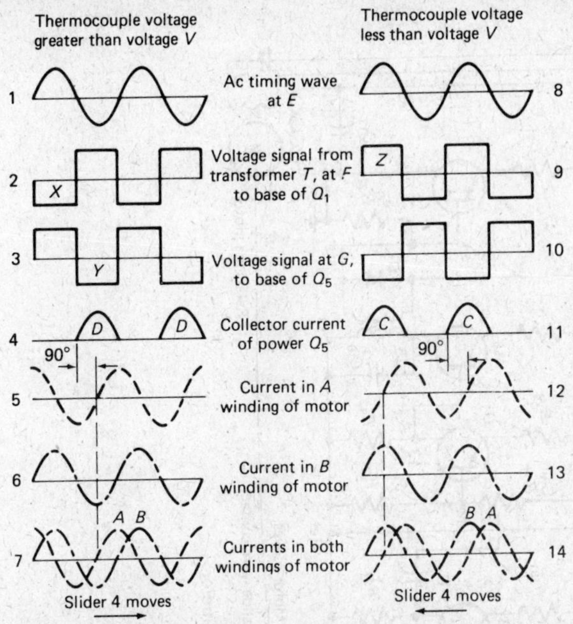

Figure 25-2 Voltage signals and motor-current waves in Fig. 25-3.

still vibrates, the motor does not move as long as V is in balance with the thermocouple voltage.

If the temperature now decreases so that the thermocouple voltage becomes less than V, the slider is too far to the right; electrons flow *away* from midtap 3 through transformer T, out of contacts 1 and 2 toward the slide-wire. The resulting voltage that T produces at F is shown by curve 9 of Fig. 25-2; curve 9 is in phase with timing wave 8, whereas curve 2 is reversed, or 180° out of phase with the timing wave. Next we may see how these signals (curve 2 or 9) are amplified so as to turn the motor.

25-2 THE HONEYWELL CONTINUOUS-BALANCE POTENTIOMETER

The amplifier circuit of this temperature instrument is shown in Fig. 25-3. At F, transformer T_4 supplies the input signal to transistor Q_1; this signal is the square wave (curve 2 or 9 of Fig. 25-2) described above. Four PNP transistors are used in common-emitter stages in the amplifier, while the collector output of Q_5 controls the current in winding A of the balancing motor.

The entire unit receives ac supply power through transformer T_1 above; this includes the timing wave E for the converter. Through diodes D_1

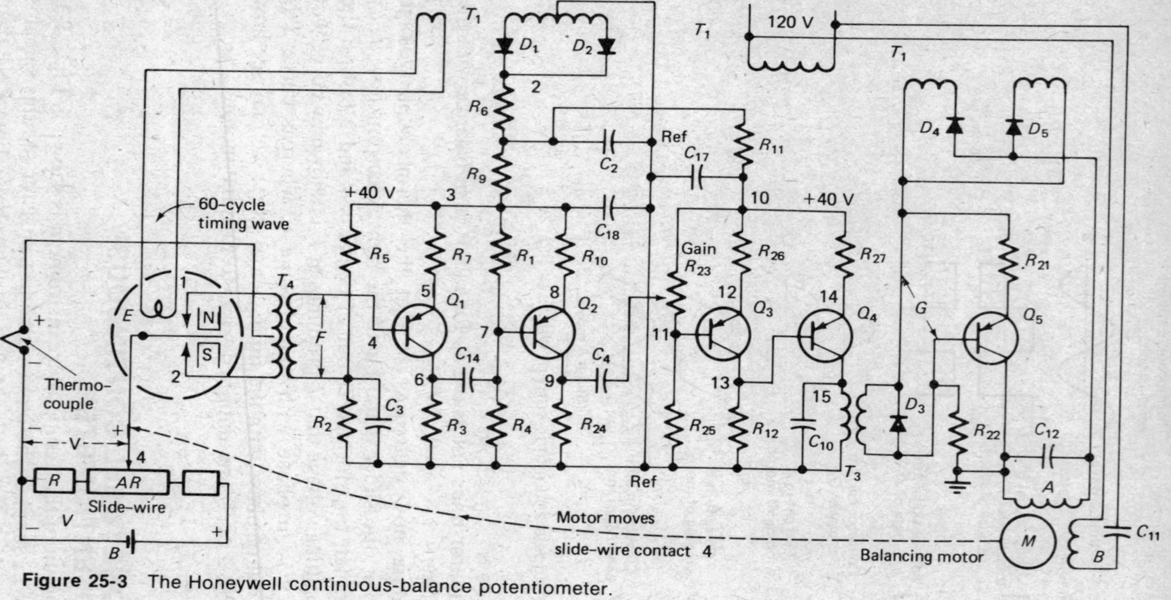

Figure 25-3 The Honeywell continuous-balance potentiometer.

and D_2, full-wave rectified output is received at point 2; this is filtered by C_2 and C_{18} so that a smooth 40 V dc supply appears between point 3 and the bottom reference line (*Ref*) for transistors Q_1 and Q_2, while C_{17} filters the similar voltage at point 10 for Q_3 and Q_4. Figure 25-3 omits many filter capacitors or circuit features that are included in this equipment.

When no signal voltage appears at F (as when the thermocouple voltage is equal to V), the voltage divider R_2 and R_5 holds the base of PNP transistor Q_1 steadily at 4 V above *Ref;* meanwhile divider R_3 and R_7 holds emitter 5 at 5 V above *Ref*. Since the P-type emitter is about 1 V more positive than the base, this junction is forward-biased; as a steady collector current flows through R_3, collector 6 is about 1 V above *Ref*, so that the collector-base junction is reverse-biased by 3 V. Likewise, the divider R_1-R_4 holds base 7 of Q_2 at 9 V above *Ref*, while divider R_{10}-R_{24} holds emitter 8 at 10 V; this forward bias lets Q_2 pass steady current through R_{24}, holding collector 9 at 5 V. (Coupling capacitor C_{14} is charged to the voltage difference between points 6 and 7 and has no further action, so long as no signal appears at F; C_4 also is charged to the steady voltage between 9 and the gain adjuster.) While Q_3 has a similar bias that lets steady collector current flow through R_{12}, the resulting 15-V potential at point 13 is applied also at the base of Q_4; since the emitter 14 of Q_4 is held at 16 V, a small steady collector current is supplied to T_3. This transformer provides inductive coupling between the output of Q_4 and the input to the base of Q_5; with steady current from Q_4, no signal is produced by T_3.

The ac output from separate windings of transformer T_1 is rectified by diodes D_4 and D_5 so that a pulsing full-wave voltage is applied across transistor Q_5 in series with winding A of the balancing motor. (This pulsing voltage is received also at G by the low-voltage winding of T_3, so that a 120-Hz voltage is induced at collector 15 of Q_4. Diode D_3 is added across T_3 to prevent surge voltages that could damage Q_4 when ac power is switched on or off at T_1.) The first half cycle hereafter is called C, while D refers to the second half cycle. When no signal is received through T_3, collector current flows in Q_5 during both C and D; the resulting direct current through winding A does not turn this motor, which is an ac induction motor. So, until a signal voltage appears at F, all five transistors pass current steadily but the motor does not turn.

25-3 CAPACITOR-COUPLED AMPLIFIERS

In Fig. 25-3, suppose that the furnace temperature rises, increasing the thermocouple voltage; since this voltage now is greater than V, a signal voltage appears at F, as shown in curve 2 in Fig. 25-2. During the half wave X, the base of the PNP transistor Q_1 is made more negative, increasing the collector current. Similar to the action described in Sec. 6-12, collector 6 of Q_1 is coupled by C_{14} to the base of Q_2; only a fast decrease in F signal can cause a decrease in Q_2 collector current. Similarly, when current decreases in Q_2, it increases in Q_3. As collector 9 falls, capacitor C_4 tries to discharge to the decreasing voltage 9-to-*Ref*; as C_4 discharges, its current causes a voltage drop across R_{25} and the gain potentiometer R_{23}; so that base 11 of Q_3 becomes more negative, thus increasing the Q_3 collector current. (When the slider on R_{23} is moved toward the lower end, a larger portion of the decrease at collector 9 appears across R_{25} and is used to change the Q_3 current through R_{12}; thus the gain of the whole amplifier is increased.) As the voltage across R_{12} increases, base 13 of Q_4 is raised, decreasing the Q_4 current. which passes through the primary winding of T_3. This *change* of current makes T_3 produce a secondary voltage at G in Fig. 25-3; this drives the base of Q_5 more positive during this first half cycle, so that collector current cannot flow in Q_5 during the C half cycles. However, during the next half cycle, the Q_5 base is driven negative (as shown at Y in Fig. 25-2) so that collector current flows in Q_5 during each D half cycle. The amount of this Q_5 current increases if the F signal (curve 2) becomes larger.

25-4 RUNNING THE BALANCING MOTOR

From the above, it is seen that Q_5 passes current during only the D half cycles, whenever the thermocouple voltage is greater than V. These current pulses (curve 4 in Fig. 25-2) must be changed into complete cycles of alternating current before they reach motor winding A. To do this, capacitor C_{12} is added (in Fig. 25-3), which is large enough to be resonant (at 60 Hz)[24-3] with the inductance of the motor winding A. Current now flows back and forth in winding A and in and out of capacitor C_{12}. This alternating current is started and kept flowing because of the pulses from Q_5. Similarly, although we give short sudden pushes (always in the same direction) to a rope swing, the swing moves smoothly back and forth (like a sine wave of current). The swing is pushed when it is barely moving, at a point near one limit of its travel; the swing reaches full speed later, at the middle of its travel. Similarly, when Q_5 "pushes" the swinging circuit (of C_{12} and winding A), the greatest current flows in this circuit about 90° after the push; thus the wave of current in the A motor winding (curve 5 of Fig. 25-2) lags 90° behind the wave of Q_5 current (curve 4).

This balancing motor in Fig. 25-3 is a two-winding induction motor (like those operated on two-phase ac power supply). The motor does not turn unless alternating current flows in both its windings. The B winding is connected to the ac supply, so that alternating current always flows. Since this winding is inductive, its current lags behind the voltage; capacitor C_{11} is added so that the current in the B winding is kept in phase with the ac supply voltage, as shown in curves 6 and 13 of Fig. 25-2.

When Q_5 passes current during only the D half cycles, the current in the motor's A winding is shown by curve 5. This is shown again in curve 7, which also includes curve 6 (current in the *B* winding). Notice that the *A*-winding current is to the left of the *B*-winding current and leads by 90°; these combined currents make this induction motor turn so as to move slider 4 toward the right, and so that the pen mark shows a rising temperature.

When the furnace cools so that the thermocouple voltage becomes less than *V*, the signal voltage at *F* becomes like curve 9 of Fig. 25-2. Recall that, during the half cycle Z when the converter reed is up, touching contact 1, the voltage at *F* is now positive—opposite to the curve-2 condition. Since the Q_1 base 4 is made positive during this half wave, Q_1 collector current decreases, Q_2 current increases, Q_3 current falls, and Q_4 current rises; at *G* the base of Q_5 is driven more negative, as shown in curve 10. Therefore, Q_5 lets collector current flow during only the *C* half cycles, in curve 11. These pulses make alternating current flow in the motor's *A* winding and resonant capacitor C_{12}, as before; this alternating current (curve 12) lags 90° behind the wave of Q_5 current (curve 11). However, since the *C* pulses occur a half cycle later (than the *D* pulses of curve 4), the wave of current in the *A* winding is also later. In the combined curves 14, the *A*-winding current is to the right of the *B*-winding current, and lags by 90°. These combined currents make the induction motor turn so as to move slider 4 toward the left, indicating lower temperature.

From this study of Fig. 25-3, we realize that the timing wave *E* (which drives the converter reed) must always be in step with the ac voltage wave applied to power transistor Q_5. Note also that the motor begins to turn instantly to bring the slider to the required position of balance; this provides the continuous-balance feature.

25-5 AC BRIDGE SIGNAL FOR THE AMPLIFIER

The continuous-balance type of amplifier may receive its signal also from an ac bridge or potentiometer circuit, such as is shown in Fig. 25-4; any voltage unbalance in such a circuit gives a signal that is an ac voltage and therefore does not need a converter such as is used with the thermocouple in Fig. 25-1. In Fig. 25-4, resistors R_1 and R_2 are both connected across an ac

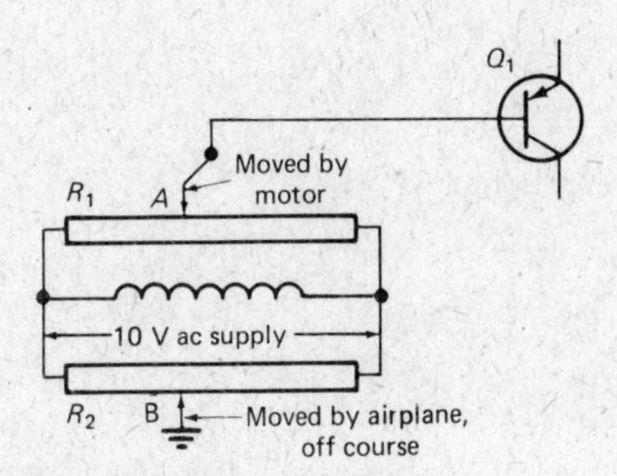

Figure 25-4 Ac bridge circuit controls transistor Q_1.

voltage (which must be supplied by the same generator or system that feeds the power transistor and motor of the main amplifier circuit). All of Fig. 25-4 is in the input circuit of the first amplifier tube (or Q_1 of Fig. 25-3).

When slider A is exactly above slider B, there is no voltage between these sliders and no ac signal is given to the tube at F. But suppose that, inside an airplane, resistor R_2 is held steady by a gyro so that its slider B is moved slightly to the left when the airplane starts to get off its course. Perhaps slider B moves so little that its potential changes only 0.1 volt (V), yet this produces an ac wave of 0.1 V at F. As described above, this ac voltage is strengthened in the amplifier circuit until it can operate a motor or a valve; this device moves the flaps or the rudder to bring the plane back on its course, and it also moves slider A to the left until the two sliders are again in line, with zero voltage between them.

26 MAGNETIC AMPLIFIERS

Amplifiers of voltage, current, and power are described in Chaps. 5 and 6 using transistors. Amplification is the control of a larger output quantity by the variation of a small input quantity; such amplification is provided also by a magnetic device such as the saturable reactor described below. By itself a saturable reactor long has served as a low-gain amplifier of large loads; it may be called a *saturable reactor amplifier*. Since about 1940 the gain and usefulness of this magnetic device have been increased greatly by the addition of rectifiers in its output circuit; this combination of a saturable reactor with rectifiers is called a *magnetic amplifier* (or a self-saturated amplifier). It is better first to study the saturable reactor alone; in Sec. 26-4 the rectifiers are added so as to produce a magnetic amplifier.

26-1 THE SATURABLE REACTOR

This device acts as a variable inductance, connected in series with a load across an ac power supply. It looks like a transformer, having two or more windings around a core of steel. However, one of these windings receives a small direct current which acts as an input signal that controls the amount of alternating current that can flow through other windings and the load. The output current and load voltage are increased as the dc input is raised.

A reactor can have a single core and only one ac winding or coil, as shown in Fig. 26-1*a*; this type seldom is used, since the alternating current in the upper winding produces an objectionable ac voltage in the lower winding or coil that may disturb or damage the dc control circuit. Therefore, most saturable reactors include two identical cores as in Fig. 26-1*b*; each steel core has its own ac winding, while the dc coil surrounds one leg of each core. Here the two ac windings are connected in parallel but the connections to the lower coil are reversed so that, at the instant when flux moves to the right

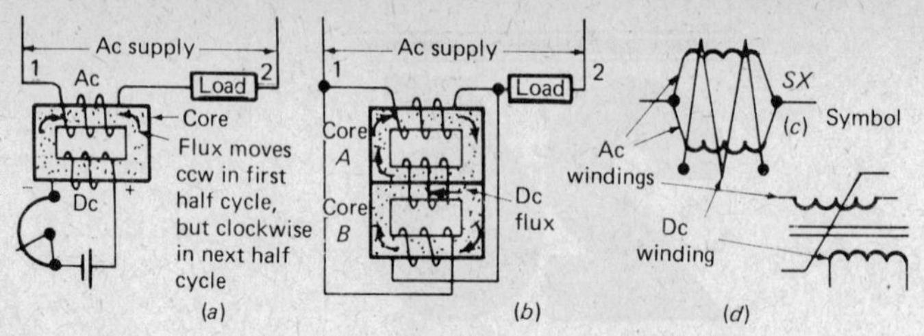

Figure 26-1 Saturable reactor windings and symbols.

within the upper ac coil, an equal flux moves to the left within the lower ac coil. Within the dc coil these two flux movements are in opposite directions at the same time; therefore, any voltages produced in the dc coil offset or cancel, so that no objectionable ac voltage is induced in the dc circuit. (In small reactors the two ac windings may be connected in series; this provides faster response but increases the voltage drop across the reactor.)

A symbol long used for a saturable reactor, in Fig. 26-1*c*, shows two ac windings in parallel and a single dc control winding. The output current passes through the ac coils, which also are called gate windings. The ohms of inductive reactance $= 2\pi fL = X_L$; so this saturable reactor often is called *SX*. In Fig. 26-1*d* the symbol is shown for a saturable reactor as now used in small units and in magnetic amplifiers.

26-2 INDUCTANCE OF A STEEL CORE

Any magnetic material such as iron or steel easily is magnetized when current flows through a wire coiled around the steel. Flowing in one turn of the coiled wire, an ampere (A) causes a certain amount of magnetic flux to flow in the steel. Since 5 A flowing in a 400-turn coil produces the same amount of flux as is caused by 2 A flowing in a 1000-turn coil at the same location, the magnetomotive force (mmf) of either coil is said to be 2000 A-turns. (This mmf that causes flux in the magnetic circuit is similar in action to an emf that causes current in the electric conduction circuit.) If we vary the current in such a coil, the resulting amount of flux varies; for an ordinary steel core, Fig. 26-2 shows this relation, known as the magnetization or saturation curve, the B-H curve, or the hysteresis loop of this core material. If the current in these turns is only a small alternating wave shown as *VW* the resulting change of flux is nearly a straight line *YZ*. But when a large changing current applies the bottom wave in Fig. 26-2, the flux loop *ABCDEF* is produced. Between *A* and *B*, the flux curve has less upward slope, showing that the steel is becoming saturated, so that the amount of flux increases by a smaller amount.

The inductance of a coil wound around this material is shown by the change of flux that is caused by a change of current; therefore, the ability of a

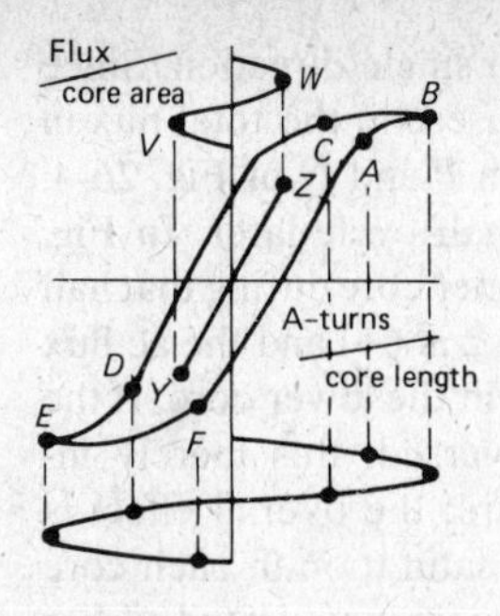

Figure 26-2 B-H or magnetization curve of ordinary steel.

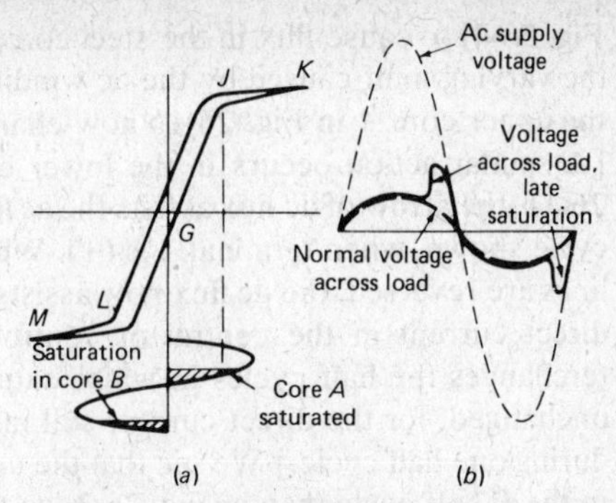

Figure 26-3 (*a*) Magnetization curve of alloy steel; (*b*) ac voltage waves showing saturation.

coil to impede the flow of alternating current is shown by the slope of its B-H curve. When operating between *A* and *B* in Fig. 26-2, this ac winding has less inductance than when it operates between *Y* and *Z*. (During any short time when the core becomes saturated, such as between *A* and *B* in Fig. 26-2, or between *J* and *K* in Fig. 26-3, the coil is less able to oppose alternating current, as though the steel core had been removed from within the coil during that short time.)

The core of most saturable reactors is made of special steel (a spiral winding of grain-oriented silicon-iron or nickel-iron alloys) that has a narrow magnetization curve, as shown in Fig. 26-3, and a sharp knee or bend at *J* and *L*. So long as no direct current flows in the signal or control winding, the reactor has large (nearly constant) inductance if it operates only on the steep slope between *L* and *J*. The resulting voltage across the load is only a small part of the ac supply voltage, and may be nearly a smooth wave, as indicated by the dashed line in Fig. 26-3*b*.

But a larger ac supply voltage can force enough current to flow (as is shown at the bottom in Fig. 26-3*a*) so that each core is partly saturated during the latter part of one half wave. Since this decreases the inductance *L* and the ohms of X_L during only the latter parts of the applied voltage wave, the current in *SX* and the voltage across the load may have the solid-line waveshape shown in Fig. 26-3*b*. For this condition, an ac ammeter in the output circuit indicates a small amount of load current, shown at *A* in Fig. 26-5.

26-3 DIRECT CURRENT INCREASES REACTOR SATURATION

When a small direct current is passed through the turns of the input or control winding of the reactor, a definite steady mmf is applied (as at *B* in

Fig. 26-4) to cause flux in the steel core, always in a single direction. Since the varying mmf caused by the ac windings also is present, the total flux in the upper core A in Fig. 26-1b now changes between P and Q of Fig. 26-4. [A similar action occurs in the lower core, but a half cycle later. In Fig. 26-1b, the arrow of dc flux assists the ac flux in the upper core during that half cycle shown, when terminal 1 is (+). When terminal 2 is (+) and the ac flux lines are reversed, the dc flux now assists the ac flux in the lower core. If the direct current in the central or control coil is reversed, this merely interchanges the half cycles in which saturation occurs; the overall effect is unchanged, for the direct current still increases the saturation in each core during one half cycle.] We see that the upper core becomes saturated earlier in the P half cycle than in Fig. 26-3, so that a larger wave P appears across the load, as in Fig. 26-4b. A half cycle later, the lower core similarly is saturated earlier by this direct current at B, so that a larger wave Q appears at the load. The average value of the load current has risen to the value shown at B in Fig. 26-5.

If the amount of direct current is increased further, corresponding to the value C in Fig. 26-4, the total mmf (or ampere-turns) varies from R to S in the upper core; the load current and voltage increase to the values shown at R and S in Fig. 26-4c, and at C in Fig. 26-5.

A large value of direct current, corresponding to D in Fig. 26-4, causes the mmf to vary from T to U; since the flux varies along the flat portion of the magnetization curve (between J and K), the core is almost completely saturated during T. Such a small change of flux results in so little inductance that nearly all the supply voltage appears across the load, as shown in Fig. 26-4d. The load current approaches its largest value, as at D in Fig. 26-5. (Receiving this large dc control signal D, the upper core is saturated during the entire half cycle T; but recall that this saturated core is in parallel with the lower core, which is not saturated during this same half cycle. By increasing the dc control signal to E in Fig. 26-4, we force each core to be saturated during both half cycles; since both cores now are saturated at all times, the load current becomes maximum, at E in Fig. 26-5.)

When current values are used in Fig. 26-5 to show the typical behavior of a small saturable reactor, the current amplification (or gain, as a current amplifier) is shown to be about 6:1 in this example; on the slope between B and C, the ac load current increases by 300 milliamperes (mA) when the dc control current is raised 50 mA. [This 6:1 ratio indicates that N_C (the number of turns in the control winding) is 6 times N_L (the number of turns in the ac or load winding). The mmf $I_C N_C$ (or product of control amperes $\times$ control turns) is equal to $I_L N_L$.] Note also that this curve is symmetrical; if the direction or polarity of the dc control signal is reversed, the ac change from F to G is like that from B to C. Thus the simple saturable reactor gives minimum ac output to its load when it has no dc input signal; an increasing direct current of either polarity causes its output to increase.

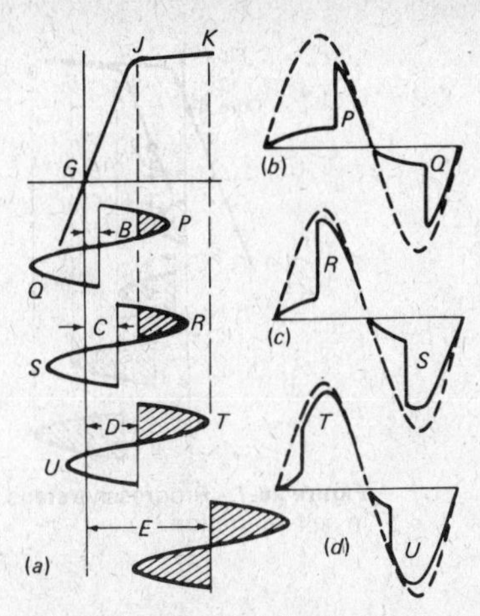

Figure 26-4 Greater direct current increases saturation and ac output.

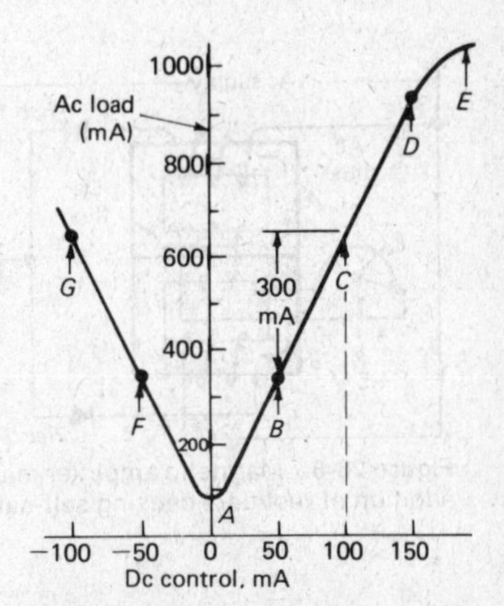

Figure 26-5 Ac output of saturable reactor versus dc control input.

When a half wave of current flows in the ac winding on a core in the circuit discussed above, it produces flux in the core; but note that this flux quickly is reset or reversed in the following half cycle, since the same amount of current flows in the opposite direction in the same ac winding. Therefore, the average value of ac flux here is zero; thus the average total flux and the amount of saturation depend entirely upon the amount of direct current in the signal or control winding. As indicated in Fig. 26-5, about 100 dc milliamperes may be needed to control about 600 ac load milliamperes.

In the next section, rectifiers are inserted so as to prevent the reverse flow of current in each ac winding of the saturable reactor. Since these rectifiers prevent current flow during the RESET half cycle, the action within the saturable reactor becomes quite different from that previously described; without direct current, this reactor becomes saturated.

26-4 RECTIFIERS ARE ADDED TO CAUSE SELF-SATURATION

The circuit of Fig. 26-1*b* is shown again in Fig. 26-6, but a silicon diode is added in series with each ac winding of the saturable reactor. On upper core *A*, current now can flow in the ac or gate winding and through the load only when supply terminal 1 is (+). Current flows in the core-*B* gate winding and the load only when terminal 2 is (+). Thus the load receives both half cycles of alternating current, but each core is magnetized by only a half cycle of current.

It is important to learn the condition of these cores before any direct cur-

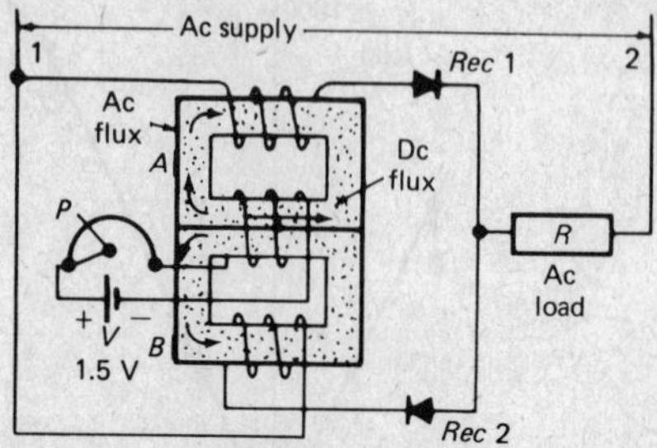

Figure 26-6 Magnetic amplifier made by addition of rectifiers causing self-saturation.

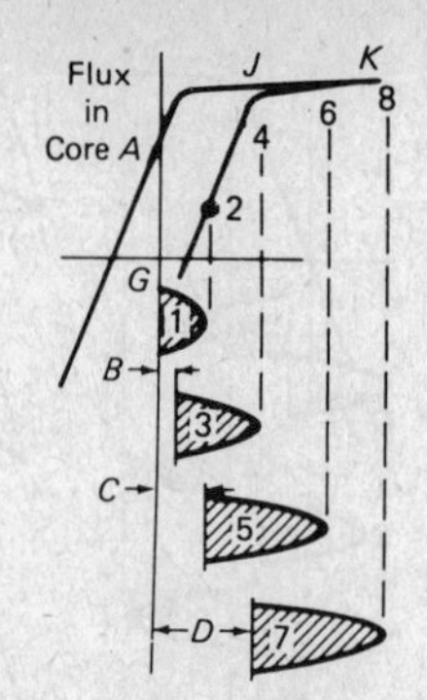

Figure 26-7 Progressive steps in self-saturation.

rent is sent through the central control winding. In the following description, the action that occurs within a few cycles is slowed so that it can be observed gradually in steps.

The magnetization curve of Fig. 26-3 is shown again in Fig. 26-7, but is widened to show greater detail. Only the upper part of this curve concerns the operation of upper core *A*, during that half cycle when current flows in its ac winding; the lower half of the magnetization curve can show similar action in core *B*, but occuring a half cycle later.

When ac power first is connected to the circuit of Fig. 26-6, when terminal 1 is (+), a small magnetizing current flows in the upper ac winding; these ampere-turns are shown at number 1 in Fig. 26-7, and they produce an initial flux in core *A*, as shown at 2. During the following half cycle this flux is not reset and some of it remains, because the diode Rec 1 blocks the reverse current. The dc or average value of this number-1 half wave is shown at *B* in Fig. 26-7; the total mmf is increased by this amount *B* (as though a small direct current had been added in the ac coils).

From the ac supply, the next half wave (numbered 3) combines with *B* and raises the core flux to point 4; after reverse current again is blocked by Rec 1, the flux remaining in the core is greater than before and the average value of mmf has increased to *C*. When ac half wave number 5 raises the total core flux above the knee of the magnetization curve, at *J*, core *A* loses some of its inductance, so that it permits greater current to flow in the ac winding; the total flux rises to 6, and the average mmf has increased to *D*. At half wave 7 it is seen that the flux is driven to point 8, so that the core operates along the flat portion of the magnetization curve throughout the entire half cycle. Here the steel of core *A* is saturated, so that the coil inductance has decreased greatly; the saturable reactor now has such low impedance that a large alternating current flows through the load. (Meanwhile, similar action during the alternate half cycle has saturated the lower core *B*. The core-*B* flux flows through the central leg in Fig. 26-6 in the same direction as does the core-*A* flux.)

Thus, although no direct current yet flows in the control or signal winding on the central legs of the cores, the reactor has become self-saturated, entirely because of the action caused by its ac coils combined with the rectifiers. If the flux produced by the upper ac coil passes always from right to left through the central core leg within the dc coil, then the flux produced by current in the lower ac coil also passes right to left within the dc coil. This is not an alternating flux; therefore, it can be aided by the flux produced by current in the dc coil, or it can be opposed by that dc flux if the direct current is reversed; this action is explained next.

26-5 DC CONTROL OF THE SELF-SATURATED REACTOR

When the reactor is in the self-saturated condition described above, the load shown in Fig. 26-6 may receive about 1000 mA, or 1 A, of alternating current, as indicated at point *D* in Fig. 26-5; but this condition exists while no dc signal current flows. Therefore, this point *D* is shown again in Fig. 26-8, on the vertical line where the dc ampere-turns or mmf = 0. To control or vary the amount of this ac load current, a small direct current may be passed through the control winding around the central core legs. (For this example we may assume that this dc control coil has 2000 turns. When a current of 2 mA flows in this coil, this also may be described as 0.002 A × 2000 turns = 4 A-turns. Such values are used in the horizontal scale in Fig. 26-8.) If the direction of this control current is chosen so that it produces in the cores a dc flux that assists the fluxes produced by the ac windings, this combined flux drives the cores into more complete saturation, thereby increasing the load current to its largest value, as shown at *E* in Figs. 26-5 and 26-8. This type of action rarely is found useful.

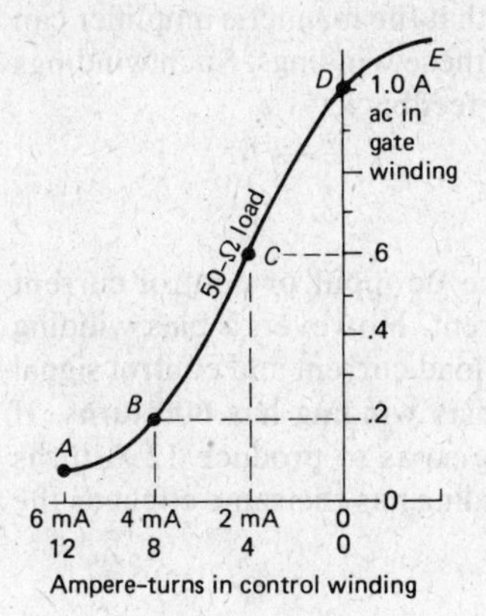

Figure 26-8 Ac output of magnetic amplifier versus dc control input.

Instead, the dc control circuit is arranged as is shown in Fig. 26-6, so that the mmf of the dc winding opposes the mmf of the ac windings. Thus, as the amount of control current in the dc winding is increased, the total mmf is decreased and the core is less saturated. (Details of this action are given in Sec. 26-10.) In Fig. 26-8, as the control current is increased to 6 mA (toward the left), the ac load current decreases from 1 to less than 0.1A.

The important point is this: whereas Fig. 26-5 shows that only a large control current (more than 150 mA) can drive the core *into* saturation, Fig. 26-8 shows that only a few milliamperes is needed to drive the same core *out* of saturation. Thus the gain provided by this self-saturated reactor is much greater than the gain of the saturable reactor alone. In Fig. 26-8, the self-saturated reactor (which now is called the magnetic amplifier) gives the greatest gain when it is operated between B and D on the steep part of the curve. Here the current gain is

$$\frac{1.0 - 0.2\text{A}}{0 - (-4)\,\text{mA}} = \frac{800\,\text{mA}}{4\,\text{mA}} = 200$$

In the dc control circuit of Fig. 26-6, a 1.5-volt battery V easily can supply the signal current, which is adjusted by rheostat P. At point D in Fig. 26-8, no control power is used; the output power to a 50-ohm (Ω) load R is $I_{ac}{}^2 R = (1\text{A})^2 \times 50\ \Omega = 50$ watts (W). When the amplifier operates at point B, the battery V supplies $4\text{ mA} \times 1.5\text{ V} = 0.006\text{ W}$; the output power has decreased to $(0.2\text{A})^2 \times 50\Omega = 2\text{W}$. Therefore, the power gain $= (50 - 2) / 0.006 = 8000$.

We may notice in Fig. 26-8 (for use in Sec. 26-6) that the addition of 12 A-turns, in the direction toward the left, reduces the ac load current to its lowest value, at A. To supply this current, battery V in Fig. 26-6 is connected so its left side is (+).

Since a magnetic amplifier can be controlled by so few milliamperes of direct current, the control winding usually is made of such small wire that it requires very little space. A number of similar windings may be placed around the central core, and in such a manner that the magnetic amplifier can be controlled by a direct current in any one of these windings. Such windings are shown in Fig. 26-10, to provide bias and feedback.

26-6 THE BIAS WINDING

In Figs. 26-6 and 26-8 we observe that the dc input or control current must be decreased to cause greater load current. However, a bias winding may be used, as in Fig. 26-10, so that both the load current and control signal can increase together. Suppose that such a bias winding has 600 turns. If battery W forces 20 mA through this winding so as to produce 12 A-turns that oppose those of the ac coils, this bias winding has the same effect as the

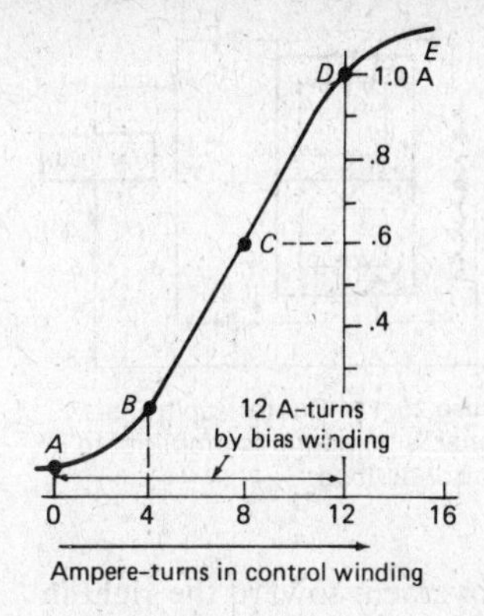

Figure 26-9 Use of bias winding so that greater control current causes greater load current.

control winding used in Sec. 26-5, so that the whole reactor becomes unsaturated and operates at point *A* in Fig. 26-8. Meanwhile, zero current flows in the control coil; so Fig. 26-9 shows zero control ampere-turns or mmf at the vertical line through *A*, where the ac load current is smallest.

Now, to increase the load current to point *B* in Fig. 26-9, the control-winding current must be increased to 2 mA, giving 4 A-turns (toward the right); this requires that the movement of the direct current in the control coil must be made opposite to its previous direction in Fig. 26-6. Thus the battery *V* polarity is reversed in Fig. 26-10, so that its right side is (+).

Thus, by adjustment of the milliamperes or ampere-turns of the bias winding, the zero-current point of the control winding can be moved to any desired point on the curve of ac load current.

26-7 MAGNETIC AMPLIFIER WITH DC LOAD

The magnetic amplifier must be operated from an ac supply, but it can furnish either ac or dc output. Every circuit that has been discussed this far is arranged so that the controlled load receives alternating current. The ac output from the amplifier in Fig. 26-6 may be rectified for use with a dc load, merely by the addition of diodes 3 and 4 in Fig. 26-10 and the relocation of the load as shown. In this way all four diodes form a full-wave bridge rectifier (as in Sec. 4-6). In the first half cycle, any current through the upper gate winding flows through diodes 1 and 3, so that the upper load terminal is (+). In the following half cycle, current in the lower gate winding flows also through diodes 2 and 4, still holding positive the upper load terminal.

A full-wave dc load voltage also is available from the circuit of Fig. 26-11 (for which the central legs and control coils are the same as in Fig. 26-10); this requires a transformer with center tap, also rectifiers with greater voltage rating for this two-leg circuit.[4-10] Since diode 2 is reversed (as compared with Fig. 26-10), the connections to the lower ac winding must be in-

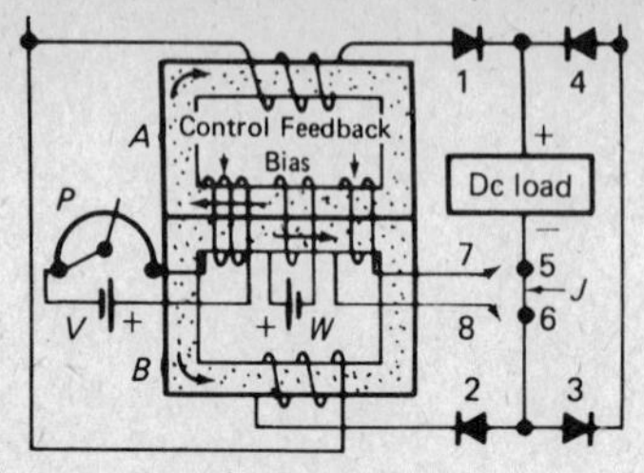

Figure 26-10 Magnetic amplifier with bias and feedback windings. Rectifier bridge permits control of dc load.

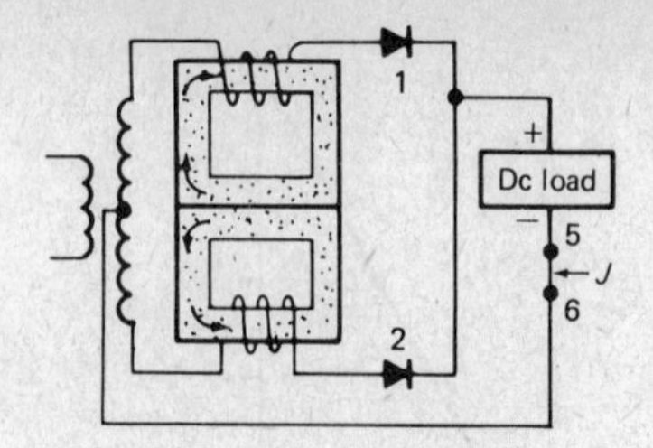

Figure 26-11 Center-tap transformer with magnetic amplifier to control dc load.

terchanged as shown, to retain the same flux movement toward the right in the lower core. [To control a load that is inductive, the bridge circuit of Fig. 26-10 is preferred. When the load current tries to decrease (during the early part of each half cycle, when the reactor cores are not yet saturated), the energy stored in the inductive load generates a voltage that is (+) at the lower load terminal. This voltage can force current through diodes 3 and 4; thus the inductive "kick" is drained away from the amplifier circuit.]

26-8 THE FEEDBACK WINDING

In Fig. 26-10 or 26-11 the output current flows through the load and through a wire *J*, joining points 5 and 6. If *J* is removed and 5 is joined to terminal 7, and 6 to 8, the load current passes through the feedback coil so as to produce flux toward the left within the central core; thus the load current may feed a signal back to the core. If *P* is turned clockwise to increase the current and flux of the control winding, the load current increases so that the feedback coil provides extra ampere-turns. Here this feedback flux assists the flux of the control coil so that the total flux becomes larger, thus further increasing the load current; this action is called *positive feedback*. Here the feedback signal has the same direction as the control signal, or is said to be in phase with the control signal.

Instead, if 5 is connected to 8, and 6 to 7, the load current flows through the feedback coil in a direction that produces flux toward the right within the central core; this feedback flux opposes the flux of the control coil. Thus, as *P* is turned clockwise to increase the load current, the feedback flux offsets or prevents some of this increase; this action is called *negative feedback*. Here the feedback signal opposes the control signal (or is 180° out of phase with it).

26-9 EFFECTS OF FEEDBACK

Since the load current in the feedback winding is much larger than the current in the control winding, very few turns are needed in the feedback wind-

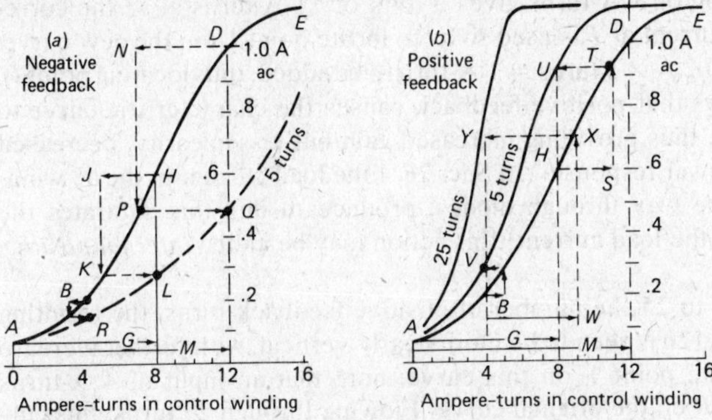

Figure 26-12 Effects of negative versus positive feedback on output current.

ing. In an example to show the effect of negative feedback, assume that only 5 turns are wound in the feedback coil in Fig. 26-10. We wish to learn what effect this coil may have on the magnetic amplifier characteristic curve given in Fig. 26-9; this curve is shown again by the solid curve in Fig. 26-12*a*.

Operation begins at point *A* on the curve; here the resistance in rheostat *P* permits almost no current in the control winding. If *P* now is turned to permit 8 A-turns, this moves the control point to *G* in Fig. 26-12; at *H* on the curve, the load current is seen to be 0.6 A. Flowing through the 5 turns of the feedback coil, this current produces 3 A-turns; in negative feedback, these 3 A-turns oppose the 8 control A-turns, so that only 5 A-turns produce the net flux, as marked at *J* in Fig. 26-12*a*. The load current resulting from these 5 A-turns is shown at *K* on the original curve. This value of load current *K* is plotted again at *L*, to become the first point on a new approximate curve. Thus, for 8 A-turns in the control winding, the negative feedback has decreased the load current from *H* to *L*. (The load current at *L* produces about half as many ampere-turns as does the current at *H*; therefore, the final new curve lies about midway between *L* and *H*.)

If *P* is turned to increase the input signal to a total of 12 A-turns, at *M*, Fig. 26-12 shows the 1-A load current at *D*. When 5 A-turns are subtracted, at *N*, the value (on the original curve at *P*) is plotted as point *Q* on the new curve that includes feedback. Another point also can begin at *B*, where the 0.2-A load current produces 1 A-turn, to be subtracted; thus the new point *R* is located.

The resulting curve *RLQ* shows that the current gain of the amplifier has been decreased because of the negative feedback. This new curve is more nearly a straight line; negative feedback provides a more linear output, greater stability, and faster response.

We now may anticipate the result when connections are interchanged so as to reverse the current direction in the feedback coil and thus to provide positive feedback. In Fig. 26-12*b*, at point *H* on the original curve at 0.6-A load, the addition of 3 A-turns gives a total of 11 A-turns at S; the corresponding load current at T is used so as to locate point U on the new curve. Similarly, at B, 0.2 A × 5 turns = 1 A-turn to be added, thus locating point V. Curve VU shows that positive feedback causes the characteristic curve to become steeper, thus providing increased gain but less linearity, decreased stability, and slower response. (In Sec. 26-4 the load current in the ac windings, passing one way through diodes, produces a flux that saturates the core, increasing the load current; this action may be called *internal positive feedback*.)

By increasing to 25 the number of positive feedback turns, the resulting curve in Fig. 26-12*b* is seen to be more nearly vertical, with further increase in gain. To locate point Y on this curve, note that an input of 4 A-turns causes 0.2 A at B on the original curve. Flowing through 25 turns, this current produces 5 A-turns, increasing the total to 9 A-turns at W. The value of load current at X is used again at Y to show the new load current that corresponds to a control signal of 4 A-turns, assisted by positive feedback in a 25-turn coil.

In Sec. 26-14, large positive feedback is used to make a magnetic amplifier suitable for purposes of switching.

26-10 OUTPUT WAVESHAPE OF MAGNETIC AMPLIFIER

Returning to the magnetic-amplifier circuit in Fig. 26-6 (which has no bias or feedback winding), as discussed in Sec. 26-5, we wish to study the waveshape of voltage appearing across the load during each half cycle, while the amount of opposing mmf of the dc winding gradually is increased, thus lowering the load current as shown in Fig. 26-8.

When there is no dc control mmf, Fig. 26-7 shows that the core is self-saturated, and operates between J and K on the flat portion of the magnetization curve. This curve is shown again in Fig. 26-13; here D shows the average amount of mmf provided by the upper ac winding in series with Rec 1. This saturating mmf is produced during the half cycle when current flows in the ac or gate winding; this is called the *gating* half cycle. Because of Rec 1, no mmf is produced that can reset this flux during the following or RESET half cycle. Since the core now is operating between J and K during the entire gating half cycle, the flux at J shows the core condition at the start of this half cycle; the core is saturated right from the start, so that the voltage across the load, as shown in Fig. 26-14*a* is nearly equal to the sine wave of supply voltage.

If now the direct current is increased in the control coil so as to produce about 2 A-turns that oppose the mmf of the ac winding, we say that the dc control mmf (acting during the RESET half cycle) can reset a portion of the core flux, so that, at the start of the next gating half cycle, the core flux has been lowered to point 2 on the magnetizing curve. During the early part P of

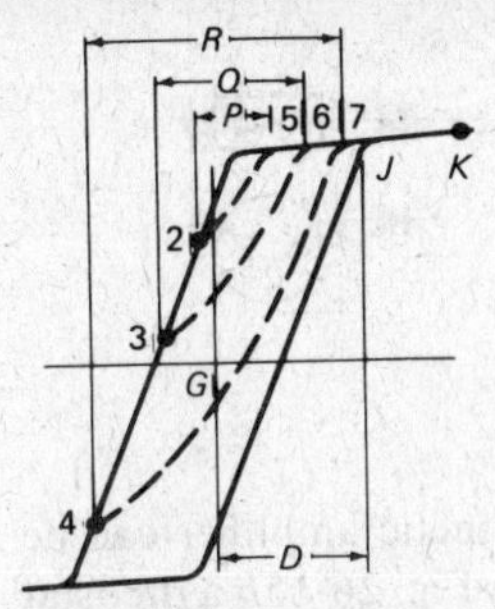

Figure 26-13 Dc ampere-turns reset the flux, varying the duration of flux change.

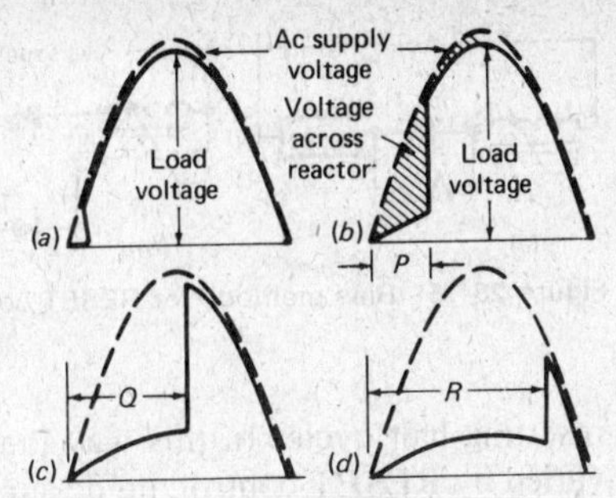

Figure 26-14 Load-voltage waveshapes are varied by amount of ampere-turns in Fig. 26-13.

the next gating half cycle, the flux changes along the dashed-line path from 2 to 5; therefore, during P in Fig. 26-14b, the core is not saturated; so the load voltage is very small. To the right of 5 the flux changes very little; so the core is saturated during the remainder of the half cycle, letting most of the supply voltage reach the load.

A further increase (to about 5 dc control ampere-turns in Fig. 26-8) may reset the core flux to point 3 in Fig. 26-13; thus the core is not saturated during the early portion Q of the following gating half cycle, as the flux increases from 3 to 6. The voltage across the load is very low during Q, in Fig. 26-14c; then suddenly it rises to full voltage for the rest of the half cycle. This voltage wave resembles a load voltage that is phase-controlled by an SCR as in Fig. 9-7.

A large increase (to 9 control ampere-turns in Fig. 26-8) resets the core flux to point 4 in Fig. 26-13. Now a major portion R elapses in the following half cycle, before the flux rises from 4 to 7; the core becomes saturated very late in the gating half cycle, so that only a small part of the supply voltage wave reaches the load, and the load current also is small.

26-11 RESET CONTROL

Above it is shown that the direct current in the control winding can reset part or all of the core flux during that half cycle when Rec 1 prevents the flow of current in the gate winding. If Rec 1 should permit considerable leakage current during this time, this reverse current flowing through the ac gate winding would tend to reset the core flux; thus we may realize that only high-quality diodes with negligible reverse or leakage current are suitable for use in a magnetic amplifier.

Leakage current in a diode flows as if through a large resistance R connected across the diode, as in Fig. 26-15a. By purposely decreasing the resistance of R, the reactor core can be driven out of saturation during each

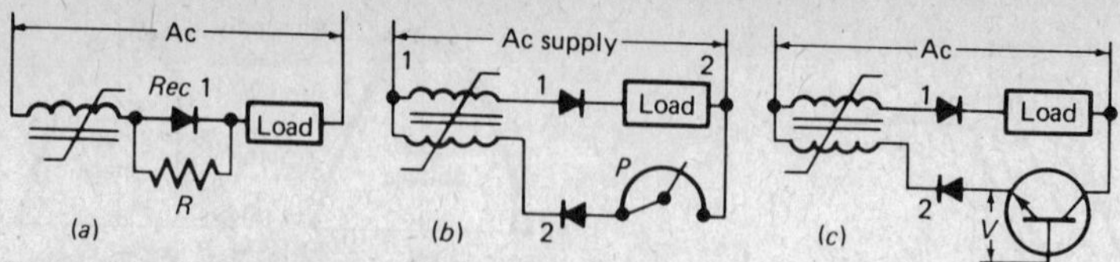

Figure 26-15 Bias methods for RESET control.

resetting half cycle. In this way the output of a magnetic amplifier can be varied by RESET control; no dc supply is needed. In Fig. 26-15*b* a rheostat *P* is in series with diode 2 and a control winding, connected across the ac supply; during the half cycle when terminal 2 is (+), the resistance of *P* determines how much current flows through the control winding to produce an mmf (ampere-turns) that tends to reset the core. In turn, this controls the point at which the core becomes saturated in the following gating half cycle.

Similarly, a transistor is used in Fig. 26-15*c* to vary the load current by means of RESET control. When signal voltage *V* raises the base potential of this NPN transistor, the increasing collector current produces mmf in the control winding so as to reset the core flux and decrease the average load current flowing in the next half cycle.

26-12 SPEED OF RESPONSE

Since a saturable reactor is an inductance by nature, it tries to delay any change of current within its windings. When we apply or change a signal at its input winding, the resulting change at the output or load may occur several cycles later. Figure 26-16*a* shows the result when the dc voltage across the control coil suddenly is decreased (for the magnetic amplifier of Fig. 26-6); the current and mmf of the control winding decrease more slowly. Several alternations or cycles of the ac supply occur before the amount of alternating current approaches its new final value. The rate of increase of load current (as shown by the dashed line or envelope that touches each current peak) is similar to the rise of voltage across a charging capacitor.[3-5]

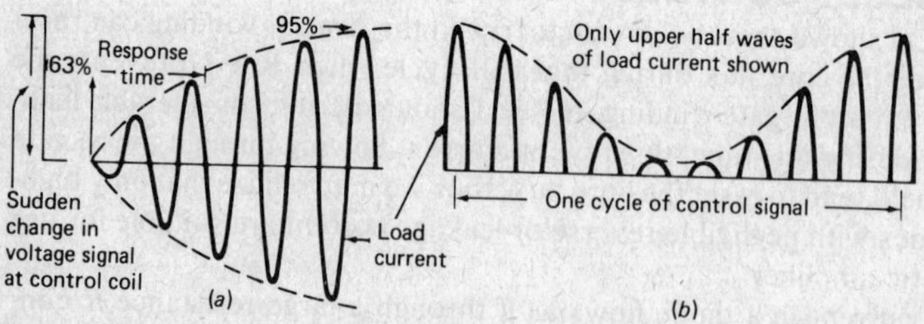

Figure 26-16 Magnetic-amplifier speed of response (*a*) to sudden change and (*b*) to cyclic change.

The response time of the reactor (as shown in Fig. 26-16) is stated as the number of cycles of the ac power supply that pass before the output rises to 63 percent of its final value. This 63 percent is mentioned in Sec. 3-4, and is used to measure the time constant of the reactor. To reach 95 percent of final value, three times as many cycles of ac supply must pass. [If RESET control is used, the current in each winding (in Fig. 26-15) changes within a half cycle; this amplifier responds in less than one cycle.]

The response of a saturable reactor requires a certain number of ac cycles, regardless of the applied ac frequency measured in hertz (or cycles per second). Thus if 5 cycles pass, in Fig. 26-16*a*, before the load current reaches 95 percent, this is a time lag of $^5/_{60}$, or 0.083 sec, if the circuit operates on 60-Hz power. However, if this same circuit is transferred to a 400-Hz supply (as is used in large aircraft), the time lag still is 5 cycles, but this now is $^5/_{400}$, or 0.012 sec; the operation or response is nearly 7 times as fast. Thus frequencies up to 2000 cycles per second commonly are used for magnetic amplifiers, to speed their response and to reduce the weight of the required core.

When the input to the control winding varies continually, as is shown in Fig. 26-16*b*, the frequency of this input-signal variation generally should not exceed one-eighth of the frequency of the ac power supply; on 60 cps, or 60 hertz, the signal might change 8 times per second.

Various means are used to speed further the response of the magnetic amplifier so that some such units can be made to respond within one cycle. The time lag is increased at the higher gain obtained by the use of positive feedback.

26-13 A PUSH-PULL MAGNETIC AMPLIFIER

Each magnetic amplifier described this far has no more than two gate windings; it can control its output current or voltage in only one direction or polarity. During a positive half cycle of the ac power, an ac load current can be controlled from a maximum positive value (with core saturated) to a minimum value that still is above zero. As such, each is called a *single-ended amplifier*.

Two such amplifiers (each complete with its two cores and all windings mentioned above) often are connected together in a push-pull arrangement (similar to the push-pull operation of transistors described in Sec. 6-3). So combined, they form one *double-ended amplifier* wherein a single control signal can be varied to cause an output of either polarity or phase relation; the output current can be adjusted to zero.

In Fig. 26-17 two single-ended amplifiers *G* and *H* are joined to form a push-pull circuit. By itself, amplifier *G* is connected at the left to the supply transformer *T* with center tap, in the same manner as in Fig. 26-11; its full-wave dc output voltage appears across R_1 at the right. Amplifier *H* also is

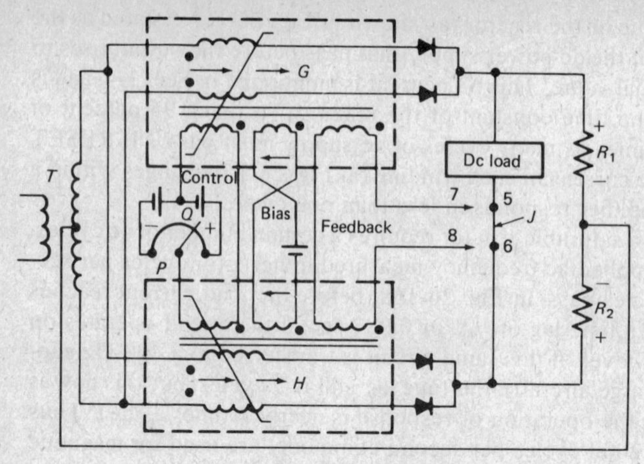

Figure 26-17 Push-pull magnetic amplifier with bias and feedback windings.

connected to T and produces its dc output across R_2. The resistance of R_1 equals the resistance of R_2 and is not much greater than the resistance of the load. When the current from amplifier G is equal to the current from H, the voltage drop across R_1 exactly opposes the voltage drop across R_2, so that zero voltage appears across the dc load, and the load current is zero.

Each amplifier is self-saturated and performs as shown in Fig. 26-8; no current flows in the feedback winding. However, the bias is adjusted to about 4 A-turns (instead of the 12 A-turns used in Fig. 26-9) so that each amplifier operates near point C; when the control-winding current is zero, the load current in each amplifier is 0.6 A, or about one-half of the greatest current it would have (if fully saturated) at E. Since the voltages across R_1 and R_2 in Fig. 26-17 change in proportion to these currents from G and H, half of the greatest voltage appears across each of these resistors so long as the control-winding current is zero.

The combined performance of the two amplifiers is shown in Fig. 26-18, where the curve of output current or voltage of amplifier G appears above the zero centerline; the corresponding curve for amplifier H is shown below zero (as if rotated through 180° into the opposite quadrant) because, in this push-pull circuit, the output current or voltage of H opposes that of G. The curve of resulting load current is obtained by subtracting the H curve from the G curve; thus, at point K, the height or output $KN = MN - NL$.

To adjust the current or the dc mmf (ampere-turns) of the control winding in Fig. 26-17, potentiometer P is used, connected across two equal batteries in series. When the slider of P touches at its center, its potential is the same as that of point Q above it; so no current flows in either control winding. With zero control mmf each amplifier operates at its point C in Fig. 26-18; thus the load receives no voltage and the load current is zero.

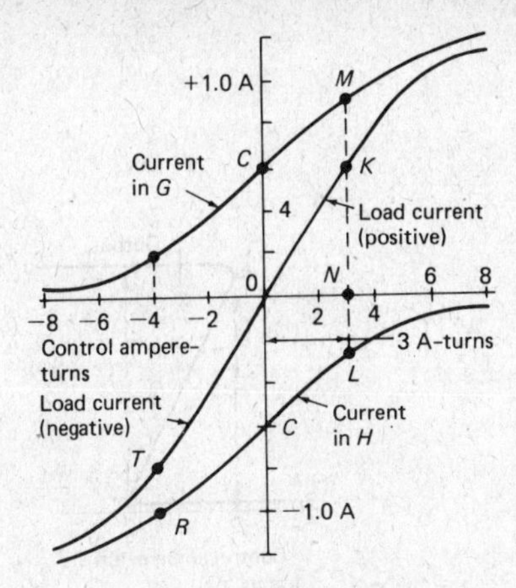

Figure 26-18 Load current can be reversed in push-pull magnetic amplifier of Fig. 26-17.

If P now is turned clockwise toward (+), both amplifiers are made to operate farther to the right (as at N in Fig. 26-18), where the control winding provides +3 A-turns. This signal current flows toward the right in the control winding of H, so that the output of amplifier H is decreased from C to L; the same signal current flows toward the left in G, so that the output at M now is greater than the (−) output at L, the dc load receives the output at K, so that the top of the load is (+) and conventional current flows downward through the load.

In contrast, if P is turned from its center position toward (−) in Fig. 26-17, a signal current flows toward the left in H, increasing the H output to a more negative value such as R in Fig. 26-18; this same signal, flowing toward the right in G, decreases the positive G output to S. The difference voltage, at T, is negative; the top of the load is more negative than the bottom, so that the load current flows upward.

Since the output curve, from T to K in Fig. 26-18, has twice the slope of the amplifier-G (S to M), we see that the gain of this double-ended or push-pull amplifier is twice the gain of amplifier G by itself. As a further advantage in push-pull, any fluctuation in ac supply voltage has little effect on the output; although a rise of ac voltage may increase the output of each amplifier, the change in G offsets the change in H so that no change appears at the load.

26-14 POSITIVE FEEDBACK TO CAUSE SWITCHING ACTION

For the push-pull amplifier described above and shown in Fig. 26-17, the output curve is shown again at $T-K$ in Fig. 26-19; here the feedback windings are not yet used. If wire J now is removed below the dc load (in Fig.

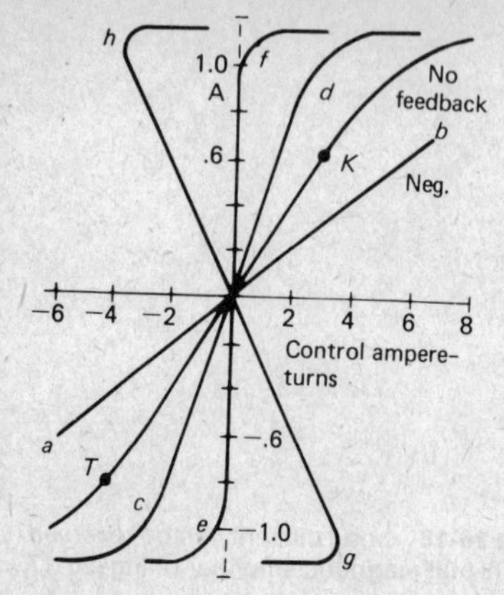

Figure 26-19 Feedback alters shape of curve of load versus control.

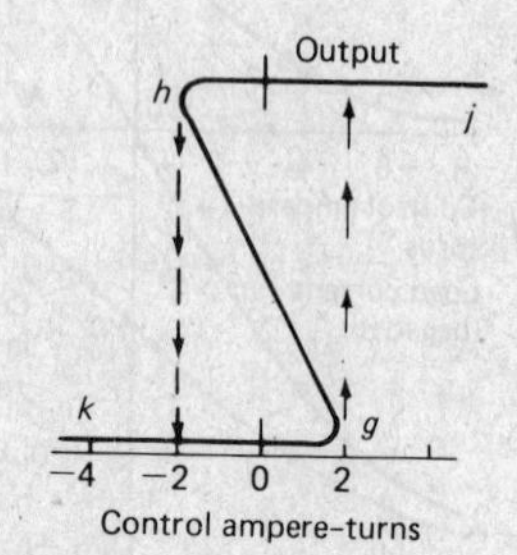

Figure 26-20 Positive feedback can provide snap action by a magnetic amplifier.

26-17) and this load current is passed instead through the feedback coils, line *ab* in Fig. 26-19 shows the effect of negative feedback, similar to the action in Fig. 26-12*a*; this lesser slope is desirable for linear control, greater stability, and faster response. However, if connections are made (5 to 7 and 6 to 8) so that the flux of the feedback winding on each amplifier assists the flux of its control winding, curve *cd* in Fig. 26-19 shows the steeper slope resulting from a few turns of positive feedback.

The number of positive feedback turns may be increased until the vertical curve *ef* results, showing an unstable and unpredictable condition; with zero control mmf, amplifier *G* may provide full output while *H* provides none [thus causing full (+) output and operation at *f*], or *H* may provide full output and *G* none [causing full (−) output and operation at *e*]. A further increase in positive feedback turns produces curve *gh*, which is seen to have a negative slope; this large amount of positive feedback gives the magnetic amplifier a snap action, so that it can act like a relay contact that is either closed (maximum output current) or open (minimum output).

The curve *gh* appears again in Fig. 26-20. If the signal winding supplies −4 A-turns, the amplifier operates at *k*; this may be used as zero output from a switching circuit, for the amplifier represents an open contact. If potentiometer 4*P* (in Fig. 26-17) gradually is turned clockwise, the control mmf decreases to zero and then increases to (+) values. At about +2 control A-turns, at *g* in Fig. 26-20, the amplifier suddenly snaps or switches up to the line *hj* (which is regarded as being full output), thus representing a closed contact. If *P* now is turned counterclockwise, the control mmf returns to zero and increases to (−) values; at *h* (−2 A-turns) the amplifier suddenly switches down to the line *kg*, again representing an open contact.

In many complex control equipments, we now may eliminate relays and many tubes by the substitution of magnetic amplifiers, thus producing "static control." Here each small plug-in unit may contain a push-pull magnetic amplifier, including cores with rectifiers, control and feedback windings, and multitap bias windings, for selection of the desired type of operation.

Problems

26-1 True or false? Explain why.

(a) A magnetic amplifier can use a magnetic circuit that has a core consisting entirely of air or wood.

(b) A steeper magnetization or B-H curve indicates greater inductance.

(c) A saturable-core reactor (without rectifiers) permits the same flow of ac through it if the dc is reversed in its control winding.

(d) A coil wound around a brass core retains the same inductance at all values of current in the coil.

(e) The magnetic amplifier has greater gain than the saturable reactor because the resetting action of the negative half wave is blocked.

(f) Between points B and C in Fig. 26-8, the current amplification is 100.

(g) The addition of a bias winding changes the available gain of a magnetic amplifier.

(h) A feedback magnetic amplifier uses no fewer than four windings in its reactor.

(i) If 1 mA flows in the dc control winding of a magnetic amplifier while its ac output is 1 A, this amplifier has a gain of 1000.

(j) A separate dc supply always is needed for control of a magnetic amplifier.

(k) Positive feedback can cause faster response in a magnetic amplifier.

(l) RESET control gives faster response than dc control.

(m) The ac load current in a single-ended magnetic amplifier can be controlled to zero value.

(n) RESET control can be used with double-ended amplifiers.

(o) Snap on-off action is provided by negative feedback.

27

AUTOMATIC CONTROL OF DC MOTORS

Many types of general-purpose electronic dc motor equipment have had years of useful service on machine tools and other industrial drives.

27-1 MOTOR CONTROL BY ONE SCR

For half-wave control of a $^3/_4$-hp dc motor, a single silicon controlled rectifier SCR is used at the upper right in Fig. 27-2, in a circuit provided by Reliance Electric and Engineering Company.

Single-phase ac power is supplied at the left in Fig. 27-2. When the START button picks up *M*, one *M* contact closes below the SCR. When the upper supply terminal 1 is positive, any pulse of current into gate *G* of SCR (as is explained in Sec. 27-2) permits conventional line current to flow through fuse *F*, selenium rectifier 4*SR*, SCR, contact *M*, and the motor armature. Thus a pulsing current and dc voltage (up to 75 V) are applied to the armature. As the motor speed rises, Fig. 27-1 shows that the motor armature produces a dc voltage of its own (called the *counter electromotive force*[21-5] or *back emf*): the amount of this motor voltage is a true and accurate measure of the motor speed. Although SCR may fire during the shaded half waves, current flows into the motor armature only while the shaded wave is higher (more positive) than the motor voltage. Meanwhile, the motor shunt field receives about 50 V dc and constant field current. Like the action described in Sec. 9-11, current flows from line 1 through 1*SR* and the field winding to line 2, thus storing energy in this inductive winding. During the next half cycle, when 1 *SR* prevents current from the line, the field winding produces a voltage [(+) at lower terminal 2] so that field current continues to flow, returning upward through 2*SR*.

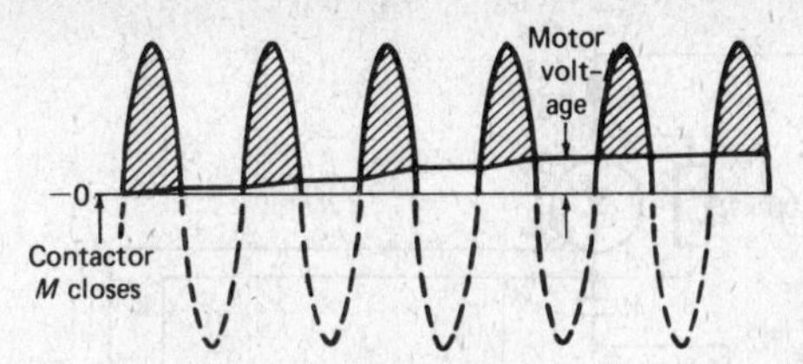

Figure 27-1 In Fig. 27-2, one SCR applies voltage (shaded) to cause armature current.

Connected between lines 1 and 2, the Thyrector[32-7] double diode provides further protection to the SCR by absorbing any sudden voltage spike, such as often is caused by the switching of contacts or by other circuit disturbances. This protector acts like two Zener diodes[7-18] connected in series back to back; any voltage surge momentarily greater than 300 V makes one of these diodes pass enough current to divert this surge away from the SCR.

When the STOP button drops out *M*, an *M* contact connects 2*R* across the armature, providing dynamic braking to stop the motor quickly.

27-2 SPEED VARIATION BY SCR CONTROL

Low in Fig. 27-2, transistor 1*Q* controls the UJT[8-7] (unijunction transistor) 2*Q*, which, through transformer 2*T*, furnishes the gate current needed to fire SCR. At the left, transformer 1*T* forces current through 6*SR* and 5*R* to charge 1*C* so that its lower terminal 9 is held steady at 20 volts below top terminal 6, which connects also to line 2 at the negative side of the motor armature. While speed selector 1*P* is being turned clockwise in Fig. 27-2, its slider is moved to a lower potential; acting through 10*R* and 12*R*, this drives more negative the N-type base of 1*Q* (in common-emitter connection, Fig. 5-9), thus increasing the collector current of this PNP transistor. This greater current flows through 15*R* to charge 4*C* more quickly; thus 1*Q* acts as a variable resistance (like R_3 in Fig. 9-8) that determines how quickly the voltage across capacitor 4*C* can raise emitter *E* of 2*Q* to the level where it fires SCR.

The SCR in Fig. 27-2 may be fired only once during each half cycle *A*, while line 1 is positive; the SCR continues to pass current to the motor armature during the rest of that half cycle. During the preceding half cycle *B* while 1 is negative, the lower terminal 9 of the 1*T* secondary winding is positive; so current flows upward through 8*SR*, 7*SR*, and 7*R*. At this time 8*SR* acts as a "clamp" across 4*C*; since the voltage drop across 8*SR* is very small while conducting, the voltage across 4*C* likewise is very small and is negative. Just as top line 1 rises above zero potential, at the start of each positive half cycle *A*, terminal 9 becomes negative so that 8*SR* no longer conducts; this removes the clamp from 4*C*, so that 4*C* begins to be charged by current through 15*R*, always at the start of each half cycle *A*. As the voltage across 4*C* increases, it raises emitter *E* of the UJT 2*Q*; just as *E* reaches a potential

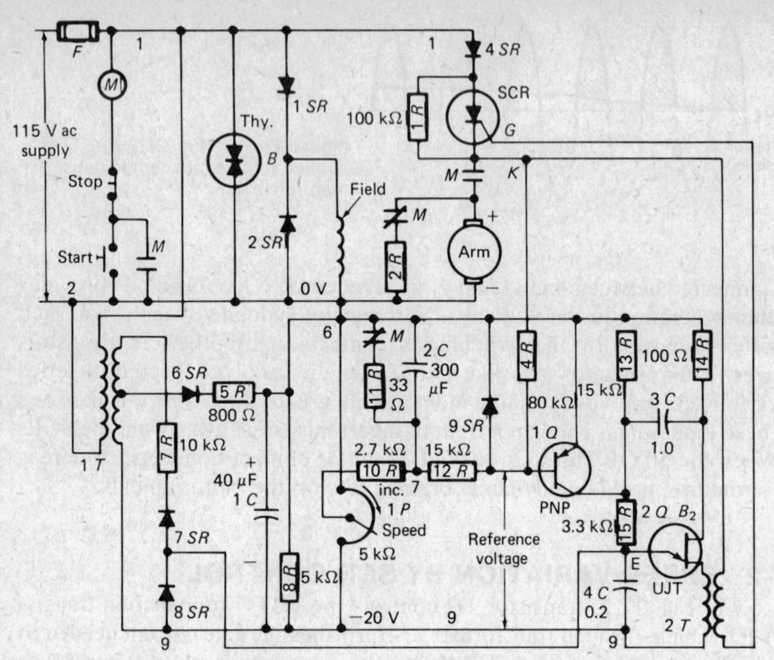

Figure 27-2 Circuit of SCR control for 3/4-hp motor. *(Reliance Electric and Engineering Company.)*

about 12 V above bottom line 9 (determined by the standoff ratio η of the UJT[8-7]), a small current flows in E and "triggers" the UJT. The internal resistance of the lower portion of UJT decreases abruptly, so that $4C$ discharges quickly through UJT and the primary winding of transformer $2T$; the $2T$ secondary winding produces a 4-volt pulse during less than 10 μsec, but this is enough to fire the SCR.

When $1P$ is set for low speed so that $1Q$ has very little collector current, $4C$ is charged slowly by the current through $13R$ and $15R$; as shown in Fig. 27-3a, the $4C$ voltage at E does not reach 12 V until near the end of half cycle A. The SCR is fired so late in half cycle A that the motor armature receives only a small wave of current. In contrast, when $1P$ is set for high speed, the larger collector current of $1Q$ charges $4C$ more rapidly, as shown in Fig. 27-3b; emitter E is raised to 12 V earlier in half cycle A, so that SCR is fired earlier, causing a much larger wave of armature current; thus the motor produces greater torque and runs at higher speed.

Whereas the potential at the $1P$ slider sets the desired speed, the base of $1Q$ receives also a signal from the motor-armature voltage, which is fed back through $4R$. With $1P$ turned clockwise, this lower potential turns on $1Q$, so that SCR is fired earlier. As the motor speed rises, the greater back

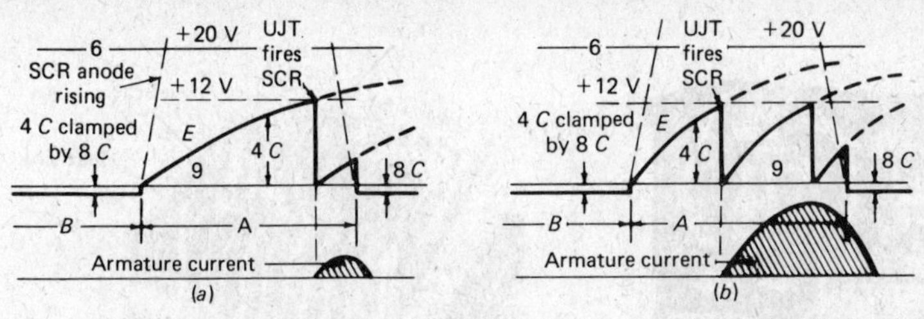

Figure 27-3 UJT fires SCR in Fig. 27-2 (*a*) late for low speed and (*b*) early for high speed.

voltage generated by the armature raises the potential at its upper terminal *K*; acting through 4*R*, this raises the potential of the base of 1*Q* so as to decrease the 1*Q* current and delay the firing of SCR until a balance is reached. (Too much rise of the base above the 1*Q* emitter is prevented by 9*SR*. Capacitor 3*C* prevents switching transients and ac voltage ripple from affecting the charging of 4*C* or causing unwanted triggering of 2*Q*.) This feedback circuit helps the motor to hold nearly constant speed, although its shaft load may change. Increased load tends to slow the motor; but lower speed decreases the voltage at *K*, so that the base of 1*Q* is lowered, thereby further turning on 1*Q*, and SCR fires earlier in its half cycle and supplies greater current so as to return the motor speed to normal.

Each time the motor is started, capacitor 2*C* (center of Fig. 27-2) provides that the motor speed shall rise slowly to the value selected by 1*P*. Before relay *M* is picked up, its normally closed contact discharges 2*C*; thus 2*C* terminal 7 and the base of 1*Q* are held more positive near line 6, so that 1*Q* has no collector current. When the START button makes *M* open its contact across 2*C*, terminal 7 gradually becomes more negative as 2*C* charges through 10*R* to the potential of the 1*P* slider. This gradual lowering of 7 and the 1*Q* base increases the collector current, thus raising slowly the average voltage applied through SCR to the motor armature.

27-3 HALF-WAVE STATOTROL DRIVE (3SRA71)

A General Electric equipment is shown in Fig. 27-4 for control of a $^3/_4$-hp dc motor, by the use of one silicon controlled rectifier (SCR). For this control, Fig. 27-5 resembles the diagram in Fig. 27-2, except that the SCR firing circuit is shown only as a block. All devices and connections in this block are molded within a plastic capsule or module for protection from dirt, moisture, and shock; the entire module can be replaced as a unit; so its internal circuit details are not disclosed.

The starting contactor *M* and the surge-protective Thyrector operate as described in Sec. 27-1; also, the SCR and diode 1*D* (for limiting PRV[4-10]) conduct current to the motor armature during only those half cycles when upper line 1 is more positive than line 2. Relay *OL* is for motor overload pro-

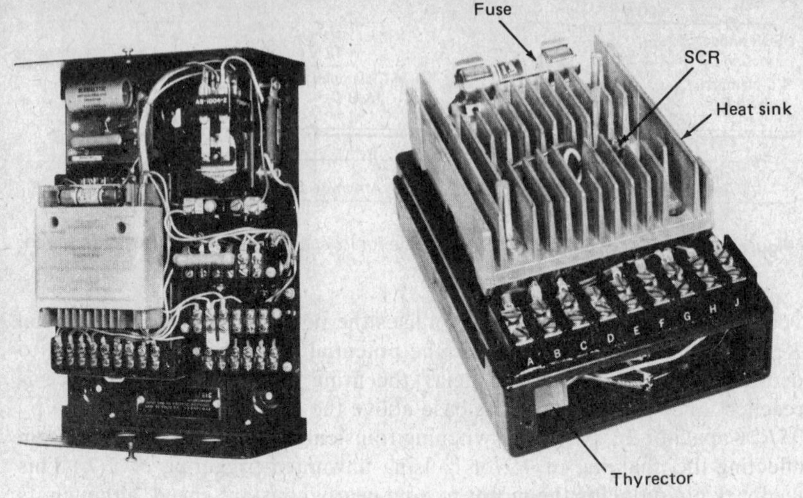

Figure 27-4 Half-wave GE Statotrol (and module) for 3/4-hp motor (3SRA71).

tection, while the fast-acting fuse *FU* protects the rectifier units. The motor shunt field is supplied by two diodes; diode 2*D* conducts field current from line 2 during those half cycles when the SCR cannot provide armature current from line 1; 3*D* lets the field inductance make current continue to flow when 2*D* disconnects the field from line 2.

In Fig. 27-5 the speed selector 1*P* is turned clockwise to raise the motor speed; the 1*P* slider 8 applies more positive potential to the firing circuit to fire SCR earlier in its half cycle. Thus SCR applies greater dc or average voltage and current to the rotating armature. Also, the amount of voltage between slider 8 and bottom line 2 serves as a reference voltage *RV* that indicates the speed desired. Meanwhile, as the motor speed increases, the armature generates greater back voltage or counter emf; the upper terminal of the armature becomes more positive, thus raising the potential of point 6, the cathode of SCR. This voltage between 6 and 2 (like that of a tachometer generator) is used as a feedback signal *FV*, which shows directly the motor speed obtained. (Similar speed regulation is described in Sec. 21-12.)

In the firing circuit the resulting speed *FV* is compared with the desired speed *RV*; any error or difference between *FV* and *RV* is used to adjust the firing point of the SCR within its half cycle. While 1*P* is being turned clockwise so that *RV* becomes greater than *FV*, the SCR is fired early to provide greater current to raise the motor speed. But when *FV* rises above *RV*, the SCR is fired later and provides so little average current that the motor coasts to a lower speed. The motor tries to run at a steady speed that makes *FV* about equal to *RV*. At a fixed setting of 1*P*, this circuit tends to hold constant motor speed, although the shaft load may change. When

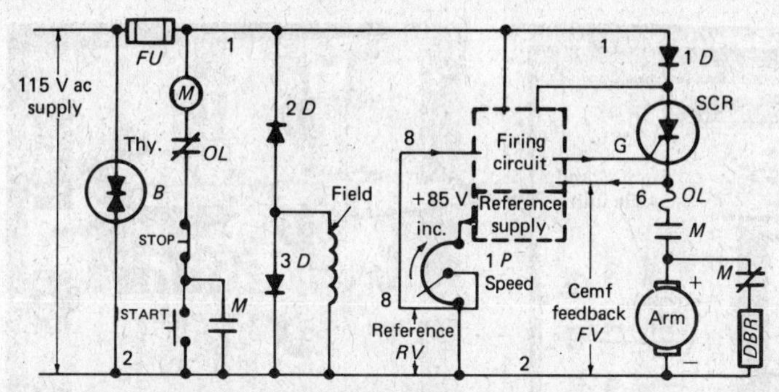

Figure 27-5 Circuit of General Electric SCR Statotrol drive.

greater load slows the motor, voltage *FV* becomes smaller; this fires SCR earlier, to increase the average voltage and current to the armature so that the motor speed returns nearer to its previous value.

Such automatic speed regulation is one form of servo action, described in the next chapter.

27-4 THREE-PHASE 20-HP SCR SPEED VARIATOR

Larger dc motors may receive power from a three-phase full-wave circuit that uses three controlled rectifiers (SCR) and three silicon diodes. Such equipment (5 to 20 hp at 230 V) is shown in Fig. 27-6, and its circuit is outlined in Fig. 27-7.

The rectifier circuit in the right-hand half of Fig. 27-7 is similar to the six-diode circuit of Fig. 22-7, if diodes *A*, *B*, and *C* are replaced by Re_1, Re_2, and Re_3, and diodes *D*, *E*, and *F* are replaced by the SCRs. After SCR_1 is fired by gate-pulse generator 1 (in the lower -left portion), conventional current flows from line 6 through Re_3 to the motor armature at the right; this current continues down through a smoothing reactor *X* and a dropping resistor *RS* to the bottom point 2, then up through SCR_1 to line 4. When pulse generator 2 fires SCR_2 one-third cycle later, current flows from line 4 through Re_1 and the motor armature, returning through SCR_2 to line 5. Again 120° later, current flows from line 5 through Re_2 and the armature, returning through SCR_3 to line 6. In this way the motor armature receives current that flows always in the same direction; the average amount of this current is controlled by varying the point in the ac wave at which each SCR is fired, similar to the phase-shifting action described in Sec. 22-10. Thus the motor speed is controlled by the turning of dials (like P_1 at the lower left) which control the gate-pulse generators, as described in the following section.

Meanwhile, rectifier Re_4 serves as a bypass across the motor so that any voltage, induced by a decreasing armature current, can force current through Re_4 instead of interfering with SCR operation.

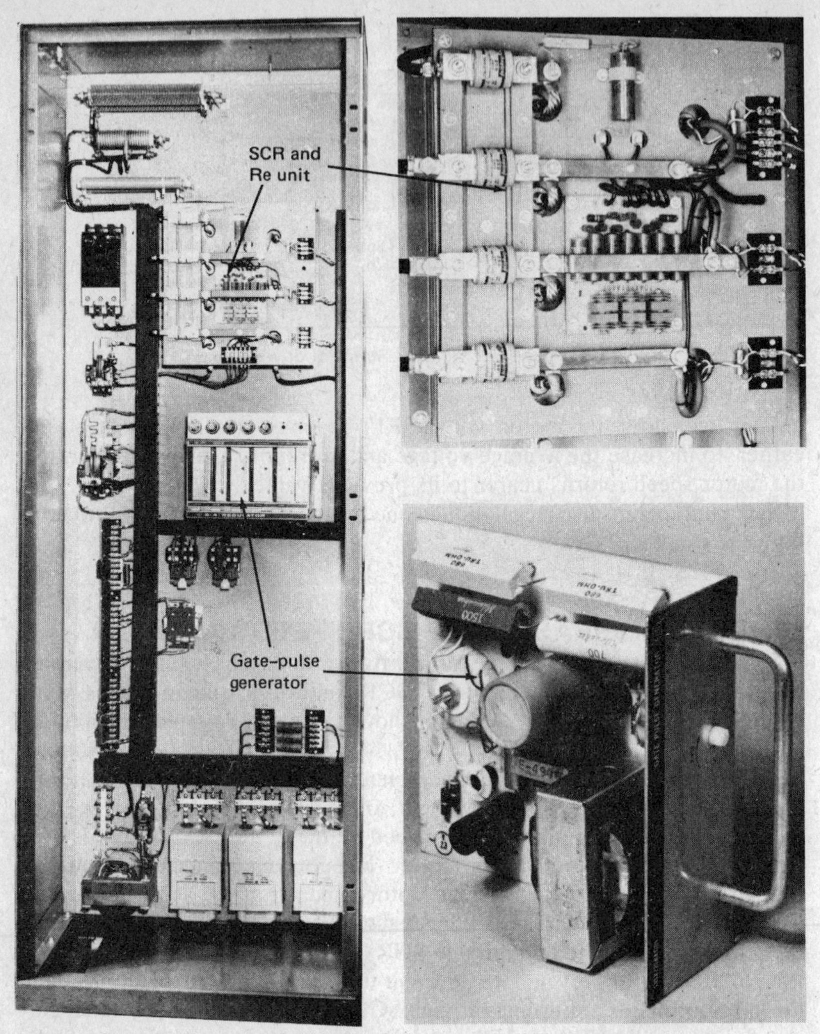

Figure 27-6 General Electric SCR power unit for 20-hp dc motor.

The shunt field of the motor receives 120 V dc from the voltage across Re_3, during the two-thirds cycle while lines 4 and 5 are more positive than 6. An M contact closes the armature circuit when the START button picks up relay I; this M contact opens to stop the motor if the voltage disappears from across the motor field winding.

27-5 GATE-PULSE GENERATOR

This circuit, shown at the lower left in Fig. 27-7, includes a magnetic amplifier SX which has control, feedback, bias, and gate windings; SX becomes saturated at the instant when SCR_1 is to be fired. Similar to the waveshapes shown in Fig. 26-4*c*, this instant of saturation can be varied by the speed adjuster P_1; the resulting current pulse through the SX gate winding turns on transistor Q so that capacitor C_3 discharges a pulse of current through gate G, to fire SCR_1.

Gate-pulse generator 1 receives 208 volts (V) from the ac lines 4 and 6. During the half cycle when line 4 is more positive so that diode D_1 cannot conduct, the upper point 7 falls nearly 100 V more negative than line 4, as shown at B in Fig. 27-8*a*; but when line 6 is more positive, D_1 holds 7 at the same potential as line 4. This half-wave B voltage forces current through P_2 to charge C_1 and apply nearly steady voltage to the bias winding of SX. As discussed in Secs. 26-5, 26-6, and 26-10, the bias mmf (adjusted by P_2) and the speed-control mmf (adjusted by P_1) together determine to what value the total SX flux is reset during each half cycle B; this determines what portion of the following half cycle A must elapse before SX suddenly becomes saturated. (With P_1 set for zero control mmf, P_2 is adjusted so that SX does not reach saturation until the extreme end of half cycle A; thus SCR_1 is not fired.) Until this saturation occurs, the gate winding of SX acts like an open circuit; meanwhile, observe other action in circuits near this gate winding.

The changes in voltage (between 7 and 4, as shown in Fig. 27-8*a*) pass easily through capacitor C_2 to the primary winding of transformer T, but the dc portion of this wave is blocked. The resulting waveshape of T secondary voltage is shown in Fig. 27-8*b*; the areas C and D are equal. During each C period, both secondary windings of T combine their voltages to force conventional current out of terminal 8 and through D_2 to charge capacitor C_3 to about 6 V; this current returns through R_3 and D_4 to terminal 9 of T.

If P_1 now is turned clockwise so as to increase the mmf in the SX control winding, this reactor becomes saturated earlier in half cycle A. At this instant of saturation, the SX gate winding acts like a switch that closes suddenly; thus the SX gate completes a circuit, so that current flows instantly from T terminal 8 through D_2, upward and from emitter to base in transistor Q_1 returning through the SX gate, R_2, and D_3 to terminal 10 of T. This emitter current turns on Q completely, so that its emitter-to-collector circuit connects capacitor C_3 to R_4 and gate G of SCR_1; this sharp current pulse fires SCR_1 immediately after SX is saturated.

But this turn-on current pulse in gate G should last no longer than 30°, even though C_3 has only partially discharged. To limit the length of this pulse of gate current, inductance L is connected from T terminal 8 to the base of Q; thus L provides a current path parallel to the path through D_2 and the emitter-to-base circuit of Q. At the instant when SX saturates, the sudden rise of current through the SX gate winding cannot pass at once through L,

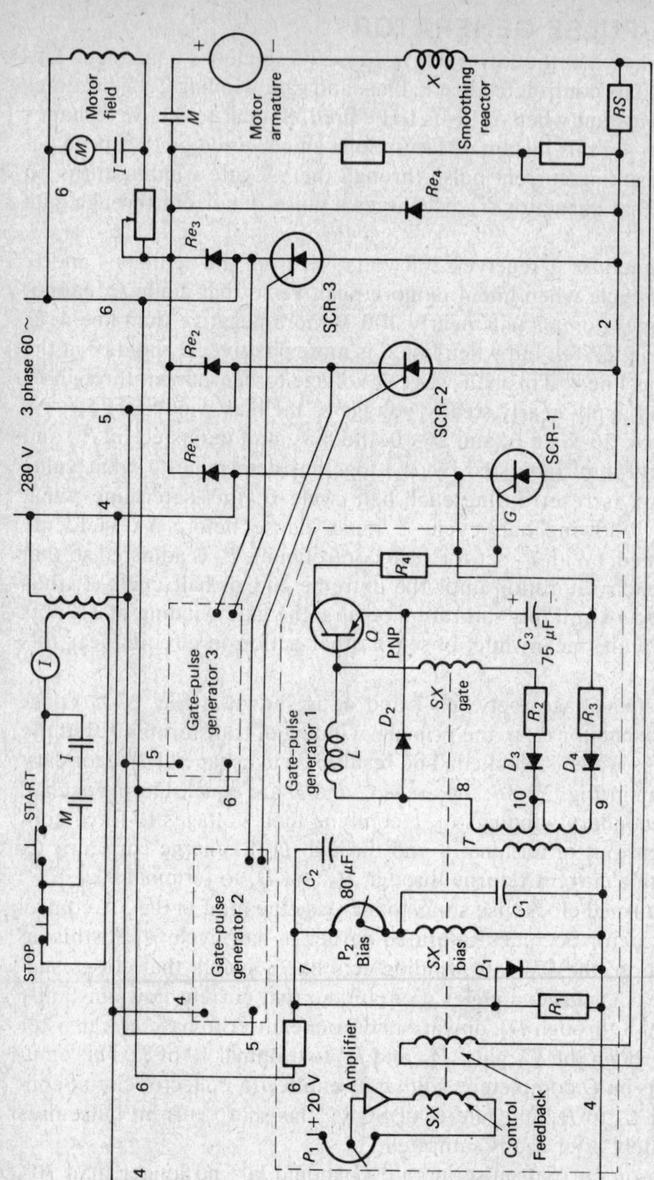

Figure 27-7 Partial circuit diagram of 20-hp SCR Speed Variator drive.

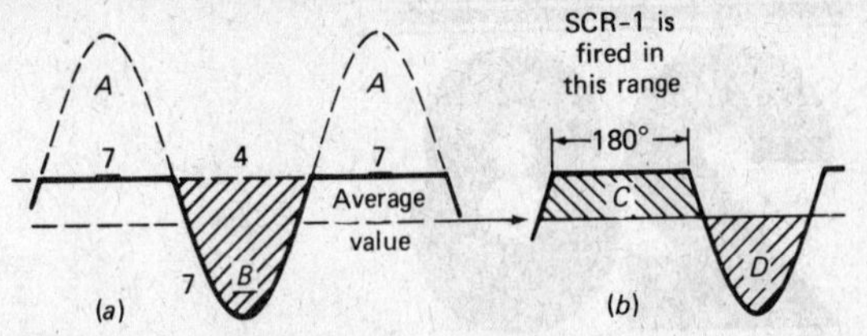

Figure 27-8 Waveshapes of voltage in gate-pulse generator.

since such inductance generates a voltage that opposes a sudden change of current through it: therefore the *SX* gate current must flow first through D_2 and *Q*. But the current through *L* increases steadily; after a millisecond, *L* no longer opposes current flow; so the current through the *SX* gate now passes through *L* rather than through *Q*. Since *Q* no longer receives emitter-to-base current, its collector current stops also, thus disconnecting C_3 and ending the pulse of gate current in SCR_1.

The feedback winding of *SX* furnishes mmf that corresponds to the voltage drop across resistor *RS*; thus it supplies a signal so that *SX* may be controlled also by the amount of motor-armature current.

A duplicate gate-pulse generator 2 provides similar control of SCR_2, but this occurs 120° later, because the input voltage from lines 4 to 5 lags 120° behind the 6-to-4 input voltage to generator 1.

28

CLOSED-LOOP SYSTEMS: SERVOMECHANISMS

The name "servomechanism" or "regulator" may describe a complete system that provides *automatic* control of an object or quantity as desired. Such a system may include many electrical, mechanical, or hydraulic devices; by their use, a person can control large power (or move a large object) with greater speed and accuracy than that person alone can provide. (While this chapter describes electrical control systems, including electronic amplifiers, the same basic ideas may apply also to hydraulic or mechanical systems.)

28-1 OPEN-LOOP AND CLOSED-LOOP SYSTEMS

Many controls start or stop the flow of power when a person touches a button; this turns on a light or starts a fan motor; these on-off controls are open-loop systems (also called "open-cycle" systems).

Perhaps a dial is turned to make the radio louder. Similarly, the voltage of a generator is adjusted by turning a rheostat until the voltmeter shows the desired value. When there is no device that automatically holds these quantities (radio sound or generator voltage) at the desired levels, these are open-loop systems. Only the sound or the voltmeter can show the operator whether the desired value is obtained.

Suppose that you are required to start your electric-refrigerator motor every 20 min, and you must then open the motor switch when a thermometer shows low enough temperature; such a system is not automatic and would be called an open-loop system. You may complete or close the control loop by adding the usual thermostat—a device that closes a contact to start a motor when the refrigerator box is too warm and that stops the motor when the box is cold enough. You adjust the thermostat for the desired temperature or *standard*. By responding to the actual temperature inside the box, the thermostat closes its contact if the box is warmer than the standard; when the box becomes cooler than the standard, the contact opens to stop the motor. Thus the thermostat feeds back a signal that regulates or holds the box temperature nearly constant; this is a closed-loop system.

28-2 REGULATORS AND SERVOMECHANISMS

Automatic regulators of quantities such as generator voltage, motor speed, water level, or room temperature are commonly used (see Chap. 21). Since 1940 there has been intense interest in servomechanisms; these are closed-loop systems that can control the mechanical movement of large units so that their *position* will follow or agree with the position of a director or control device. Examples include the gun directors on warships and aircraft, the automatic-tracking radar, the steering of ships, or the autopilots for planes. Similar servos now are used in industry in the automatic "follow-up" control of precision machine tools, the remote handling of dangerous materials, the "automation" of production lines.

Specifically, a *regulator* is a closed-loop system that holds a steady level or quantity (such as speed, voltage, current, pressure, or temperature); often it needs no moving parts. A *servomechanism* is a closed-loop system that moves or changes the position of the controlled object so that it will "follow up" or agree with the position of a control device or director (that may be smaller and at a distance); it includes a motor to cause such mechanical movement. The shorter term *servo* is commonly used to apply to any type of closed-loop system; in these chapters servo refers to regulators and servomechanisms alike.

In response to a "command" or signal input of low power level, it is expected that a servo will control a much greater amount of power—it amplifies finger pressure so as to move huge gun turrets. A good servo gives close "lineup" or high accuracy at standstill; it provides fast response when moving to a a new required position; it permits control of equipment from a remote position. By the nature of its self-checking action, it decreases the errors expected from any variation in the parts of which it is made. It is smooth in its action. It provides unattended control. It reduces the effects of any disturbances; thus, on ship or aircraft, the gun direction is held steady in spite of wind pressure or the roll and pitch of the craft.

To obtain high accuracy and fast response, servos require careful and precise design so as to prevent unstable operation—the violent oscillation or undesirable movement of the heavy controlled unit. The more accurate regulators may cause a bad variation of voltage or speed known as "hunting" unless "antihunt devices" are included in the design. Since any servo continually is exposed to outside disturbance, it is considered to be stable only if it is designed so that the effects of such disturbance quickly disappear.

Stability is the greatest problem in the design of a modern closed-loop system. Texts on this subject necessarily use higher mathematics to explain the rapid changes within the system, like those in Sec. 28-15. However, later chapters present general ideas of servo behavior by showing some of the graphic methods often used by engineers as they analyze or design a closed-loop system. It is hoped that this may encourage study in other texts, such as those listed below.[1]

[1] F. I. Barker and G. J. Wheeler, "Mathematics for Electronics," Addison-Wesley, Reading, Mass., 1968.
J. J. D'Azzo and C. H. Houpis, "Feedback Control System Analysis and Synthesis," 2d ed., McGraw-Hill, New York, 1966.
P. Dransfield, "Engineering Systems and Automatic Control," Prentice-Hall, Englewood Cliffs, N.J., 1968.
B. C. Kuo, "Automatic Control Systems," 2d ed., Prentice-Hall, Englewood Cliffs, N.J., 1967.
J. L. Melsa and D. G. Schultz, "Linear Control Systems," McGraw-Hill, New York, 1969.
F. H. Raven, "Automatic Control Engineering," 2d ed., McGraw-Hill New York, 1968.
C. J. Savant, "Basic Feedback Control System Design," 2d ed., McGraw-Hill, New York, 1964.

28-3 BASIC PARTS OF A SERVO

As is shown in the block diagram of Fig. 28-1, every closed-loop system contains the following devices or features: (1) a steady device giving an input signal R (often called the *command* or *reference input*) that sets the desired level or position the servo is asked to hold; (2) the controlled quantity C, which is the resulting level or position of the voltage, gun, etc., that is being controlled by this system; (3) a feedback path or element H (often merely two resistors acting as a voltage divider) to supply a feedback signal B that truly indicates the size or position of C; (4) an error-detecting device that receives the feedback signal B and compares it with the reference input signal R; any error or difference between B and R produces an output or actuating signal E; (5) control-system elements G that receive and amplify the actuating signal E so that larger external power is applied in order to restore C to the desired size or position.

Following the arrows in Fig. 28-1, the actuating signal E asks for a change in C; so E passes through G in a "forward" direction so as to control C; part of the result is fed through H until signal B reports the change back to the error-detecting device, thus completing a chain or loop of signals; this sequence produces the closed-loop system.

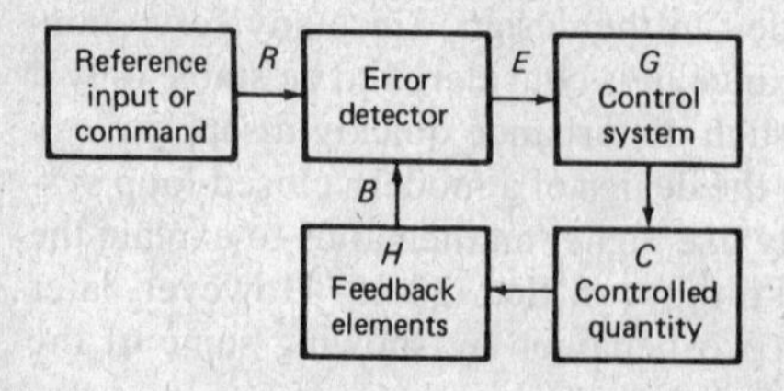

Figure 28-1 Parts of a closed-loop system.

28-4 AMPLIFIERS AND ERROR CORRECTORS

In a good servo, the control system G must include some form of amplifier, part of which usually is electronic. Any device that controls large power in response to a smaller power signal may serve as an amplifier. Some common devices used in this way are listed in Table 28-1.

The large power, controlled by the amplifier, is applied to an actuator or device that corrects the system error by causing the right change in the controlled quantity C. In a servomechanism, this error corrector must produce motion so as to change the position C; therefore, some form of motor or thrust device is indicated, as shown among error correctors in Table 28-1. In a regulator, the actuator or corrector may take the form of a furnace, an increased flow of electric current, or other sources of energy that do not necessarily involve motion.

28-5 ERROR DETECTORS AND TRANSDUCERS

Error detectors also are listed in Table 28-1; such a device must receive and compare *two* signals. When the transistor is so used, one signal is applied to its emitter and the other to its base; the resulting collector current is a measure of the error. (As an example, transistor Q of Fig. 21-13 detects the difference between the reference voltage RV and a fixed portion of the generator G armature voltage, across R_2. Here Q serves also as part of the amplifier.) A vacuum tube may be used in a similar manner.

A differential gear[28-15] compares the two speeds at its input shafts; its third shaft turns at a speed equal to the error or difference between the other two. Most electric bridge circuits are sensitive networks that compare two voltages; any difference between them is used as an error or actuating signal.

Some servos compare mechanical measurements such as speed or fluid pressure; the resulting error can be changed into a corresponding electric signal. A device that makes such a change is called a *transducer*. Many familiar devices act as transducers. A microphone converts sound into electricity; a phonograph pickup converts needle vibration into an electric signal. Similarly, a thermocouple[25-1] and a strain gage[32-8] change a temperature

TABLE 28-1

Error detectors	Amplifiers	Error correctors
Transistor or vacuum tube	Electronic device	Solenoid
Differential gear	Metal contact	Electric motor
Bimetal thermostat	Valve (fluid)	Hydraulic motor
Synchro (selsyn[32-5])	Electric relay	Steam or gas engine
Bridge circuits	Steam throttle	Piston or jet
Bellows	Electric generator	Oil burner
Reluctance motion pick-off	Saturable reactor	Water pressure

signal or a small movement into corresponding electric signals. A tachometer generator produces a voltage proportional to speed. A selsyn changes angular position into an output signal. A motor converts a voltage into torque or motion. An oscilloscope changes an electric signal into a visible pattern. A shaft may turn a potentiometer to produce a voltage related to the angle of shaft movement. All these are transducers.

28-6 COMPLETE SERVO DIAGRAM; LOOP GAIN

The basic parts described in Sec. 28-2 are shown again in Fig. 28-2, but here the control system G is divided into the parts just described. The external power supply passes through the amplifier to make the correcting device keep the controlled quantity C at the desired value. If the power applied to C is 90 times greater than the power contained in the actuating signal E, this becomes a "forward gain" of 90; we may call this gain by the letter K.

The feedback path H often includes a divider that reduces the feedback signal B to only a fraction of the voltage across C. In Fig. 28-2, if the voltage at B is $^1/_3$ of the voltage fed from C into H, this is a 3-to-1 *loss*, or a gain of 1 to 3; the feedback factor (called β, beta) is $^1/_3$. Therefore, the total gain all around the loop, from E to C and back to B, is equal to $K \times \beta$, or we say that the *open-loop gain* $=K\beta=90\times{}^1/_3=30$. The size of this loop gain determines the standstill or follow-up accuracy of the servo, as is discussed in Sec. 28-8.

Although the command or reference input R may be held constant, the servo still may need to give a correction to C, because a disturbance is introduced at N in Fig. 28-2. For example, a voltage regulator tries to hold constant output voltage C from a dc generator. If the load current of the generator increases, this is a disturbance that makes the generator produce less output voltage. This decreased voltage at C feeds back a similar decrease to B. Since B decreases while R remains constant, an error or actuating voltage is produced at E which (by acting through the control circuits G that increase the field current supplied to the generator) restores the output voltage C to very nearly its original value.

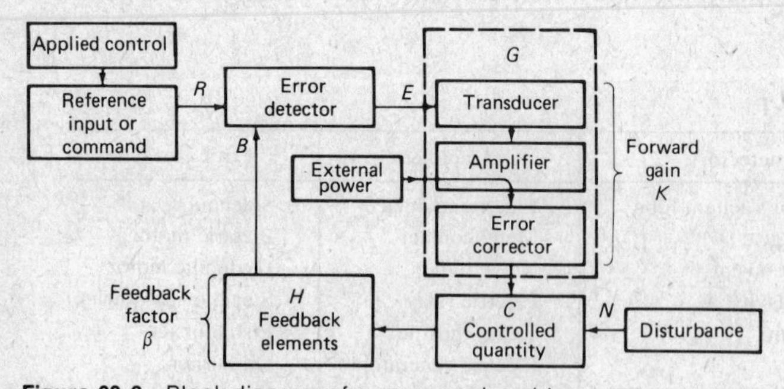

Figure 28-2 Block diagram of a servo or closed-loop system.

In the above example, the generator voltage C may have been 125 volts. An operator who wants to change this value to 115 volts turns a dial that decreases the value of the reference input R; this action is called "applied control." This reduces R below the value of feedback B; so an actuating voltage E is produced (but of opposite direction to that in the example above, so that the field current of the generator is decreased); this lowers the output voltage C to the new value of 115 V. At this lower value of C, the feedback B also is decreased until it nearly matches the new reduced value of R, so that the error E returns nearly to zero.

28-7 AN OIL-FURNACE TEMPERATURE REGULATOR

The oil furnace for heating the home is controlled as a closed-loop system; it aims to hold the room temperature close to the value set by the thermostat, regardless of changes in the weather. In Fig. 28-3, the thermostat is a bimetal strip that moves its lower contact clockwise when the room temperature rises. The arrow contact is adjusted for the desired temperature, say 70° F. When a disturbance (an open door or the usual heat loss through the walls) lowers the room temperature below 70°, the contact closes at this reference value R and lets a low voltage energize or pick up relay A. Here A acts as an amplifier, for its contact controls the larger power needed to run the motor. The motor in turn pumps the oil; the burner uses the heat energy of the oil (as an error-correcting device) to raise the room temperature. As the warmer air reaches the thermostat, its bimetal contact turns clockwise and (at perhaps 71°) moves away from the arrow contact; this stops the pump motor, but the burner continues to supply the stored heat remaining, perhaps causing the temperature to "overshoot" to 73°.

In this servo, the thermostat acts also as the error-detecting device; by its coiled position, it compares the room temperature with the desired value. When cool, its contact closes to give an actuating signal E to the amplifier relay A. Rising room temperature decreases the error so that the thermostat removes its E signal and A opens its contact. If lower temperature is desired during the night, the thermostat is reset by moving the arrow contact upward, thus lowering the temperature reference value R. The bimetal strip now may move farther upward (cooler) before it closes the contact that starts the furnace.

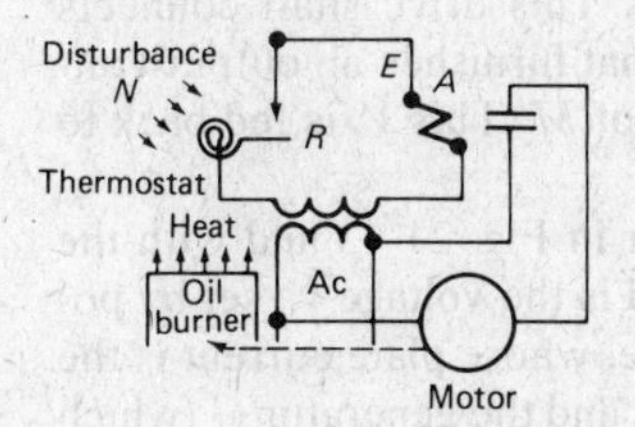

Figure 28-3 Home-heating regulator as a closed loop

28-8 STANDSTILL OR STATIC ACCURACY

Because they used lower amplification or gain, earlier closed-loop systems were less accurate than today's servos; also, they had less tendency to hunt or become unstable. Modern servos seek to provide closer lineup or standstill accuracy; therefore, they are designed with greater gain. They also use greater power so as to provide fast follow-up when a rapid change in position or value is needed; here the servo is designed to respond better to changes at high frequency, or the servo is said to have better frequency response.

In Sec. 28-6, the overall open-loop gain of a servo is expressed as $K\beta$. (This loop gain can be measured by disconnecting the feedback B from the error detector in Fig. 28-2. Now increase the size of the reference voltage R by a certain amount, say 0.1 V; by a suitable meter, measure the resulting *change* in the voltage fed back at B. If this B voltage changes by 3 V, the open-loop gain = 3V/0.1 V = 30 = $K\beta$.) For example, let this servo be the voltage regulator for a generator. If this regulator is disconnected so that the generator voltage C is adjusted only by hand, this voltage may drop, perhaps 5 V, when the load current is increased by 60 amperes (A). Suppose that this regulator now is returned to service; note what change in voltage C results from the same 60-A increase in load. If the overall open-loop gain of this regulator is $K\beta = 30$, it can be shown (as in Sec. 28-13) that the final change in voltage C now will be $1/(1 + 30)$, or $^1/_{31} \times 5$ V = 0.161 V. The regulator holds voltage C with only $^1/_{31}$ as much error; so the steady accuracy of the voltage C now is increased 31 times, since $31 \doteq 1 + K\beta$. A servo having open-loop gain = 300 provides about 10 times the standstill accuracy of a servo having $K\beta = 30$. The static or standstill accuracy is also called the *stiffness* of the servo.

28-9 SPEED-REGULATING SYSTEM

As a further example of a closed-loop system, Fig. 28-4 shows a regulator circuit which aims to hold constant the speed of a dc motor M, although the torque required by its load may vary. The field of M is separately excited, while its armature voltage V_a is supplied by generator G, driven at constant speed. The field current of G is controlled by the 6L6 beam tube, whose grid voltage depends on the 6J5 triode. At the left in Fig. 28-4, potentiometer P adjusts V_r, the amount of negative v_G of the 6J5 tube, and thereby sets the desired speed of motor M. The torque output of M drives the load, which requires a constant torque T_L. This drive shaft connects also to a tachometer generator (called a *tach*) that furnishes an output voltage V_t that is exactly proportional to the speed of M. This V_t is fed back to the 6J5 grid if switch S is in position B.

Compare this circuit with the speed regulator in Fig. 21-13 and with the servo block diagram in Fig. 28-2. The command is the voltage V_r set by potentiometer P. The error detector is the 6J5 tube, whose plate current is the error signal E. The amplifier includes both tubes and the generator G (which is an electromagnetic amplifier). The error corrector is the dc motor M; the controlled quantity is the speed of M and the load. The feedback element H is the tach generator, whose V_t is the feedback signal B. External power into the amplifier comes from the tube plate batteries and from the engine that drives generator G.

Let the disturbance be an increase in load torque that tends to reduce the speed of M. This reduces the output of the tach, which is so connected that this decrease in V_t lets the 6J5 grid become more negative. Less 6J5 plate current decreases the voltage drop across the 5-kilohm (kΩ) resistor, so that the 6L6 control grid becomes less negative; the current increases in the field of G. Greater voltage V_a is applied to motor M, so that its speed rises toward its original and desired value.

28-10 OPEN-LOOP ACTION

If switch S is moved up to position A in Fig. 28-4, the feedback signal V_t is not used; so this circuit acts as an open-loop system. Now, for a given setting of P, a constant voltage V_a is supplied to M. The speed-torque curves for motor M appear in Fig. 28-5; for each value of applied V_a, a slanting line shows that the motor rpm decreases if the load torque is increased.

Since M is a separately excited 1-hp 250-V 875-rpm dc motor, its rated full-load torque is 6 lb-ft, and is shown at point R on the 250-V line in Fig. 28-5. For purposes of this study, let the motor run at 680 rpm while it delivers rated torque to its load. At point X, we see that $V_a = 200$ V must be applied to motor M.

Now other circuit values may be determined when $V_a = 200$ V. First, certain factors are given, as follows. The tachometer generator delivers 0.15 V/rpm. The 6J5 tube (with $\mu = 20$, $r_p = 7500$, load $= 5$ kΩ) shows a gain of 8, assumed to be constant. Generator G produces 1.6 V for each milliampere in its field, or 1600 V/A. Since the current in the 1000-Ω field of generator G must be 200 V/1.6 V = 125 mA, this is also the 6L6 plate current.

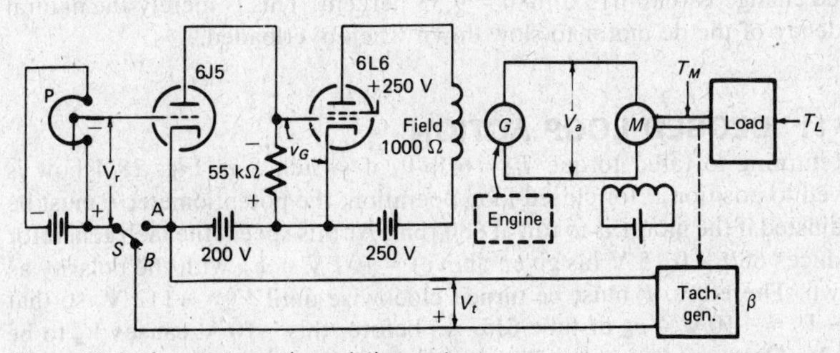

Figure 28-4 A motor-speed-regulating system.

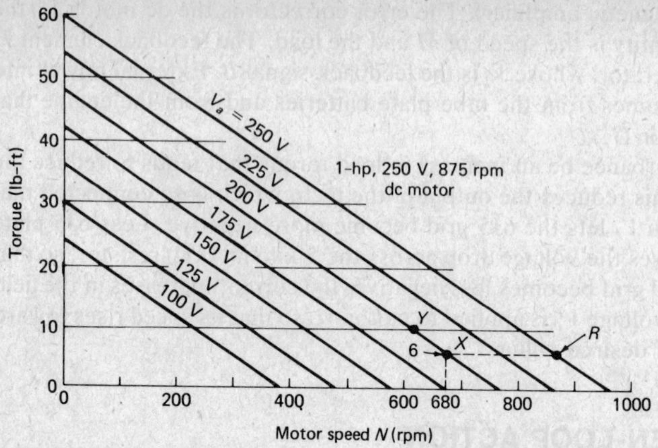

Figure 28-5 Speed-torque curves for motor M in Fig. 28-4.

From 6L6 curves, and using $V_{PP} = 250$ V and a 1000-Ω load line, we may see that 125 mA will flow when $v_G = -5$ V. Also (for later use), since the load line crosses $v_G = 0$ at 170 mA and crosses $v_G = -10$ V at 95 mA, a *change* of 10 V at the 6L6 grid causes a *change* of 75 mA; this tube performance is 7.5 mA output per volt input, or 0.0075 A/V.

To obtain $v_G = -5$ V at the 6L6 a current of 1 mA must flow through the 5-kΩ resistor; therefore, the 6J5 plate current = 1 mA. Using tube curves, with $V_{PP} = 200$ V and a 5-kΩ load line, the required $v_G = -10$ V. Therefore, for motor M to run at 680 rpm and deliver 6 lb-ft, potentiometer P must be adjusted so that $V_r = -10$ V, while switch S touches at A.

Now observe how an increased load torque affects the motor speed while the loop still is open. If T_L is raised to 10 lb-ft, the load change or $\Delta T_L = 4$ lb-ft. Since no change is made at the 6J5 grid, the generator V_a remains at 200 V. Figure 28-5 shows the new operating point at Y on the 200-V line, and the motor speed now is 615.2 rpm. So, for open-loop operation, the speed change is (680-615.2)/680 = 9.53 percent. This is merely the natural tendency of the dc motor to slow down when overloaded.

28-11 CLOSED-LOOP ACTION

Returning to rated torque $T_L = 6$ lb-ft, if switch S in Fig. 28-4 now is moved to position B for closed-loop operation, the potentiometer P must be readjusted if the motor is to run at 680 rpm. At this speed, the tach generator produces 680 × 0.15 V (as given above) = 102 V = V_t, with the polarity as shown. Therefore, P must be turned clockwise until $V_r = -112$ V, so that $V_r - V_t = -10\text{ V} = v_G$ of tube 6J5. As before, this −10 V causes V_a to be 200 V. Thus set, P is not to be moved; so V_r is constant.

In this section, the performance of the system in Fig. 28-4 is to be observed after a change of load has caused certain other changes throughout the system. The transient behavior before reaching this new steady state is not considered until Sec. 28-15.

Now if the load torque T_L is increased by ΔT_L, the resulting speed drop ΔN causes also a decrease ΔV_t. These changes are marked in Fig. 28-7, which is a block diagram for the circuit of Fig. 28-4. To determine the closed-loop regulator performance, values must be found for the blocks marked K_1, K_2, 1/D, and β. For each block, the value needed is Δ output/Δ input.

The input signal to the 6J5 is $\Delta V_r + \Delta V_t$; if P is not moved, $\Delta V_r = 0$. The gain of the entire amplifier block is marked K_1, which is $\Delta V_a/(\Delta V_r + \Delta V_t)$; therefore, K_1 includes the individual gains of each tube and of generator G, as given or determined in Sec. 28-10. So

$$K_1 = \underset{\substack{\uparrow \\ \text{6J5}}}{8} \times \underset{\substack{\uparrow \\ \text{6L6}}}{0.0075} \text{ A/V} \times \underset{\substack{\uparrow \\ \text{G}}}{1600} \text{ V/A} = 96$$

$$= \frac{\Delta V_a}{\Delta V_r + \Delta V_t} = K_1 \tag{1}$$

28-12 MOTOR PERFORMANCE

For Fig. 28-7, the values of blocks K_2 and $1/D$ can be found from the motor curves of Fig. 28-5. Here the symbol D refers to *viscous friction*, which may need explanation. In contrast to static friction and coulomb friction (during movement, but constant for all speeds), there is viscous friction, which increases in proportion to the speed. In servo work the term *viscous damping* may describe the natural behavior of a dc motor, whereby its net output torque decreases as its speed rises, as though a part of its developed torque is being consumed by overcoming internal viscous friction. To show this effect, the basic motor equations are recalled:[21-3]

Applied armature voltage $V_a = V_g + I_a R_a$.

Back emf V_g is proportional to flux ϕ and speed N(rpm).

Motor output torque T_M is proportional to ϕ and armature amperes I_a. The separately excited motor M in Fig. 28-4 has constant ϕ; so $V_g = K_N N$, where K_N is in volts generated per rpm. From the above,

$$I_a = \frac{V_a - K_N N}{R_a} \quad \text{or} \quad T_M = K_T \left(\frac{V_a}{R_a} - \frac{K_N N}{R_a} \right) \tag{2}$$

where K_T = lb-ft/ampere.

This output torque T_M also is T_L, the torque required by the load. In equation (2), $K_T V_a / R_a$ is a constant, called the *developed torque* T_d; this T_d is the value shown in Fig. 28-5, where each slanting V_a line crosses the vertical

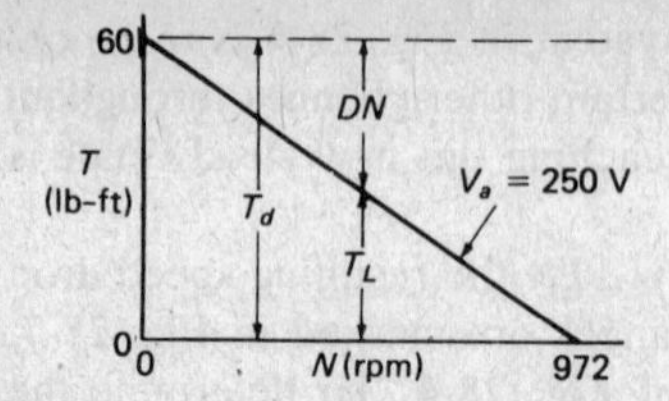

Figure 28-6 Load torque T_L shown as $T_d - DN$.

axis. Using the highest line, for $V_a = 250$ volts, we see that $T_d = 60$ lb-ft. But when $V_a = 0$, $T_a = 0$. Therefore, K_2, which is

$$\frac{\Delta T_d}{\Delta V_a} = \frac{60 \text{ lb-ft}}{250 \text{ V}} = 0.24 \text{ lb-ft/volt} = K_2 \tag{3}$$

In equation (2) the second term $K_T K_N N / R_a$ is a torque that is proportional to speed and is called DN. On this basis $T_L = T_d - DN$, as is sketched in Fig. 28-6. So

$$N = \frac{T_d - T_L}{D} \tag{4}$$

Since D is the slope of each motor speed-torque line in Fig. 28-5, the value of $D = 60$ lb-ft/972 rpm. Therefore

$$\frac{1}{D} = \frac{\Delta N}{\Delta T_d} = \frac{972}{-60} = -16.2 \text{ rpm/lb-ft} \tag{5}$$

Here the minus sign shows that a torque increase causes a speed decrease. The motor characteristics are responsible for both K_2 and $1/D$; yet Fig. 28-7 locates $1/D$ in the block marked "load"; here any viscous friction of the driven load may be combined with the motor viscous damping D, which acts like a load that slows the motor as torque T_L increases.

The feedback factor β is the performance of the tach generator, which was given earlier as 0.15 V/rpm. So

$$\beta = \frac{\Delta V_t}{\Delta N} = 0.15 \text{ V/rpm} \tag{6}$$

28-13 LOOP GAIN AND SPEED CHANGE

For any servo the *forward gain* K includes the gains of all those parts between the reference input and the controlled quantity. Figure 28-7 shows that

$$K = K_1 \times K_2 \times \frac{1}{D} = 96 \times 0.24 \frac{\text{lb-ft}}{\text{V}} \times (-16.2) \frac{\text{rpm}}{\text{lb-ft}} = -373 \text{ rpm}$$

per volt of change at the 6J5 grid. For the entire system, the *open-loop gain* is

$$K\beta = \frac{K_1K_2\beta}{D} = -373\frac{\text{rpm}}{\text{V}} \times 0.15\frac{\text{V}}{\text{rpm}} = -56 \tag{7}$$

This value of $K\beta$ can be found experimentally as follows. (*a*) In Fig. 28-4 switch S is thrown to position A for open-loop operation; (*b*) P is moved to more negative potential so as to cause a change ΔV_r; (*c*) the resulting positive change ΔV_t is measured; (*d*) then open-loop gain $K\beta = \Delta V_t/\Delta V_r$.

From the value of motor speed N as given in equation (4), the change in speed

$$\Delta N = \frac{\Delta T_d - \Delta T_L}{D} \tag{8}$$

This equation may be expressed in terms of open-loop gain $K\beta$ by the following steps:

(*a*) If V_r is not varied in Fig. 28-7, then

$$K_1K_2\beta = \frac{\Delta V_a}{\Delta V_t} \times \frac{\Delta T_d}{\Delta V_a} \times \frac{\Delta V_t}{\Delta N} = \frac{\Delta T_d}{\Delta N}$$

So
$$\Delta T_d = K_1K_2\beta\Delta N$$

(*b*) From (8)

$$D\,\Delta N = K_1K_2\beta\,\Delta N - \Delta T_L \qquad \text{or} \qquad D = K_1K_2\beta - \frac{\Delta T_L}{\Delta N}$$

(*c*) Since $\Delta T_L/\Delta N = K_1K_2\beta - D$, then

$$\Delta N = \frac{\Delta T_L}{K_1K_2\beta - D} = \frac{-\Delta T_L}{D - K_1K_2\beta}$$

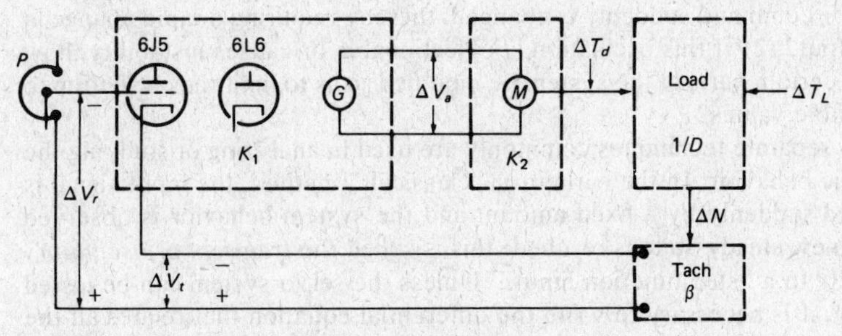

Figure 28-7 Block diagram for servo system of Fig. 28-4.

(d) Dividing each quantity by D,

$$\Delta N = -\frac{(1/D)\ \Delta T_L}{1 - K_1K_2\beta/D} \quad \text{or} \quad \Delta N = -\frac{(1/D)\ \Delta T_L}{1 - K\beta} \tag{9}$$

Substituting the values from the system of Fig. 28-4,

$$\Delta N = -\frac{(-16.2) \times 4}{1 - (-56)} = 1.14 \text{ rpm}$$

The closed-loop speed change is 1.14/680 = 0.167 percent. In comparison, it is shown in Sec. 28-10 that the open-loop speed change is 64.8 rpm (as obtained from the geometry of Fig. 28-5). Now 64.8 rpm/1.14 rpm = 57, which is equal to 1−(−56), or $1 - K\beta$. So we see that

$$\Delta N \text{ (closed loop)} = \frac{1}{1 - K\beta} \times \Delta N \text{ (open loop)}$$

So, if loop gain $K\beta = -56$, the closed-loop regulator restricts the speed variation to 1/57 of the open-loop speed variation. (A similar ratio was obtained for a voltage regulator in Sec. 28-8.)

In the above study of the static characteristics of the closed-loop system, it seems desirable to use very high amplifier gain so as to decrease the effect of a load disturbance. From an earlier course the student may recall that similar results are obtained in a negative-feedback amplifier. Moreover, there is a practical limit to the gain that may be used since, at certain signal frequencies, the feedback amplifier can become an oscillator. That is, the phase of the feedback signal may become shifted until the amplifier has positive feedback and becomes unstable, or oscillates. In a similar way, a closed-loop servo system may become unstable when the feedback signal $K\beta$ has sufficient size and phase shift, as is discussed in Sec. 29-3.

28-14 DYNAMIC RESPONSE

To study the dynamic behavior of any automatic system or servo, certain questions are: (1) To what extent does the system oscillate when the input signal or command suddenly is changed, thereby requiring a rapid change in the output? (2) If this oscillation is objectionable or causes instability, how should certain parts of the system be modified so as to limit the oscillation to acceptable values?

Two separate techniques commonly are used in analyzing or studying the dynamic behavior. In the earlier, or "classical," method, the input signal is changed suddenly by a fixed amount and the system behavior is observed until a new steady state is reached; this is called the *transient* or *oscillatory response* to a "step function input." Unless the servo system can be tested directly, it is necessary to write the differential equation that relates all the motions or forces that occur in the whole system. After solving this equation to determine its roots, certain facts regarding the transient behavior of the system are known or can be foreseen; these data may be plotted to determine whether the system is stable. Since most closed-loop systems involve differential equations of third or higher degree, the solution is difficult; here the Laplace transform commonly is used to facilitate a solution and to obtain the roots. Further information may be gained from these root values by a procedure called the *root-locus method*, described in Chap. 30.

In the second kind of study of dynamic behavior, a sine-wave command or signal of fixed size is applied at the input; a corresponding wave is fed back after passing through the system. The size and phase lag of this feedback wave are recorded while the frequency of the input signal is varied through a wide range. This is called the *frequency-response method*. Since tests of an existing system seldom can be made, the proposed system is expressed in equation form; this involves the use of "transfer functions."[29-4] If the size and phase angle of the feedback signal are plotted in polar coordinates on the complex plane, this is part of the Nyquist approach to the stability study.[29-6] However, if these data are plotted instead on rectangular logarithmic coordinates (decibel gain versus log frequency), this forms a Bode diagram.[29-11]

The student should be familiar with all methods mentioned above. In practice, engineers may use the Bode diagram in early trial stages of system design. Later they may make the more laborious Nyquist plot within a certain frequency range of interest, or may make a root-locus plot. The final results may be confirmed by solution of the diffential equation and a plot of its roots.

28-15 TRANSIENT RESPONSE

The first of the above methods next is discussed: the transient response of a simple servo. This section also describes natural frequency ω_n and damping ratio ζ and percent overshoot, to be used in Chap. 29.

Similar to the servo block diagram of Fig. 28-2, a rotating system is shown in Fig. 28-9, wherein a motor is made to turn a load until its angular position matches that of a handwheel. (This control of a position identifies this servomechanism as a type-1 servo, as discussed in Sec. 29-9.)

A differential gear is used as the error detector. This differential resembles the gear that drives two wheels of an automobile by a single engine shaft; however, this servo differential has two input shafts R and B and only one output shaft E, as shown in Fig. 28-8. When R and B turn in the same direction at identical speeds, shaft E does not turn, as next explained. Identical spur gears 6 and 7 merely turn shaft C in a direction opposite to shaft B. On suitable bearings, shaft C passes through frame F; shaft R passes through gear 4, which is solidly connected to F. Shafts R and C turn identical bevel gears 1 and 2 so that the gear teeth at G move toward you as fast as the teeth at H move from you; therefore, gear 3 merely idles on its shaft D, turning in a bearing mounted on frame F, which now does not move.

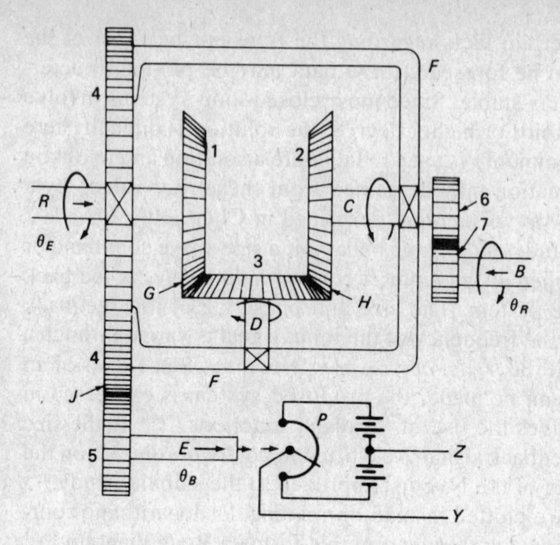

Figure 28-8 A differential gear.

If θ_R is made greater than θ_B so that shaft R turns faster than shaft C, the teeth at G move faster than the teeth at H; this forces shaft D to move toward you, thus turning the entire frame F and gear 4 about the RC axis. Gear teeth at J move toward you, turning gear 5 and the output or error shaft E so as to rotate potentiometer P clockwise, making terminal Y more negative than Z.

When θ_R is less than θ_B, the teeth at H move faster than those at G; sc shaft D and the teeth at J move away from you, turning shaft E and P so that Y is more positive than Z.

In Fig. 28-9, if the angular displacement θ_B, fed back by the motor-driven load shaft, is equal to the angular displacement or command θ_R as set by the handwheel, no movement or displacement θ_E occurs at the error shaft.

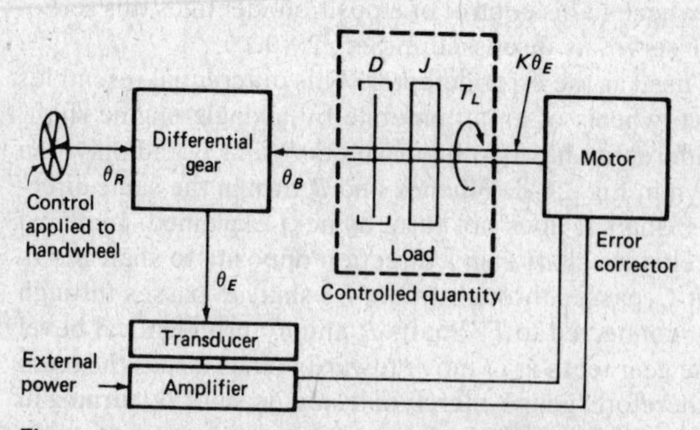

Figure 28-9 Type-1 servo that controls angular position of load.

Any difference between θ_R and θ_B turns the error shaft and changes θ_E so that the motor is made to turn in the right direction to make θ_B line up with θ_R; thus $\theta_E = \theta_R - \theta_B$.

The load to be overcome or turned by the motor consists of D, J, and T_L, where D = damping torque due to viscous friction,[28-12] in pound-feet per radian per second at the motor-driven shaft; J = inertia of load and motor, in slug-ft^2; T_L = coulomb friction at the motor-driven shaft, in lb-ft, independent of speed.

Since the error θ_E is amplified, then converted into torque by the motor, let K represent this entire gain, in pound-feet produced by the motor for each radian of displacement θ_E.

When time $t = 0$, if the handwheel suddenly is turned through a given angle A, the motor cannot change θ_B instantly, because of J and D. Therefore, the error shaft moves through angle θ_E and the motor applies to the load a torque $= K\theta_E$.

$$K\theta_E = J\frac{d^2\theta_B}{dt^2} + D\frac{d\theta_B}{dt} + T_L \tag{10}$$

This equation involves the movement of two shafts θ_E and θ_B; but θ_B can be expressed in terms of θ_E, as shown next.

Since A is a known or constant displacement, and $\theta_B = A - \theta_E$, therefore

$$\frac{d\theta_B}{dt} = 0 - \frac{d\theta_E}{dt} \quad \text{and} \quad \frac{d^2\theta_B}{dt^2} = 0 - \frac{d^2\theta_E}{dt^2} \quad \text{when } t > 0$$

Substituting, equation (10) becomes

$$J\frac{d^2\theta_E}{dt^2} + D\frac{d\theta_E}{dt} + K\theta_E = T_L \tag{11}$$

This is a second-order differential equation, and Fig. 28-9 shows a second-order system.

The solution for θ_E contains a steady-state part and also a transient part. After a long enough time, the transient part becomes very small (and the derivative terms become zero), so that steady-state error

$$\theta_E = \frac{T_L}{K} \tag{12}$$

Note that little steady-state error can exist if the load torque T_L is very small, and that the error approaches zero if the gain K is made very large.

To find the transient error, the equation

$$J\frac{d^2\theta_E}{dt^2} + D\frac{d\theta_E}{dt} + K\theta_E = 0$$

is solved by means of the auxiliary equation $Js^2 + Ds + K = 0$, where s represents $d\theta/dt$ and s^2 shows the second derivative. By use of the quadratic formula, the roots

$$s = \frac{-D \pm \sqrt{D^2 - 4JK}}{2J}$$

or

$$s = -\frac{D}{2J} \pm \sqrt{\frac{D^2}{4J^2} - \frac{K}{J}} \tag{13}$$

This transient error may include a sinusoidal oscillation that tends to die out at a rate set by the size of the first term, $D/2J$. So long as oscillations continue, their angular frequency ω(in rad / sec) is set by the value of the radical

$$\sqrt{\frac{D^2}{4J^2} - \frac{K}{J}}$$

If the viscous damping torque D is zero, the system continues to oscillate indefinitely, at the natural frequency

$$\omega_n = \sqrt{\frac{K}{J}} \tag{14}$$

As the damping torque D is increased, the oscillations die out more quickly; when D is made so large that $D^2/4J^2 = K/J$, the radical in equation (13) becomes zero and all oscillation disappears. At this value of D we say the system is critically damped, and

$$D_{\text{crit}} = 2\sqrt{KJ}$$

From this comes the term *damping ratio* ζ (zeta), which is the ratio of the actual system damping D to the critical damping, or

$$\zeta = \frac{D}{2\sqrt{KJ}} \tag{15}$$

In terms of these values for ζ and ω_n, a set of curves can be plotted for this system, as in Fig. 28-10, showing how the time length of oscillation decreases as the damping ratio ζ is increased. Here the input signal θ_R suddenly is changed from zero to a new value of -1.0 (a unit step function or an initial error = 1) and the resulting error finally decreases to zero for all values of ζ greater than zero. [Any underdamped system (or ζ less than 1.0) tends to travel beyond the final position of zero error; Fig. 28-10 shows 72 percent overshoot if ζ is 0.1. Similarly, a ζ of 0.4 is chosen to limit overshoot to 25 percent.] Although critical damping provides the fastest approach to *zero* error, a damping ratio of $\zeta = 0.7$ or 0.5 may reduce the error more quickly to within a specified useful tolerance, such as ± 10 percent. The time required for the error to decrease and remain within this tolerance is called the *settling time*.

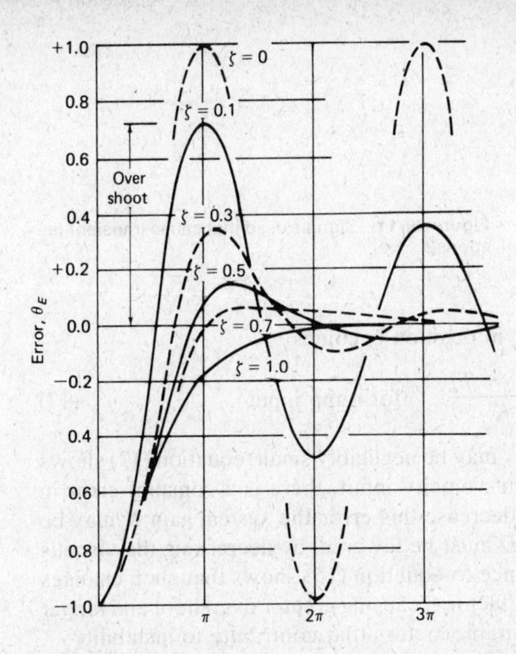

Figure 28-10 Transient response of positional servo to initial step input.

28-16 RESPONSE TO CONSTANT-VELOCITY SIGNAL

In addition to using the step function input described in Sec. 28-14, it is common practice to observe how a servo may respond to an input signal that changes at a constant rate. The upper part of Fig. 28-11 shows the "step function" change of input signal θ_R, while below is shown the constant change of θ_R with time. From its up-slope comes the term "ramp input"; since here $d\theta_R/dt$ is constant ($t>0$), this is also a constant-velocity input signal $= \Omega_R$.

For a ramp input, equation (10) still describes the system operation. The differential gear operates so that the velocities of its shafts are related by $\omega_E = \omega_R - \omega_B$. But since the input signal is a known constant velocity, and $d\theta_B/dt = \Omega_R - d\theta_E/dt$, then

$$\frac{d^2\theta_B}{dt^2} = 0 - \frac{d^2\theta_E}{dt^2}$$

Substituting in equation (10), the system equation becomes

$$J\frac{d^2\theta_E}{dt^2} + D\frac{d\theta_E}{dt} + K\theta_E = D\Omega_R + T_L \tag{16}$$

The final steady-state velocity of the load shaft will equal the input signal velocity Ω_R; so the final $d\theta_E/dt = 0$, and the error shaft stops turning. How-

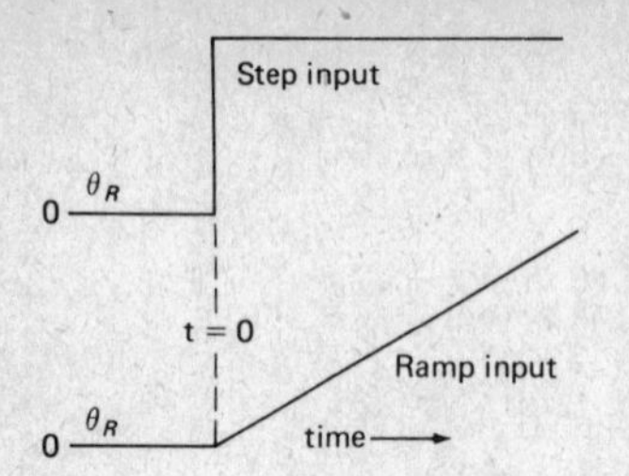

Figure 28-11 Signals used that cause transient response.

ever, at steady state the error in position becomes

$$\theta_E = \frac{D\Omega_R + T_L}{K} \qquad \text{for ramp input} \tag{17}$$

Even though the load torque T_L may be negligibly small, equation (17) shows that, during a ramp or constant-velocity input, there is a constant error in position equal to $D\Omega_R/K$. To decrease this error the system gain K may be raised or the damping torque D must be lowered, by decreasing the viscous or running friction. But reference to equation (15) shows that such changes also will decrease the damping factor ζ, causing greater overshoot and longer settling time, which are undesirable factors that contribute to instability.

28-17 USE OF ERROR-RATE CONTROL

The above difficulty can be solved so as to keep low positional error and also low overshoot by adding into the servo system a circuit or element that produces a signal proportional to the rate of change of the error. In Fig. 28-12 a second transducer is added (to the original system of Fig. 28-9) so that the electrical signal into the amplifier includes the original voltage V_1 proportional to position θ_E, and also a new voltage V_2 proportional to the rate of change of θ_E. Therefore, the motor delivers both its original torque $K\theta_E$ and another torque $M(d\theta_E/dt)$. If both of these torques now are included in the left-hand side of equation (10) and substitutions are made similar to those for equation (16), the result is

$$J\frac{d^2\theta_E}{dt^2} + (D + M)\frac{d\theta_E}{dt} + K\theta_E = D\Omega_R + T_L \tag{18}$$

Since the transient portion of equation (18) is the same as in equation (10) except that $(D + M)$ has replaced D, further reference to equation (15) shows that the new damping ratio is

$$\zeta = \frac{D + M}{2\sqrt{KJ}} \tag{19}$$

If the value of M is increased, the amount of frictional damping D now may

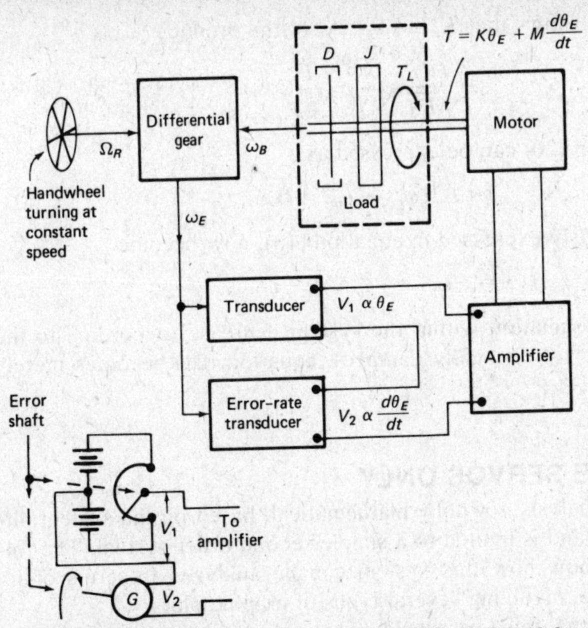

Figure 28-12 Error-rate control added to system of Fig. 28-9.

be decreased to reduce the positional error (with ramp input), yet ζ can remain large enough to keep the overshoot within desired limits.

In Fig. 28-12 the positional transducer may be a potentiometer, while the error-rate transducer may be a tachometer generator G whose output V_2 depends on the speed of the error shaft, and therefore on $d\theta_E/dt$.

28-18 DIMENSIONLESS FORM

Often control systems are described in terms of their undamped natural frequency ω_n and damping ratio ζ, as defined in equations (14) and (15). In this way the actual values of inertia J, damping torque D, and gain K are replaced by a frequency and a ratio that have no dimensions. For example, equation (11) gives the differential equation of the positional servo of Fig. 28-9; its transient error is found by using the auxiliary equation $Js^2 + Ds + K = 0$, from which is obtained

$$s^2 + \frac{D}{J}s + \frac{K}{J} = 0 \qquad (20)$$

(Here s merely replaces $j\omega$, as is mentioned further in Sec. 30-2, step I.)

But equation (14) shows that $K/J = \omega_n^2$. Also, the product $\zeta\omega_n$ is

$$\frac{D}{2\sqrt{KJ}}\sqrt{\frac{K}{J}} = \frac{D}{2J}$$

Therefore equation (20) can be expressed as

$$s^2 + 2\zeta\omega_n s + \omega_n^2 = 0 \tag{21}$$

The roots, previously expressed in equation (13), now become

$$s = -\omega_n\zeta \pm j\omega_n\sqrt{1-\zeta^2} \tag{22}$$

This shows that oscillation within the system decreases according to the term $\epsilon^{-\omega_n\zeta}$. If ζ is 1.0 (critically damped), equation (21) becomes merely $(s + \omega_n)^2 = 0$.

28-19 SIMPLE SERVOS ONLY

The foregoing analysis is wholly mathematical, based on the system differential equation, and is limited to a simple second-order system. The following chapters show how this system can be analyzed in terms of its frequency response, involving several types of graphic plots.

We must realize that this text considers only ideal simple servos that contain only a single feedback loop and linear components. Servos containing more than one loop generally must be "reduced" to an equivalent single loop; thereafter the solution may be like that described here, except that the system is more complex. Nonlinear systems, including features such as backlash of gears or the saturation of magnetic elements, require advanced study at a higher mathematical level.

Problems

28-1 True or false? Explain why.

(a) An error detector compares only quantities that are electrical.

(b) Open-loop gain usually is greater than forward gain.

(c) An alarm clock is a closed-loop device.

(d) An oil-furnace regulator could hold steadier temperature if the furnace could instantly deliver room heat and could stop such heat quickly when turned off.

(e) To produce a specified change in the controlled quantity, the reference potentiometer must be turned the same amount, whether the feedback loop is open or closed.

(f) A pushbutton is a transducer.

(g) If forward gain is 76, and one-fourth of the output voltage is fed back, the output error is only 5 percent as great as it would be without feedback.

(h) If B exceeds R, E may have the same polarity or direction that E has when R exceeds B.

(i) If a simple system has inertia of 5 slug-ft^2 and a damping torque of 20 lb-ft/rad/sec, a gain of 20 is needed to make $\zeta = 1.0$.

(j) If forward gain is 120, and one-fifth of the output voltage is fed back, the output error is only 4 percent as great as it would be without feedback.

(k) ζ always is small when D is small.

(l) Damping affects only a signal that is changing.

28-2 (*a*) Describe the operation of the circuit of tubes A, B, C, D, and E, acting as a motor-armature-voltage regulator. Identify each part as is done in a servo block diagram. (*b*) For each 1-volt (V) change at the grid of tube C, the rectifier tubes will change by 50 V the average dc voltage applied to M. Find the open-loop gain. (*c*) If capacitor C becomes short-circuited, how much worse does the voltage regulation become?

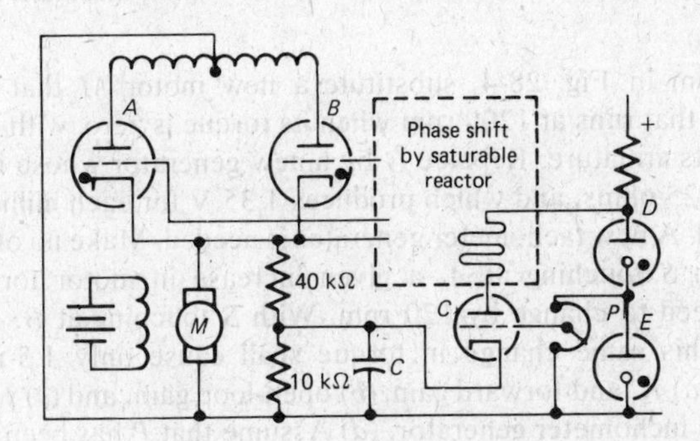

Figure Problem 28-2

28-3 The open-loop gain of this voltage-regulator system is −75. The voltage P changes 50 V for each ampere change of generator-G field current. The tube plate current changes 12mA/V change in v_G. The output of generator A changes 0.5 A/mA change in its control field. Find (*a*) forward gain K, (*b*), β, and (*c*) value of R_2. (*d*) If a given change of load decreases P by 0.5 V while the loop is closed, find the change of P for open-loop operation.

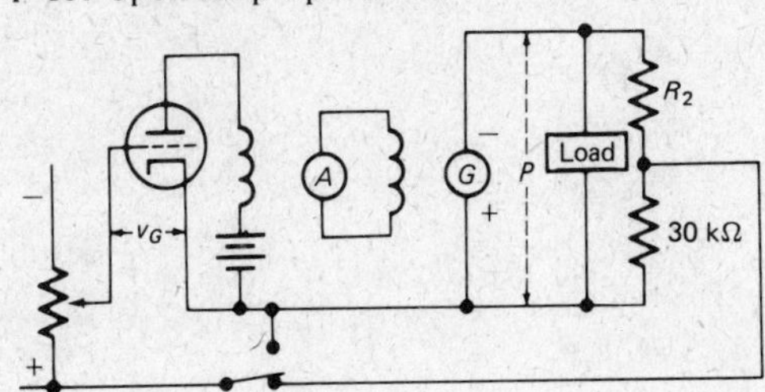

Figure Problem 28-3

28-4 Voltage P changes 400 volts for each 1-V change in v_G, which causes 5-mA change in plate current. The output of generator A changes 800 A per control-field ampere. $R_2 = 120\ k\Omega$. Find (*a*) the open-loop gain, and (*b*) the change in P per ampere change in field current of generator G. (*c*) If a certain change of load decreases P by 0.15 V while the loop is closed, find the change of P for open-loop operation. (Use diagram of Fig. Prob. 28-3.)

28-5 For the system in Fig. 28-4, replace the 6J5 by a new tube Q having different gain. Substitute a new tachometer generator that delivers 80 V at 500 rpm, and a new motor M that, with 250 V applied to its armature, delivers 70 lb-ft when stalled, but runs at 1134 rpm when its torque is zero. Make no other changes. With S touching at B, a given increase in torque makes V_t of the tachometer drop 0.17 V. With S touching at A, this same change in torque makes V_t drop 15.8 V. Find (*a*) open-loop gain, (*b*) forward gain, and (*c*) voltage gain of tube Q. (*d*) At constant torque, find the voltage change needed at P to reduce the motor speed by 50 rpm, for each position of S. Which direction is P moved?

28-6 For the system in Fig. 28-4, substitute a new motor M that has $K_2 = 0.2$, and that runs at 1200 rpm when its torque is zero, with 250 V applied to its armature. Replace G by a new generator whose field resistance is 625 ohms, and which produces 1.35 V for each milliampere in its field. A new tachometer generator is needed. Make no other changes. With S touching at A, a given increase in motor torque causes the speed to change by 120 rpm. With S touching at B, it is desired that this same change in torque shall cause only 1.5-rpm change. Find (*a*) K_1 and forward gain, (*b*) open-loop gain, and (*c*) volts per rpm of the tachometer generator. (*d*) Assume that P has been adjusted so that M turns 500 rpm; the motor torque is 5 lb-ft and is constant. Now if P is turned clockwise to change V_r by 0.9 V, find the new motor speed, for each position of S.

29 FREQUENCY RESPONSE OF SERVO SYSTEMS

The behavior and ability of a servo may be studied by applying a smoothly alternating wave or command signal to the input, and observing or calculating the nature of the wave that is fed back after passing through the system. Then, by making this input wave occur faster or at higher frequency, similar results may be tabulated at each frequency, thereby recording the frequency response of this servo. From such data, easily obtained for the open-loop system, it then is possible to determine the closed-loop response by the use of methods or plots as described in this chapter and the next chapter. The parts of the system that cause varying results as the frequency increases are first described.

29-1 TIME CONSTANT OF AN INDUCTIVE WINDING

In Sec. 28-8 the standstill accuracy of a voltage regulator is described; here an increase in load current tends to reduce the generator voltage, but the regulator increases the generator field current so as to restore the voltage. Although the final generator voltage in this regulator example may be nearly the same as the starting voltage, there may be a time lag before it reaches this final value. Such a delay or lag is caused by any portion of the regulator circuit that stores energy. Since the generator itself is perhaps the only moving part in the above regulator system and its speed probably is constant, the energy stored in moving parts is not the cause of delay in this example. However, the field winding of the generator is highly inductive. When current flows through such an inductance, a considerable amount of energy is stored in its magnetic field; any change in this field current causes a voltage reaction that opposes the change. Therefore, when the regulator applies larger voltage to the field and tries to increase the field current, this current does not increase instantly; the increase of current lags behind the increase of applied voltage. The amount of lag caused by this inductive winding can be stated in terms of its time constant. Just as the time constant of a capacitor-resistor circuit is equal to RC seconds (ohms × farads, or megohms × microfarads, as studied in Sec. 3-3), the time constant of an inductance-resistance circuit is equal to L/R seconds. If the generator field winding has 50 ohms resistance and 25 henrys of inductance, the time constant of this field = 25 henrys/50 ohms = 0.5 sec. When a voltage is applied suddenly across this field winding, 0.5 sec will pass before the current rises to nearly two-thirds of its final value. [After a time equal to L/R sec, the current = (1 − 0.368) or 0.632 of its final steady value. This same relation applies to the charging of a capacitor or the increase of voltage across it, as is described in Sec. 3-5.]

To obtain fast follow-up or higher-frequency response, the major controlled element in the servo is designed to have as small a time constant as possible.

29-2 FAST RESPONSE

Since the average regulator aims for high steady-state accuracy rather than fast follow-up, it is better here to consider the servomechanism in Fig. 29-1 for the control of gun position. The gun director is pointed easily at the desired target by the gunner, who may be at some distance from the gun. The pointing of this director delivers a command signal R. The actual gun position feeds back a signal B. When B differs from R, an error or actuating signal E is amplified so as to make a motor turn the gun turret in the right direction so that the gun points in the same direction as the director. Of course, the steady-state accuracy must be high—the servo must point the gun in exactly the required direction. Moreover, since the target may be moving rapidly and the gunner may turn the director quickly, the heavy gun must follow with very little lag or delay; it must have good *dynamic response*. To obtain this fast response, so much power must be applied through the motor that it may turn the heavy gun beyond the required direction. So proper servo

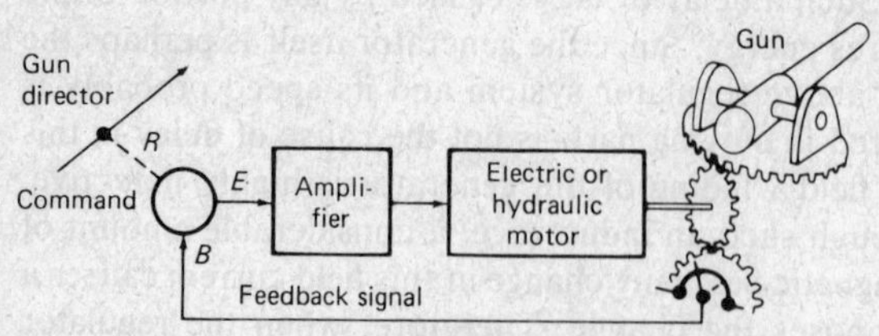

Figure 29-1 Servomechanism for control of gun position.

design includes features that provide fastest followup with least overtravel (or overshoot, as shown in Fig. 28-10).

In any such position-control servomechanism, the error-correcting motor must accelerate from standstill in order to move the gun; here again is a time delay, for the maximum motor output naturally occurs later than the signal that starts the motor.

To study or determine how fast a servo will follow up or respond, the designing engineer can analyze such response by applying (at R in Fig. 28-2) an input signal or command that is varying steadily up and down at a certain rate or frequency, like a sine wave. If the gun director is turned smoothly back and forth through 90°, once per minute, the gun follows easily and accurately. However, when the director is moved through the same angle in only 6 sec, the gun position may lag at a small angle. At still faster movement, the sine-wave input signal R may change at 1 cycle per second; perhaps the gun now lags 2° behind the director —a "phase lag" of 2°. When the change in R is increased to 2 or 3 cycles per second, the gun now may be far from the end of its desired travel when the R signal has reversed; the total swing of the gun decreases so that the size or amplitude of its response has decreased. When the command signal at R is a sine wave that varies at 10 cycles per second, the gun barely moves—its response is weakened, or "attenuated," until its amplitude is nearly zero. Moreover, whatever movement remains now occurs nearly 90° behind the signal R.

As illustrated above, the gain or output of a servo at low frequencies may be very high, giving excellent accuracy; the controlled quantity C lags very little behind the command R. As the frequency of the input signal increases, the output decreases in amplitude and it lags at a greater angle behind the input signal. As is explained later, at a higher signal frequency the servo output may lag nearly 180°, so that the feedback signal B produces the same effect as the varying R signal; at this frequency the servo may set up a self-oscillation that continues even when the R signal is removed. Even though the servo may not be expected to operate with fast input signals, accidental disturbance signals must be considered that can make the system oscillate or become unstable.

29-3 CAUSE OF UNSTABLE OPERATION

Since a servo consists of many parts or devices, probably two to five of these parts may store energy; every capacitor, inductive winding, or moving element is an "energy-storage component." As indicated in the example above, there is a time constant for each element or circuit of this kind; each such element attenuates or weakens the loop gain and causes a delay, or lag, that becomes greater at increased input-signal frequency until the lag of each element may approach a limit of 90°. At high frequency, three such elements in one servo easily can combine their lags, so that 60° apiece causes a total lag of 180°. If the system has high gain, so that the loop gain remaining at this high frequency still is greater than 1, the servo will oscillate and will not be stable.

As an example of this combined phase-lag action, Fig. 29-2 shows the circuit of a *phase-shift* oscillator, wherein a total shift of 180° is purposely produced. Most oscillators (like those of Sec. 24-5) are of the resonant type, requiring a tank circuit containing certain amounts of L and C; such resonance is not used here. Instead, Fig. 29-2 shows three RC groups that feed to the base a current that is obtained from the collector voltage. At the desired oscillating frequency f, the size of capacitor C_1 is selected so that its reactance ($1/2\pi fC$) is 1/1.73 times the resistance of R_1. (Capacitors C_2 and C_3 are chosen to have this same ratio to R_2 and R_3.) Therefore, when the collector current oscillates and causes a varying voltage to appear between top line a and bottom line k, the alternating k-to-b voltage across C_1 now lags 60° behind the k-to-a voltage (because C_1 is an energy-storage device). Similarly, the k-to-c voltage across C_2 lags another 60°. The final voltage across C_3 lags another 60° behind the k-to-c voltage; so the k-to-d base voltage of the transistor is 180° out of phase with the k-to-a collector voltage; this fulfills one requirement for oscillation (as is mentioned in Sec. 24-5). [Recall that a rope swing is made to oscillate by pushing the swing *from* you just when it reaches its greatest travel *toward* you. The push (at the base) is 180° out of phase with the (collector) wave of the swing.] But notice that the voltage across C_2 is only half as large as the voltage across C_1; this shows the attenuation, or decrease of amplitude, mentioned above. Because of three such reductions, the base voltage is only one-eighth of the collector voltage; therefore, to cause oscillation, this transistor circuit must include an initial gain greater than 8, so that a gain larger than 1 can remain at the base.

The oscillator of Fig. 29-2 shows how three time constants or phase lags purposely are combined to produce a feedback base current that will cause oscillation. Similarly, in a servo, three or more time constants (energy-storage elements, including motors that start and stop) can combine their phase lags to cause undesired oscillation.

These examples show why the stability of a servo depends on the phase

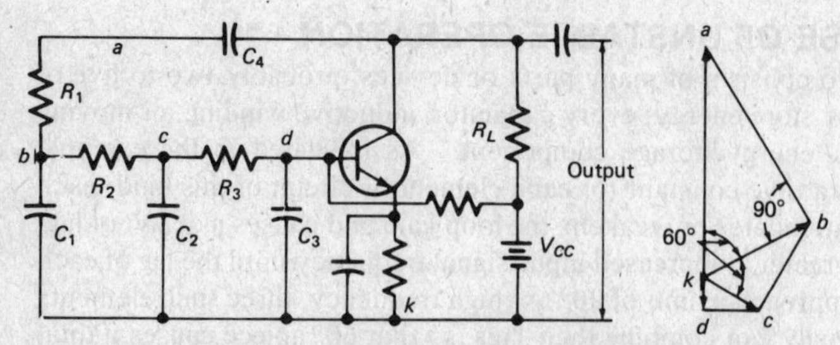

Figure 29-2 Phase-shift oscillator uses the sum of three RC phase lags = 180°.

lags produced by certain elements in the closed loop. To cause severe oscillation, which occurs at that signal frequency that causes a total phase lag near 180°, the remaining loop gain must be nearly equal to 1.

29-4 THE TRANSFER FUNCTION

While engineers or designers are mainly interested in the overall phase lag and gain of the total closed-loop system, they also study the behavior of each energy-storage element or circuit portion by itself. For each element they use an equation that states the ratio of the output voltage of the element to its input voltage, expressed as v_{out} / v_{in}; such an equation is called the *transfer function* of that element. Since the amount of voltage across a capacitor or an inductance depends on the frequency f, this fact must be included in the equation. [The ohms of reactance represented by an inductance of L henrys (H) is equal to $X_L = 2\pi fL$. In servo work, $2\pi f$ is replaced by ω (the angular velocity of the signal or alternating voltage, expressed in radians per second): so $X_L = \omega L$. Similarly, the ohms of reactance of a capacitor of C farads (F) is equal to $X_C = 1 / 2\pi fC = 1 / \omega C$. When a current i flows through a series circuit consisting of R, L, and C, this current produces a voltage across R equal to iR, which is in phase with i; across L is the voltage iX_L or $i\omega L$, which is 90° ahead of i; across C is the voltage iX_C or i / C, which lags 90° behind i. This 90° relation is now shown by the letter j; a voltage shown as $ji\omega L$ is 90° ahead of a voltage iR; a voltage jiR is 90° ahead of a voltage $i / \omega C$. (ω = omega.)]

In the simple RC circuit shown in Fig. 29-3, the input voltage v_i forces an alternating current to flow through R and C in series; this current produces across R a voltage that always leads 90° ahead of the voltage across C. The voltage across C is $iX_C = i / \omega C$ and also is the output voltage v_o. The input v_i is the phasor sum of iR and $i / \omega C$. So the transfer function of this circuit is

$$\frac{v_o}{v_i} = \frac{i / \omega C}{i / \omega C + jiR} = \frac{1}{1 + j\omega RC} = \frac{1}{j\omega\tau + 1}$$

In servo work the time constant of an element often is represented by τ, which therefore can replace RC, as shown in the final equation given above; this form of transfer function is used commonly for any circuit con-

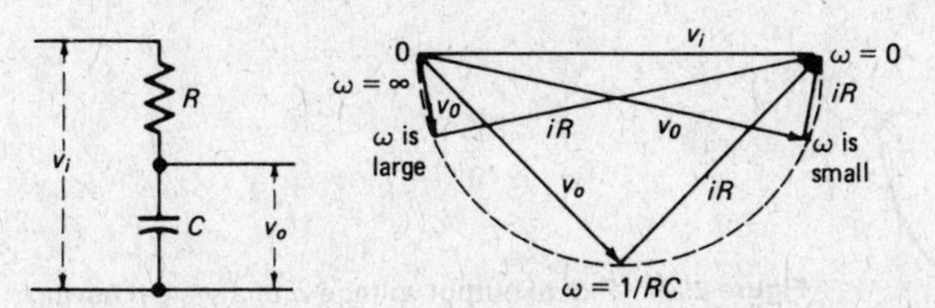

Figure 29-3 Input and output phasors for RC phase-lag network.

taining a single time constant τ (whether $\tau = RC$ for a capacitor circuit or $\tau = L / R$ for an inductive circuit). (τ = tau.)

The phasor diagram in Fig. 29-3 shows how the length of v_o becomes a smaller portion of v_i as the input signal frequency ω increases; the phase lag, or angle between v_o and v_i, also increases. When $\omega = 0$, no current flows through C or R; so $v_o = v_i$. (In such servo networks it is assumed that no current flows to an output circuit at v_o, for v_o may be the voltage applied between grid and cathode of a vacuum tube, biased so that its grid remains negative.) At that frequency where $\omega = 1 / RC$ or $1 / \tau$, it is seen that $1 / \omega C = R$; so the voltage v_o across C is equal to the voltage across R. The phasor length shows that v_o now is $0.707 v_i$, and v_o lags 45° behind v_i. (This relation occurs at a break or corner frequency of the Bode diagram, as discussed in Sec. 29-12.) At much higher frequency, ω is so large that $1/\omega C$ becomes very small; v_o is small and lags nearly 90° behind v_i. Thus this arrangement of R and C is seen to be a phase-lag element.

The semicircle in Fig. 29-3 is the locus or path traced by the tip of the v_o arrow or phasor, while its tail end is held at 0; this path is a picture or plot of the transfer function of this RC element, as ω increases from zero toward infinity (∞).

29-5 EQUATION FOR A REGULATOR LOOP

When two energy-storage elements, each having its own time constant, are used in a loop circuit, their separate actions may be combined in a single transfer function shown as $v_o / v_i = 1 / (j\omega\tau_1 + 1)(j\omega\tau_2 + 1)$. The locus or plot of this v_o is similar to Fig. 29-4; here notice that as ω increases and v_o becomes very small, v_o now lags nearly 180° behind v_i.

We now may study the complete loop of a regulator that contains three energy-storage elements or lags. As is shown in Fig. 29-5, perhaps two of these lags are caused by the inductive fields of machines and their time constants are τ_1 and τ_2; the third lag is that caused by a capacitor, shown in the feedback portion of the loop. The transfer function or equation for the whole loop becomes

$$\frac{v_o}{v_i} = \frac{1}{(j\omega\tau_1 + 1)\,(j\omega\tau_2 + 1)\,(j\omega\tau_3 + 1)} = \frac{B}{E}$$

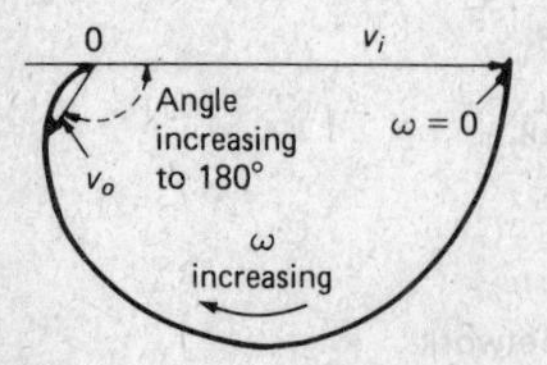

Figure 29-4 Plot of output voltage v_o of a system having two phase lags.

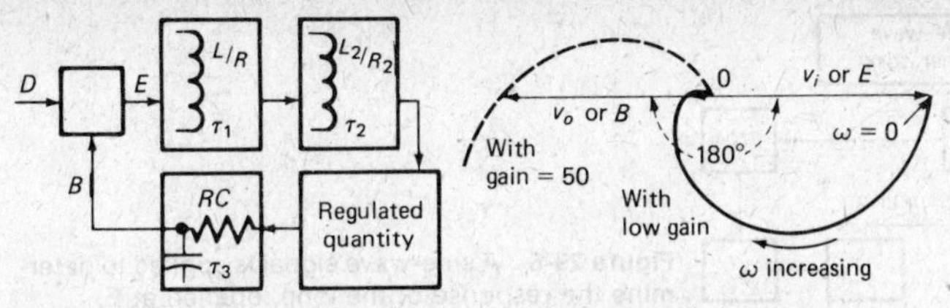

Figure 29-5 Regulator having three energy-storage elements.

Here realize that the actuating signal E is the input v_i while the feedback signal B is the output v_o of the whole loop. If there is no gain or amplification of E within the loop, the plot of v_o is like the solid line in Fig. 29-5. At large values of ω, the combined lag action of the three energy-storage elements definitely brings the v_o phasor to a position 180° behind v_i, however, since this v_o phasor is small, so that the gain or ratio of v_o / v_i is much less than 1, the system is stable.

But any useful servo includes amplifiers that increase the size of input E after it enters the loop. If this open-loop gain is 50 (as if the size of v_i is increased 50 times), the signal fed back at B becomes 50 times larger than first was plotted in Fig. 29-5 and now is shown by the dashed line. (Also, the number 50 replaces the 1 above the line in the transfer equation.) We quickly see that the v_o arrow (when it lags 180° behind v_i) now is as large as the original input arrow v_i; B is as large as E. The loop gain (or ratio v_o / v_i) now is 1, accompanied by a total phase shift of 180°; so this servo will act as an oscillator and will not be stable.

29-6 ANALYSIS OF A SERVO; THE NYQUIST APPROACH

To test a servo, some engineers apply a sudden change (a unit-step input) to the command R; then they measure or calculate the resulting errors, the overshoot, the length of time for any oscillation to die out; this method is discussed in Sec. 28-15. Most engineers prefer to apply a continually changing sine-wave signal input at R, then measure the loop gain and the phase lag for various input frequencies; this is known as the Nyquist approach to the problem. Many years ago Dr. H. Nyquist of the Bell Laboratories developed this method, which divides the problem into several steps; its use here is intended mainly for the study of simple servos.

As the first step, shown in Fig. 29-6, the loop of the servo is left open at the error detector. A sine-wave voltage of small constant size is used to supply the actuating signal E; after this varying signal passes through G to the controlled quantity C, the size of the signal fed back at B is measured; the phase angle by which B lags behind E also is measured. Now, as the frequency of the sine-wave input gradually is increased, the corresponding

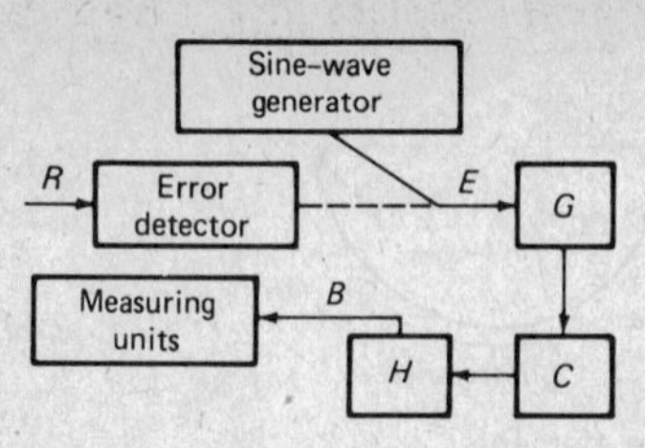

Figure 29-6 A sine-wave signal is applied to determine the response of the loop, opened at E.

readings at B are taken. It is seen that such readings give the data to plot a curve like that in Fig. 29-5. For a sample set of readings as recorded below, the resulting polar or "Nyquist plot" is shown in Fig. 29-7. On the horizontal line, the actuating signal E is shown as 1 volt in length. The corresponding length for B (when $\omega = 0$) is shown as 10 volts in length; this shows that the open-loop gain is 10 at standstill.

The second step uses the above plot (of the open-loop system response) to calculate or observe whether the servo can be expected to operate satisfactorily when the loop is restored or closed. To judge such closed-loop performance, most engineers use the ratio between the input command signal R and the resulting feedback B. To plot or find this ratio B/R, notice how the test data (like those plotted in Fig. 29-7) can be used.

With E and B reconnected into the circuit, the purpose of the error detector is to produce a value of E equal to $R - B$; therefore, $R = E + B$. Since the Nyquist plot in Fig. 29-7 shows the phasor B (variable in size

Frequency input at E		Volts at B* (for 1-volt input at E)	Phase lag*
ω, radians per sec	f, cps		
0	0.00	10.0	0°
1	0.16	8.9	33°
2	0.32	6.9	58°
3	0.48	5.3	76°
4	0.64	4.1	89°
5	0.80	3.3	100°
7	1.11	2.2	116°
10	1.59	1.4	133°
15	2.39	0.7	149°
20	3.18	0.4	166°
30	4.78	0.2	184°

*These values are obtained from

$$\frac{B}{E} = \frac{10}{(j\omega 0.5 + 1)\,(j\omega 0.1 + 1)\,(j\omega 0.0167 + 1)}$$

(See Sec. 29-13.)

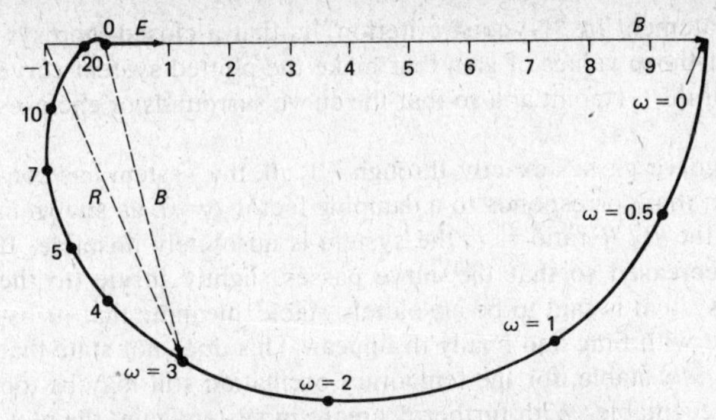

Figure 29-7 Nyquist plot of an example servo system.

and direction) and indicates that E is a constant phasor 1 unit long, the desired length and position of phasor R can be drawn as the sum of these phasors B and E. By relocating phasor E so that its arrow tip is at 0, its tail now is at -1. Any line drawn from this -1 point to any point on the locus curve of phasor B represents the phasor sum of E and B; so it is also the value of R.

Part of the plot of Fig. 29-7 is shown again in Fig. 29-8; here the dashed phasors show B and R when the feedback signal B is lagging by nearly 90°; here B is smaller than R. At a higher frequency (or a larger value of ω) where B lags by 133°, B becomes larger than R; the ratio B/R here is near 1.4. At the frequency where B lags by 180°, B is about one-fourth as large as E, so the gain is much less than 1.0; this system probably is stable at the gain of 10 used here.

If the loop gain now is increased until B in Fig. 29-8 is equal to or greater than E (at the 180° position where the plotted curve crosses the negative horizontal axis), the servo will have violent oscillation or hunting.

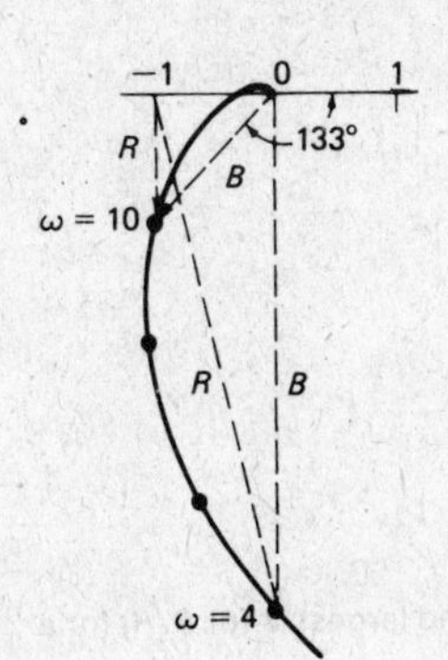

Figure 29-8 Part of Fig. 29-7, showing B/R ratio.

So the guiding statement or "Nyquist criterion" is that a closed-loop system is unstable at those values of gain that make the plotted system curve cross to the left of the -1 point and so that the curve surrounds or encloses this -1 point.

If this plotted curve passes exactly through $-1, j0$, the system has continuous oscillation that corresponds to a damping factor $\zeta = 0$, as shown in Fig. 28-10; here the B / R ratio $= \infty$; the system is absolutely unstable. If system gain is decreased so that the curve passes slightly inside (to the right) of -1, the system is said to be absolutely stable, meaning that its oscillations decrease with time and finally disappear. This does not state that the system is *usefully* stable, for the temporary oscillation still may be too prolonged to be acceptable. With further decrease in system gain, the plotted curve moves farther away from $-1, j0$, and the B / R ratio decreases; this indicates that less oscillation can occur, and the damping factor has risen nearer to 1.0. By experience, engineers have learned to avoid using B/R ratios greater than 1.5 or 2 at any signal frequency; this provides an upper limit to useful stability.

29-7 *M* CIRCLES

By increasing the loop gain, the size of B also can be increased (at every point in the curve) so as to increase this B/R ratio to the maximum desired value. To help find what amount of gain can be permitted, you may use M circles, where M is merely this B/R ratio. If $M = 1$, then $B = R$. Figure 29-9 shows that all points that meet this requirement (of $M = 1$) lie on the straight vertical line halfway between -1 and 0. But if $M = 1.4$, the size of

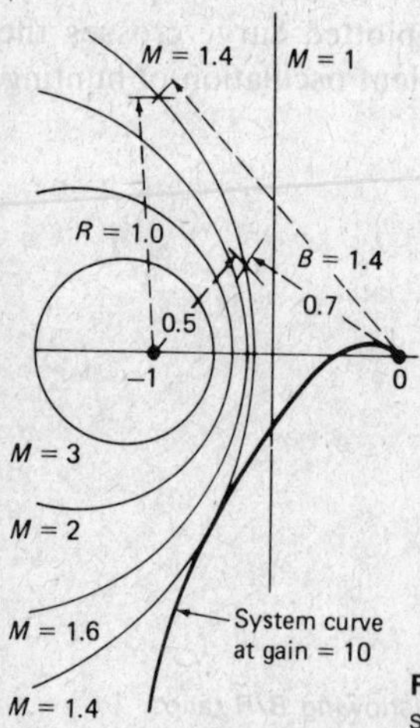

Figure 29-9 Use of *M* circles to find largest *M* (or *B*/*R*) for a system.

B must be 0.7 when $R = 0.5$; B must be 1.4 when $R = 1.0$; using compass arcs to plot these values, it is seen that all such points lie on a circle. Similarly, the circle for $M = 2$ may be plotted; it is smaller in size and does not have the same center point as the previous circle. [The M circles need not be plotted point by point; as made with a compass, each circle has a radius $= M/(M^2 - 1)$ and its center is to the left of 0 by the amount $M^2/(M^2 - 1)$. Thus the circle for $M = 2$ has its center at -1.33 and its radius is 0.67.] After a series of such circles is prepared, the curve of the studied servo is plotted on the same sheet, probably using values obtained when the loop gain $K\beta$ of that servo is some small amount such as 1 or 10. If the servo curve of Fig. 29-8 is used in this way, the heavy line in Fig. 29-9 shows the result. Notice that this servo curve just touches the circle of $M = 1.4$. If we believe (based on previous experience or others' advice) that an M ratio of 1.6 can be used, we increase the loop gain until the servo curve touches but does not cross the circle of $M = 1.6$.

29-8 CORRECTIVE OR ANTIHUNT NETWORKS

From previous discussion it may appear to be necessary to reduce the loop gain in order to stabilize a servo. But high gain is needed for high accuracy and fast response; so engineers have learned to provide stability by adding corrective networks into the closed loop; all such units may be called "antihunt" devices. Some of these networks may cause a leading phase angle, intended to offset the lag that is inherent or natural in most energy-storage elements. [When an electronic amplifier is used as part of the closed-loop system, the corrective network is placed in this electronic portion, for here the needed parts (capacitors, etc.) may be much smaller and are more easily changed to attain the desired results.]

First recall the arrangement of R and C in Fig. 29-3, which causes a phase-lag action; if the positions of R and C are interchanged as shown in Fig. 29-10, an alternating input signal v_i may produce an output v_o that leads by nearly 90°. However, this simple circuit is not used in a servo, for its output v_o becomes zero as the signal frequency ω is lowered toward 0, the steady-state condition; a loop containing this circuit has no gain at standstill and therefore has low accuracy.

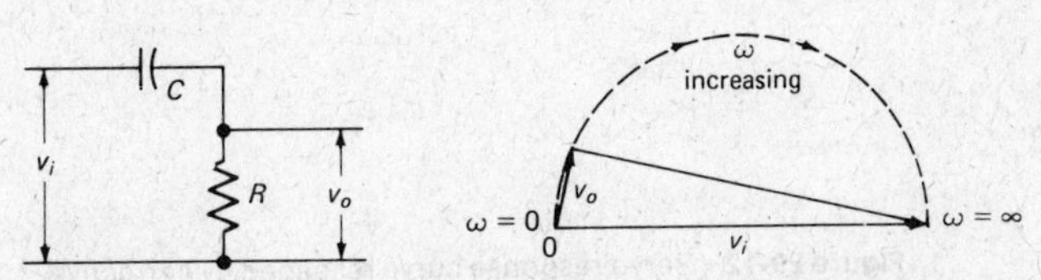

Figure 29-10 Phase-lead circuit having no gain at low frequency.

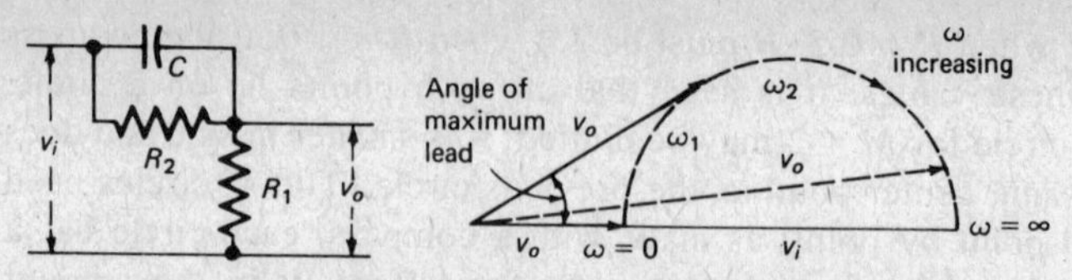

Figure 29-11 Useful *RC* phase-lead circuit.

If another resistor R_2 is added across C as shown in Fig. 29-11, this becomes a useful phase-lead circuit. {At low frequency (or when $\omega = 0$) in Fig. 29-11, the current in C is negligible; R_2 and R_1 act as a simple voltage divider so that $v_o = v_i \times [R_1 / (R_1 + R_2)]$.} If R_1 has half as many ohms as R_2, $v_0 = {}^1/_3 v_i$; this loss of steady-state gain may be offset by increasing the amplifier gain in the loop. The phasor plot shows that this circuit provides no leading angle when ω is very large or very small. For frequencies between ω_1 and ω_2, the leading angle reaches a nearly constant value (still much less than 90°), then it decreases at higher values of ω. At very high frequency, C becomes a short circuit around R_2, so v_o becomes as large as v_i. This phase-lead circuit is used again in Sec. 29-17.

By careful selection of the values of R and C in such phase-lead networks, we can change the shape of the plotted curve of the servo loop so that it will pass well inside -1, to provide better stability. For example, the dashed curve in Fig. 29-12 represents a servo that is unstable, for the curve surrounds the -1 point. If certain corrective networks are added, part of this servo curve may be reshaped so as to follow the solid line, thus decreasing the loop gain for frequencies between ω_1 and ω_2; this retains the high gain desired at lower frequencies and at standstill.

Other antihunt devices include transformers, tachometer generators, or capacitors that are connected so that they feed back a corrective signal only when the controlled quantity is changing. Such rate-of-change correction often can stabilize a servo better than can the error signal itself, as illustrated

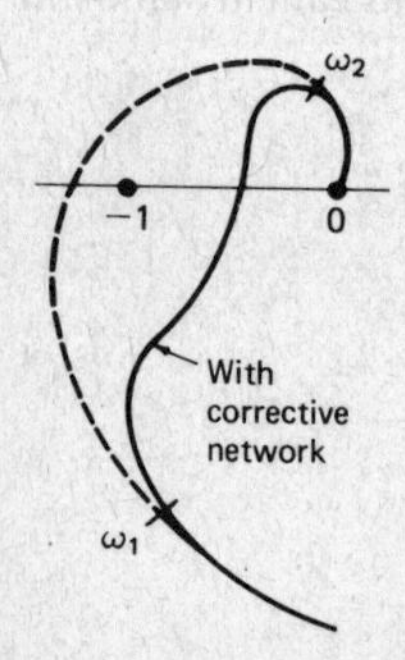

Figure 29-12 Servo response curve reshaped by corrective network.

next. [When a new driver is learning to steer an automobile, and sees that the car is going too far to the right, the wheel is swung to the left. Now the car goes too far to the left, so the wheel is swung back to the right. The car is hunting for the center of the road; here the corrective movements of the steering wheel are related directly to the size of the error in car position; these corrections are so large and so fast that the car crosses the road center but cannot stay in the center. But an "antihunt" action is used when this driver learns to move the wheel smoothly—when the wheel is straightened quickly after each small turn away from center. When the car is moving slowly toward the road edge (so the error in car position is changing slowly), a good driver turns the wheel very little; usually this small correction is all that is needed. However, if the car is leaving the road faster, the driver turns the wheel more sharply, then straightens it again. Notice that the wheel is turned, not so much because of a small error in car position, but because that error is fast increasing. The greater the rate of change in error, the more correction is needed. This is *error-rate* control.] Such antihunt devices (as used in the control of an amplidyne) are described in Sec. 32-3.

29-9 SERVO TYPES 0, 1, 2

Only regulators of level or quantity are used as the servos whose curve plots are shown in examples above; these servos include no motor to cause a change of position. Engineers refer to such a regulator system as a "type-0 servo"; it always has some small amount of steady-state error.

A "type-1 servo" is the usual servomechanism that includes the start-stop action of a motor so as to correct the *position* of the controlled object. The natural delay, while the motor comes up to its correction speed, introduces a phase lag of 90° into the servo loop, regardless of the frequency of the input command signal R. (Mathematically, we state that the position controlled by the motor is a summation of the preceding motor actions and is therefore the *integral* of the sine-wave variation of motor speed; this integral is the $-\cos$, or a phasor that lags 90° behind v_i.) As is shown in Table 29-1, the Nyquist plot of a type-1 servo differs in that (at standstill, when $\omega = 0$) the v_o arrow lags 90° behind the v_i arrow, so that the servo curve enters from the bottom of the chart and can more easily surround the -1 point to indicate instability. As is derived in Sec. 29-10, the transfer function of this servo type includes a term $j\omega$ in the denominator; when $\omega = 0$, v_o is infinitely large. There is no error at standstill, but there may be an error in position during a follow-up or velocity action.

A "type-2 servo" is a less common position-control servomechanism that includes two start-stop motor actions. For example, the actuating signal E may start one motor to turn a rheostat, which thus applies voltage to start the second motor to turn and correct the position of the controlled object. Each of these motors causes a 90° lag at any frequency; so the plotted curve of

TABLE 29-1

Servo type	Type 0	Type 1	Type 2
Used as	Regulator of level or quantity	Position control with no standstill error	Position control with no velocity error
Start-stop motors	0	1	2
Typical transfer function	$\frac{200}{(j\omega\tau_1+1)(j\omega\tau_2+1)(j\omega\tau_3+1)}$	$\frac{200}{j\omega(j\omega\tau_1+1)(j\omega\tau_2+1)}$	$\frac{200}{(j\omega)^2(j\omega\tau_1+1)(j\omega\tau_2+1)}$
Nyquist plot. Correction – – –	−1 0	0 −1	0 −1
Stabilization	Not difficult	Requires care	Needs precise corrective design
Initial slope on Bode diagram	0	1-unit slope 20 dB/decade	2-unit slope 40 dB/decade

such a system enters from the left, at 180°, and always surrounds the −1 point unless corrective devices are added. The type-2 transfer function includes $(j\omega)^2$ in the denominator.

29-10 TRANSFER FUNCTION OF A MECHANICAL SYSTEM

Looking ahead to the *RL* circuit of Fig. 29-15, the electrical student will recognize that

$$v_i = L\frac{di}{dt} + iR$$

The transfer function is

$$\frac{1}{j\omega L / R + 1}$$

In similar form, for the mechanical system shown in Fig. 29-13, the applied torque $= T = J\, d\omega / dt + D\omega$. Here $\tau = J / D$. In terms of angular ve-

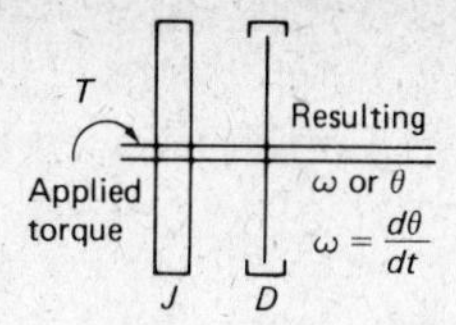

Figure 29-13 Mechanical system for obtaining transfer function of type-1 servo.

locity ω, the transfer function is

$$\frac{\Omega \sin \omega t}{T \sin \omega t} = \frac{1/D}{j\omega\tau + 1}$$

However, in terms of an angular loadshaft displacement $\theta = \Theta \sin \omega t$, the applied torque

$$T = J\frac{d_2\theta}{dt_2} + D\frac{d\theta}{dt}$$

Since

$$\frac{d\theta}{dt} = \omega\Theta \cos \omega t \quad \text{and} \quad \frac{d^2\theta}{dt^2} = -\omega_2 \Theta \sin \omega t$$

Therefore

$$T = \Theta(-\omega^2 J + j\omega D)$$

so that the transfer function is

$$\frac{\Theta \sin \omega t}{T \sin \omega t} = \frac{1}{j^2\omega^2 J + j\omega D}$$

Dividing all terms by D, the result is

$$\frac{1/D}{j^2\omega^2\tau + j\omega}$$

so the transfer function is

$$\frac{1/D}{j\omega(j\omega\tau + 1)}$$

Here we see that a system element, whose inertia is to be accelerated, has a displacement transfer function that includes a separate $j\omega$ term in the denominator. Thus, as ω approaches 0, the steady-state response approaches infinite size, and the phase angle $= -90°$.

The typical Nyquist plot of this type-1 servo takes the forms shown in Fig. 29-14. Moreover, since the input signal vector R and the feedback vector B both extend to $-\infty$, they are identical in length and angle. Therefore, the steady-state displacement error is zero (for $\omega = 0$) in any positional follow-up system that contains a start-stop element having inertia.

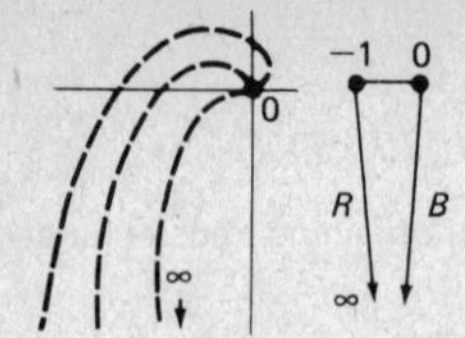

Figure 29-14 Nyquist plots of type-1 servo.

29-11 THE BODE ATTENUATION DIAGRAM

To give an easier method for plotting and analyzing the response of a servo system, an attenuation diagram is suggested by Dr. H. W. Bode of the Bell Laboratories. Whereas tedious point-by-point measurements or calculations are needed for the Nyquist plot described in Sec. 29-6, the Bode method requires only that the gain of the servo system be known at one frequency (often at $\omega = 1$ rad/sec), together with the time constants of the main energy-storage elements in the system. If we draw straight lines (as explained below), the response curve of the servo is easily located; this single curve shows both the gain and the phase lag for each signal frequency applied to the system. Various corrective elements may be inserted or changed without needing to replot the whole response curve. To show a change in system gain, the whole curve merely is raised or lowered on the chart.

This Bode diagram uses logarithmic scales (like those on a slide rule or as used also in Fig. 18-8). If the values of system gain (available from the table in Sec. 29-6) are plotted for various signal frequencies (angular velocities, ω) on such a logarithmic chart, the result is shown by the lower dashed curve in Fig. 29-17. Notice how this curve closely follows the straight lines drawn from points M and N; the method for locating points J and K (like M and N) is explained below.

In a Bode attenuation diagram like that in Fig. 29-17, the open-loop gain of the servo is plotted on a vertical scale of decibels (dB); each value of decibels corresponds to a certain gain ratio as shown below, but it is related

Gain	dB*	Gain	dB	Gain	dB
0.5	−6	7	17	100	40
0.7	−3	10	20	177	45
1	0	18	25	316	50
2	6	32	30	560	55
4	12	56	35	1000	60

*The decibel (dB) = $20 \log_{10} K$, where K = gain.

to the *logarithm* of that gain, so that a linear (uniformly spaced) scale of decibel values is also a logarithmic scale of gain values. Note that a system gain of 1 is represented by 0 dB; larger gains are shown above the 0-dB line. So, for the system in Sec. 29-6, a gain of 20 dB is plotted at the left in Fig. 29-17 to show the open-loop gain ratio of $B/E = 10$ at low frequency.

29-12 THE BODE DIAGRAM FOR ONE ELEMENT

Here note how the action of a single inductive winding (described in Sec. 29-1) is plotted on a Bode diagram. Such a winding includes resistance of R ohms as well as L henrys of inductance, as shown in Fig. 29-15; its time constant $\tau = L/R$. With the ac signal voltage v_i applied to this group, its transfer function is

$$\frac{v_o}{v_i} = \frac{iR}{ji\,\omega L + iR} = \frac{1}{j\omega L\,/\,R + 1} = \frac{1}{j\omega\tau + 1}$$

When ω is near 0, inductance L acts like a short circuit; so the gain of this group is 0 dB, since its ratio $v_o\,/\,v_i = 1$ at very low frequency. In the same manner as is shown in Fig. 29-3, when the signal rate $\omega = 1/\tau = R/L$, the ac voltage across R is the same size as the voltage across L; v_o now lags 45° behind v_i and is only 0.707 as large as v_i. This ratio or gain of 0.707 is about $-$ 3 dB, or it is a loss of 3 dB. When similar values are calculated for many frequencies, as in the table, the resulting plot of decibels versus frequency is shown by the dashed curve in Fig. 29-15. At the higher values of ω, notice that the decibel value decreases by 6 dB each time the frequency is doubled. Since such a doubling of frequency is called an *octave*, the greatest downward slope of the curve in Fig. 29-15 is said to be 6 dB per octave. At this slope, the calculations show also that a phase lag of 90° finally is reached, caused by this single inductive winding.

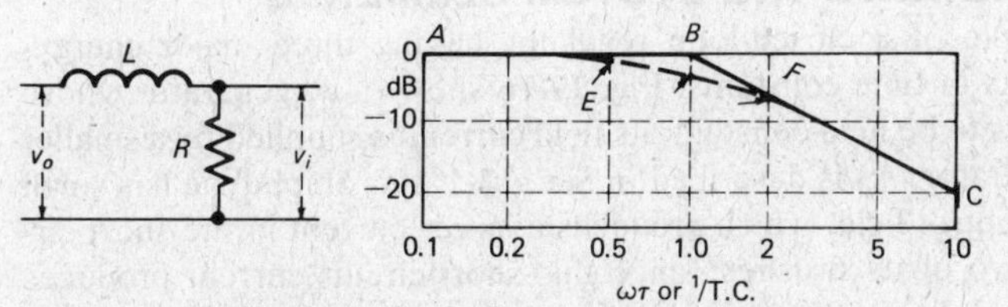

Figure 29-15 Bode diagram for *RL* phase-lag network.

$\omega\tau$	$v_o\,/\,v_i$	dB	Lag	$\omega\tau$	$v_o\,/\,v_i$	dB	Lag
0.5	0.895	−1	27°	10	0.095	−20	84°
1.0	0.707	−3	45°	20	0.050	−26	87°
2.0	0.447	−7	63°	40	0.025	−32	89°
5.0	0.196	−14	79°	80	0.012	−38	90°

In place of calculating and plotting the points of the above curve, the Bode method substitutes two straight lines. In Fig. 29-15, one of these lines is drawn from A to B along the 0-dB line. Point B is located at that frequency where $\omega\tau = 1$, or $w = 1/(\text{time constant})$. From point B, the second straight line is drawn toward C with a downward slope of 6 dB per octave. (At point C the value of ω is 10 times as large as at B; this ratio of 10 is called a *decade*. Since C is 20 dB lower than B, the slope of line BC also is known as 20 dB per decade, or a *unit slope*.)

We see that these two solid lines coincide with the dashed line of the plotted system curve except near the bend or break B where the two straight lines meet. Since $\omega = 1/\tau$ at B, point D on the true system curve in Fig. 29-15 is about 3 dB below the junction of the two lines; the error between the true curve and the straight lines never exceeds 3 dB.

Similarly, at points E and F, one octave distant from D, the true curve is within 1 dB of the straight lines. The slope of the curve at D represents a phase lag of 45°, for its slope is halfway between the slopes of the two straight lines that meet at B.

As demonstrated in the above example, the effect of any energy-storage element in a closed loop may be shown on the Bode diagram by constructing a break [at the "corner frequency" of $\omega = 1/(\text{time constant})$] so that the straight line continues to the right at a slope that differs (by 6 dB per octave) from the slope of the straight line that enters this break from the left.

29-13 COMBINING THE SYSTEM ELEMENTS

As an example of a closed-loop regulator having three major energy-storage elements or time constants, Fig. 29-16 shows a dc generator whose output voltage is to be held constant; its field current is supplied by a smaller amplidyne generator. As is described in Sec. 32-1, this amplidyne has small current in its control field, which produces a larger current in the short circuit between two of its brushes; since this short-circuit current produces another field that is at 90° or "in quadrature" to the control field, this is called the quadrature circuit. A feedback signal from the output voltage of the main generator returns to the amplifier, which controls the tiny current in the control field of the amplidyne, thus completing the system loop. This voltage regulator is a type-0 servo.

In Fig. 29-16 the main generator field has 50 ohms of R and 25 henrys of L,; so its time constant $L/R = {}^{25}/_{50} = 0.5$ sec; it will cause a break at $\omega = 1/0.5$, or at 2 radians per second (rad/sec). The quadrature circuit of the amplidyne has 2 Ω of R and 0.2 H, a time constant of $0.2/2 = 0.1$ sec;

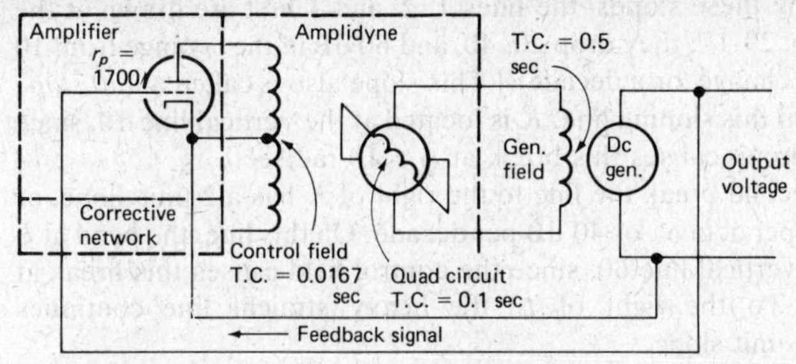

Figure 29-16 Time constants in a closed-loop system to regulate generator voltage.

it causes a break at $\omega = 1/0.1$, or at 10 rad/sec. Since the control field of the amplidyne is in series with a vacuum tube, the plate resistance of 1700 Ω is added to the 1600 Ω of the control-field winding; with 3300 Ω of R and 55 H, its time constant is $^{55}/_{3300} = 0.0167$ sec; its break occurs at $\omega = 1/0.0167$, or at 60 rad/sec. Thus three breaks will occur, at $\omega = 2$, $\omega = 10$, and $\omega = 60$ rad/sec.

The performance of this system (of Fig. 29-16) can be shown on the Bode diagram of Fig. 29-17 if a value is calculated or assumed for the overall amplification or loop gain of the system. (This identical system is used for the data shown in the table on page p. 462; the lower dashed curve in Fig. 29-17 shows the performance of this system at a low loop gain of 10, shown as 20 dB.) Using a high gain (such as 316 times, or 50 dB), the first heavy line is drawn horizontally at 50 dB in Fig. 29-17. At J the first break occurs, caused by the main generator field ($\omega = 2$). To the right of J, a line is drawn downward toward R at a slope of 6 dB per octave, or 20 dB per decade. [As

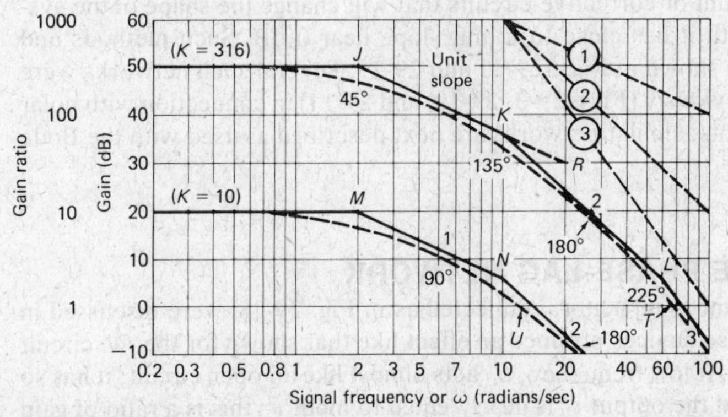

Figure 29-17 Bode diagram for study of regulator system of Fig. 29-16.

a guide in drawing these slopes, the lines 1, 2, and 3 first are drawn at the upper right in Fig. 29-17; they drop 20, 40, and 60 dB in the ω range from 10 to 100 (a 10-to-1 change, or a decade).] This slope also is called a *unit slope* (or slope of 1). On this sloping line, K is located at the vertical line 10, since the quadrature circuit causes this break at $\omega = 10$ rad/sec.

Beyond this second break the line to the right of K has a 2-unit slope, or decreases 12 dB per octave, or 40 dB per decade. On this line, the bend at L is located at the vertical line 60, since the control field causes this break at $\omega = 60$ rad/sec. To the right of L, the heavy straight line continues downward at a 3-unit slope.

29-14 STUDY OF THE BODE DIAGRAM

The true curve of system response next is drawn smoothly (as shown by the upper dashed curve in Fig. 29-17) so as to pass about 3 dB below each corner or break at J, K, and L. Not only does this curve show the amount of loop gain remaining at various signal frequencies; its slope indicates the amount of phase lag. Where the curve is parallel to a unit slope of 6 dB per octave, the phase lag of the system is 90°; a 2-unit slope indicates 180° lag. Beneath bend K the phase lag is 135°, increasing to 225° beneath L.

Since a system will hunt if the feedback signal lags by nearly 180° (when the loop gain is 0 dB or somewhat more), the high-gain upper curve in Fig. 29-17 indicates an unstable system, for the phase lag has reached 180° before the system line crosses the 0-dB line at T. However, the lower line MN shows how this system may become stable when the loop gain is reduced, for now the phase lag is not yet 180° at the point where the curve reaches 0 dB, near U.

After drawing the system action as in Fig. 29-17, designers may expect that the system will hunt, have poor response, or be unstable if the sloping true curve of the system has much more than a unit slope when it is near the 0-dB line. Therefore, to stabilize the high-gain system of Fig. 29-17, they will add antihunt or corrective circuits that will change the shape of the system curve until it has close to a unit slope near 0 dB. Such methods and results will be shown in Figs. 29-21 and 29-25. Several such networks were discussed previously (Figs. 29-3, 29-10, and 29-11) in connection with polar or Nyquist plots; similar networks are next described as used with the Bode diagram.

29-15 THE PHASE-LAG NETWORK

A resistor and a capacitor, connected as in Fig. 29-18, were discussed in Sec. 29-4; these devices produce an effect like that shown for the RL circuit in Fig. 29-15. At low frequency, C_1 acts almost like an open circuit; it has so little effect that the output v_o is nearly equal to input v_i; this is a ratio or gain

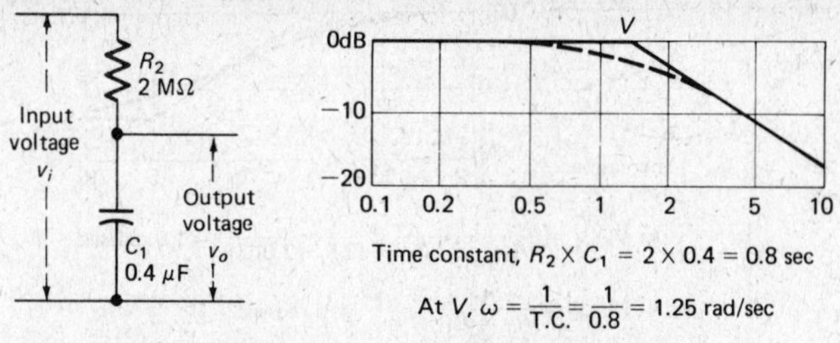

Figure 29-18 Bode diagram for *RC* phase-lag network.

of 1 and is shown as 0 dB in Fig. 29-18. However, as the signal frequency increases, more alternating current flows in C_1 and R_2, causing a voltage drop across R_2; the output v_o decreases (along a unit slope or a slope of 6 dB per octave), causing a loss in system response. At very high frequency, C_1 becomes almost a short circuit, so that nearly all the input is lost across R_2; the response curve continues downward to large (−dB) values or zero gain; a phase lag of 90° is produced. The break or corner in the curve is centered at V, where $\omega = 1/RC = 1.25$ rad/sec..

If this network is added into the system near a tube (as in Fig. 29-19), with the capacitor at position C_x, the conditions are the same as in Fig. 29-18. However, if the capacitor is placed instead between tube grid and anode, its 0.4 microfarad (μF) may be more effective at C_1 than at C_x. If the tube has a gain of 8, C_1 acts like $(8 + 1) \times 0.4$ μF, and the corner or break is moved to the left accordingly (to 1.25/9, or 0.139 rad/sec).

Returning to the circuit of Fig. 29-18, if next a resistor R_1 is added in series with C_1 as shown in Fig. 29-20, this network causes *limited* lag or slowdown. The first corner, at V, is nearly the same as in Fig. 29-18; the time constant of $(R_1 + R_2) \times C_1 = \tau_1$ and causes the first break; so at V, $\omega_1 = 1/(0.5 + 1)0.4 = 1$ rad/sec. At high frequencies where C_1 becomes nearly a short circuit, R_1 and R_2 now act as a voltage divider, so that v_o becomes a fixed portion of v_1; there is no further loss in output at still higher

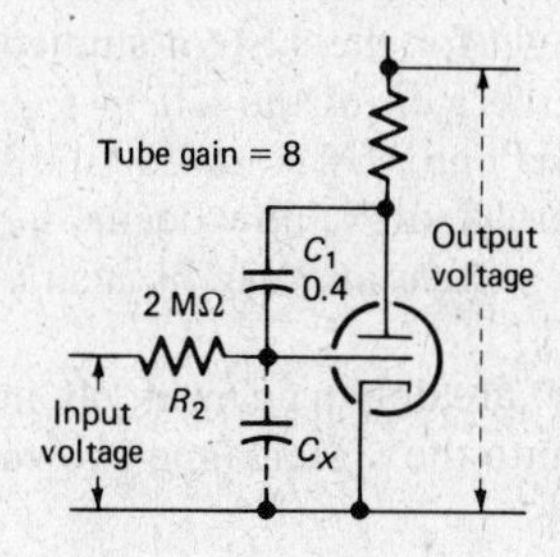

Figure 29-19 Anode-to-grid capacitor C_1 has greater effect than C_X.

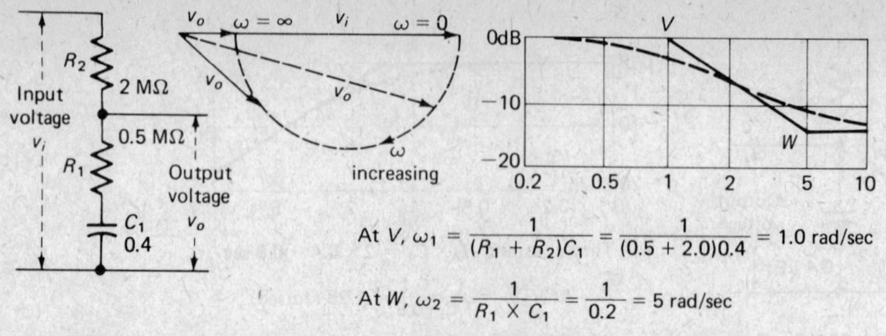

Figure 29-20 Addition of R_1 forms a *limited* phase-lag network.

frequencies; so the system curve again becomes horizontal. The second corner, at W in Fig. 29-20, depends on R_1 and C_1; so here $\omega_2 = 1/(0.5\ \text{M}\Omega \times 0.4\ \mu\text{F}) = 5$ rad/sec.

The transfer function or equation of this whole circuit is

$$\frac{v_o}{v_i} = \frac{j\omega\tau_2 + 1}{j\omega\tau_1 + 1}$$

The numerator term τ_2 is associated with the phase-lead action shown at W, which decreases the 1 downslope to a zero slope. The denominator value τ_1 is larger than τ_2 and causes the phase-lag action shown at V. When $\omega = 0$, the value of this equation is 1, which also is 0 dB. However, when ω reaches high values so that 1 is negligible compared with $j\omega\tau$, this equation reaches the value $j\omega\tau_2 / j\omega\tau_1 /$ or τ_2 / τ_1, which also is $R_1 / (R_1 + R_2)$. The voltage-divider action of R_1 and R_2 makes the output voltage $= 0.5 / (0.5 + 2.0)$, or 0.2, times the input voltage. A gain of 0.2 corresponds to -14 dB; so the horizontal line (to the right of W in Fig. 29-20) is lowered by 14 dB.

In any phase-lag network, notice that the capacitor is in a circuit *across* the output voltage; since the voltage of the capacitor does not change instantly, it "braces" the circuit against sudden changes, thus slowing the circuit action.

29-16 STABILIZING WITH A LAG NETWORK

Now see how the lag network of Fig. 29-20 is used to stabilize a closed-loop system. In Fig. 29-21, the solid line is drawn for the system studied previously in Figs. 29-16 and 29-17; however, the gain at the left in Fig. 29-21 is adjusted to 30 dB, so that the whole solid line MN is raised 10 dB higher than before. Since the second corner or break, at N, now occurs far above the 0-dB line, the feedback signal of this system may lag by nearly 180° at 0 dB, so hunting may be expected.

For comparison, the network lines of Fig. 29-20 are drawn again at VW in Fig. 29-21. If R_1, C_1, and R_2 now are connected into the system (and shown

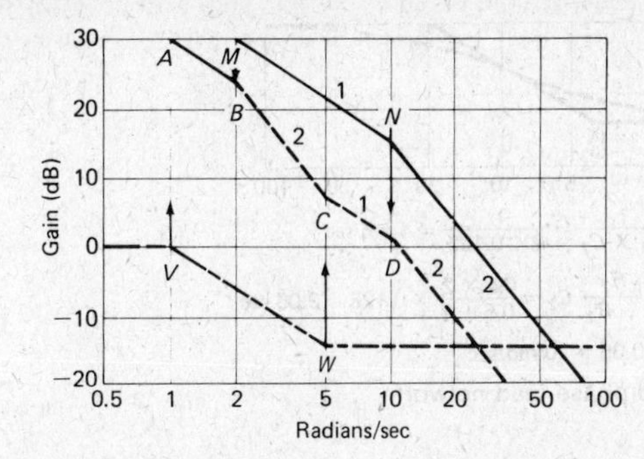

Figure 29-21 Network of Fig. 29-20 used to stabilize a system at higher gain.

as the corrective network in Fig. 29-16), the effect of this added network can be shown in Fig. 29-21. Starting at the left at a system gain of 30 dB, the corner at *V* causes a similar break at *A*; the system gain decreases, following the downward slope of 1. The corner at *B* is caused by the large generator field at *M*; the system quickly loses gain, along a slope of 2. The end of the downward slope at *W* causes a similar decrease of slope at *C*. The lag at *N*, caused by an amplidyne field, makes a similar break at *D* so that the system line returns to a slope of 2, below the 0-dB line. The slope of the true system curve, where it crosses the 0-dB line near *D*, has a value between the 1 and 2 slopes and indicates a phase lag of about 145°. This shows that the system now may be stable after adding the lag network. But gain is sacrificed, shown by the vertical distance between the solid line and the new dashed line.

29-17 THE PHASE-LEAD NETWORK

When two resistors and a capacitor are connected into a system as shown in Fig. 29-22 (also shown in Fig. 29-11), a phase lead or a speedup action is produced, thereby causing higher output of the system at higher signal frequencies. (Notice here that the capacitor is in a circuit *in series* with the signal; the signal must pass through C_2 or through resistor R_2 that parallels it. For an instant after a sudden signal is applied at the input, the C_2 voltage remains unchanged, making the entire signal appear at the output; then as C_2 changes its charge to match the signal, only part of the input signal remains at the output. In this way C_2 causes a forcing action each time that the input signal changes.) At a low signal frequency, capacitor C_2 passes very little current; so R_1 and R_2 act as an ordinary voltage divider; the output voltage v_o is a fraction (0.5/2.5 or 0.2) of the input v_i, so that the low-frequency gain is −14 dB, actually a loss. Such loss usually is offset by increasing the gain of the amplifier of the system.

As the signal frequency or ω rises, more ac passes through C_2 and R_1, increasing the output voltage across R_1; the loss in this network decreases as

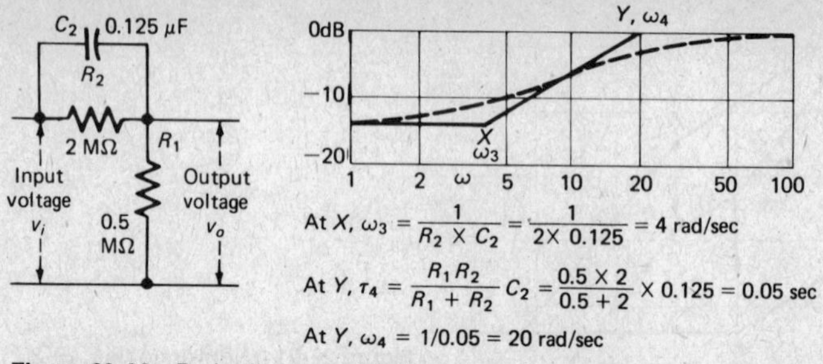

Figure 29-22 Bode diagram of limited phase-lead network.

ω rises. Finally, at high frequencies that make C_2 act as a short circuit across R_2, the output voltage equals the input voltage; so the gain becomes constant at 1, or at 0 dB.

The transfer function of this limited-lead network is

$$\frac{R_1}{R_1 + R_2} \times \frac{j\omega\tau_3 + 1}{j\omega\tau_4 + 1}$$

The numerator term τ_3 causes the phase lead at X, while τ_4 is associated with the phase lag at Y. Since τ_3 is larger than τ_4, then ω_3 is less than ω_4, so that X is to the left of Y. When $\omega = 0$, the value of this equation is $R_1/(R_1 + R_2) = 0.5/(0.5 + 2.0)$, or 0.2. Since a gain of 0.2 corresponds to −14 dB, the horizontal line (to the left of X in Fig. 29-22) is lowered by 14 dB. Now as ω reaches high values so that 1 is negligible compared with $j\omega\tau$, this equation reaches the value $R_1/(R_1 + R_2) \times \tau_3/\tau_4$, which is a gain of 1, or is 0 dB.

To determine the time constant that corresponds to ω_1 at V (Fig. 29-20), or to ω_4 at Y (Fig. 29-22), we must consider that the input voltage v_i is short-circuited. Thus, in Fig. 29-20, C_1 discharges through R_1 and R_2 in series, so that $\tau_1 = (R_1 + R_2)C_1$. However, in Fig. 29-22, C_2 discharges through R_2 and also discharges through a parallel circuit formed by R_1. For R_1 and R_2 in parallel, $\tau_4 = R_1R_2C_2/(R_1 + R_2)$.

29-18 BODE DIAGRAM OF A TYPE-1 SERVO

As we discussed in Sec. 29-9, the type-1 servo includes a motor that must start from rest so as to correct the *position* of an object; this is indicated by a separate $j\omega$ term in the denominator of the transfer function of such a system. As a simple example, the system

$$\frac{316}{j\omega(j\omega 2 + 1)\,(j\omega 0.004 + 1)}$$

is considered; its Bode plot appears in Fig. 29-23. For this plot, the gain of

316 will be shown as 50 dB (at R). For the time constants of 2 and 0.04 sec, bends occur at 0.5 and 25 rad/sec.

But the separate $j\omega$ term must be included. At very low frequencies, as ω nears 0, the $j\omega$ term (in the denominator) makes the equation approach infinite value. Consider first the equation $1/j\omega$; this shows a phase lag of 90° and has a value of 1 when $\omega = 1$; if $\omega = 0.5$, the line value = 2, which is 6 dB. As is shown in the lower left corner of Fig. 29-23, the Bode plot of $1/j\omega$ is a straight downward slope of 6 dB per octave that crosses 0 dB at $\omega = 1$ rad/sec.

Similarly, $316/j\omega$ is shown by a straight line of unit downward slope that crosses 50 dB at $\omega = 1$ rad/sec. (This line also crosses 0 dB where $\omega = 316$ rad/sec.) For the complete system, this line P to R is drawn first. Since the term $j\omega 2 + 1$ *increases* the slope by one unit, at Q a line is drawn with 2 slope, or at 12 dB per octave; at S (for $j\omega 0.04 + 1$) a line is continued at 3 slope. When the true curve of this system is shown by the dashed line in Fig. 29-23, it passes about 3 dB below Q, and here its phase lag is 135°; also, about 3 dB below S, the line slope corresponds to a lag of 225°.

For this system, the true curve is far below R when $\omega = 1$ rad/sec. The line P to R merely locates the initial unit slope of this type-1 servo before the time constants have any effect. When the value 1 is used for ω in the complete system equation, the mathematical result shows a gain of 141 at a phase lag of 156°. Since a 141 gain is 43 dB, this value is shown by the true curve at U.

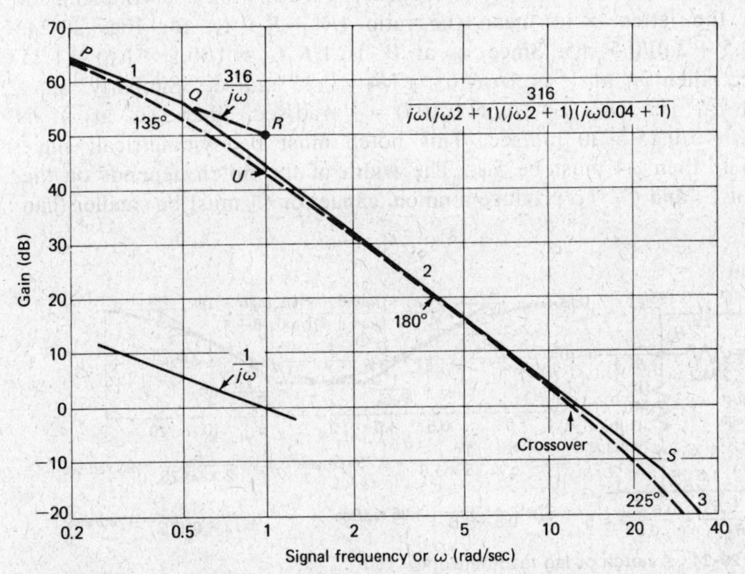

Figure 29-23 Bode diagram of type-1 servo.

Figure 29-23 shows that this type-1 servo is not stable, even though it has only two time constants. The system reaches 180° phase lag at a point about midway between Q and S, at which point the gain still is 20 dB. At the point where the true curve crosses 0 dB, the phase lag has increased to 200°, called the *crossover angle;* this occurs where $\omega = 11$ rad/sec, called the *crossover frequency.* Without decrease of gain at low or very high frequencies, the unstable system of Fig. 29-23 can be made stable by the use of the notch network next described.

29-19 THE NOTCH, OR LAG-LEAD, NETWORK

For use in stabilizing a high-gain servo, the phase-lead network of Sec. 29-17 usually is combined with a phase-lag network; this combination is called a "notch network." The lead network of Fig. 29-22 is made into a notch network merely by inserting a capacitor C_1 in series with R_1, as shown in Fig. 29-24. Here C_1 is 1.6 μF, or is four times the size of the C_1 used in Fig. 29-20; therefore, the bends at V and W now occur at 0.25 and 1.25 rad/sec, just one-fourth of their former values. Except for this change, we see that the slanting-line diagram of this network is like that of Fig. 29-20 added to that of Fig. 29-22. This combined diagram shows (at $VWXY$) the notch shape from which this network is named; the four time constants appear in the transfer function shown above the notch.

The choice of R_1 and R_2 determines the depth of the notch and also the ratio of ω_1 to ω_2. In Fig. 29-24, the voltage-divider ratio $R_1/(R_1 + R_2) = 0.2$, so the notch depth is -14 dB. Many servo engineers assign the letter α to mean the ratio $(R_1 + R_2)/R_1$; for Fig. 29-24, $\alpha = (0.5 + 2.0)/0.5 = 5$. Since ω_2 at W is $1/R_1C_1 = 1/(0.5 \times 1.6) = 1.25$ rad/sec, then ω_1 at V is $1/\alpha R_1 C_1 = 1/4 = 0.25$ rad/sec. Similarly, since ω_3 at X is $1/R_2C_2 = 1/(2 \times 0.125) = 4$ rad/sec, then ω_4 at Y is $\alpha/R_1C_1 = 5/0.25 = 20$ rad/sec. This notch must be symmetrical; since $\omega_2 = 5\omega_1$, then $\omega 4$ must be $5\omega_3$. The width of the notch depends on the sizes of C_1 and C_2. To produce a notch, capacitor C_2 must be smaller than C_1/α.

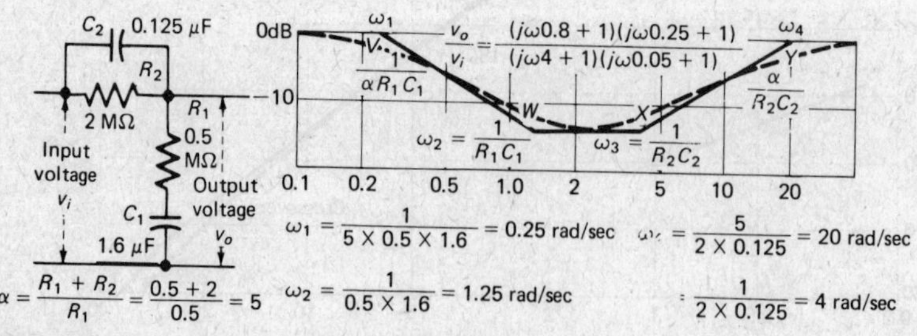

Figure 29-24 A notch or lag-lead network.

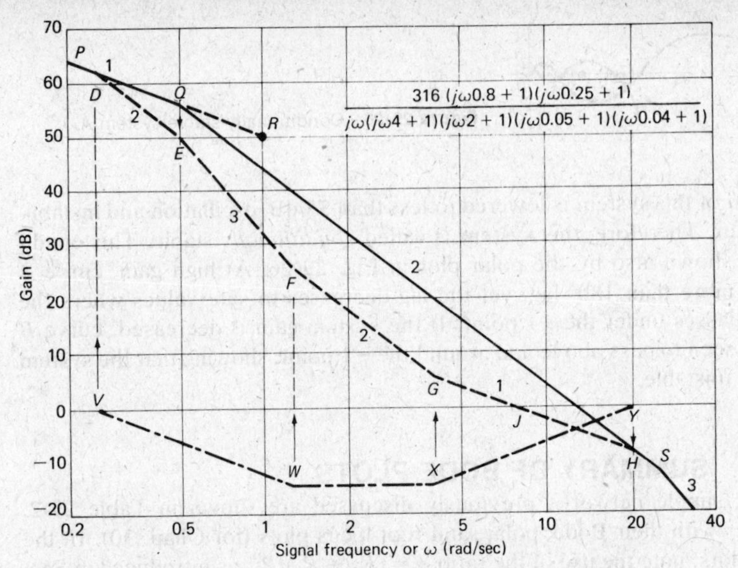

Figure 29-25 Notch network of Fig. 29-24 used to stabilize a system.

29-20 STABILIZING WITH A NOTCH NETWORK

To illustrate how this network may be applied, Fig. 29-25 shows again the solid line *PQS* from Fig. 29-23; lines *VWXY* are added from Fig. 29-24.

If the notch network now is connected into the circuit of the system, the effect of this added network can be shown by the dashed line *DEFGH* in Fig. 29-25. The first break, at *D*, corresponds to corner *V* of the notch. The effect of the large system time constant at *Q* causes a second break at *E*, so that the system gain decreases rapidly along a slope of 3. The notch corner *W* causes the break at *F*, decreasing the slope. A short distance above the 0-dB line, another corner *G* is caused by the upward bend of the notch network (at *X*); this decreases the slope so that the line *GH* has only a unit slope when it crosses the 0-dB line. This fulfills the main requirement in this Bode diagram, to show that this corrected system now may be stable. The break at *H* is caused by the notch network (at *Y*); here the system line returns to a slope of 2, then later to a slope of 3 (because of the smaller time constant of the original system, at *S*).

Because of the added notch network, the true system curve now crosses 0 dB at *J*, at a phase lag of only 160° This can be confirmed by substitution of the crossover frequency $\omega = 8$ into the complete transfer function shown in Fig. 29-25.

The line *DEFGH* includes a 3 slope between *E* and *F*, and the true curve has greater than 180° phase lag within this section. However, so long as this 180° lag does not occur below the 10-dB line, it does not cause instability. If

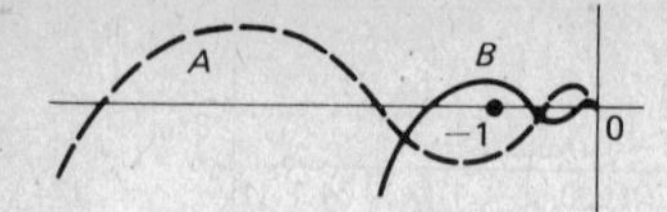

Figure 29-26 Conditionally stable system *A*.

the gain of this system is lowered to less than 35 dB, oscillation and instability occur. Therefore, this system is called *conditionally* stable. This condition is shown also by the polar plot in Fig. 29-26. At high gain, curve *A* shows more than 180° lag, yet the lag decreases to safe values where the curve passes under the −1 point. If the system gain is decreased, curve *B* now is seen to pass above and around the −1 point, showing that the system now is unstable.

29-21 SUMMARY OF BODE PLOTS

Four simple networks previously discussed are shown in Table 29-2, together with their Bode, polar, and root-locus plots (for Chap. 30). In the Bode plots, note the use of the ratio $\alpha = (R_1 + R_2)/R_1$, as introduced in Sec. 29-19.

Any logarithmic or Bode diagram consists of only four kinds of term or "building block"; three of these have been used above.

TABLE 29-2

Network	Equation	Bode lines	Polar plot	Root locus
R_2, C_1; Lag	$\dfrac{1}{j\omega\tau_1 + 1}$; $\tau_1 = R_2C_1$	ω_1	$\omega = 0$, V_i, V_o, ω; See Fig. 29-3	$1/\tau_1$
R_2, R_1, C_1; Limited lag	$\dfrac{j\omega\tau_2 + 1}{j\omega\tau_1 + 1}$; $\tau_1 = (R_1 + R_2)C_1$; $\tau_2 = R_1C_1$	$\omega_1 = \omega_2/\alpha$; $\dfrac{1}{R_1C_1} = \omega_2$	$\omega = \infty$, V_i, V_o, ω; See Fig. 29-20	$1/\tau_2$, $1/\tau_1$
C_2, R_1; Lead	$\dfrac{\omega\tau_4}{j\omega\tau_4 + 1}$; $\tau_4 = R_1C_2$	ω_4	V_i, ω, V_o, $\omega = \infty$; See Fig. 29-10	$1/\tau_4$
C_2, R_2, R_1; Limited lead	$\dfrac{R_1(j\omega\tau_3 + 1)}{(R_1 + R_2)(j\omega\tau_4 + 1)}$; $\tau_3 = R_2C_2$; $\tau_4 = \dfrac{R_1R_2}{R_1 + R_2}C_2$	$\alpha\omega_3 = \omega_4$; $\omega_3 = \dfrac{1}{R_2C_2}$	V_o, ω, $\omega = 0$, V_i; See Fig. 29-11	$1/\tau_4$, $1/\tau_3$

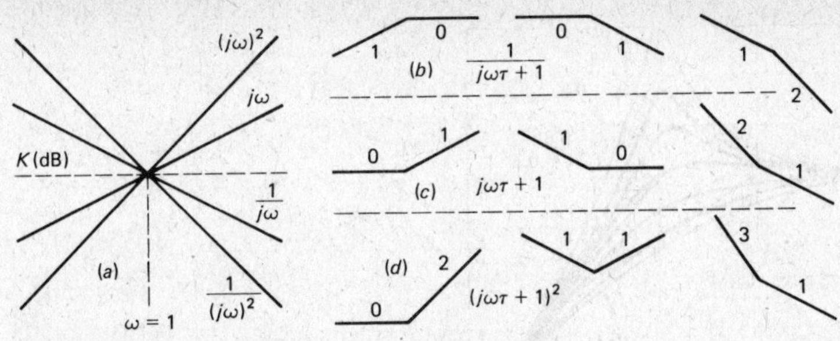

Figure 29-27 Basic terms used in Bode diagrams.

1. A constant, such as K or the ratio $(R_1 + R_2)/R_1$. This term is not affected by ω or frequency; so it is a horizontal straight line of constant dB value.
2. The term $(j\omega)^{\pm n}$. If $n = -1$, the resulting $1/j\omega$ is the term that identifies a type-1 servo; it is plotted as a straight line having downward slope of 1. Similarly, $(j\omega)^{-2}$ shows the type-2 servo, plotted as a straight line sloping downward at 12 dB per octave. As shown in Fig. 29-27*a*, any one of these lines crosses $\omega = 1$ at a value of dB corresponding to the system gain K.
3. The term $(j\omega\tau + 1)^{\pm n}$. If $n = -1$, the resulting $1/(j\omega\tau + 1)$ is the familiar downward bend or break caused by a time-constant term located in the denominator; this term always causes the amount of phase lag to increase by 1 unit of slope, as in Fig. 29-27*b*. Similarly, when $n = +1$, the $(j\omega\tau + 1)$ is a numerator term, and is associated with an upward bend that decreases the phase lag by 1 unit, as in Fig. 29-27*c*. For $(j\omega\tau + 1)^2$, two numerator or phase-lead terms have the same time constant and the same value of ω; at this bend, the phase lead is increased by 2 units of slope, as shown in Fig. 29-27*d*.
4. The fourth kind of term shows what happens in a system that contains two equal time constants, as this system becomes underdamped. (Damping ratio ζ is discussed in Sec. 28-15.) In Fig. 29-28, the bottom curve A shows the response of the system $1/(j\omega 0.2 + 1)\,(j\omega 0.05 + 1)$, which has breaks at $\omega = 5$ and $\omega = 20$ rad/sec. As is discussed in Sec. 30-5, these two separate time constants or roots indicate that the system is overdamped. As damping decreases, these two roots move together until they become equal. The equation $1/(j\omega 0.1 + 1)^2$ has a break at $\omega = 10$ for each of the two roots, so that the phase lag increases from 0 slope to a downward slope of 2. The true curve, at B, passes about 6 dB below the corner at $\omega = 10$; this is the condition called *critical* damping, where damping ratio $\zeta = 1.0$. The denominator portion of $1/(j\omega 0.1 + 1)^2$ corresponds to the quadratic $(s + 10)^2$ as shown in Table 30-1; this expands to $s^2 + \zeta 20s + 100$, when $\zeta = 1.0$. With further

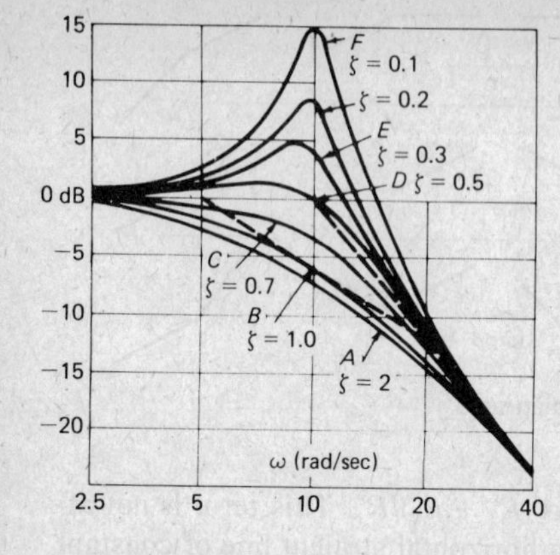

Figure 29-28 Bode diagrams of two-pole system as ζ is varied.

decrease in damping until $\zeta = 0.7$, the quadratic equation becomes $s^2 + 14s + 100$ and the corresponding system performance is shown at C. For $\zeta = 0.5$, giving $s^2 + 10s + 100$, the curve D in Fig. 29-28 shows increased gain near the resonant or natural $\omega = 10$; in this way the Bode plot shows that this system tends toward oscillation and toward the overshoot shown in Fig. 28-10. A damping factor as low as $\zeta = 0.3$ sometimes is used (causing 36 percent overshoot in Fig. 28-10), so that the system gain increases by about 5 dB as shown at E. A value of ζ as low as 0.1 cannot be tolerated because of its high overshoot; at F, Fig. 29-28 shows the 15-dB (or 6 times) increase in gain that makes this system oscillatory and useless.

The behavior of the roots of the system equation, as just now discussed, is used in the root-locus method described in the next chapter.

Problems

29-1 True or false? Explain why.

(a) A motor may be added to convert a regulator into a servomechanism.

(b) Some servos do not need to be stable, since they are intended for use with steady signals.

(c) Steady-state accuracy of a servomechanism is better than that of a regulator.

(d) A servo with better frequency response is less likely to be unstable.

(e) Every device that stores energy has a time constant.

(f) Automobile power steering is a type-1 servo.

(g) If a system element decreases the phase lag, it weakens the response.

(h) A servo should not be a good oscillator.

(i) Any feedback signal that lags 180° behind the input signal causes instability.

(j) Transfer function is another name for voltage efficiency of a circuit.

(k) A system having one large time constant has better frequency response than a system (with the same steady-state gain) that has three or four small time constants.

(l) If the time constant τ is stated in seconds, then the frequency $1/\tau$ is given in cycles per second.

(m) The numerical value of almost any transfer function changes when the input frequency changes.

(n) Most servo systems have only a single loop.

(o) Using a Bode diagram, the true response of the system falls exactly along a number of straight lines.

(p) Using the data tabulated in Sec. 29-6, B/R is close to 2.5 when gain $K = 20$.

(q) The polar plot of this system $\frac{800}{(j\omega 5 + 1)(j\omega 2 + 1)}$ passes through $-1.1, j0$.

(r) A regulator that contains four phase lags, at $\tau_1 = 1$ sec, $\tau_2 = 0.1$ sec, $\tau_3 = 0.02$ sec, $\tau_4 = 0.01$ sec, is stable if its steady-state gain $= 20$ dB.

(s) A system tends to become less stable if one large phase lag τ is added.

Figure Problems 29-2 to 29-6

29-2 Curve B shows the performance of a system whose transfer function is $\dfrac{6}{j\omega(j\omega\tau_1 + 1)(j\omega\tau_2 + 1)}$, wherein 6 is the system gain $K\beta$. (*a*) By trial measurements find the largest value of B/R. (*b*) If the gain is doubled, find the largest B/R. (*c*) Using an M circle, find the system gain that limits B/R to 2.3.

29-3 Curve D applies to a system when its gain $K\beta = 16$. (*a*) For what value of M is a circle drawn that is tangent to curve D at $-0.9, -j0.2$? (*b*) Find the largest B/R ratio when $K\beta = 8$. (*c*) Find the value of $K\beta$ that causes constant continuous oscillation (indicated because the system curve passes through $-1, j0$). (Curves are shown in Fig. Prob. 29-2.)

29-4 Curve E applies to a system when its gain $K\beta = 40$. (*a*) Find the largest value of B / R and describe the stability of the system at this gain. (*b*) If the gain is decreased to 20, find the greatest B/R and describe the system stability.

29-5 Curve C applies to a system when $K\beta = 12$. (*a*) By trial measurements find the largest value of B/R. (*b*) Describe system stability at this gain. (*c*) Find the largest gain at which B/R is not greater than 2.

29-6 Curve A applies to a system when its gain is 4. (*a*) By inspection determine the largest B/R ratio at this gain. Find the largest gain at which B / R is not greater than (*b*) 2.0 and (*c*) 4.0.

29-7 For a servo whose transfer function is $K\beta/j\omega(j\omega\tau_1 + 1)(j\omega\tau_2 + 1)$, find what value of loop gain $K\beta$ will produce a B/R ratio of 2, by constructing suitable M circles and by plotting the system curve. Let $\tau_1 = 0.5$ sec and $\tau_2 = 0.1$ sec.

Note: to obtain reasonable accuracy in such plots, the distance between -1 and 0 should be at least 4 inches.

29-8 Repeat Prob. 29-7, letting $\tau_1 = 0.2$ sec and $\tau_2 = 0.06$ sec. Find $K\beta$ and ω for a B/R ratio of (*a*) 1.7, and (*b*) 2.6.

29-9 A regulator has only two dynamic elements, at $\tau_1 = 0.2$ sec and $\tau_2 = 0.05$ sec. When the open-loop gain is 30, plot the polar curve between values of $\omega = 40$ and $\omega = 100$ rad/sec. (*a*) From this curve, find the greatest value of B/R, and the system frequency at which this occurs. (*b*) Find ω when the phase lag is 90°. (*c*) Repeat (*a*) and (*b*) when open-loop gain is reduced to 20.

29-10 Plot the transfer function $\dfrac{K}{j\omega(j\omega\tau_1 + 1)(j\omega\tau_2 + 1)}$ for $K = 10$, at the points between $\omega = 4$ and $\omega = 12$ rad / sec. $\tau_1 = 0.2$ sec and $\tau_2 = 0.05$ sec. Find the maximum allowable gain K and the corresponding frequency if the output-input ratio is not to exceed (*a*) 1.75, or (*b*)

3.0. (*c*) To retain the same B/R ratio as found in (*a*) of Prob. 29-9, find the change in gain K that is needed because of the $j\omega$ term added in Prob. 29-10.

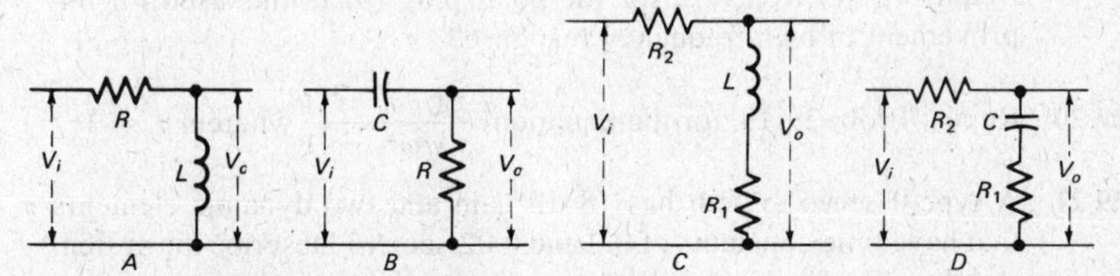

Figure Problems 29-11 to 29-16

29-11 (*a*) Write the transfer function for network A, showing numerical values. Let $R = 32$ ohms (Ω), $L = 8$ henrys (H). (*b*) Draw the Bode plot, labeling the true curve with values of dB and ω, at three points. (*c*) Show the polar plot, to scale.

29-12 Repeat Prob. 29-11, for network B. Let $R = 500$ kΩ, $C = 0.2$ μF.

29-13 Repeat Prob. 29-11, for network C. Let $R_1 = 30$ Ω, $R_2 = 120$ Ω, $L = 20$ H.

29-14 Repeat Prob. 29-11, for network C. Let $R_1 = 25$ Ω, $R_2 = 175$ Ω, $L = 50$ H.

29-15 Repeat Prob. 29-11, for network D. Let $C = 0.1$ μF, $\tau_1 = 0.2$ sec, $\tau_2 = 0.025$ sec. (*d*) Find the ohms of each resistor.

29-16 Repeat Prob. 29-11, for network D if the shortest $\tau = 0.02$ sec and $R_2 = 600$ kΩ. As ω changes from 0 to ∞, v_o varies a total of 12 dB. (*d*) Find R_1 and C.

29-17 A corrective network has the polar plot shown in E. (*a*) Show a circuit for this network, giving values for each R and C used. (*b*) Draw the corresponding Bode plot, showing numerical values of ω and dB.

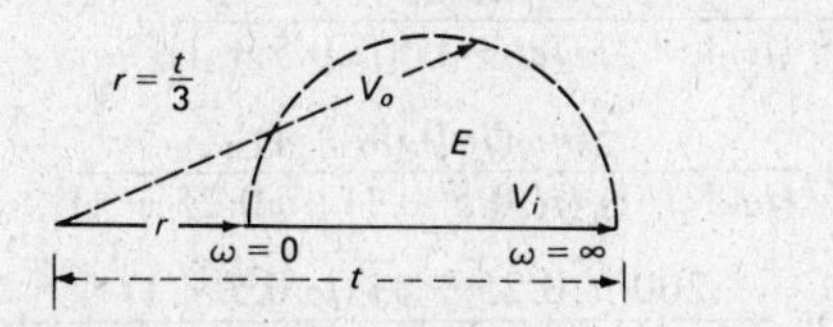

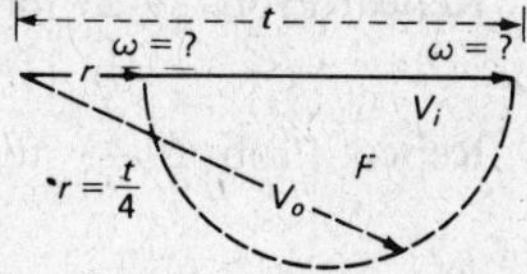

Figure Problem 29-17

29-18 Repeat Prob. 29-17 for the plot shown in F. Add values of ω on the F plot.

29-19 A corrective RC network has the equation $\dfrac{j\omega\tau_1 + 1}{j\omega\tau_2 + 1}$, wherein $\tau_2 = 4\tau_1$. (*a*) Sketch the circuit and select suitable values of R and C. (*b*) Show the Bode plot and label it with values of amplitude and frequency. (*c*) Repeat *b* for the polar plot. (*d*) Is this used for improvement of high-frequency response?

29-20 Repeat Prob. 29-19, for the equation $\dfrac{\tau_2(j\omega\tau_1 + 1)}{\tau_1(j\omega\tau_2 + 1)}$ wherein $\tau_1 = 3\tau_2$.

29-21 A type-0 servo system has 18 dB gain and two dynamic elements that have time constants of 0.2 and 0.02 sec. (*a*) Describe the system stability. (*b*) How much better is the steady-state accuracy than it would be if the system were an open loop?

29-22 A system has been found to be stable, and it contains no time constant longer than 0.07 sec. However, the network shown is inserted later in the amplifier of the system, and the amplifier gain also is increased by 20 dB. (*a*) Describe the purpose or results of this change. (*b*) What is the effect on the stability?

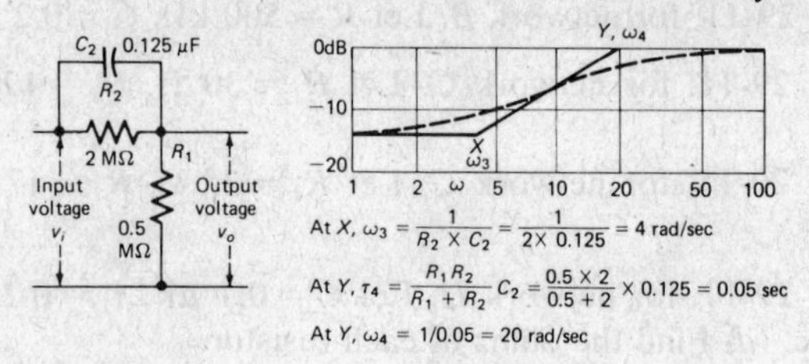

29-23 A system function is $\dfrac{560(j\omega 0.1 + 1)}{j\omega(j\omega 0.5 + 1)(j\omega 0.01 + 1)}$. (*a*) Plot the Bode diagram of the system. (*b*) Find the crossover frequency (rad/sec). (*c*) Comment on the system stability.

29-24 Repeat Prob. 29-23 for $\dfrac{560\,(j\omega 0.05 + 1)}{(j\omega 2 + 1)(j\omega 0.5 + 1)(j\omega 0.005 + 1)}$.

29-25 Repeat Prob. 29-23 for $\dfrac{40\,j\omega(j\omega 0.25 + 1)}{(j\omega 4 + 1)(j\omega + 1)(j\omega 0.5 + 1)}$.

29-26 Repeat Prob. 29-23 for $\dfrac{56 j\omega(j\omega 0.08 + 1)}{(j\omega 2 + 1)(j\omega 0.5 + 1)(j\omega 0.25 + 1)}$.

29-27 Repeat Prob. 29-23 for $\dfrac{200(j\omega 0.25 + 1)(j\omega 0.5 + 1)}{j\omega(j\omega 0.05 + 1)(j\omega + 1)(j\omega 2 + 1)}$. (*d*) If $(j\omega 2 + 1)$ is in the original system before correction, explain whether the other time constants form a symmetrical notch network, of the type shown in Fig. 29-24.

30

SERVO ANALYSIS BY THE ROOT-LOCUS METHOD

Feedback control systems often are analyzed by the root-locus method, proposed by W. R. Evans; this involves making a plot of the roots of the open-loop equation of the servo system. As the gain of the closed-loop servo is increased, the position of each root changes gradually and thereby traces a path or locus; by observing these paths, we may select the permissible amplifier gain or the corrections needed.

By use of the methods described in Chap. 29, we may study the system response as the frequency of the input signal is varied. In contrast, the root-locus method is not based on frequency response; instead, this chapter deals with the transient response, and lets us find what gain can be used without exceeding the permissible overshoot (described in Sec. 28-15 and Fig. 28-10).

30-1 OUTLINE OF PROCEDURE

The root-locus method is mainly graphic. The steps to be followed are listed here, to be explained in later sections.

1. Determine the time constants and write the equation or transfer function of the servo system being studied; this then is expressed in terms of the transform operator s, and in normalized form.
2. In the s or complex plane, plot the roots of the above open-loop equation. These also are the roots of the closed loop when gain $= 0$ (or with no feedback signal).
3. After closing the loop, trace the movement or locus of each root, as the system gain K_0 is increased; this "180° locus" is obtained by graphic procedure as is outlined later in Rules A to G.[30-9]

4. Calibrate this closed-loop locus by finding graphically the values of K_o that must exist at various points in the locus.
5. From this root locus select the desired K_o for this system, or determine what form of correction is needed. After each correction is added in the system, a new root-locus diagram must be plotted.

30-2 SYSTEM EXAMPLE 1

A type-1 servo is shown in Fig. 30-1, which includes a motor M that positions a load in response to the command signal R as set by dial P_1. The motor and load have the time constant $\tau_1 = J/D = 0.4$ sec. (Recall that D includes motor behavior called *viscous damping*, as mentioned in Sec. 28-12.) Generator G furnishes a gain, and has the time constant $\tau_2 = L/R = 0.125$ sec. Let K_o equal the total overall forward gain of the system, including tube and generator-G gains, and motor constant $1/D$ (which appears in the transfer function derived in Sec. 29-10). Let feedback factor β of the potentiometer P_2 be unity (1 volt per radian).

Step 1. The transfer function of this system of Fig. 30-1 is

$$\frac{K_o}{j\omega(j\omega\tau_1 + 1)(j\omega\tau_2 + 1)}$$

In terms of operator s (for initial conditions = 0), this becomes

$$\frac{K_o}{s(0.4 + 1)(0.125s + 1)}$$

Here the letter s merely replaces each $j\omega$ in the system equation. Each numerical value of s must be found, for it becomes a root of the equation. To normalize this equation, the term $(0.4s + 1)$ is multiplied by 2.5, to become $(s + 2.5)$; the numerator likewise is multiplied by 2.5, so as not to

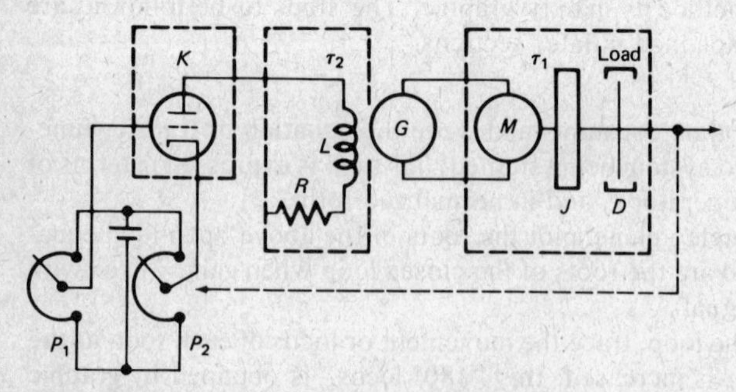

Figure 30-1 System Example 1 (a type-1 servo).

change the value of the equation. Similarly, the term $(0.125s + 1)$ is multiplied by $1/0.125$, or 8, to become $(s + 8)$; the numerator is multiplied by 8 also. Therefore, above the line a figure 20 is inserted (which is 2.5×8). The resulting

$$\frac{20K_o}{s(s + 2.5)(s + 8)}$$

has the same value as the original equation, but is in normalized form.

Now the root values are found by giving zero value to each term containing s; thus $(s + 2.5) = 0$, or $s = -2.5$. Similarly, $(s + 8) = 0$, so $s = -8$. The first s term in the denominator of the equation above is a root, $s = 0$. Each of these values is a "real" root, to be located on the horizontal centerline (called the *real axis*) in a plane as shown in Fig. 30-2.

Looking ahead to a second example (Sec. 30-8) where the system equation contains the term $(s^2 + 5s + 25)$, the values of s are found by use of the quadratic equation, so that

$$s = \frac{-5 \pm \sqrt{5^2 - 4 \times 1 \times 25}}{2} = -2.5 \pm j4.32$$

Here j represents $\sqrt{-1}$, an imaginary quantity that is plotted vertically, at an angle of 90° with the real axis. Now s has two values, located at equal distances of 4.32 above and below the real axis, and on a vertical line passing through -2.5 on the real axis. These are called a *conjugate pair* of complex roots. The plane or area on which both the real quantities and j quantities are plotted is called the *complex* plane or s plane. Thus the equation of Example 1, when normalized to make all coefficients of s equal to unity, becomes

$$\frac{20K_o}{s(s + 2.5)(s + 8)}$$

where 20 is the *normalizing constant*, but K_o still is the system gain.

Step 2. The roots of this equation, $s = 0$, $s = -2.5$, $s = -8$, are shown in Fig. 30-2, plotted on the real axis of the complex or s plane. The symbol × is used to indicate that each of these roots is located in the denominator of the system equation and is called a *pole*. Similarly, in a system equation that includes *numerator* terms like $(s + 1.5)$, as shown in Example 2 in Sec. 30-8, this numerator root $s = -1.5$ is indicated by a circle symbol ○; this is called a *zero*. (As such a root approaches 0, it causes the whole equation to become zero.)

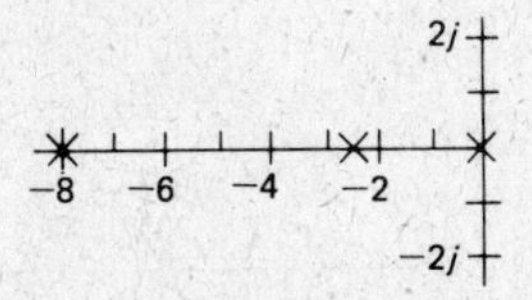

Figure 30-2 Plot of open-loop real roots in a complex plane.

30-3 STEP 3. CLOSING THE LOOP

The roots, as plotted in Fig. 30-2, are obtained from the open-loop transfer function, and are used as starting points for the study of closed-loop conditions.

Figure 30-3 shows the block diagram for a closed loop. At the error detector (shown as ⊗, called also a *summing point*), the feedback B is subtracted from the command R to produce the error E; thus $E = R - B$. The controlled quantity is C. Gain K is the constant portion of open-loop gain, not affected by signal frequency; G is the transfer function or frequency-sensitive portion (containing $j\omega$ terms) of the forward loop, while H is the similar transfer function of the feedback elements. Here $C = KGE$ and $B = HC$. Since error $E = R - HC$, then $R = E + HC = E + HKGE$. The input-output or closed-loop equation is

$$\frac{C}{R} = \frac{KGE}{E + KGHE} \quad \text{or} \quad \frac{KG}{1 + KGH}$$

Here the denominator has roots whose combined values equal $KGH = -1$; each of the roots that make up this total must be located. (To simplify later discussion, it is assumed here that the H elements $= 1$ and can be omitted.)

The root-locus method helps to find these closed-loop denominator roots by recognizing that a value of -1 is obtained when a $+1$ (an arrow 1 unit long, pointing to the right) is rotated through 180°. Thus $KGH = +1 \ \underline{/180°}$, and this says that the product of the sizes of all these roots must equal 1, and the sum of all their angles = 180°. Therefore, the root-locus method first locates and plots all values of s that make the KGH equation have a total phase shift of 180° (or 540° or 900°, etc.).

In Fig. 30-4 a trial point s_1 has been selected on the s plane, along with the poles plotted in Fig. 30-2. The angle from each pole to s_1 is marked; here angles $A + B + C = 20° + 56° + 104° = 180°$. Since the combined angles to s_1 total 180°, this trial point s_1 lies on the 180° locus. Note that the same angle values can be measured from the single point s_1, as shown at D, E, and F; this easier form of adding angles is used in Figs. 30-5 and 30-8.

When many such trial points are located, like s_1 above, a line may be drawn through them; each such line is called a 180° locus. Two or more such lines become the 180° loci of the system.

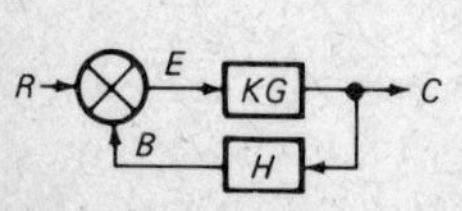

Figure 30-3 Block diagram for closing the loop.

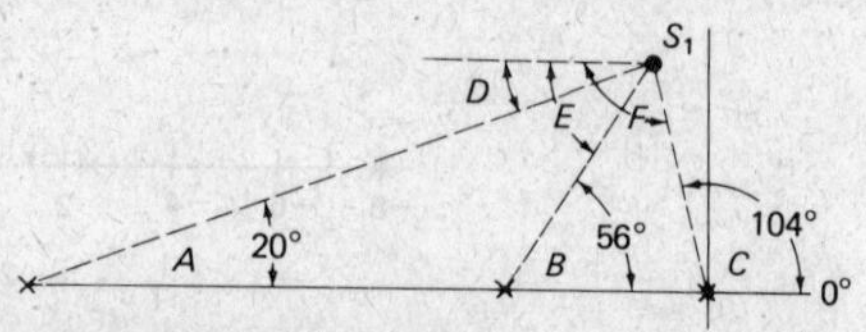

Figure 30-4 Angles measured from open-loop roots to a trial point s_1.

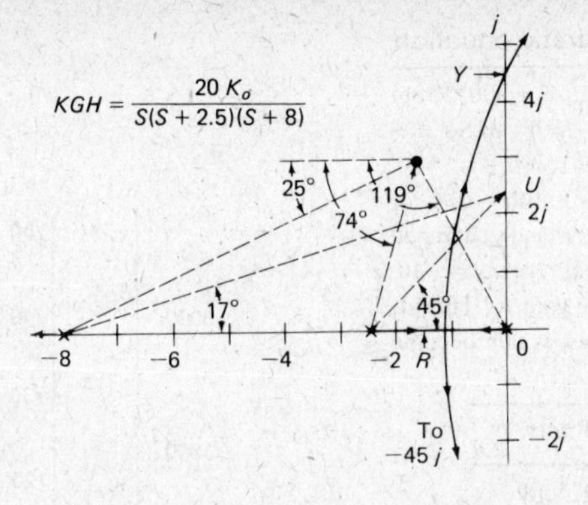

Figure 30-5 Steps to locate the 180° loci.

When a closed loop has zero gain, it acts like an open loop. Thus each open-loop root plotted in Fig. 30-2 becomes also a closed-loop root when $K_o = 0$; as such it serves as a starting point for one 180° locus. The problem is to find how the values and locations of these closed-loop roots change as the system gain K_o is increased.

For the system of Fig. 30-1, the open-loop equation is shown again in Fig. 30-5; the open-loop roots are shown at ×.

30-4 PORTIONS OF LOCI IN THE REAL AXIS

Step 3 may be started by locating those portions of the 180° loci that lie in the real axis. To do this, some value s_1 is selected on the real axis, as shown at point R in Fig. 30-5. Since R is directly to the right of the root at −2.5, the angle is 0° from this root to s_1. Similarly, the angle from −8 to s_1 is 0°. However, since R is directly to the left of the root located at 0, an angle of 180° exists from this origin root to s_1. Since the sum of these three angles is 180°, the locus of the 180° points lies all along the real axis between −2.5 and 0, and is so marked by the heavy line. But a total of 360° exists when s_1 is chosen between −2.5 and −8; this acts as 0°; so no 180° locus lies here.

Another portion of the 180° locus exists along the real axis for values of s to the left of the root at −8; here the angle from each open-loop root to s is 180°; so the total of 540° acts the same as 180°.

30-5 LOCI LEAVING THE REAL AXIS

As the system gain K_o becomes greater than zero, the closed-loop roots move from −2.5 and 0 toward each other along the real axis. As they meet, they leave the real axis at 90°; one root moves upward, the other moves downward, thus forming a conjugate pair of complex roots. This is the normal action of a quadratic equation, whose two roots behave in a similar fash-

TABLE 30-1 Plot of roots of quadratic equation

Consider a system with $D = 40$, $J = 2$, $K = 200$. From equation (20) of Sec. 28-18, $s^2 + Ds/J + K/J = 0$. So $s^2 + 20s + 100 = 0$. From equation (21), $s^2 + 2\zeta\omega_n s + \omega_n^2 = 0$, $\omega_n^2 = 100$, so $\omega_n = 10$. $s^2 + 20\zeta s + 100 = 0$, or $(s + 10)^2 = 0$. So the above system is critically damped ($\zeta = 1.0$), and there are two real and equal roots, $s = -10$.

Now hold D at 40, J at 2, but vary the gain K. This affects ω_n and D_{crit}. Plot the resulting roots, which become complex when K exceeds 200.

K	ω_n	Equation	Roots, s
72	6	$s^2 + 20s + 36$	$-2, -18$
150		$s^2 + 20s + 75$	$-5, -15$
200	10	$s^2 + 20s + 100$	$-10, -10$
400	14+	$s^2 + 20s + 200$	$-10 \pm j10$
800	20	$s^2 + 20s + 400$	$-10 \pm j17+$
1800	30	$s^2 + 20s + 900$	$-10 \pm j28+$
5000	50	$s^2 + 20s + 2500$	$-10 \pm j49$

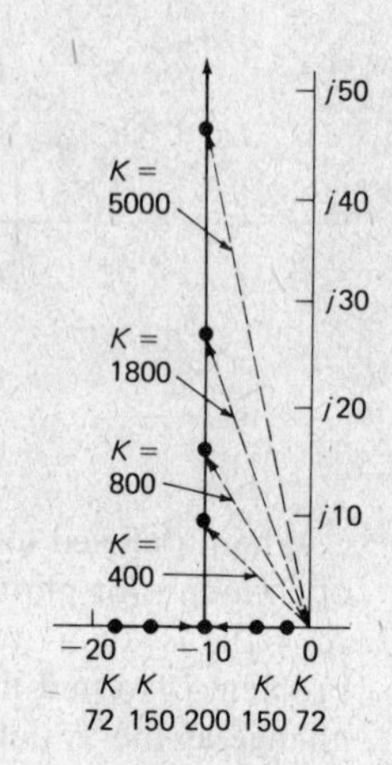

Now vary only the damping D and plot the resulting roots, which become complex at ζ less than 1.0.

D	ζ	Equation	Roots, s
85	2.1+	$s^2 + 42.5s + 100$	$-40, -2.5$
50	1.25	$s^2 + 25s + 100$	$-20, -5$
41	1.02	$s^2 + 20.5s + 100$	$-12.5, -8$
40	1.00	$s^2 + 20s + 100$	$-10, -10$
28	0.7	$s^2 + 14s + 100$	$-7 \pm j7.14$
20	0.5	$s^2 + 10s + 100$	$-5 \pm j8.67$
12	0.3	$s^2 + 6s + 100$	$-3 \pm j9.54$
0	0.0	$s^2 + 100$	$0 \pm j10$

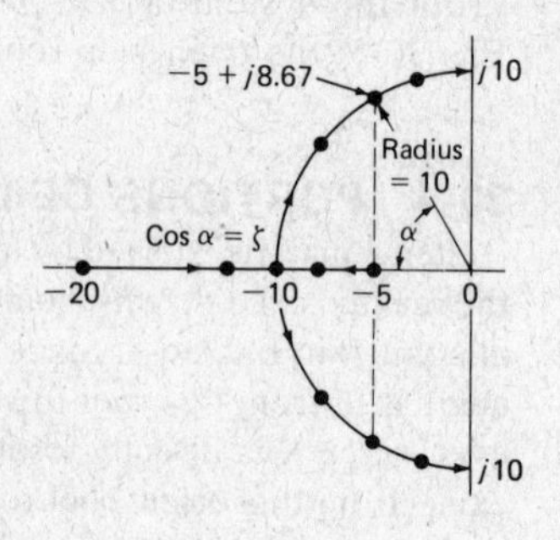

ion. A review of this feature is given in Table 30-1; the upper portion, plotting the roots as gain K is varied, is of direct interest here.

When the closed-loop roots become complex and the loci have left the real axis, such points on the 180° locus are found by trial, using a protractor to measure angles. When s is chosen at point T, Fig. 30-5 shows angles of 25, 74, and 119°, whose sum is greater than 180°; but if s is chosen at U, the corresponding angles of 17, 45, and 90° total less than 180°. Further trials reveal that the 180° locus lies along the curved line, and crosses the j axis as shown at Y. The 180° locus always is symmetrical above and below the real axis, since any complex roots appear always in conjugate pairs.

To interpret the results in Fig. 30-5, it can be shown that this system has "absolute" stability only so long as all its closed-loop roots lie at the left of

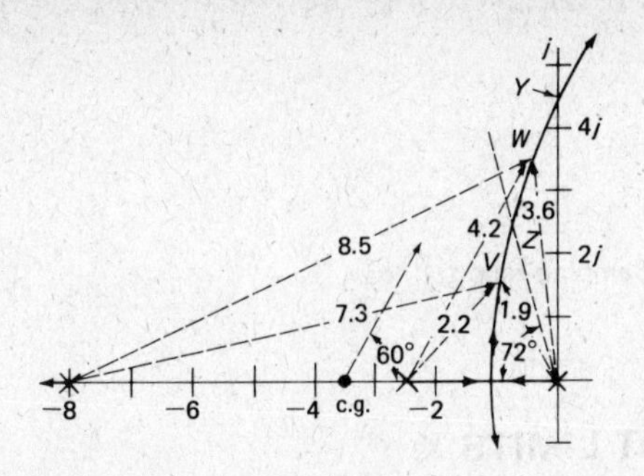

Figure 30-6 Lengths for finding gain K_0 at points V and W

the j axis. When any pole has a value of s that is negative or has a negative real part, the term is ϵ^{-st}; so the term decays with time to zero, and is called a stable root. When a root s lies on the j axis, the system oscillates endlessly. If s is positive or has a positive real part, ϵ^{+st} expands, and is called an *unstable root*. Therefore, in Fig. 30-5, it becomes necessary to determine what values of system gain K_o can be used without causing the 180° locus to reach the j axis. Thus the 180° locus next must be calibrated in values of K_o.

By means of a device called a Spirule, we quickly may add angles so as to locate the 180° locus, and then may combine distances so as to calibrate the locus. (Spirule Company is at 9728 El Venado, Whittier, Calif.)

30-6 STEP 4. CALIBRATING THE LOCUS

The 180° locus for Example 1[30-2] appears again in Fig. 30-6. To find the value of K_o that causes a closed-loop root s to lie at point V, the distances are scaled from each open-loop root to V, thus giving the values shown. These lengths are inserted in the equation, giving

$$KGH = \frac{20K_o}{1.9 \times 2.2 \times 7.3} = 1$$

(since the value of KGH must be +1 if the closed-loop roots are to lie on the 180° locus). From this, $K_o = 30.5/20 \approx 1.53$. Similarly, measurements to point W give

$$KGH = \frac{20K_o}{3.6 \times 4.2 \times 8.5} = 1$$

so here $K_o = 128.5/20 = 6.42$. In this manner, the entire 180° locus curve can be calibrated in values of K_o. Arrows show movement along the locus as K_o is increased; as gain becomes infinite, each locus moves to infinity. The locus to the left of −8 similarly can be calibrated; but since this locus moves away from the j axis, it is of less interest.

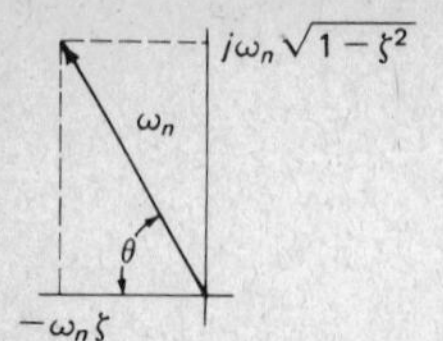

Figure 30-7 Damping ratio $\zeta = \cos\theta$.

30-7 STEP 5. OVERSHOOT LIMITS K_o

From the calibrated root locus, the desired value of K_o now may be chosen. Where K_o is near 10, the root lies on the j axis, at Y, and here the system has continuous oscillation. (This corresponds to the value of gain that causes the Nyquist polar plot of this system to pass through $-1, j0$, as shown in Sec. 29-8.) Therefore, a value of $K_o = 10$ is too high to use for this system.

The upper limit for K_o often is determined by the permissible amount of overshoot after applying a step input; this overshoot usually is caused by complex roots in the closed-loop relation. As shown in Fig. 28-10, the overshoot is related to damping ratio ζ. To limit the overshoot to 35 percent, $\zeta = 0.3$.

Section 28-18 shows how the dimensionless equation for this kind of system has the roots $s = -\omega_n\zeta \pm j\omega_n\sqrt{1-\zeta^2}$. When such a root is plotted in Fig. 30-7 the diagonal becomes merely ω_n, so that $\cos\theta = \omega_n\zeta/\omega_n$, and damping ratio is indicated as an angle θ whose $\cos = \zeta$. Since $\cos^{-1} 0.3 \approx 72°$, a line is drawn at 72° in Fig. 30-6. Where this line intersects the 180° locus, as shown at Z, the corresponding value of $K_o = 3.2$ is read from the calibrated curve; this is the largest gain that may be used with this system so long as the overshoot is limited to 35 percent.

30-8 SYSTEM EXAMPLE 2, A TYPE-2 SERVO

Another system whose transfer function is

$$\frac{K(0.67j\omega + 1)}{(j\omega)^2[0.04\,(j\omega)^2 + 0.2j\omega + 1]}$$

is studied because this type-2 servo has complex roots, and has a phase-lead element shown in the numerator. When normalized, this becomes

$$KGH = \frac{16.7K_o(s + 1.5)}{s^2(s^2 + 5s + 25)}$$

The denominator contains two poles at 0 or the origin, and complex poles $s = -2.5 \pm j4.32$ (see Sec. 30-2) marked × in Fig. 30-8. The numerator root $s = -1.5$ is a "zero," designated as ○. Since a zero contributes a lead-

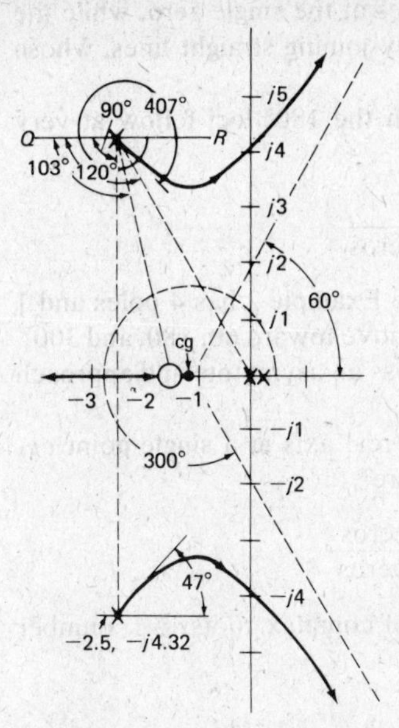

Figure 30-8 Location of cg, asymptotes, and breakaway angle for Example 2.

$$KGH = \frac{16.7\ K_0(s + 1.5)}{s^2\ (s^2 + 5s + 25)}$$

ing phase angle, this must be subtracted from the total angle caused by the denominator roots or poles.

To shorten the search for the 180° locus, note that 180° cannot exist along the real axis at the right of −1.5, since any value of s here has 0° angle measured from the zero at 1.5. Each pole at the origin is considered separately; each contributes 180° if s is (−), or 0° if s is (+).

30-9 RULES FOR LOCATING LOCI

Solution of Example 2[30-8] continues in Sec. 30-10, with the help of the following rules.

Rule A A 180° locus is found in any part of the real axis that lies to the left of an *odd* number of roots (including both poles and zeros). In this calculation, the angles from any complex roots offset each other and so are omitted.

Rule B There are as many branches of the 180° locus as there are poles. Since each open-loop pole is also a closed-loop pole when K_o is 0, one branch of the 180° locus must start from each pole. At infinite gain, one branch ends at each zero, while the remaining branches end at infinity. Thus there are four branches to be located in Example 2, two above and two below the real axis. Each branch is a continuous single-valued locus. At very high gain, one of the four branches terminates at the single zero, while the other three must move toward infinity, finally joining straight lines, whose locations are found next.

Rule C The straight-line asymptotes, which the 180° loci follow at very high gain, lie at angles found by

$$\alpha = \frac{(k)180°}{\#\text{ poles} - \#\text{zeros}}$$

where $k = 1, 3, 5, 7$ (any odd number). Since Example 2 has 4 poles and 1 zero, three of the branches of the 180° locus move toward 60, 180, and 300°. No asymptote ever lies at 0°. A locus can cross an asymptote and approach it from the far side.

Rule D The asymptotes cross or leave the real axis at a single point *cg*, called the *center of gravity* of the roots, where

$$cg = \frac{\Sigma\text{ poles} - \Sigma\text{ zeros}}{\#\text{ poles} - \#\text{ zeros}}$$

(Σ = sum of values, including real portions of complex roots. # = number of items.)

In Fig. 30-8,

$$\text{cg} = \frac{(0 - 0 - 2.5 - 2.5) - (-1.5)}{4 - 1} = \frac{-3.5}{3} = -1.167$$

Rule E The *breakaway point*, where two branches of the 180° locus leave the real axis, may be found by trial calculations, as shown in Sec. 30-10. This method also will locate the point where two branches *enter* the real axis, as shown in Fig. 30-12. In most cases, loci leave or enter the real axis vertically.

Rule F From each complex pole, a branch of the 180° locus leaves at a *breakaway angle* found as follows. From a horizontal reference line drawn through the upper complex pole in Fig. 30-8, angles are measured from Q to each of the other three poles and to the zero. These angles are combined, using (−) for a pole but (+) for a zero. When 180° is subtracted from this sum, the resulting total is the break-away angle, measured from R as reference. Therefore, in Fig. 30-8, $-90° - 120° - 120° + 103° = -227°$. Then $-227° - 180° = -407°$, which is the angle of breakaway from the root at $-2.5, j4.32$, and is measured clockwise from R.

If the system contains complex zeros, a branch of the 180° locus *enters* each zero at an angle calculated as shown above (remembering that the other complex root is also a zero), but the final angle is measured counterclockwise from R.

Rule G For the linear systems considered in this text, a root-locus plot always is symmetrical about the real axis. Only those loci lying in and above the real axis need be located. The 180° locus from a single pole cannot leave

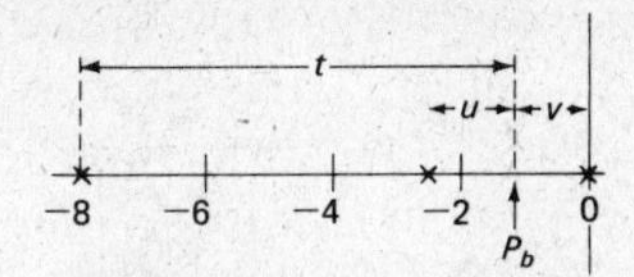

Figure 30-9 Location of p_b, point of breakaway from real axis (for three real poles).

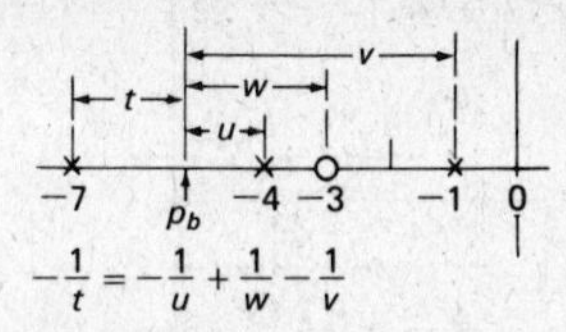

Figure 30-10 Location of p_b (for real poles and zero).

the real axis, since the locus from a second pole also must leave the real axis at the same point, to maintain symmetry.

30-10 BREAKAWAY POINT FROM REAL AXIS

For a simple system consisting only of two real poles, the 180° loci break away from the real axis at a point p_b midway between the poles. When there are more than two roots, each root affects the *breakaway point* p_b inversely to its distance from p_b. As used in Fig. 30-5, three poles are shown again in Fig. 30-9, and located at 0, −2.5, and −8. Here the breakaway point p_b will be located by trial, so that $1/t + 1/u = 1/v$.

Trying p_b at $-1.2 = v$, then $t = -6.8$ and $u = -1.3$:

$$-\frac{1}{6.8} - \frac{1}{1.3} \stackrel{?}{=} -\frac{1}{1.2} \qquad \text{or} \qquad -0.147 - 0.77 = -0.917 \; (\neq -0.83)$$

Trying p_b at $-1.1 = v$, then $t = -6.9$ and $u = -1.4$:

$$-\frac{1}{6.9} - \frac{1}{1.4} \stackrel{?}{=} -\frac{1}{1.1} \qquad \text{or} \qquad -0.145 - 0.715 = -0.86 \neq -0.91$$

Trying p_b at $-1.13 = v$:

$$-\frac{1}{6.87} - \frac{1}{1.37} \stackrel{?}{=} -\frac{1}{1.13} \qquad \text{or} \qquad -0.145 - 0.73 = -0.875 = -0.875$$

Therefore, the loci of Fig. 30-9 break away from the real axis at −1.13.

If a zero is added, as at −3 in Fig. 30-10, it acts like a pole of opposite sign; so its term $1/w$ is included as (+). Trying p_b at −5:

$$-\frac{1}{2} \stackrel{?}{=} \frac{1}{1} + \frac{1}{2} - \frac{1}{4} \qquad -0.5 \neq -0.75$$

Trying p_b at −5.3:

$$-\frac{1}{1.7} \stackrel{?}{=} -\frac{1}{1.3} + \frac{1}{2.3} - \frac{1}{4.3}$$

$$-0.588 \stackrel{?}{=} -0.77 + 0.435 - 0.233 \qquad -0.588 \approx -0.568$$

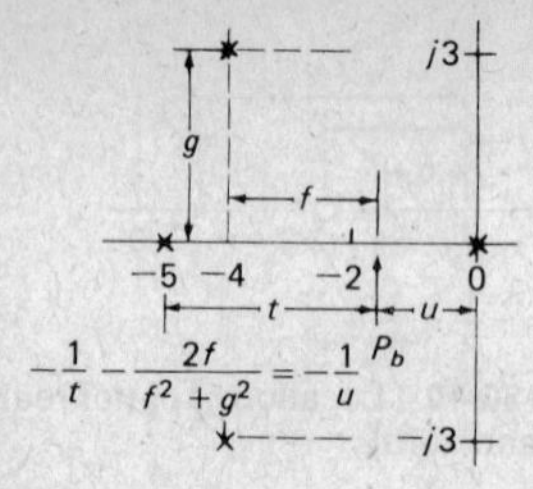

Figure 30-11 Location of p_b (for complex poles).

Therefore, the loci of Fig. 30-10 break away from the real axis at −5.28. Complex poles appear at $-4 \pm j3$ in Fig. 30-11. If these complex poles are ignored, the p_b lies midway between the real poles, or at −2.5. The effect of each complex pole varies inversely as the square of its distance from the real axis. The effect of a pair of complex poles is included by the term $-2f/(f^2+g^2)$. (If g becomes 0 so that these poles enter the real axis, this term becomes $-2/f$, being the same as 2 real poles at distance f from p_b.)

Trying p_b at −1.8, then $f = 2.2$, $g = 3$, and $t = 3.2$:

$$-\frac{1}{3.2}-\frac{2\times 2.2}{(2.2)^2+3^2}\overset{?}{=}-\frac{1}{1.8} \quad \text{or} \quad -0.313-0.318 \neq -0.555$$

Trying p_b at −1.6:

$$-\frac{1}{3.4}-\frac{2\times 2.4}{(2.4)^2+3^2}\overset{?}{=}-\frac{1}{1.6} \quad \text{or} \quad -0.294-0.325 \approx -0.625$$

Therefore, p_b in Fig. 30-11 lies at −1.6.

The system used in Fig. 30-12 shows loci entering the real axis between −3 and −2.5. A zero lies at −1.5, while poles lie at 0, 0, and at $-2.5 \pm j4.32$. Trying p_b at −3.0:

$$0 \overset{?}{=} +\frac{1}{1.5}-\frac{1}{3}-\frac{1}{3}-\frac{2\times 0.5}{(0.5)^2+(4.32)^2}$$

$$0 \overset{?}{=} +0.667-0.333-0.333-0.053 \qquad 0 \neq -0.053$$

Trying p_b at −2.85:

$$0 \overset{?}{=} +\frac{1}{1.35}-\frac{1}{2.85}-\frac{1}{2.85}-\frac{2\times 0.35}{(0.35)^2+(4.32)^2}$$

$$0 \overset{?}{=} +0.74-0.35-0.35-0.037 \qquad 0 \approx 0.003$$

Therefore, $p_b = -2.85$.

30-11 RESULTS OF EXAMPLE 2

Continuing with Example 2,[30-8] all four branches of the 180° locus are plotted in Fig. 30-12, which shows also the angles measured in locating

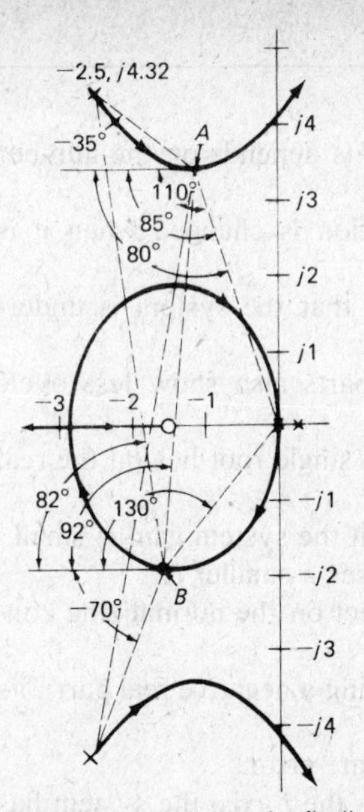

Figure 30-12 Angles for finding 180° loci in Example 2.

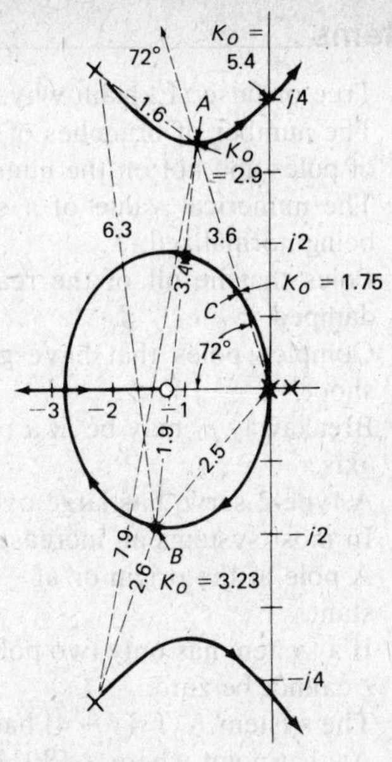

Figure 30-13 Lengths to calibrate 180° loci in Example 2.

points A and B. At A, $-35° + 80° + 110° + 110° - 85° = 180°$. Each pole at the origin contributes 110°; the 85° measured to the zero is subtracted. At B, angles $-70° + 82° + 130° + 130° - 92° = 180°$.

To calibrate this 180° locus, sample measurements are shown in Fig. 30-13; here also the 72° line is drawn to locate the points in the 180° locus that correspond to $\zeta = 0.3$ and 35 percent overshoot.

At point A:

$$KGH = \frac{16.7K_o \times 3.4}{3.6 \times 3.6 \times 1.6 \times 7.9} = 1 \quad \text{so} \quad K_o = \frac{164}{56.7} = 2.9$$

At point B:

$$KGH = \frac{16.7K_o \times 1.9}{2.5 \times 2.5 \times 2.6 \times 6.3} = 1 \quad \text{so} \quad K_o = \frac{102.4}{31.7} = 3.23$$

To hold this system to less than 35 percent overshoot, the gain must not exceed 2.9, nor may it be less than 1.75, the value of K_o at intersection C. (These values of system gain K_o are too small to be useful in a servo; low gain values result from the selection of low-valued roots that can be shown conveniently in the plots of this example.)

Problems

30-1 True or false? Explain why.

(a) The number of branches of the 180° locus depends on the number of poles and not on the number of zeros.

(b) The numerical value of a system equation is changed when it is being normalized.

(c) Poles that lie off of the real axis show that the system is underdamped.

(d) Complex poles that have greater real parts also show less overshoot.

(e) Breakaway p_b may be at a point where a single root lies on the real axis.

(f) A type-2 servo has large overshoot when the system gain is small.

(g) In most systems an increase in gain causes a smaller ζ.

(h) A pole at the origin or at −1 has no effect on the normalizing constant.

(i) If a system has only two poles (each having a negative real part), its ζ cannot be zero.

(j) The system $K_0 / s(s+4)$ has a steady-state error.

(k) At that point where a 180° locus crosses the j axis, the system has continuous oscillation and is absolutely unstable.

(l) A network consisting of a pole at −3 and a zero at −6 decreases the high-frequency response by about 6 dB.

(m) The system $K_o / s(s^2+25)$ can be stable at some value of gain.

(n) A network consisting of a zero at −1 and a pole at −4 decreases the low-frequency response by about 12 dB.

(o) For a system that has only three roots, all lying on the real axis, no branch of the 180° locus ever leaves the real axis if the middle root is a zero.

(p) $\dfrac{16K_o}{s(s^2+2s+16)}$. This system has about 40 percent overshoot when a step input is applied, at low gain.

Note: To make the plots requested in these problems, a scale of 2=1 inch should be used. Where no complex roots exist, only the portion above the real axis needs to be plotted.

30-2 A system consists of one pole at −0.5, one at −2, and one at −4. (*a*) Write the transfer function of this system in normalized form, showing the numerical value of each root and of the normalizing constant. (*b*) Find values of cg and asymptotes. (*c*) Find p_b. (*d*) Without search for points by angle summation, sketch each 180° locus and mark the direction of increasing K_o.

30-3 Repeat Prob. 30-2 for a system having single poles at 0, at −2, at −5, and at −8.

30-4 Repeat Prob. 30-2 for a system having single poles at 0, at −3, and at −4, and one zero at −2.

30-5 Repeat Prob. 30-2 for a system having single poles at −1, at $-4 + j3$, and at $-4 - j3$. Also express the complex poles in quadratic form and, for (*c*), find instead the breakaway angle from the upper complex pole.

30-6 Repeat Prob. 30-5 for a system having single poles at −6 and at $-3 \pm j4$.

30-7 A system transfer function is $\dfrac{AK_o(s+2)}{(s+4)(s+6)(s+3+j4)(s+3-j4)}$. (*a*) Find A, the normalizing constant. (*b*) Plot the roots. Find (*c*) cg, (*d*) the asymptotes, (*e*) the breakaway angle from the upper complex pole. (*f*) Without search for points by angle summation, sketch each 180° locus and mark the direction of increasing K_o.

30-8 Repeat Prob. 30-7 for $\dfrac{AK_o(s+5)}{s^2(s+6)(s+4+j3)(s+4-j3)}$.

30-9 Repeat Prob. 30-7 for $\dfrac{AK_o(s+4)}{s(s+2)(s+16)}$. Add (*g*) plot a Bode diagram of this system when $K_o = 40$, and comment on the stability.

30-10 Repeat Prob. 30-9 for $\dfrac{AK_o(s+2)}{s(s+3)(s+7)}$. In (*g*) let $K_o = 100$.

30-11 A system has a zero at −8, two poles at −1, a single pole at −4, and a pair of complex poles expressed by $(s^2 + 14s + 100)$. (*a*) Write the transfer function of this system in normalized form with all numerical values. (*b*) Find values of cg and asymptotes. (*c*) Find the breakaway angle from the upper complex pole. (*d*) Without search for points by angle summation, sketch each 180° locus and mark the direction of increasing K_o.

30-12 Repeat Prob. 30-11 for a system that has a zero at −2, single poles at 0, −3, −5, and −6, and a pair of complex poles expressed by $(s^2 + 8s + 25)$.

30-13 Repeat Prob. 30-11 for a system that has a zero at 0, a pair of complex poles at $-1.5 \pm j2$, and single poles at −2, −3, and −4.

30-14 Repeat Prob. 30-11 for a system that has a zero at −3, a pair of complex poles at $-2 \pm j2$, and single poles at −1, −4, and −6.

30-15 For the system in each problem listed below, find the value of gain K_o at that point where the 180° locus crosses the vertical or j axis, which is at the value given. (*a*) Prob. 30-3 at $j2.3$, (*b*) Prob. 30-5 at

$j5.7$, (*c*) Prob. 30-7 at $j8.8$, (*d*) Prob. 30-11 at $j2.8$, (*e*) Prob. 30-13 at $j3.5$.

30-16 Repeat Prob. 30-15 for (*a*) Prob. 30-2 at $j3.4$, (*b*) Prob. 30-6 at $j7.8$, (*c*) Prob. 30-12 at $j2.6$, (*d*) Prob. 30-14 at $j2.8$.

30-17 For the system $\frac{K_o}{x(0.25s+1)}$ find (*a*) cg and (*b*) normalizing constant. (*c*) If the overshoot is limited to 25 percent (Fig. 28-10 shows $\zeta = 0.4$), find the largest permissible K_o. Next insert the corrective network $\frac{0.2s+1}{0.08s+1}$ and find new (*d*) cg (*e*) normalizing constant, and (*f*) permissible *change* in gain for the same overshoot.

30-18 Plot the system $\frac{K_o}{s(0.04s^2+0.24s+1)}$. (*a*) If the overshoot is limited to 50 percent ($\zeta = 0.2$), find the largest permissible K_o. (*b*) Next insert the corrective network $\frac{0.2s+1}{0.1s+1}$ and find permissible change in gain, for the same overshoot.

Note: In each problem that follows, make a root-locus plot (at a scale of 2 = 1 in.). Find (*a*) the normalizing constant, (*b*) cg, (*c*) breakaway angle from any complex pole, (*d*) breakaway points from the real axis, and (*e*) the lowest value of K_o that causes continuous oscillation of the system. (*f*) Find the lowest and highest values of K_o that keep the overshoot below the value specified.

30-19 $\frac{K_o}{(s+1)(0.125s+1)(0.04s^2+0.32s+1)}$ 25 percent overshoot

30-20 $\frac{K_o}{s(0.2s+1)(0.1s+1)(0.05s^2+0.4s+1)}$ 25 percent overshoot

30-21 $\frac{K_o(j\omega 0.125+1)}{(j\omega 0.5+1)(j\omega 0.25+1)(j\omega 0.2+1)}$ 40 percent ($\zeta = 0.25$)

30-22 $\frac{K_o}{s(s/4+1)(s^2/36+s/6+1)}$ 40 percent

30-23 $\frac{K_o(s/4+1)}{s^2/36+s/18+1}$ 25 percent

30-24 $\frac{K_o(0.2s+1)}{(s+1)(s^2/49+0.245s+1)}$ 25 percent

30-25 $\frac{K_o(0.025s^2+0.1s+1)}{(0.25s+0)^3}$ 25 percent

30-26 $\frac{K_o(2s+1)}{0.0625s^2+0.25s+1}$ 40 percent

31

ELECTRONIC SERVICE INSTRUMENTS

Hundreds of kinds of electronic measuring devices are in use. (Chapter 25 describes temperature recorders, which are electronic instruments.) Many books describe such instruments. Here we see the circuits of four instruments, used in industry to service or check other electronic equipment and fast-moving objects. Three of these appear in Fig. 31-1. Without an electronic voltmeter and an oscillograph, good maintenance of most transistor- or tube-operated equipment is very difficult. (The cathode-ray oscillograph, whose "picture tube" is watched as its picture changes, is often called an oscilloscope or "scope.")

Detailed instruction for the use of such instruments is not intended here; instead, the circuits of these electronic instruments are studied to see how they can measure voltages and supply information far beyond the range of most electric instruments.

31-1 THE NEED FOR AN ELECTRONIC VOLTMETER

Ordinary meters may draw 1 to 10 milliamperes (mA) when measuring 100 volts (V); energy to move the meter pointer is taken from the circuit being measured, and may disturb the normal operation of that circuit.

For example, if a voltmeter draws 1 mA when connected across 100 V dc, the resistance inside this meter is 100,000 ohms (Ω); we say that this meter has 1000 ohms per volt. When we use the 30-V scale instead, the meter now has 30,000 Ω; if we try to use this meter to measure the voltage across a 10-kΩ, or 10,000-Ω resistor, the meter's 30-kΩ resistance combines in parallel with the 10 kΩ to give the effect of only 7.5 kΩ in the measured circuit, and this probably upsets the circuit behavior. The best of dc voltmeters (having about 20,000 ohms per volt) probably can be used successfully here, for its internal 600 kΩ lowers the voltage across the measured 10 kΩ by less than 2 percent. But when we try to check the voltage across higher resis-

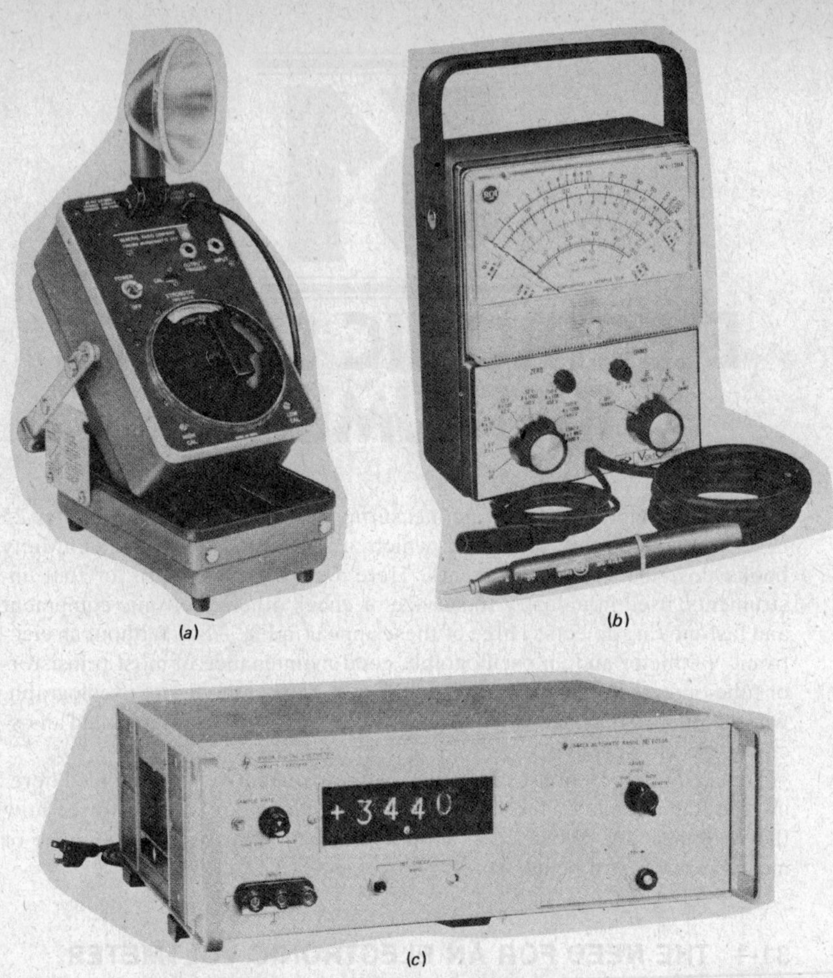

Figure 31-1 Electronic service instruments. (*a*) Strobotac 1531-A *(General Radio Company).* (*b*) Electronic voltmeter—VoltOhmyst WV-500A *(Radio Corporation of America).* (*c*) Digital voltmeter—3440A *(Hewlett-Packard).*

tances (such as the 50-kΩ, 200-kΩ, or 1-MΩ resistors found often in tube or transistor circuits), the measured circuit is disturbed by the meter's internal 600 kΩ (or even by 3 MΩ, when its 150-V scale is used).

In contrast, a vacuum-tube voltmeter connects the unknown voltage to the grid circuit of a high-vacuum tube. The tube grid draws no current from the measured circuit. A tiny current (10 μA) may pass through a voltage divider inside the instrument. A later type of instrument uses transistors, as next described. On dc measurements, it has an internal resistance of 11 MΩ; so it causes little or no disturbance when used to check most electronic circuits.

31-2 AN ELECTRONIC VOLTMETER (RCA SOLID-STATE VOLTOHMYST, TYPE WV-500A)

This battery-operated instrument measures dc or ac voltages from 0.1 volt to 1500 volts, or resistances from 0.2 ohm to 1000 megohms. The circuit in Fig. 31-2 shows the main features of operation but omits many details; the selector switches appear as single contacts to simplify the tracing of circuit action. A function-selector switch *S*2 (whose many layers of contacts appear in the upper part of Fig. 31-2) has five positions, to choose whether the indicating instrument is to be OFF or is to measure AC VOLTS, −DC VOLTS, +DC VOLTS, or OHMS. Each kind of measurement is described below.

Each measurement of voltage or ohms produces a tiny current at *H* and, through *R*34, to the base of transistor *Q*3 at the lower right. When switch *S*2 is turned away from its OFF position, battery *BT*4 applies +9 V through *R*30 to the collectors of transistors *Q*3 and *Q*4. This also forces tiny currents through 180-MΩ resistors *R*31 and *R*32 to the bases of *Q*3 and *Q*4 so that both pass collector current; *R*30 is factory-adjusted so that these transistors pass equal currents to the bases of *Q*1 and *Q*2.

The parallel batteries *BT*2 and *BT*3 apply 9 V through *R*21 and *R*22 to the *Q*1 collector at point *J*, also through *R*21 and *R*20 to the *Q*2 collector at point *I*. Whatever voltage difference appears between *I* and *J* is connected (through *S*2*C* contacts) across the indicating instrument *M*, which deflects full scale when 50 μA (0.00005 ampere) pass through it. With zero signal current in *R*34, the ZERO adjuster *R*21 (on front of the meter case) is moved until *I* and *J* have equal potentials, so that *M* reads 0.

The incoming voltage to this instrument is received between the one probe (at upper left in Fig. 31-2) and the ground clip attached to it. (These appear also in Fig. 31-1*b*.) Inside the probe is a 1-MΩ resistor that remains in series during measurement of dc voltages. But while measuring ac voltages or resistance ohms, this 1-MΩ resistor must be short-circuited by a switch on the side of the probe.

31-3 MEASURING DC VOLTS

All the contacts of selector switch *S*2 are moved by a single knob on the front of the VoltOhmyst. In Fig. 31-2, each of these arrow contacts touches at the −DC VOLTS terminal; so the meter is now set to measure the dc voltage between the ground clip and a point more negative than ground, which is touched by the pointed probe. Inside the meter, the ground clip connects directly to all points marked ⏚ ; thus the base of *Q*4 connects through *R*33 to the ground clip.

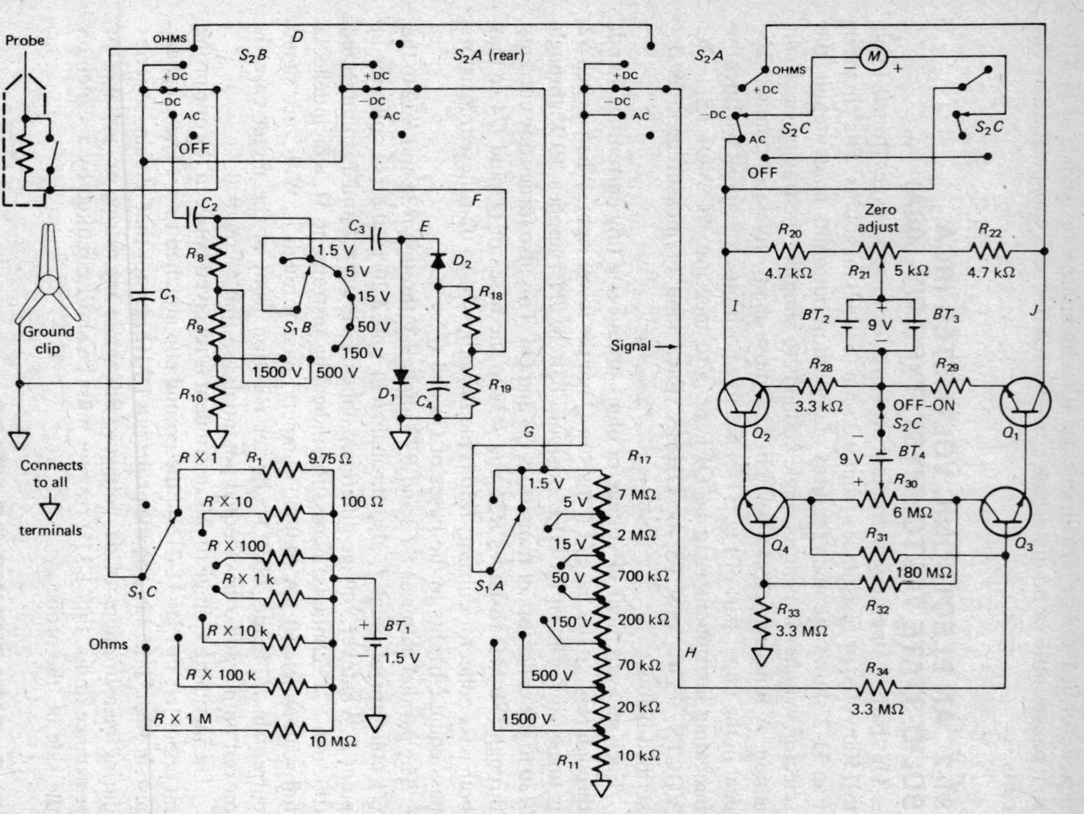

Figure 31-2 Circuit of a solid-state voltmeter (RCA VoltOhmyst, type WV-500A).

The voltage at the probe is connected through switches *S2B* and *S2A* (rear contacts) to point *G* at the top of the 10-MΩ voltage divider (R11 to *R*17, at lower center of Fig. 31-2); thus the entire dc voltage being measured is applied across the probe resistance and this voltage divider. When range switch *S1A* is set at the 1.5-V position as shown, this voltage passes through *S1A* and *S2A* (front contacts) so as to send current through *R*34. When this voltage reaches −1.5 volts, the instrument-M needle swings across the whole scale.

To measure as much as −150 V, range switch *S1A* is turned to the 150-V position. (At the same time, *S1B* and *S1C* turn also, but the voltages controlled by them are not being used while *S*2 is in the −DC VOLTS position.) While −150 V dc is applied (between point *G* and the ground clip) to the string of seven resistors in the divider, only −1.5 V (appearing across the lower three resistors) is applied through *S2A* to *H*.

As the voltage signal drives *H* more negative, the current through *R*34 decreases the *Q*3 base current so that *Q*3 passes less collector current through *R*30, and also decreases the *Q*1 base current. As the potential of the *Q*3 collector rises, it feeds back through *R*32 to increase the *Q*4 base current so that *Q*4 passes more current through the base of *Q*2. Thus, when point *G* goes more negative, the collector current increases in *Q*2 and decreases in *Q*1. The increased electrons flow from the negative terminal of batteries *BT*2 and *BT*3 through *R*28 and *Q*2 to point *I*, through *R*20 and *R*21 to the +9-V battery terminal; with this greater voltage drop across *R*20, point *I* becomes more negative and (through *S2C*) drives the left-hand side of meter *M* more negative. Meanwhile, decreased *Q*1 current lessens the voltage drop across *R*22 so that point *J* rises, applying more positive potential to the right-hand side of *M*; the *M* needle moves up-scale. If the probe is connected instead to ac voltage, *M* reads about 0. Any high-frequency part passes through *C*1 to the ground clip.

31-4 MEASURING AC VOLTS

The switch on the probe now is moved so that it short-circuits the 1-*M*Ω resistor within the probe. Selector switch *S*2 is turned to AC VOLTS; now the measured ac voltage signal passes through *S2B* to capacitor *C*2, through *S1B* to *C*3 and diodes *D*1 and *D*2 to *C*4; the signal continues from point *F* through *S2A* to *G* atop the voltage divider. Notice that the diodes convert the measured ac voltage into a dc signal that is equal to the peak-to-peak value of the ac voltage, as follows. During the half cycle when the probe is more positive than ground, electrons flow from the ground clip through *D*1 into *C*3, and continue through *S1B*, *C*2, and *S2B* to the probe; *C*3 becomes charged to the peak value of this positive half wave. As the measured ac voltage starts to reverse, *C*3 retains this charge, so that its terminal *E* remains more negative than the probe. As the ac probe voltage falls to its negative peak, electrons flow through *D*2 so as to charge capacitor *C*4 to the sum of the *C*3 voltage and the negative ac peak. Thus the total voltage across *C*4 equals the peak-to-peak value of the measured ac voltage; this *C*4 charge remains nearly a second, since its discharge is slowed by *R*18 and *R*19 (20 MΩ each). Half of the *C*4 voltage is fed at *F* through *S*2*A*, so that it becomes the input to the voltage divider at *G*. This rectified ac signal forces *G* more negative, thereby acting like a measurement of −DC VOLTS: thus an increasing value of ac volts forces line *H* more negative, causing deflection of meter *M* as described in Sec. 31-2. These peak-to-peak values of the ac voltage are converted also to rms values that are accurate when sine-wave ac voltages are measured. This meter responds to frequencies of 30 hertz (Hz or cps) to 3 megahertz (MHz).

Alternating-current voltages up to 150 V are applied directly through *S*1*B* to *D*1, *D*2, and *C*4. When *S*1*B* is turned to the 500- or 1500-V position, only a part of the ac voltage across the *R*8-*R*9-*R*10 divider is used for charging *C*4.

31-5 MEASURING OHMS

To measure the resistance of an external device, the ground clip is connected to one side and the probe is touched to its other side (after all power has been removed). Selector switch *S*2 is set at OHMS. (Again the switch on the probe is moved to short-circuit its 1-MΩ resistor.) At the lower left in Fig. 31-2, the ohms-measuring circuit includes switch *S*1*C* and a 1.5-volt battery *BT*1. From the negative terminal of *BT*1, electrons flow through the ground clip to the unknown resistance and return through the probe, through *S*2*B* and *S*1*C* and *S R*1 and to the positive battery terminal. Notice that *R*1 and the unknown resistance are in series across *BT*1 and act as a voltage divider, which controls the potential at top point *D*. The voltage produced across the unknown drives point *D* more positive; this is connected through *S*2*A* to point *H*. Thus the voltage across the resistance acts in the same way as +DC VOLTS, making point *H* more positive (as described late in Sec. 31-3).

If the unknown resistance has less resistance than *R*1 [9.75 ohms (Ω)], most of the 1.5 V appears across *R*1. The rest appears across the unknown and raises point *D* very little; the *M* needle remains at a low-resistance reading. If the unknown is equal to *R*1, just half of the 1.5 V raises point *D*; the *M* needle rises halfway up the scale, pointing just below 10 ohms. If the unknown has much greater resistance than *R*1, nearly the entire 1.5 V appears across the unknown and raises points *D* and *H*, so that the meter needle swings up to a higher resistance reading.

31-6 A DIGITAL VOLTMETER (HEWLETT-PACKARD 3440A)

In place of a moving pointer, this solid-state meter displays the measured voltage by showing four lighted figures or digits steadily on its front. By turning a range selector, the displayed decimal point is moved so that the "full-scale" value may be selected as 9.999 volts (V) or 99.99 V or 999.9 V. The measured voltage is applied across a divider so that this voltmeter has an internal resistance of 10 megohms (MΩ). From this divider, a portion less than 10 V is applied at the INPUT (at upper right in Fig. 31-4). Plug-in units may be inserted within the meter so that it may read also ac volts, dc milliamperes or amperes, or ohms.

Although the lighted numbers do not flicker, this meter is measuring the voltage five times each second (or the SAMPLE RATE dial may adjust this down to one voltage sample each 5 sec). During each sample, the measured voltage is converted into a display of four numbers by the steps or processes next described, and as sketched in Fig. 31-3. The meter also provides an output to permit the recording of the measured values.

Within the meter, a 2-microfarad capacitor $C6$ is charged to above +12 volts. At the start of each voltage sample (at zero time, called T_0), $C6$ starts to discharge at a linear rate, sending a constant flow of current through transistor $Q17$, so that the $C6$ voltage changes along a straight line from +12 to −12 V in exactly 60 milliseconds, reaching −12 V at time T_2 (in Fig. 31-3); this decreasing voltage is called the *ramp*. Suppose that the range switch is

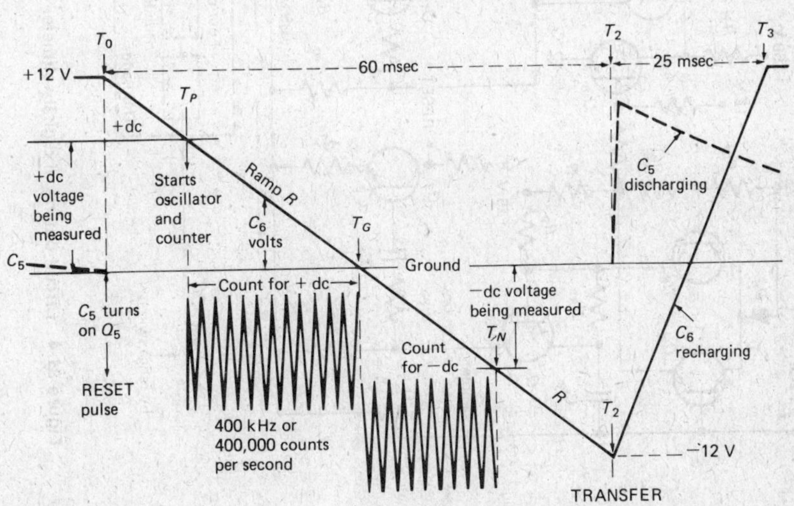

Figure 31-3 A ramp, produced in Fig. 31-4, converts a measured voltage into a digital readout.

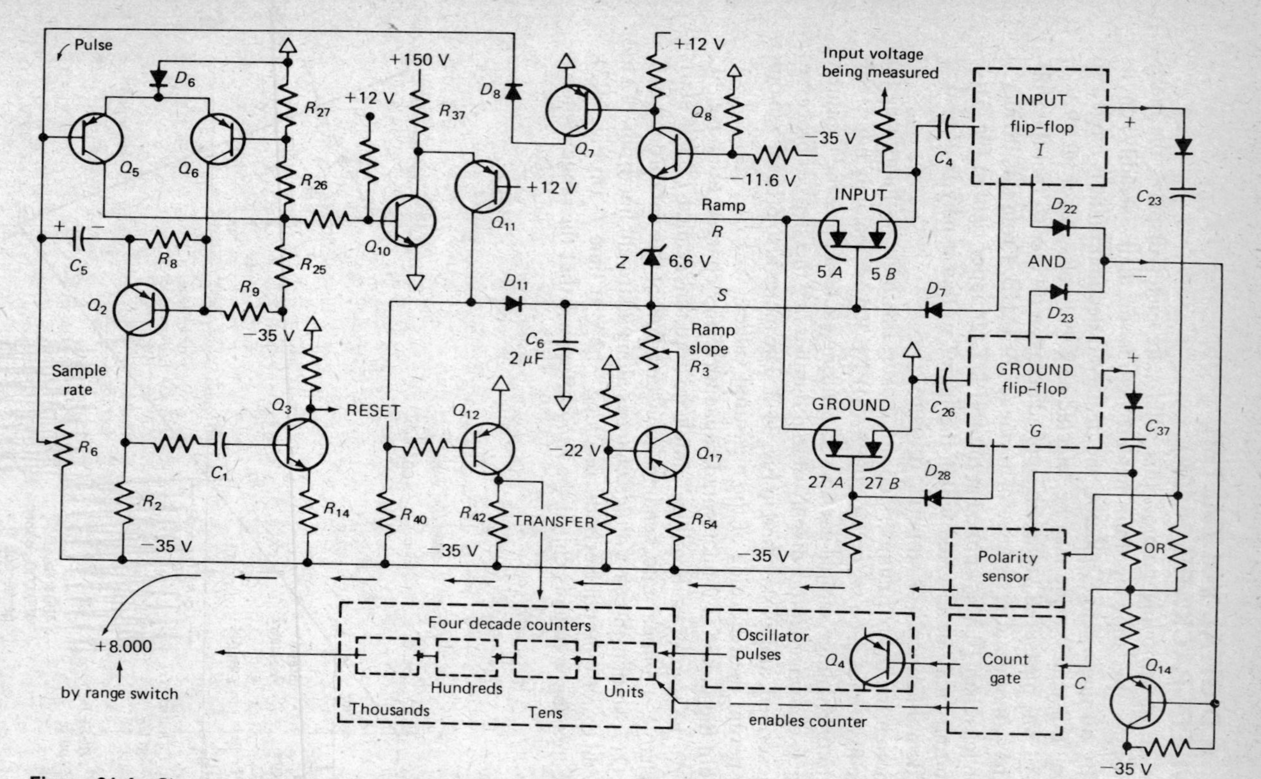

Figure 31-4 Circuit outline of digital voltmeter (Hewlett-Packard 3440A).

set to the 10-V scale and the dc voltage being measured is +8 V. At the exact instant when the ramp voltage drops below 8 V, a signal starts a transistor oscillator that produces 400,000 voltage pulses per second. These pulses are being counted by four decade counters in series, that accumulate the pulse count in thousands, hundreds, tens, and units. When the ramp voltage drops below ground or zero volts, the oscillator pulses stop; the count ends but the counters continue to hold their number values. At T_2, another signal transfers this count so as to light up the corresponding glow lamps that produce the numbers appearing on the meter display.

Thus the meter actually is measuring the time required for the capacitor $C6$ voltage to change from 8 to 0 volts (V). The slope of this $C6$ voltage ramp is 24 volts in 60 milliseconds; thus the ramp falls from 8 to 0 V in 20 msec. The oscillator produces 400 pulses per millisecond; in 20 msec it produces $20 \times 400 = 8000$ pulses. The counter causes the digits 8000 to be displayed; the position of the range switch lets the decimal point appear after the 8, so as to read 8.000 volts.

Figure 31-4 shows only a few of the circuits and one-sixth of about 75 transistors included in this meter; many desirable features and calibration circuits are not mentioned. Not shown, an input transformer and two diode-bridge rectifiers furnish 150 V (for internal glow lamps and digit-display devices); there are regulated supplies of +12 and −35 V. The many connections to power-supply ground are shown as ▽.

31-7 FORMING RAMP R OF FIG. 31-3

At the upper left in Fig. 31-4, transistors $Q5$ and $Q6$ operate as the sample-rate multivibrator (similar to Fig. 24-8, as described in Sec. 24-8). Here $Q5$ conducts while the voltage is being sampled (from T_0 to T_2 in Fig. 31-3). At time T_0, the $Q5$ collector current through $R25$ raises the base of NPN transistor $Q10$ so that it conducts. The $Q10$ current through $R37$ lowers the $Q11$ emitter below its base; this turns off PNP $Q11$, whose collector drops toward −35 V. Before $Q11$ was turned off, the top of capacitor $C6$ (at the center of Fig. 31-4) was more than 12 V positive, having been charged by electrons flowing from ground to $C6$ and continuing through diode $D11$ and $Q11$ and $R37$ to +150 V. Now diode $D11$ becomes reverse-biased and acts as an open circuit; this lets $C6$ discharge through the RAMP SLOPE adjuster $R3$ and transistor $Q17$ toward −35 V.

Whereas the current and voltage across a discharging capacitor usually have an exponential shape (as shown in Fig. 3-2), the discharge current of $C6$ is kept constant by $Q17$ as it holds constant voltage across $R54$. Aided by three other transistors (not shown), the upper terminal S of $C6$ is made to follow a straight-line slope downward to −20 V. Above Q 17 is a Zener diode Z that holds its top R always at 6.6 V above S; this point R has the ramp voltage shown in Fig. 31-3, where the R line is seen to cross ground potential at T_G (30 msec later than T_0). Then 60 msec after T_0, R reaches −12 V at T_2; here ends the voltage-sample time.

As ramp R reaches −12 V, it lowers the $Q8$ emitter below its base (at the top of Fig. 31-4); this NPN transistor conducts, thus lowering the base of PNP $Q7$. As $Q7$ conducts, it sends a positive pulse through diode $D8$ back to the base of $Q5$; this turns off $Q5$ at time T_2, thus turning off $Q10$. The $Q11$ emitter rises above its base, so that $Q11$ passes a constant current that forward-biases diode $D11$, letting $C6$ be recharged in 25 msec (until time $T3$). This $Q11$ current raises the potential at the top of $R40$; this turns off $Q12$, whose collector drops to −35 V to give the negative TRANSFER pulse mentioned in Sec. 31-10.

31-8 SAMPLE RATE IN FIG. 31-4

While $Q5$ conducted (during the voltage sample), it connected capacitor $C5$ through diode $D6$ to ground. Meanwhile, $Q6$ had no current; so the $Q6$ collector was at −35 volts (V) and applied this potential through $R8$ to the right-hand side of $C5$ in Fig. 31-4. (The $Q2$ current also charged $C5$.) But when $Q5$ is turned off at T_2, its current in $R25$ stops, and this lowers the base of PNP $Q6$. As $Q6$ conducts, its collector rises near to ground (and turns off $Q2$); the charge on $C5$ continues to hold the $Q5$ base above ground, keeping $Q5$ off. But electrons flow now from −35 V up through $R6$ so as to decrease the $C5$ potential. After a minimum of 140 msec, the left-hand side of $C5$ has gone negative so as to turn $Q5$ on, to start another voltage sample. An increase of SAMPLE RATE $R6$ resistance slows this $C5$ discharge so that $Q5$ is turned on only at 5-sec intervals, for a slow sample rate.

Each time that $Q5$ turns on, at T_0, its current through $R25$ turns off $Q6$. As the $Q6$ collector drops toward −35 V, this turns on $Q2$ to restore the $C5$ charge; as the $Q2$ current through $R2$ raises the base of PNP $Q3$, the $Q3$ collector current through $R12$ produces a negative RESET pulse, which is used to reset all counters to zero and to prepare other circuits for the start of a new voltage sample. Also at T_0, the falling $Q6$ collector turns off an NPN transistor $Q1$ (not shown) so as to light a neon indicator lamp whose flashes show the sample rate.

31-9 THE DOWNWARD RAMP STARTS AND STOPS THE PULSE COUNT

As the ramp voltage at R decreases along its slope between T_0 and T_2 in Fig. 31-3, it must cause a signal at T_P, just as R becomes less than the value of the positive input voltage being measured; it also must give a separate signal at T_G, just as R becomes less than ground potential. So the ramp R voltage is connected to diode $5A$ of an INPUT comparator (at the right in Fig. 31-4), and is connected also to diode $27A$ of a GROUND comparator, just below. Since Zener Z holds 6.6 volts between R and S, diode $5A$ passes constant current and reverse-biases diode $D7$. Just after T_0, the ramp R is more positive than the INPUT voltage being measured, so diode $5B$ is reverse-biased. But at that instant when ramp R becomes more negative than the INPUT, $5B$ conducts and draws current from capacitor $C4$ so as to trip the flip-flop I. This INPUT flip-flop now sends a positive pulse through $C23$ to raise line C at the COUNT gate (thus to start the oscillator and counters in Sec. 31-10) and applies a positive voltage through $D7$ that reverse-biases both diodes $5A$ and $5B$, to stop current drawn from the ramp or from the INPUT. Flip-flop I also applies a negative potential so as to reverse-bias diode $D22$ below it.

As the ramp-R voltage is decreasing toward ground potential, diode $27A$ conducts, reverse-biasing both diodes $27A$ and $D28$. But at that instant when R becomes more negative than ground (at T_G), diode $27B$ conducts and draws current from capacitor $C26$ so as to trip the flip-flop G. This GROUND flip-flop now sends a positive pulse through $C37$ (to be used as described below) and applies a positive voltage through $D28$ that reverse-biases diodes $27A$ and $27B$. More important, flip-flop G applies a negative potential so as to reverse-bias diode $D23$ above it. Since diode $D22$ already is reverse-biased by flip-flop I, both $D22$ and $D23$ become open circuits, letting the base of transistor $Q14$ drop toward −35 V (at lower right in Fig. 31-4). Here $D22$ and $D23$ serve as an AND gate. Thus, at time T_G, the G flip-flop turns on $Q14$; this lowers line C so that the COUNT gate stops the oscillator and the counters.

While a positive or +dc voltage is being measured, ramp R trips the INPUT flip-flop before it trips the GROUND flip-flop. The positive pulse from each flip-flop is applied also to a POLARITY SENSOR; since I trips before G, the SENSOR lights a + sign at the left of the meter's display of lighted digits. In contrast, when a negative or −dc voltage is being measured, ramp R trips flip-flop G before it trips I (at time T_N in Fig. 31-3). At the right in Fig. 31-4, G sends its positive pulse through $C37$ to the COUNT gate to start the oscillator and counters; G also reverse-biases diode $D23$. At a later time (T_N), the I flip-flop reverse-biases diode $D22$, letting $Q14$ stop the count. Since the POLARITY SENSOR receives the G pulse ahead of the I pulse, it lights a negative or − sign at the left of the displayed voltage digits. Note that either G or I can pulse through the OR gate to start the count, but both G and I must trip before the AND gate can make $Q14$ end the count.

31-10 THE OSCILLATOR AND COUNTERS PREPARE THE NUMBER DISPLAY

When a pulse from flip-flop I or G raises the C input (at lower right in Fig. 31-4), the COUNT gate sends a signal to the oscillator that turns on a transistor $Q4$, which acts like the closing of switch S in the Colpitts oscillator circuit of Fig. 24-3. Instantly, this oscillator sends 400,000 sharp pulses per second into the decade-counter group. The COUNT gate sends a signal also to the units counter that enables it to respond to the oscillator pulses.

Each of the four decade counters operates somewhat like the counter shown in Fig. 10-3, except that the output of each counter lights one of ten glow lamps, each displaying a digit from 0 to 9. After each 10 pulses into the units counter, it sends 1 pulse to the tens counter; each total of 100 into the hundreds counter sends 1 pulse to the thousands counter. When the ramp reaches T_G for +dc, or T_N for −dc, the conduction by $Q14$ trips the COUNT gate so as to turn off $Q4$ and stop the oscillator; the enabling signal is removed from the counter.

During the count, the displayed numbers are clamped steadily at the values reached in the previous count. But at the end of each new count, at T_2, transistor $Q12$ turns off, sending a negative TRANSFER signal into each counter so that its new count value is transferred and the lighted numbers match the new count.

At T_2, a PRINT command also is given to an external digital recorder, if used.

31-11 THE CATHODE-RAY TUBE

A cathode-ray oscillograph is an instrument (also called a "scope") that includes a cathode-ray tube (like a small TV picture tube) instead of a meter. Such an instrument is used as a voltmeter. (This applies to the type of tube described here. Some cathode-ray tubes use coils outside to move the electron beam; such a tube responds to current in the coils and is used like an ammeter.) The measured voltage moves a spot of light, seen at the end of the tube, instead of moving a pointer. Since this spot of light can move much faster than a pointer, the oscillograph shows quick changes of voltage; it traces curve pictures on the end of the tube that show how a circuit acts within a small part of a second.

The working parts of a cathode-ray tube are shown in Fig. 31-5 and again at the right in Fig. 31-10. This tube is about 12 in. long; narrow at one end, it widens at the other end to a circle 3 or 5 in. across. The bright spot, or "picture," is seen in this circle; so this end of the tube appears at the front of the oscillograph.

Many different voltages are connected to the tube to make it work. Figure 31-5 shows that this high-vacuum cathode-ray tube has a filament, a heated cathode, a control grid, and an anode; so far, this tube is merely a high-vacuum triode. It has also a second anode and two pairs of deflecting plates.

Electrons from the heated cathode are attracted toward both anodes. The second anode is 1100 volts more positive than the cathode; so the electrons reach such high speed that most of them shoot past the anode and strike the circle end of the cathode-ray tube. The inside of this glass-tube circle or

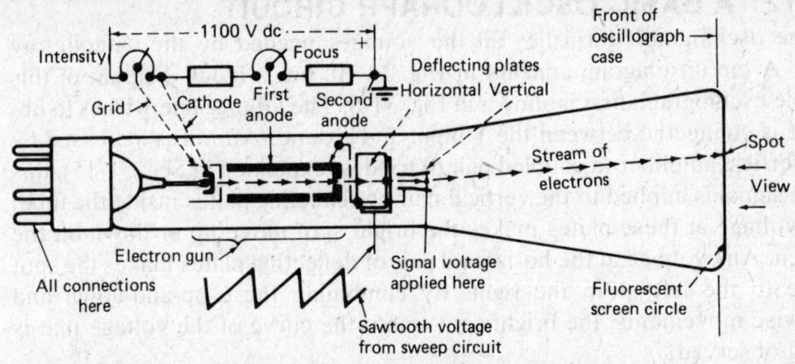

Figure 31-5 Parts of a cathode-ray tube and their connections.

screen is coated with a fluorescent "paint," which glows when the electrons strike it at high speed. (Fluorescent lights also glow when electrons strike such a "paint" on the inside wall of the glass tube.[23-12]) Instead of letting the electrons scatter over a large portion of this painted end, the voltage between the first and second anodes bends the paths of the electrons so that they all strike at one tiny spot on the tube end, or screen. This focusing of the beam of electrons is adjusted by a slight change of potential at the first anode.

Here the cathode, control grid, and two anodes act as an *electron gun*; together they "shoot" a narrow stream of electrons toward the target, or screen. (The grid is a solid piece of metal with one small hole, which is the only path by which electrons may pass toward the anodes. The second anode also has a small hole, which aims the electrons between the deflecting plates. Similar electron guns are used in television tubes and in the electron microscope.) After leaving this gun, the stream of electrons may be controlled or bent by the voltage connected to either pair of deflecting plates, as the direction of a bullet may be changed by the wind or by gravity. Since the electrons have a negative charge, the electron stream is attracted or bent toward a deflecting plate that is more positive. (A magnet held near the tube also will bend the electron stream and move the bright spot.) By making that deflecting plate more negative, the stream is repelled so that it strikes the screen at a different spot. So by changing the potential of a deflecting plate inside the tube, the bright spot is moved across the face of the tube screen.

Many lines or curves may appear on the screen at the same time; all these curves are made by the same spot, or electron beam, which moves back and forth across the screen so many times each second that one's eye sees all these movements at once. The "paint" used on most cathode-ray-tube screens holds the bright marks for perhaps $^1/_{10}$ sec after the electron beam has passed; this helps to produce a steady picture or curve, without flicker. After the electrons strike the screen, they return (to ground) through a circuit "painted" inside the glass of the tube.

31-12 A BASIC OSCILLOGRAPH CIRCUIT

The oscillograph furnishes all the voltages needed by the cathode-ray tube. A circuit diagram appears in Fig. 31-10, but a block diagram of this simple oscillograph first is shown in Fig. 31-6. The voltage one wishes to observe is connected between the *Y* input and ground. After it is increased by the vertical amplifier (a coupled pair of triodes, explained in Sec. 31-15), this input signal is applied to the vertical pair of deflecting plates inside the tube; any voltage at these plates makes the bright spot move up or down on the screen. Any voltage at the horizontal pair of deflecting plates makes the spot move to the left or to the right. By combining these up-and-down and sidewise movements, the bright spot traces the curve of the voltage that is being observed.

When no voltage is applied to either pair of deflecting plates, a single bright spot is seen on the screen. (The tube may be damaged if this bright spot remains still for a long time.) If only the vertical plates receive voltage, the spot traces a straight line up and down on the screen; the height of this line increases if the observed voltage increases. Rapid changes in this voltage cannot be seen unless the bright spot is moved from left to right at the same time. This sidewise movement usually is produced by a "sweep circuit" inside the oscillograph, which makes a "sawtooth" waveshape, shown in Fig. 31-5. When switch 1*S* is set so that this voltage is applied through the horizontal amplifier, it gradually makes one of the horizontal plates more positive, so that the bright spot moves from left to right at a constant rate; in this way, any sudden changes in observed signal voltage are seen as breaks in a curve. When the bright spot reaches the right-hand side of the screen, it returns very quickly to the left, to start another left-to-right movement. This return trace often is "blanked," or made invisible, by a circuit that forces negative the grid of the cathode-ray tube during this instant of spot return. The height of the pattern on the screen is adjusted by the Y AMPLITUDE dial; the width of the pattern is adjusted by the X AMPLITUDE dial.

To hold the observed wave still on the screen, a synchronizing signal is applied to the sawtooth generator, as is explained in Sec. 31-17. In Fig. 31-6, switch 2*S* is set to hold the wave in step with the *Y*-input signal through the vertical amplifier; 2*S* may be turned to use some external signal for this synchronizing action.

31-13 AC SIGNALS AT *X* AND *Y* INPUTS

For most purposes, switch 1*S* is set as shown in Fig. 31-6, so that the internal sweep circuit is used as the *X* input; thus the observed *Y*-input signal is seen on a linear time scale as the bright spot moves to the right. However, if ac signals are applied at both the *X* and the *Y* inputs (and 1*S* is turned so that this ac input at *X* is applied through the horizontal amplifier to the horizontal deflecting plates), interesting patterns, called Lissajous figures, are

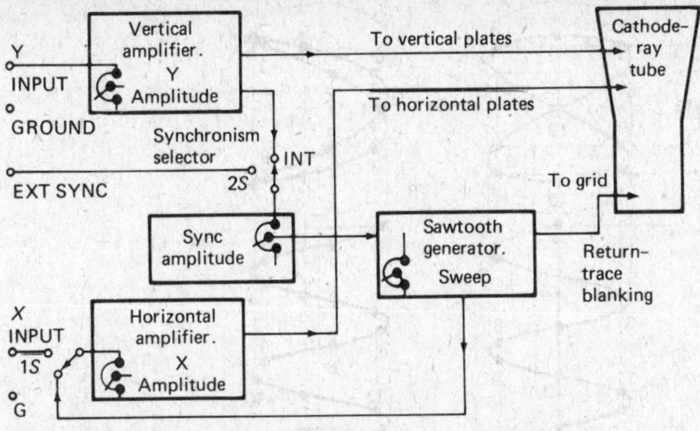

Figure 31-6 Block diagram of a cathode-ray oscillograph.

produced on the screen. The shape of a Lissajous figure may be used to find the ratio between the frequencies of the two ac signals and the phase difference between them.

Suppose that the *X* and *Y* AMPLITUDE dials are set so that the screen pattern is as wide as it is tall. If the ac signals applied at *X* and *Y* have the same frequency and there is no phase difference between them, the screen shows a straight angling line, as in Fig. 31-7*a*. Then Fig. 31-7*b* and *c* shows how this image becomes an ellipse or a circle if one of these ac signals lags behind the other while their frequencies remain the same.

If the frequency of the *X*-input signal is made twice the *Y*-input frequency, the screen may show a figure-8 pattern, as is explained in Fig. 31-8. During each $^1/_{60}$ sec, the 60-hertz (Hz or cps) wave (at the *Y* input and vertical plates) is moving the bright spot up and down once; during this same $^1/_{60}$ sec, a 120-Hz wave (at the *X* input) moves the spot horizontally through two complete cycles. Each of these $^1/_{60}$-sec signals is shown divided into 12 equal parts. When the *Y* wave at point 2 moves the spot upward, the *X* wave at point 2 moves the spot to the right; if dashed lines are drawn (as shown at *A* in Fig. 31-8) from point 2 of each wave, their intersection locates the bright spot at that instant. If pairs of dotted lines are drawn from the other numbered points in the same way their intersections form the figure-8 curve in *A*. Here both input curves cross the zero axis at the same time, at point 1. Part

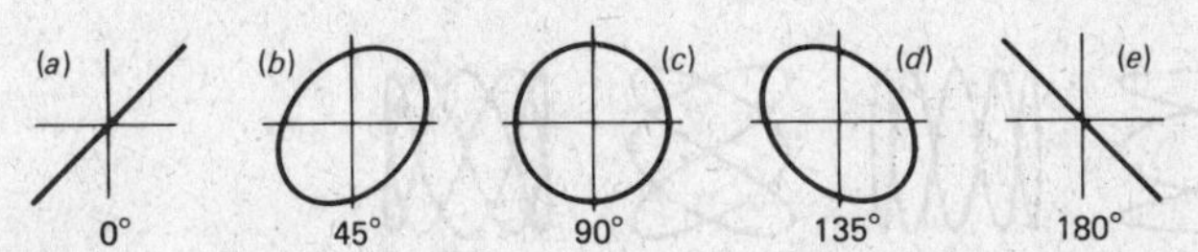

Figure 31-7 Patterns shown when signals applied to *X* and *Y* inputs have the same frequency but varying phase angles.

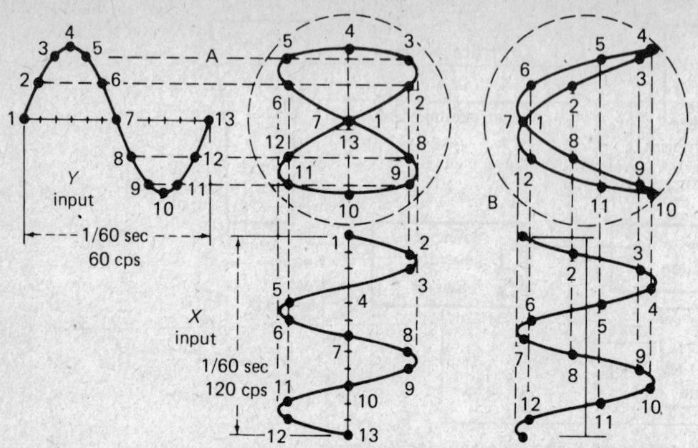

Figure 31-8 Forming of patterns when the *X*-input frequency is twice the *Y*-input frequency.

B of Fig. 31-8 shows the change in pattern when the *X*-input voltage wave lags nearly 90° behind the *Y*-input wave; the figure 8 approaches a *C* pattern.

If either of these patterns in Fig. 31-8 is considered to be bounded by a square, notice that the figure-8 curve touches the top or bottom only once while it touches each side twice; this shows that the *X* frequency is twice the *Y* frequency. Similarly, if a Lissajous pattern touches the top boundary twice while it touches either side three times, frequency at *X* is $^3/_2$ times the frequency at *Y*. Patterns for simple frequency ratios appear in Fig. 31-9.

31-14 A CATHODE-RAY OSCILLOGRAPH (DU MONT TYPE 292)

Figure 31-10 shows the circuit of the oscillograph that is described briefly in Sec. 31-12. At the left, tubes 4 and 5 rectify ac power to provide 400 volts dc between upper line 1 and ground bus 2, while 1100 volts dc appear between 2 and bottom line 3 and is applied to the electron gun of cathode-ray tube 6 at the right, as shown also in Fig. 31-5.

With 115 V ac applied, the INTENSITY dial switch 33*R* (at the bottom of Fig. 31-10) closes the circuit to the supply transformer. After about 20

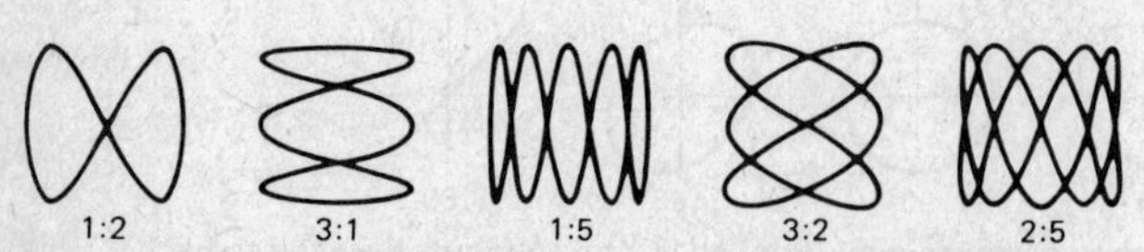

Figure 31-9 Lissajous figures for simple *X*/*Y* frequency ratios.

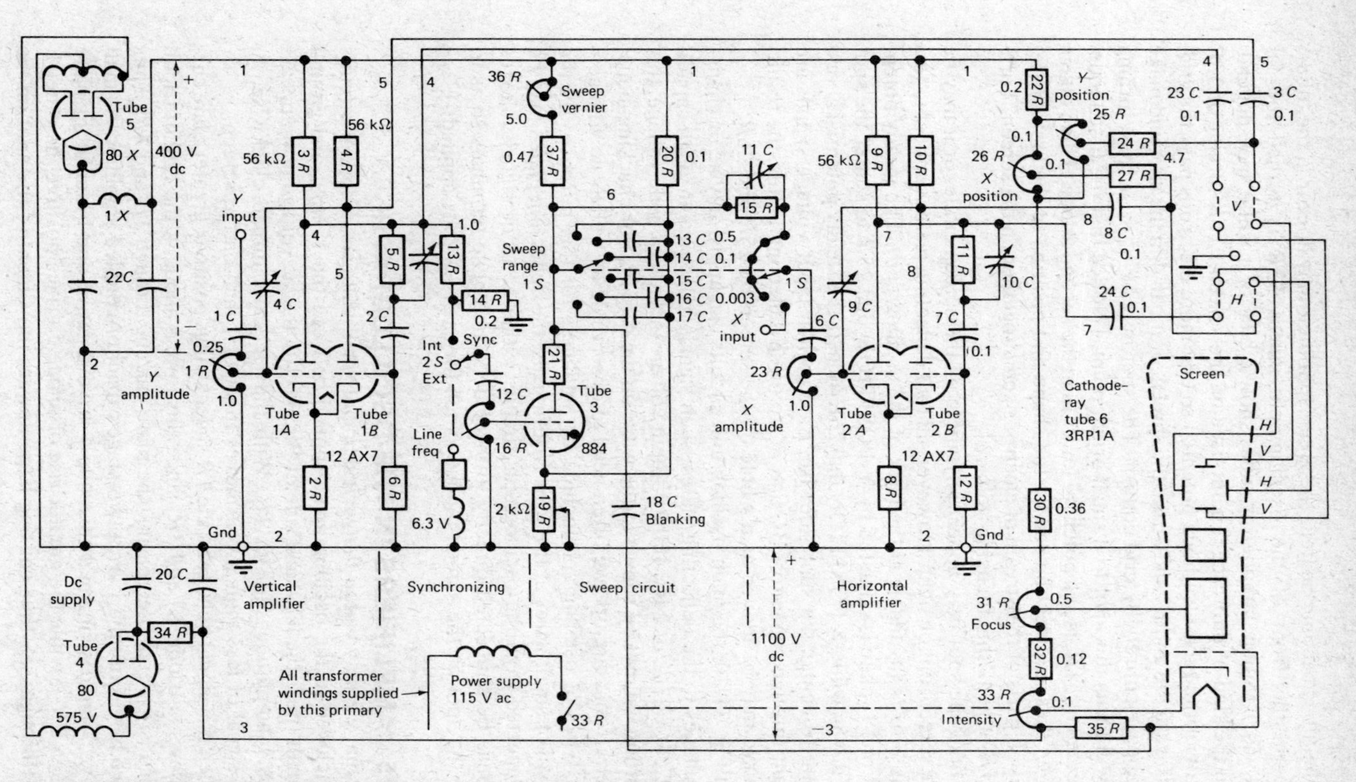

Figure 31-10 Circuit of a cathode-ray oscillograph (Du Mont type 292).

sec, the tubes become heated; the green spot then may appear in the tube-6 circle on the front of the oscillograph, unless 33*R* is turned too far (clockwise). (Some cathode-ray tubes show a blue or a white spot, depending on the kind of fluorescent paint used on the screen.) This turning of 33*R* may lower the tube-6 cathode potential so that more electrons pass the grid, rush toward the anode, and strike the screen, or it can dim the spot and make it disappear entirely by grid control. The spot may be $^1/_4$ in. across; turning 31*R* will focus this spot to a small bright point. [Notice that the first anode, connected to 31*R*, is at a potential lower than the second anode. This voltage between these anodes (helped by the shape and position of the first anode) makes all parts of the stream of electrons come together on the screen. Turning 31*R* adjusts this focusing voltage].

At first, the spot may appear anywhere on the screen circle, or it may be off the screen, out of sight. However, all four deflecting plates connect to terminals *V* or *H* (available at the back of the oscillograph). The steady potential at one *V* plate is adjusted by Y POSITION dial 25*R* to center the spot up or down, while X POSITION dial 26*R* adjusts the steady potential at one *H* plate to center the spot sidewise. Later, when input voltage signals are brought through capacitors 3*C* and 8*C* to these deflecting plates, the resulting curve may be moved as a whole on the screen by 25*R* and 26*R*.

[In Fig. 31-10, the main oscillograph circuits can apply only ac or changing voltages to the deflecting plates; such signals must pass through capacitor 3*C*, 8*C*, 23*C*, or 24*C*. If the *Y*-input voltage includes any dc voltage, this dc portion will not be shown in the wave on the screen. For checking industrial electronic circuits, we often need to observe dc as well as ac voltages; many types of oscillograph include dc amplifiers for this purpose. By the removal of small wires at the *V* or *H* terminals, the deflecting plates may be disconnected from the oscillograph circuits; either ac or dc signal voltages then may be connected directly to these deflecting-plate terminals so as to move the spot on the screen (about 1 inch for each 30 volts applied).]

31-15 AMPLIFIERS IN THE OSCILLOGRAPH

So that we may watch the waveshape of small voltages, amplifier circuits are included in the oscillograph. Applied between the *Y*-input and ground terminals (near the left-hand side of Fig. 31-10), this ac voltage now appears across *Y*-amplitude adjuster 1*R*. With the 1*R* slider turned clockwise, an input signal of less than 1 volt moves the spot 1 inch on the screen.

When this signal voltage at the 1*R* slider swings positive, greater plate current flows in triode 1*A* and 3*R*; since this lowers anode 4, the grid of triode 1*B* also is lowered, decreasing the plate current through 1*B* and 4*R*. Thus the two halves of tube 1 are a two-stage capacitor-coupled amplifier. A small positive *Y*-input swing makes anode 4 drive negative one *V* deflecting plate (through 23*C*), while the greater rise of anode 5 drives positive the other *V* plate (through 3*c*), thus causing large upward movement of the spot on the screen. If the *Y*-input signal is 350 V, the 1*R* slider is turned down so that a very small part of this voltage reaches the tube-1*A* grid; by this decrease of *Y* amplitude the bright spot or wave is kept inside the screen circle.

Similar to the above, a horizontal amplifier in Fig. 31-10 uses tube 2. If the SWEEP RANGE switch 1*S* is turned to the *X* input, an external voltage may be used to cause the sidewise spot movement (as in Sec. 31-13). A positive voltage swing applied across 23*R* (X AMPLITUDE) lowers the potential of anode 7 of tube 2*A* but causes a large rise at anode 8; through capacitors 24*C* and 8*C*, this amplified signal is applied to the *H* deflecting plates.

For most tests on industrial equipment, the SWEEP RANGE switch is turned away from the *X* input, so that tube 2 now is controlled by the changes of potential at point 6 of the sweep circuit.

31-16 THE SWEEP CIRCUIT

To move, or "sweep," the bright spot from left to right across the screen in order to see the rapid vertical changes of observed voltage, the circuit around tube 3 is used. Tube 3 is a small thyratron, as described in Sec. 20-1.

The 400-V dc supply (at the left in Fig. 31-10) forces electrons to flow from grounded point 2 through 19*R* to point 9 and up through 20*R* to positive point 1; this keeps the tube-3 cathode about 4 V above ground potential. (Meanwhile, turn 16*R* until the tube-3 grid is at ground potential.) Electrons flow through 19*R* also to charge capacitor 14*C* (or another capacitor connected by SWEEP RANGE switch 1*S*), then through 1*S*, 37*R*, and 36*R* to point 1.

When 14*C* first starts to charge, there is little voltage across 14*C*; there is not enough voltage 6-to-9 to fire tube 3. This low potential at point 6 is applied through 15*R*, 1*S*, 6*C*, and 23*R* to the grid of tube 2*A*; the decreased current in tube 2*A* permits large plate current in tube 2*B*; so its anode-8 potential is low and keeps the bright spot at the far left on the cathode-ray-tube screen. However, as the electron flow gradually charges 14*C*, the point-6 potential rises steadily; the tube-2*B* current decreases, steadily raising the point-8 potential so that the bright spot moves toward the right across the screen.

When the 14*C* voltage becomes large enough (20 to 40 V), thyratron tube 3 suddenly fires, letting 14*C* discharge almost instantly. (Electrons flow from 14*C*-terminal 9, through tube 3 and the switch 1*S* to the left-hand terminal of 14*C*.) Point 6 drops suddenly to the potential of point 9, so the tube-2*A* current stops; the potential of point 8 drops so that the bright spot returns quickly across the screen from right to left. (This return trace is not seen because of the "blanking" circuit; each time when tube 3 fires, the sudden drop at point 6 is applied through 18*C* to drive negative the grid of cathode-ray tube 6, momentarily stopping the electron flow so as to blank or dim the spot.) Since capacitor 14*C* is discharged, there is no voltage 6-to-9 and the tube-3 current stops; 14*C* then starts to recharge, again making the bright spot sweep across the screen. By this slow-charge—fast-discharge action, 14*C* and tube 3 make the point-6 potential follow the sawtooth waveshape (shown in Fig. 31-5) needed for the sweep circuit.

If a 60-hertz (Hz or cps) voltage wave is being applied to the vertical plates (through *Y* input and tube 1), a single 1-cycle wave will appear and stand still on the screen if tube 3 is fired exactly 60 times each second. The size of 14*C* is chosen so that, after adjusting the SWEEP VERNIER 36*R*, the 14*C* voltage rises and fires tube 3 at 60 times each second. (If tube 3 fires a bit too often, the 1-cycle wave moves toward the right across the screen and may cause many crossing waves to appear at the same time; if the 36*R* resistance is increased so that 14*C* charges more slowly and tube 3 fires less often, the 1-cycle wave may move to the left.)

If we wish to see three or four waves of the 60-Hz voltage on the screen at one time, we turn the SWEEP RANGE switch to connect 13*C* into circuit in place of 14*C*. This larger capacitor takes more time to charge; so tube 3 fires less often; by the adjusting of 36*R*, three, four, or five waves can appear side by side on the screen. [In other positions, 1*S* connects smaller capacitors into circuit, so that tube 3 fires hundreds or thousands of times per second. These high sweep speeds are used with high-frequency waves (such as are found in radio circuits). If tube 3 fires 300 times per second, a 60-Hz voltage (applied to the *Y* input) appears on the screen as five waves crossing each other, for the bright spot passes across the screen five times while the 60-Hz wave is changing through 1 cycle.]

31-17 SYNCHRONIZING THE WAVE

No matter how carefully the SWEEP VERNIER 36*R* is controlled, the position of the curve may move slowly across the screen. To hold this curve still, thyratron tube 3 may be fired by changing its grid potential; to do this, the tube-3 grid is connected to a voltage that is in step with the curve on the screen. This is called *synchronizing* the wave.

Near tube 3 in Fig. 31-10 is the SYNC SELECTOR switch 2*S*. When 2*S* is thrown to the INTERNAL position, the changing voltage between tube-1*A* anode 4 and ground is now applied across 16*R*. After the SWEEP VERNIER 36*R* has been set so that the curve moves very little on the screen, the slider of SYNC AMPLITUDE 16*R* is turned up (clockwise) so that more of the 4-to-ground voltage reaches the tube-3 grid; this "locks" the wave to hold it still. Each time point 4 rises, the tube-3 grid also rises. Tube 3 is fired always at this one point in the wave; so the curve on the screen always starts at the same point on the wave; the curve "stands still."

When testing 60-Hz circuits, it is better to synchronize the wave on the screen by setting 2*S* to the EXTERNAL position and by making a wire connection between the EXT and LINE FREQ terminals (as shown by the broken line in Fig. 31-10). This LINE FREQ terminal provides a test-signal voltage from a 6.3-V transformer winding. When this 6.3-volt ac signal is connected across 16R, tube 3 may be fired in step with this 60-cycle signal.

31-18 A STROBOSCOPE (GENERAL RADIO COMPANY STROBOTAC 1531-A)

When this instrument shines it flickering light on an object that is turning or vibrating at high speed, that object may appear to be standing still or moving slowly. As shown in Fig. 31-1, this stroboscope has a neon tube that gives a very short flash of light; its electronic circuit can make this light flash 25,000 times per minute. Dials may be turned to adjust this flashing rate to as low as 110 per minute. When this light makes a fast-turning motor appear to stand still, then the light is flashing once each time the motor turns; since the dial is marked to show how often the light is flashing, it also shows the motor speed. (The motor also appears still if the light flashes once for each two turns of the motor. If the light flashes twice for each turn of the motor, the motor is seen in two positions; every second flash shows the motor at the half-turn position. Select the highest flashing rate that shows the motor in only one position.)

At the upper left part of the circuit in Fig. 31-11, the ac supply voltage is increased through transformer T_1; each positive half cycle passes through diode D_3 and charges C_{12} so that the upper line 11 is held at +400 V above ground line 4. More filtering by R_{26} and C_{12A} produces a steady +250 V on line 12. Meanwhile, each negative half cycle from T_1 passes through D_1 and charges C_{13} so that the bottom line 8 is held at –400 V, or below ground. Thus a total of 800 volts appears between lines 11 and 8, since the circuit acts as a voltage doubler.

At the right in Fig. 31-11, this 800-V total is available across tube 3, which produces the flashes of light. Here capacitor C_{10} is charged to 800 V, storing enough energy to cause a short bright flash when C_{10} discharges a large current through tube 3. If this light flash lasts more than a microsecond, the fast-turning object moves far enough during the flash to be blurred. [Tube 3 is flashed rapidly. A selector handle (shown in Fig. 31-1) is turned to a position that chooses the range between 4000 and 25,000 rpm or flashes per minute; other positions select the range of 670 to 4170, or 110 to 690 rpm. Only a few of these selector S_2 contacts are shown in Fig. 31-11, and as though the instrument had only the two higher flashing ranges. In other S_2 handle positions, the instrument is connected so that the flashes are triggered by an external signal, or by a signal from the ac power-supply line.]

Strobotron tube 3 is made to flash each time when thyratron tube 2 is fired. The tube-2 cathode is at ground 4, while its grid is biased at –20 V on divider R_{16}-R_{17}. With no current through tube 2 and R_{19}, capacitor C_9 has steady charge and no voltage is applied to the primary winding of trans-

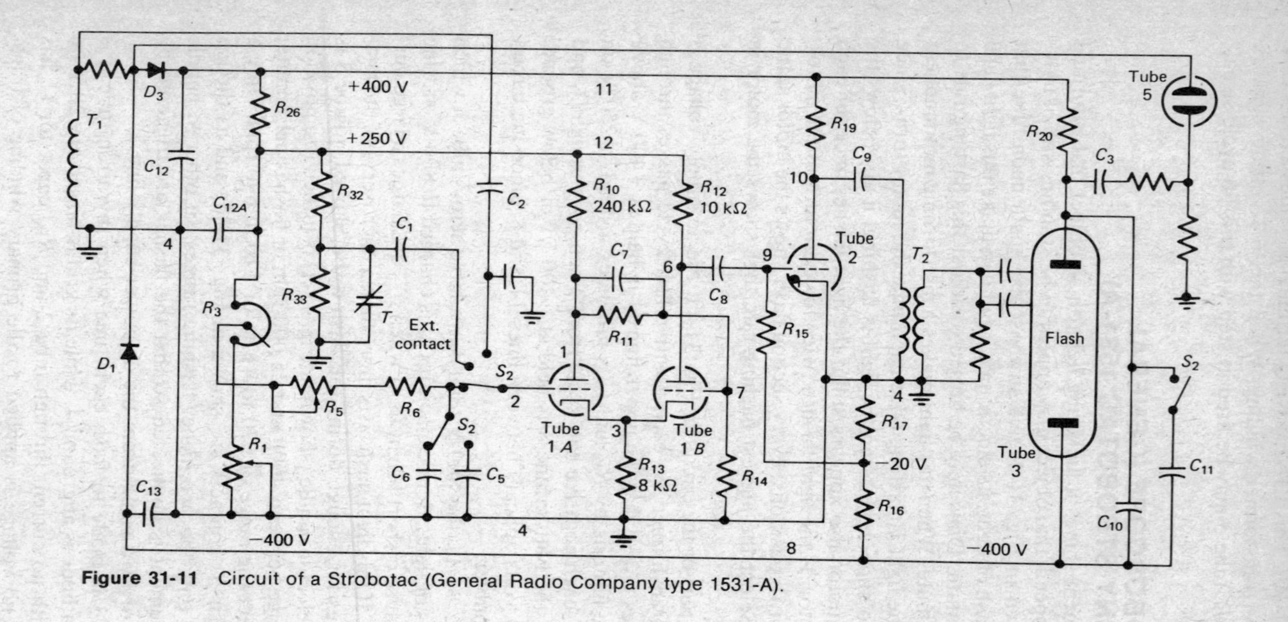

Figure 31-11 Circuit of a Strobotac (General Radio Company type 1531-A).

former T_2. When tube 2 is fired (by the momentary turnoff of tube 1B, as described below), its anode 10 drops, and C_9 discharges through tube 2 and the primary winding of T_2; the T_2 secondary is capacitively coupled to electrodes of strobotron 3 so as to fire this tube and discharge C_{10}.

Usually, thyratron 2 is fired many times per second by tubes 1A and 1B, which act as an oscillator or cathode-coupled multivibrator. Before watching this repeating action, notice how thyratron 2 can be fired once whenever a contact opens outside the instrument. (Such an outside contactor may be driven from the shaft of a motor whose motion is being studied; although the motor speed may change, each turn of the motor flashes tube 3 once.) Plugged in as an EXTERNAL INPUT, this contact T is shown at the left of tube 1A in Fig. 31-11. The selector S_2 is turned to connect the tube-1A grid to capacitor C_1; the closed contact T connects C_1 to ground. Meanwhile, cathode 3 is about 60 V above ground 4, since current flows in tube 1B and R_{13}. Little current flows in tube 1A or resistor R_{10}; so anode 1 is at high potential; divider R_{11}-R_{14} holds the tube-1B grid 7 near cathode 3, and tube-1B current through R_{12} holds anode 6 at low potential.

When external contact T opens, the voltage divider R_{32}-R_{33} sharply raises the potential at C_1, so that the tube-1A grid is driven positive for an instant. As the current increases quickly, anode 1 drops; the charge on C_7 forces the 1B grid 7 negative for an instant. Tube-1B current through R_{12} decreases, and the sudden rise at its anode 6 acts through C_8 to raise grid 9 and fire thyratron 2. The momentary decrease of tube-1B current (through R_{13}) lets cathode 3 drop to low potential, since the large resistance of R_{10} limits the tube-1A current to about 4 percent of the size of the tube-1B current.

But C_7 [only 10 $\mu\mu$F or picofarads (pF)] discharges very quickly through R_{11}, letting grid 7 rise again; the increasing current in tube 1B and R_{13} quickly raises cathode 3 of tube 1A. When contact T recloses, connecting C_1 to ground, grid 2 is driven negative; current in tube 1A stops, and the circuit is reset to await the next opening of contact T.

31-19 TIMING THE STROBOSCOPE FLASHES

To cause repeated flashing at a rate adjusted by the instrument front dial (which turns the slider of R_3 at the left in Fig. 31-11), the selector handle is turned to the RPM position so that an S_2 contact connects the tube-1A grid through R_6 to the R_3 slider. Even when R_3 is turned fully clockwise, for lower flashing rate, the potential at this slider is high enough (as shown at A in Fig. 31-12) to let grid 2 permit a sudden flow of tube-1A anode current just as S_2 is closed. As is explained above, this flow in tube 1A abruptly turns off tube 1B, so that cathode 3 drops to low potential for a very short time (shown between B and C in Fig. 31-12); during this brief interval C_6 is discharged through R_{13} and the grid-to-cathode circuit of tube 1A, so that grid 2 falls to low potential, as shown by the dotted line.

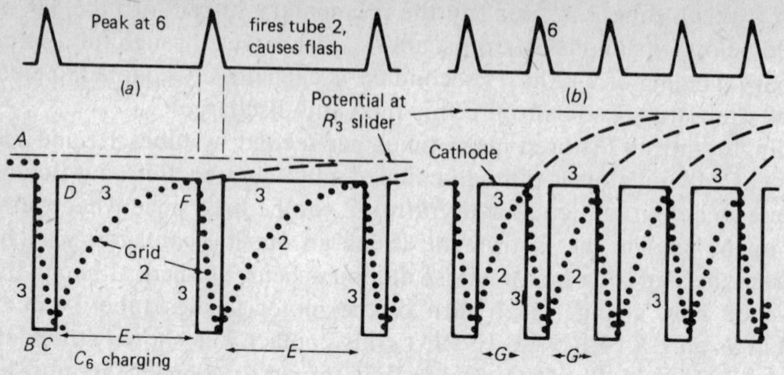

Figure 31-12 Charging of C_6 to potential set by R_3 determines flashing rate in Fig. 31-11.

The interval between *B* and *C* has been shown enlarged so that various actions can be seen separately, although they occur at the same instant: *B* to *C* is very small compared with *E* or *G*. At *C* the tube-1*B* current returns, suddenly raising cathode 3 as shown at *D*. But grid 2 rises more slowly as C_6 is recharged by electrons flowing through R_6 and R_5 toward the positive potential at the R_3 slider. After the time delay *E*, grid 2 has risen high enough (at *F*) to fire tube 1*A* again. Each time that tube 1*A* is fired, thyratron 2 fires and flashes strobotron 3; therefore, interval *E* is also the time between flashes. [Thyratron 2 operates from dc supply and is fired within 1 microsecond (μsec) by the turn-on pulse. As C_9 discharges through tube 2, it causes a pulse of current in transformer T_2; current continues to flow in this inductive winding until C_9 is recharged, becoming more negative at its terminal 10. Just as the transformer current stops, this charge on C_9 drives negative the tube-2 anode, thus stopping the thyratron current so that its negative grid can regain control.]

To increase the number of flashes per minute, R_3 is turned counterclockwise, thereby raising the potential at its slider, as is shown in Fig. 31-12*b*. Now C_6 is recharged toward this higher potential; therefore, grid 2 rises more quickly to the level of cathode 3, and after a shorter delay as shown at *G*, tube 1*A* is fired again. Thus strobotron 3 is flashed more often as the R_3-slider potential is raised, by the turning of R_3.

To make tube 3 flash at a much lower rate, the selector handle is turned to the middle range (between 670 and 4170 rpm); below tube 1*A* in Fig. 31-11, a contact of S_2 connects grid 2 to C_5 in place of C_6. Since C_5 is six times as large as C_6, it is recharged more slowly, so that the flashing rate becomes one-sixth of its previous value. At these lower flashing speeds, another contact S_2 (at the right in Fig. 31-11) adds capacitor C_{11} to C_{10}. The added charge in C_{11} causes a longer flash of light each time tube 3 fires; although flashing less often, this longer flash helps to shine as much total light on the moving object as is given in the high-speed range.

The sliders on R_1 and R_5 adjust the flashing rate at 900 and 3600 (on 60-Hz supply), with the help of glow tube 5 (at upper right in Fig. 31-11). The amount of glow increases as the voltage between its two electrodes increases. The potential at the top electrode of tube 5 varies 3600 times per minute, in step with the ac supply; the potential at the lower electrode changes with each flash of tube 3. With the R_3 dial set at 3600, R_5 is adjusted until the glow of tube 5 remains at a steady amount.

If the selector handle is turned to the LINE position, tube 3 flashes exactly in step with the power-supply frequency; a contact of S_2 now connects the tube-1A grid through C_2 to one side of supply transformer T_1. Each upward swing of this ac voltage fires tubes 1A, 2, and 3, giving 3600 flashes per minute (on 60-Hz supply).

Problems

31-1 True or false? Explain why.

(a) When the instrument of Fig. 31-2 is measuring ac volts, a dc voltage is applied to the base of transistor Q_3.

(b) When measuring ohms in Fig. 31-2 (with $S1C$ set at $R \times 1$), greater current is drawn from battery $BT1$ when the meter pointer is moved up-scale (reading higher ohms).

(c) When measuring a dc voltage with the instrument of Fig. 31-2, very nearly the only current drawn from this voltage is the current flowing through the divider (point G to ground).

(d) If the oscillator in Fig. 31-4 were to produce only 390 kilohertz (kHz), a measurement of exactly 8 volts dc would give a display of 7.800.

(e) The metal enclosing case of an oscillograph may have dangerous voltage to ground.

(f) If the same supply of voltage is connected to both sets of deflecting plates, a circle appears on the picture-tube face.

(g) A Lissajous "figure 8" changes shape continuously when the ratio of frequencies is not exactly 2:1.

(h) The V and H terminals of the cathode-ray tube are fairly close to ground potential.

(i) If 30 V dc applied at the V deflecting plates of a cathode-ray tube will move the bright spot 1 in. away from center, 30 V ac will move the spot nearly $1\frac{1}{2}$ in. from center.

(j) The focus adjustment of an oscillograph varies the grid voltage of the picture tube.

(k) In Fig. 31-11, the brightness of the flash of neon tube 3 depends on the amount of energy discharged through it by capacitors.

31-2 Showing construction lines as in *A* of Fig. 31-8, carefully draw large Lissajous figures for frequency ratios of (*a*) 1:3, (*b*) 3:4.

31-3 At *V*, how much voltage is indicated by (*a*) an electronic voltmeter, (*b*) a voltmeter having 2000 ohms per volt, using its 150-volt scale, (*c*) the volt-meter of (*b*), using its 50-volt scale?

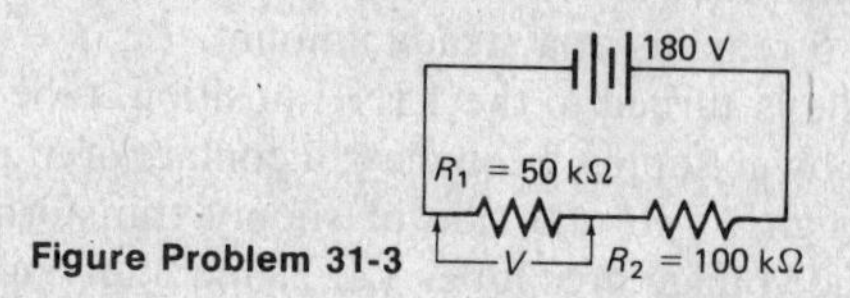

Figure Problem 31-3

31-4 Repeat (*a*) and (*b*) of Prob. 31-3, if battery $V = 300$ V, $R_1 = 250$ kΩ, $R_2 = 1$ MΩ, and the voltmeter has 1667 ohms per volt, using a 100-V scale.

31-5 A voltmeter (20,000 ohms per volt, with 15-, 50-, and 150-V scales) reads 112.5 V when connected across resistor *D*. (*a*) Find the voltage of battery *X* and the true voltage across each resistor. (*b*) Using lower scales when possible, what voltage does this voltmeter read across *A*, *B*, and *C* individually?

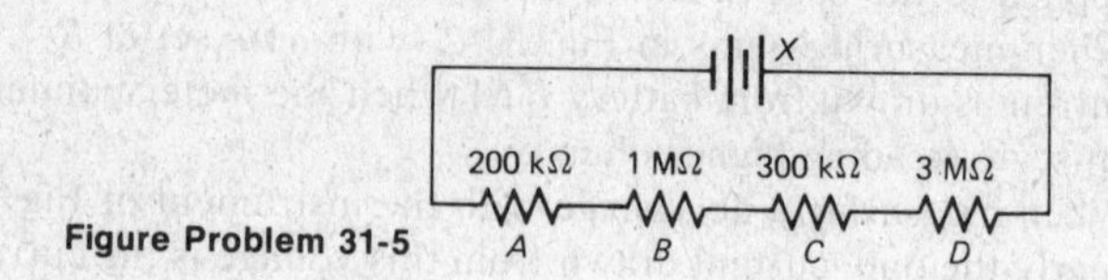

Figure Problem 31-5

32 NONELECTRONIC DEVICES

Today many of the electronic circuits in industry include devices that may not be electronic but that add greatly to the successful operation of the circuit. The amplidyne acts as an amplifier so that it may replace or may be combined with electron devices. Other devices act as transducers (as mentioned in Sec. 28-5) to produce electric signals that show changes in temperature, pressure, motion, or other nonelectrical quantities.

32-1 THE AMPLIDYNE

This rotating unit often is used as a dc generator to provide large power gain. It is usually a two-pole machine. Its armature is like that of an ordinary dc motor. If four brushes are used, two of these are short-circuited together, as shown in Fig. 32-1.

The output voltage of the amplidyne generator may be controlled by varying the current in a single field winding F. The advantage of the amplidyne is that a field current of only 20 to 100 milliamperes (less than 0.1 ampere) can control 10 to 200 amperes output from its armature circuit. (A similar increase of current is obtained when two ordinary dc generators are con-

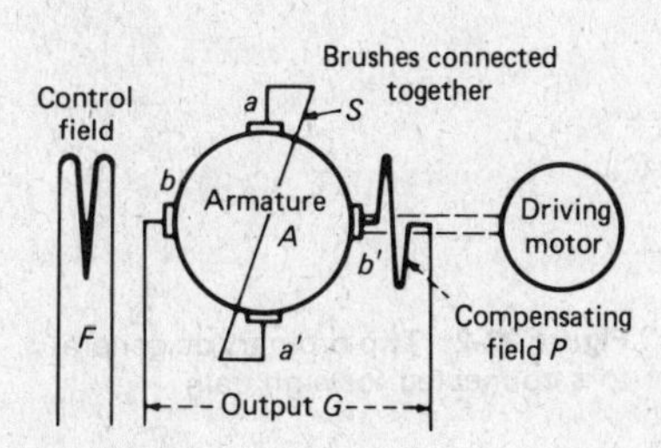

Figure 32-1 Connections of an amplidyne generator.

nected as shown in Fig. 32-2. Here a 10-watt input signal at the field of generator 1 controls the output of 10,000 watts from generator 2; however, such a combination of two separate generators is slow to respond when the input signal changes.)

In Fig. 32-1, very small current in F causes the turning armature A to generate a low voltage between brushes a and a', so that a large current flows in the short-circuit connection S. By armature reaction, this S current in the armature produces a stronger field, at 90° to the control field, so that armature A generates a higher voltage between brushes b and b^1 and greater power output at G. (The large output current flowing in the armature produces a field that opposes or weakens the flux of the control field F; this effect must be offset by passing the output current also through a compensating field winding P, so arranged that it assists F.) For a change of 1-W input at control field F, the output power at G may be changed by 2000 to 25,000 W. Of special importance, a signal change at F causes the output G to change very quickly. Since its speed of response is so much faster than that of an ordinary dc machine, the amplidyne combines well with the speed of electronic circuits. Since currents of 100 mA are easily controlled by certain high-vacuum tubes or transistors, sensitive electronic circuits may be used directly to control an amplidyne. In this way, the amplidyne itself may act as an amplifier, in turn driving loads that require many horsepower. (The amplidyne is the logical connecting link between electronic control circuits and large dc apparatus. In a similar way, the saturable reactor[26-1] or the magnetic amplifier is used as a connecting link between electronic control circuits and large ac apparatus.)

In many industrial circuits, the amplidyne is used as an exciter, supplying field current to a larger generator, as shown in Fig. 32-3.

32-2 AMPLIDYNE FIELDS

The control field winding of an amplidyne is so small that three to six like it can be placed within the available space; in this way one amplidyne generator can be controlled from several signals at the same time. Figure 32-3 shows such an amplidyne generator being controlled by four separate fields

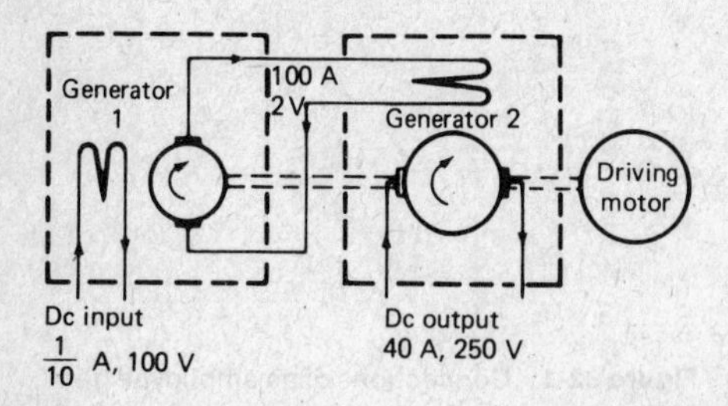

Figure 32-2 Two ordinary dc generators connected for high gain.

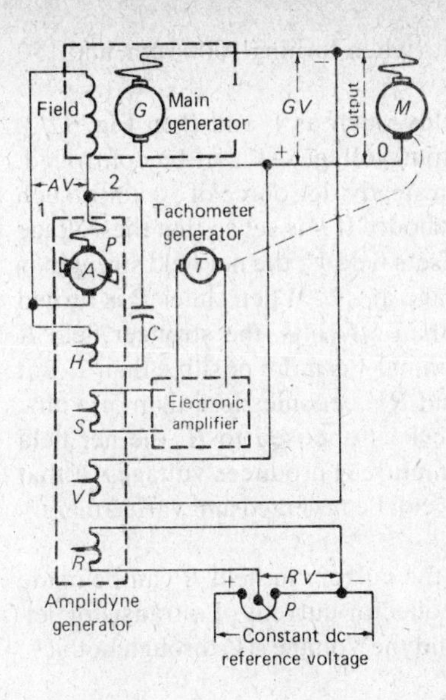

Figure 32-3 Separate fields of amplidyne exciter that regulate voltage, control speed, and decrease hunting.

H, *R*, *S*, and *V*; its armature *A* supplies direct current to the field of a larger generator *G*. We can control hundred of kilowatts of output at *O* merely by changing the 1-watt input signal at *H*, *R*, *S*, or *V*.

Field *V* is the main control field mentioned earlier; it lets the amplidyne of Fig. 32-3 act as a regulator to hold constant generator voltage at *GV*. Here the desired generator voltage is selected by turning *P*, which adjusts *RV* or the current and strength of the reference field *R*; this current comes from some standard supply, such as a battery, Zener diode, or voltage-regulator tube.[17-5] If *RV* is adjusted so that field *R* is just equal and opposite to field *V*, these fields now cause no output from amplidyne *A*; so there can be little voltage at *GV*. In operation, *RV* is increased until field *R* becomes stronger than field *V*; this difference between *V* and *R* increases the output of amplidyne *A* so that it excites generator *G* to produce voltage *GV*. If some change of load causes *GV* to decrease, the field *V* is weakened; this increases the difference between *V* and *R* so that amplidyne *A* strengthens the field of *G* to raise *GV* back to normal.

To hold constant speed (in Fig. 32-3) of a motor *M* that operates as the main load on generator *G*, amplidyne field *S* can control *A* and *G* to produce such speed control. If the speed of *M* drops, the voltage output of *T* decreases; this tiny voltage change at *T* is amplified to produce enough change of current in field *S* to boost *GV* and raise the speed of motor *M* to normal. (Similar action is described in Sec. 21-12. This tachometer generator *T* has constant field strength furnished by permanent magnets; so its output voltage has a direct ratio to the speed of the motor that drives it. For example, such a "tach" may produce 50 volts when turning 1000 rpm, and 150 volts at 3000 rpm.)

By the use of two equal amplidyne fields, such as V and R in Fig. 32-3, both the size and the polarity of the output voltage AV can be controlled. Suppose that field V is connected to only a steady dc source of 50 volts, such as the voltage across a battery or a Zener diode. If P is set so that the voltage RV also is 50 volts, the field R exactly offsets field V; the net field strength is zero, and amplidyne A produces no voltage at AV. When slider P is turned clockwise so that RV becomes greater than 50 volts, the stronger field R makes A produce a voltage AV so that terminal 1 is more positive than 2. But when P is turned counterclockwise so that RV becomes less than 50 volts, the field V becomes larger than R; since V is opposed to R, the net field strength has been reversed, so that the armature A produces voltage AV that is more positive at 2. Thus the voltage AV can be reversed and varied merely by turning the single dial P.

Instead of passing through adjuster P, the current in field R can be made the plate current of a triode tube or the collector current of a transistor; either device alone can control the the amplidyne voltage AV through both (+) and (−) values.

32-3 ANTIHUNT METHODS

In most regulating systems, such as that shown in Fig. 32-3, there is need for an antihunt, or stabilizing, circuit; without it the generator voltage GV may rise and fall (or "hunt") so rapidly that the system cannot settle down to a steady voltage, as is discussed in Secs. 28-2 and 29-8. Field H is an antihunt field; because of its connection in series with capacitor C, it can act only when circuit voltages are *changing*. When the amplidyne output voltage AV is steady or constant, capacitor C has charged to this voltage AV; no current flows now into or out of C; so there is no current in field H. If AV increases slowly, capacitor C will charge to this higher voltage by drawing so little current through H that its effect may be neglected; when AV increases quickly, the large current needed to charge C also causes such a signal in field H that it "bucks down" the amplidyne output AV. By opposing such sudden changes in amplidyne voltage, the rest of the system is likewise prevented from hunting.

Sometimes the antihunt signal is produced by using a transformer instead of capacitor C just described. In Fig. 32-4 such an antihunt transformer is shown, with its primary winding connected across the amplidyne output voltage AV. Is it strange to see an ac transformer used in a dc circuit? The dc voltage AV forces current through AHT primary (1-to-2); no voltage is produced at AHT secondary (3-to-4) as long as AV remains steady. Remember that the secondary, or output, voltage of a transformer is produced by a *change* in primary, or input, voltage. If AV suddenly

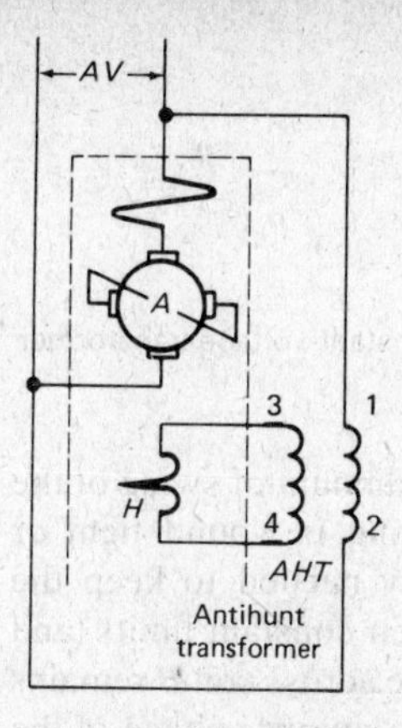

Figure 32-4 Antihunt transformer used with an amplidyne.

increases, AHT quickly produces a secondary voltage, which forces current through field H in such direction as to oppose or reduce AV.

32-4 CONSTANT-VOLTAGE TRANSFORMER, OR STABILIZER

There are many types of this voltage-regulating transformer. Generally, such a unit includes a capacitor, together with several reactors or windings on a special magnetic core. By cleverly combining the voltages across these various parts, this combination furnishes more constant output voltage. (To see how these voltages combine, a vector diagram is used, as shown in J. A. Uttal, Voltage Stabilizers, *Electronic Industries*, August 1945.) If its input or voltage supply changes, the transformer absorbs this voltage change, keeping its output rms voltage unchanged. To accomplish this, the waveshape of its output may change, but this is often unimportant, as when its output is to be rectified and filtered for a dc supply to an electronic circuit. Since there are no moving parts, the output voltage is corrected within 2 or 3 cycles after any change in the input voltage or the load.

In one type shown in Fig. 32-5, the input winding A is on one portion of the iron core and directly induces voltage only in winding D. On another portion of the core is the B winding, or coil, which is connected across capacitor C (also mounted inside the transformer case). This combination of winding B and capacitor C is resonant at 60 hertz (Hz or cps). (The size of capacitor C is chosen just large enough so that $1/2\pi fC = 2\pi fL$. Here f equals 60 for a 60-Hz transformer; C is in farads, L is in henrys.[24-3] A large current flows backward and forward through B and C, exactly in step with the 60-Hz pulse of energy received through the iron core from winding A. Notice that the amount of this oscillating current depends mainly on the henrys or farads of B and C and does not increase when the voltage across A

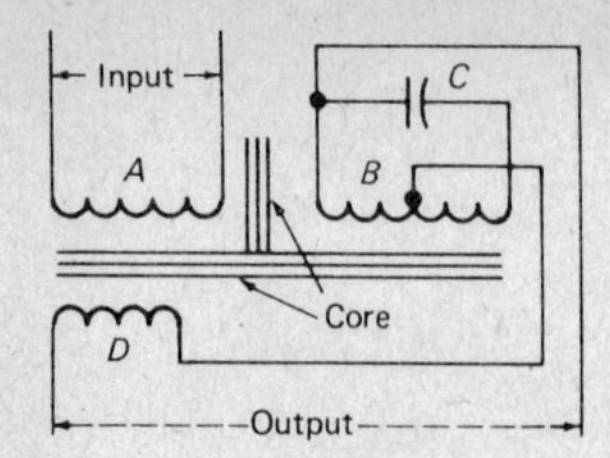

Figure 32-5 Circuit of a constant-voltage transformer (resonant type).

increases. This is like a grandfather clock, where the amount of swing of the pendulum remains the same whether the clock spring is wound tight or loose; the spring supplies only the pulses of energy needed to keep the pendulum swinging. Since this current swings between constant limits (and since the core inside *B* becomes saturated), the voltage across coil *B* remains fairly constant; part of it is used to furnish part of the output voltage of the transformer. Coil *D* furnishes a small part of the output voltage and further corrects or keeps the output voltage at a steady value.

32-5 THE SELSYN—ELECTRIC GEARING

The selsyn is a kind of motor or generator. When two selsyns are connected together electrically, any movement of the shaft of selsyn 1 causes the shaft of selsyn 2 to turn the same amount, as though the two selsyn shafts were mechanically geared together. If pointers are mounted properly on each of the selsyn shafts and selsyn 1 is pointed at a certain mark on a dial, selsyn 2 will point to the corresponding mark on a duplicate dial. For such indicating purposes, the selsyns are small units that operate from single-phase ac power supply, as is shown in Fig. 32-6.

32-6 THE DIFFERENTIAL SELSYN OR PHASE SHIFTER

In the electric circuit between the above selsyns, a third, or differential, selsyn may be inserted, shown as *D* in Fig. 32-7; the movement of *D* is equal

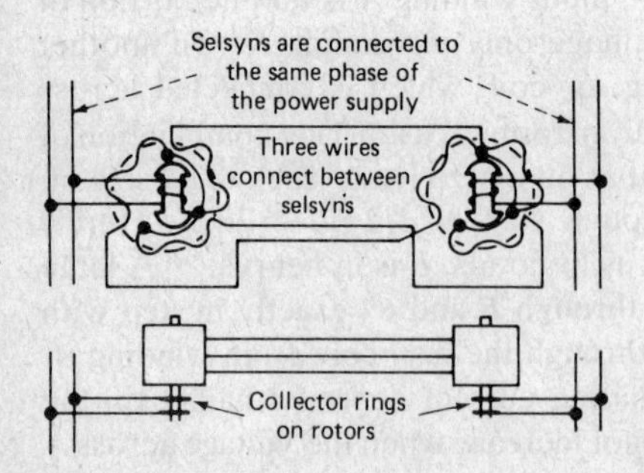

Figure 32-6 Connections of single-phase indicator selsyns.

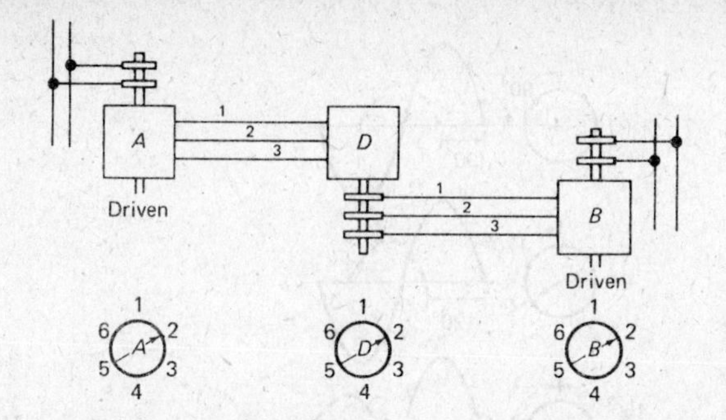

Figure 32-7 Differential selsyn D may act as a differential gear.

to the difference between the movement of A and the movement of B. If selsyns A and B are turning at exactly the same speed, D does not move; if A turns 1000 rpm forward and B turns 999 rpm forward, D turns 1 rpm backward. [The differential selsyn D has three rings (like a three-phase unit), while selsyns A and B may be either single-phase or three-phase units.]

If an arrow is mounted on each of the three selsyn shafts and pointed at 2 (in lower portion of Fig. 32-7), these things will happen: (1) If D is locked so it cannot turn, A and B will control each other as though D were not in the circuit. (2) If A is held still at 2, and D is turned from 2 to 3, B also moves from 2 to 3. (3) If B is held still at 2, and D is turned from 2 to 3, A moves from 2 to 1. (4) With A at 2, if D is turned to 5 and locked there, B points to 5, just opposite to A; if we now rotate A, B turns at the same speed as A, but is always opposite to A, or 180° from A. Although D is not turning, the position of D controls the displacement between A and B; although A and B may both be turning at 1000 rpm, D is the phase shifter by which we can make the arrows of A and B both point at 2 at the same instant, or we can displace arrow B so that it lags behind A.

In electronic control circuits, a multiphase selsyn may be used as a phase shifter to produce output ac voltages that are out of phase with the input, or supply, voltage. At one position of its shaft shown in Fig. 32-8*a*, the output voltage at its rings is in phase with the input voltage to its stator. If the shaft is moved one-sixth of a full turn, or 60°, Fig. 32-8*b* shows that the output voltage now lags 60° behind the input voltage (or the output has been shifted 60° out of phase). Turning the shaft to the other positions produces other amounts of phase shift of the output voltage in Fig. 32-8*c*, *d*, or *e*.

32-7 THYRITE

Thyrite is a resistance material used to limit overvoltage, and is made of silicon carbide and baked at high temperature. To give good electrical con-

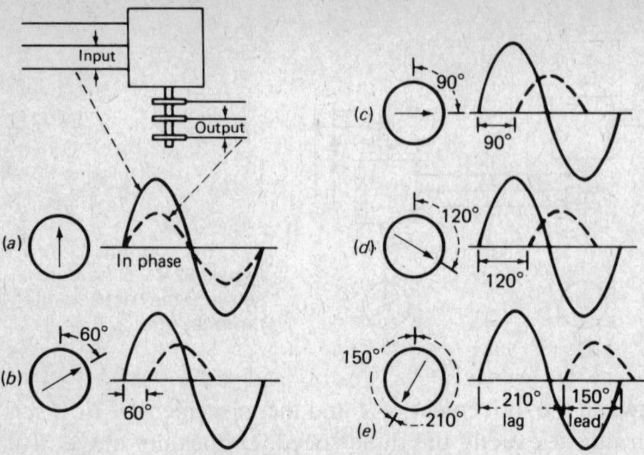

Figure 32-8 Using a selsyn as a phase shifter.

tact, its two flat surfaces are metal-sprayed. Smaller sizes may have wire leads. Thyrite is an example of a nonlinear resistance called a *varistor*.

Thyrite has a special action when the voltage across it is increased. When we double the voltage across an ordinary resistor, the current doubles also, since the amount of resistance stays unchanged. However, if we double the voltage across Thyrite, the current increases at least 11 times; this shows that the amount of resistance decreases greatly when the voltage increases. Thyrite may be used for lightning arresters; it passes very little current at ordinary line voltages; but when a lightning surge adds a high voltage, the resistance of the arrester material instantly decreases, letting the lightning pass through the arrester, protecting other equipment. When the high voltage has passed, the Thyrite resistance returns to normal. Similarly, Thyrite resistors are connected across transformers, motor fields, or other inductive windings, to absorb or bypass any voltage surge or "kick" when such circuits are opened.

Recent Thyrector selenium diodes provide similar circuit protection against transient overvoltages, especially where SCR or other semiconductor devices must be protected. (Thyrector and Thyrite are trade names used by General Electric Company.) Each Thyrector is like a Zener diode,[7-18] acting as an open circuit until the reverse voltage across it exceeds its rated value; any greater voltage peak instantly makes the diode act like a short circuit that bypasses this voltage away from the rest of the circuit. In an ac circuit, two such diodes are combined back to back, as is shown in Figs. 27-1 and 27-5.

32-8 STRAIN GAGES

These small devices may be attached or cemented onto beams, pipes, airplane structures, etc., so that they will convert any tiny movement or stretch (caused by mechanical changes of weight, force, pressure, or torque) into electrical signals that can be measured directly or observed on an oscillograph; the strain gage is a transducer that converts mechanical quantities into electrical measurements. Of the many types available, the most common are the resistance-wire gage and the magnetic gage.

In the resistance-wire strain gage, a piece of fine wire (only $^1/_{1000}$ in. in diameter, made of copper-nickel alloy) is cemented onto the material being tested; when that material is stretched by a force, the wire is stretched an equal amount. This strain or stretching lengthens the wire and decreases its cross section, both of which increase the resistance of the wire. The gage is connected into an electric circuit so that the change of its wire resistance produces a change of voltage, which directly indicates the size of the force that stretched the material.

In a commercial form of strain gage, a 1- to 6-in. length of fine wire is formed into loops (as shown in Fig. 32-9) and is bonded firmly on a backing piece of paper or Bakelite little larger than a postage stamp. This whole "stamp" then is cemented onto the sample being tested so that each wire will be stretched when the sample is stretched. (The wire is so fine and is held so firmly that it also may be compressed to *decrease* its resistance.) In use, the amount of stretch L may be less than $^1/_{1000}$ in. for each inch of length of wire; so the change in wire resistance R also is small. The ratio of the change in R to the change in L is called the *gage factor* and usually is between 2 and 5; if a 1 percent stretch in L causes a 3 percent increase in the resistance of R the gage factor of this certain unit is 3.

If the strain applied to the gage is steady or is changing slowly, the gage may be connected as one leg of a dc Wheatstone-bridge circuit, as shown in Fig. 32-10. Here the battery voltage E is applied across the gage, $3R$ and $4R$ in series, and also across $1R$ and $2R$ in series. Before force is applied or the gage is stretched, $4R$ is made zero. If $1R = 2R$, the potential of A is midway between the potentials at C and D. Now if $3R$ is adjusted until the galvanometer G reads zero, the resistance of $3R$ becomes equal to the resistance of the gage; the potential at B becomes midway between those at C and D. Since the potential at A now is the same as at B, there is no voltage across G to move the galvanometer indicator; so its reading is zero.

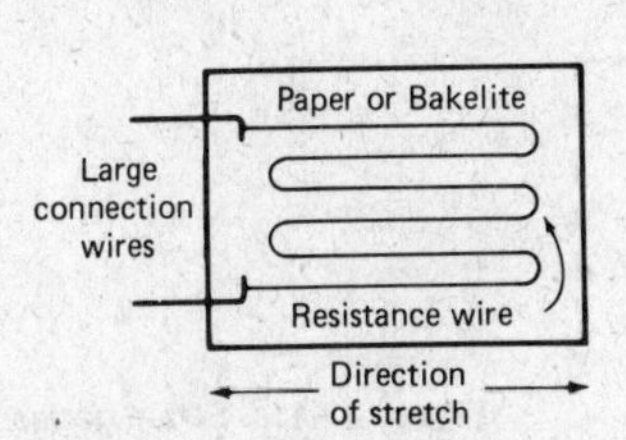

Figure 32-9 Resistance-wire strain gage.

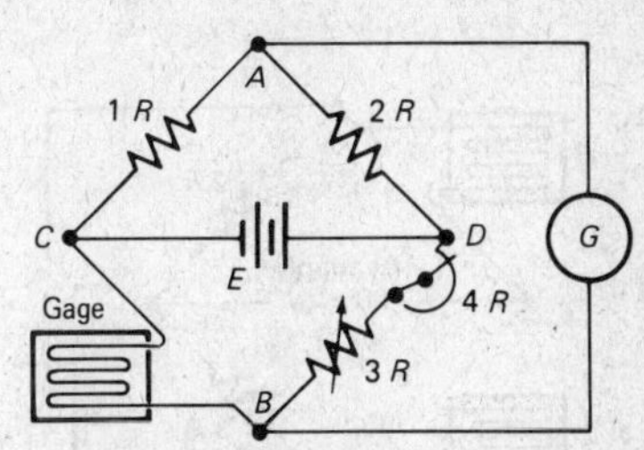

Figure 32-10 Dc bridge circuit used with strain gage.

When the gage is stretched and its ohms increase, the voltage across the gage becomes greater than the voltage across $3R$; this raises B to a higher potential than A, causing G to read up-scale. If resistance of $4R$ now is inserted until G is brought back to a zero reading, the ohms added by $4R$ will equal the *increase* of resistance of the gage; so from this the stretching force can be calculated.

To observe sudden or fast changes of force applied to the strain gage, an oscillograph is used in place of the galvanometer, as shown in Fig. 32-11. Since the output of the bridge, voltage A-to-B, changes by only a small fraction of a volt, it is passed through an amplifier before it is applied to the oscillograph or recorder. (Some recent types of oscillographs are designed to operate directly from this low strain-gage voltage, without a preamplifier.) Since an ac amplifier often works better than a dc type, ac power may be applied to the bridge circuit in place of battery E; here the frequency of this alternating current is selected so that it is 5 or 10 times greater than the fastest vibration or change that is to be measured.

In Fig. 32-11 a second gage H is used, merely as a fixed resistance in place of $1R$, to compensate for temperature changes. If gages F and H are close together, any temperature change has equal effect on the resistance of each gage, so that the balance of the bridge circuit is not changed thereby. The added gage H sometimes is placed on an opposite side of the beam being tested or is turned in a different direction, so that, when a force increases the resistance of F, the same force decreases the resistance of H; this doubles the sensitivity or gage output. [A wide variety of commercial strain-gage units is available, built into compact mechanical assemblies (such as the SR-4 devices of the Baldwin-Lima-Hamilton Corporation). Here four gage wires are cemented to the four sides of a central steel bar; when this bar is compressed (perhaps $^1/_{200}$ in.), weights up to 25 tons are measured directly by this *load cell*, having the size of a fist. Similarly, when gages are cemented to the outside of a metal tube, they respond to any stretch of the tube wall; thereby they measure changes of pressure inside this *fluid pressure cell*.]

Since each gage wire may have a resistance near 120 ohms, many such gages can be switched successfully in and out of a single measuring circuit.

In a magnetic type of strain gage, the stretching of the tested material

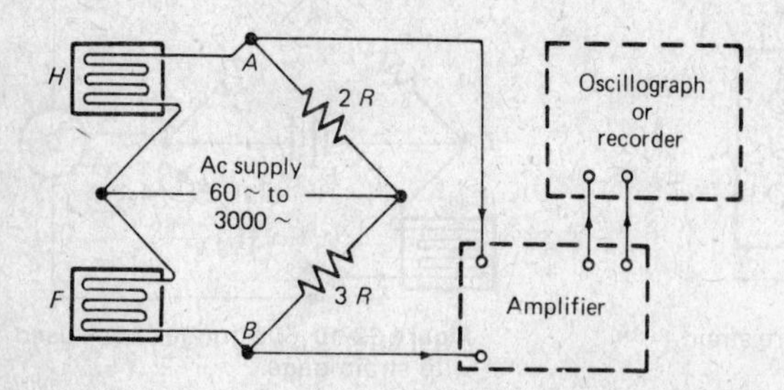

Figure 32-11 Strain gages connected so that fast changes may be observed.

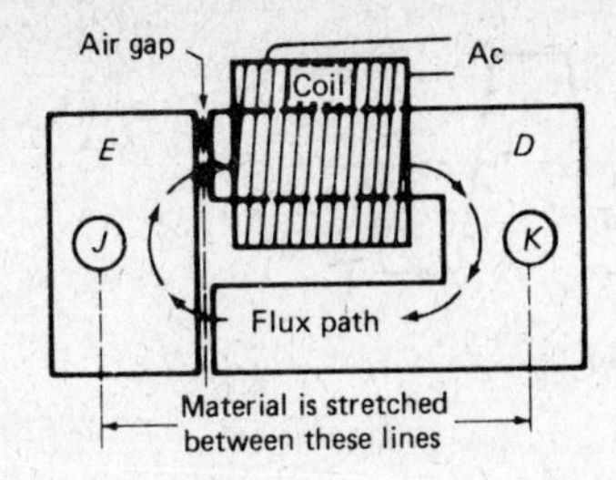

Figure 32-12 Magnetic type of strain gage.

causes a change in the reactance or inductive ohms of a coil. As shown in Fig. 32-12, the ac coil is wound around a laminated steel core *D*. When alternating current is forced through this coil, it produces magnetic flux that circulates through core *D* and also through a separate steel bar *E*. Connectors at *J* and *K* firmly attach *D* and *E* to the material being tested, leaving an air gap of perhaps $^1/_{100}$ in. between *D* and *E*.

If a force stretches the material so that *E* is pulled another $^1/_{1000}$ in. away from *D*, this small increase in the air gap makes it more difficult for flux to pass; this decrease in flux lessens the inductive ohms of the coil, increasing the current through it.

This coil may be used in place of gage *F* in an ac bridge circuit like Fig. 32-11; a duplicate coil may replace *H* to give temperature compensation.

32-9 VIBRATOR OR CONVERTOR

For use in portable electronic equipment wherein the only power supply may be a battery (such as the 12-volt automobile battery that operates a car radio), the low voltage of the battery may be converted to a higher voltage by a vibrator unit. Such a vibrator appears within the dashed rectangle of Fig. 32-13; here a set of contacts is made to vibrate so that the battery voltage is "chopped" into short intervals of (+) and (−) voltage, which, when fed through transformer *T*, produce a higher voltage secondary output; this ac may then be rectified by PN diodes to give the desired high-voltage dc.

At the left in Fig. 32-13, a piece of magnetic material *M*, together with middle contact *S*, is mounted on a spring that tries to remain in a central position, toughing neither contact *A* nor *B*. The battery forces current through the upper half of transformer *T* and through the coil of electromagnet *D*, which pulls *M* and deflects the spring until *S* touches *A*. This short-circuits coil *D*; at once the energy in the deflected spring pulls the middle contact *S* away from *A*. The inertia of *S* and *M* causes overtravel until *S* touches at contact *B*. But by now current flows again in coil *D*, pulling *M* and *S* toward *A* once more. (This is also the operating principle of the vibrating electric doorbell.) As long as the current stops and restarts in coil *D*, contact *S* is made to touch alternately at *A* and *B*.

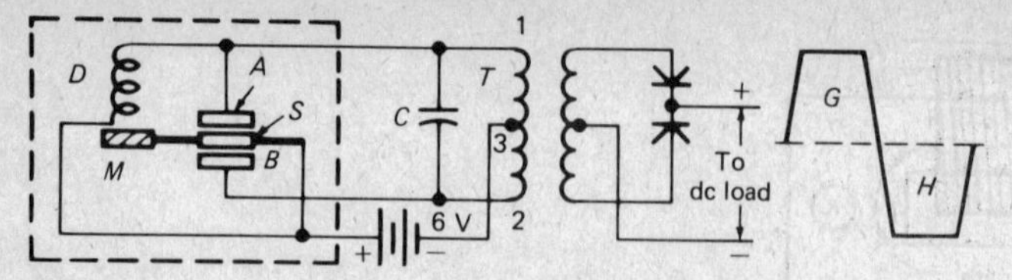

Figure 32-13 Vibrator converts low-voltage dc into ac.

While contact *S* touches at *A*, the battery voltage makes terminal 1 of transformer *T* more positive than its center tap 3; so electrons flow upward in this *T* winding. As this current increases, the resulting change of flux causes the secondary winding to produce a voltage (shown as *G*, at the right in Fig. 32-13). Contact *S* now moves from *A* to *B*, and the battery voltage makes terminal 2 of *T* more positive than center tap 3; electrons flow downward in this lower half of *T*. (When contact *S* leaves *A*, there would be an arc at the contact because of the inductive nature of the *T* winding, but capacitor *C* is added to prevent this arc.) As this current increases, the flux changes in the opposite direction and a secondary voltage *H* appears. Thus transformer *T* produces an alternating output voltage whose size can be any amount as selected in the design of the *T* windings; this ac now may be rectified to provide high-voltage dc to a load.

Problems

32-1 True or false? Explain why.

(a) Both the amplidyne and the magnetic amplifier may have two to six control windings.

(b) If 1 milliampere flows in the control field of an amplidyne while its output is 1 ampere, the amplidyne has a gain of 1000.

(c) Transistors or vacuum tubes are not large enough to control an amplidyne directly.

(d) Figure 32-3 shows a servo.

(e) The amplidyne acts as a two-stage direct-coupled amplifier.

(f) The differential selsyn can act as an error detector.

(g) Strain gages are limited to the measurement of small forces.

(h) All the devices described in Chap. 32 are transducers.

(i) To compare the positions of two shafts a mile apart, a mechanical interconnection is needed.

ANSWERS TO ODD-NUMBERED PROBLEMS

Chapter 3

3-1 (*a*) F (*b*) F (*c*) T (*d*) F (*e*) T (*f*) F (*g*) T
3-3 (*a*) 0.8 sec (*b*) 1.5 sec
3-5 (*a*) 2.75 sec (*b*) 0.44 sec
3-7 12.33 sec
3-9 0.822 μF; 236 V
3-11 (*a*) $RC = 0.12$ sec (*b*) $RC = 0.5$ sec

Chapter 4

4-1 (*a*) T (*b*) T (*c*) F (*d*) T (*e*) F (*f*) T (*g*) F (*h*) F
4-3 (*a*) 120 V (*b*) 54 V dc; 85 V ac
4-5 (*a*) 3 series, 8 parallel (*b*) 2.54 A
4-7 (*a*) $V_{ac} = 141.4$ V; $V_{dc} = 63.6$ V; $R = 5.29\ \Omega$ (*b*) 1890 W (*c*) 764 W
4-9 (*a*) 8 series, 3 parallel (*b*) 54.7 V, 1.08 A
4-11 (*a*) 88.4 V rms (*b*) 28.1 Ω
4-13 Half-wave, 2s, 4p, 8 total; center tap, 8s, 1p, 16 total; bridge, 17s, 2p, 136 total
4-15 Ripple factor = 0.475. (*b*) or (*c*) of Fig. 4-5

Chapter 5

5-1 (*a*) T (*b*) F (*c*) F (*d*) T (*e*) F (*f*) T (*g*) T (*h*) T (*i*) F (*j*) T (*k*) F
5-3 (*a*) 11 V (*b*) 1.7 mA (*c*) 2.5 to 0.9 mA; 7.2 to 15.1 V
5-5 (*a*) 167 Ω (*b*) 375 Ω (*c*) 667 Ω (*d*) no effect
5-7 (*a*) 0.08 mA (*b*) 13.8 mA (*c*) 3.6 V (*d*) 125 (*e*) 50 (*f*) 6250

Chapter 6

6-1 (*a*) F (*b*) T (*c*) T (*d*) F (*e*) T (*f*) F (*g*) T
6-3 (*a*) 13.2 mA, 3 V CE (*b*) 91
6-5 (*a*) 0.08 mA (*b*) 17 mA (*c*) 107.5 kΩ (*d*) I_B drops toward 0.04 mA, but the resulting decrease in I_C again raises I_B. Final I_C may be about 20 mA, I_B about 0.062 mA.
6-7 (*a*) 0.04 mA, 8.2 mA, 8.8 V (*b*) 8 mA p-p (*c*) 0.0145 mA

Chapter 7

7-1 (*a*) T (*b*) F (*c*) T (*d*) T (*e*) T (*f*) T (*g*) T (*h*) F (*i*) T (*j*) T (*k*) T (*l*) F (*m*) T (*n*) T
7-3 (*a*) 0.97 (*b*) 90 kΩ (*c*) PNP, since I_C and V_{CB} are negative
7-5 (*a*) $h_{ie} = 640\ \Omega$, $h_{re} = 3.4 \times 10^{-4}$, $h_{fe} = 19$, $h_{oe} = 2 \times 10^{-5}$ mho (*b*) 3.17×10^{-4} (*c*) 6.4×10^{-3}
7-7 (*a*) 21 (*b*) -641 (*c*) $-13{,}500$
7-9 (*a*) 32.6 Ω (*b*) 650 kΩ (*c*) 628 Ω (*d*) 69.6 kΩ

Chapter 8

8-1 (*a*) T (*b*) F (*c*) T (*d*) F (*e*) T (*f*) T (*g*) F (*h*) F (*i*) F (*j*) T (*k*) T (*l*) F (*m*) T (*n*) T

Chapter 9

9-1 (*a*) T (*b*) T (*c*) F (*d*) T
(*e*) F (*f*) T (*g*) F (*h*) F
(*i*) T (*j*) T (*k*) T (*l*) F
(*m*) T (*n*) T (*o*) F (*p*) F
(*q*) T (*r*) F

9-3 (*a*) 2.7 A (*b*) 0.106 H
(*c*) 45° (*d*) 120°

9-5 (*a*) 134° (*b*) 2.88 Ω

Chapter 10

10-1 (*a*) F (*b*) F, T (*c*) T
(*d*) F (*e*) T (*f*) T
(*g*) T (*h*) F (*i*) F

10-3 (*a*) 26 (*b*) 56 (*c*) 10.5
(*d*) 73 (*e*) 36.5
(*f*) 18.25 (*g*) 792
(*h*) 2080

10-5 (*a*) 100100 (*b*) 1110.11
(*c*) 1000001.1 (*d*) 1010101
(*e*) 11111010.01
(*f*) 1100110011
(*g*) 1111101000
(*h*) 11111001111

10-7 (*a*) 11101000
109 + 50 + 73 = 232
(*b*) 1110001
63 + 33 + 17 = 113
(*c*) 1000000
34 + 17 + 13 = 64

Chapter 11

11-1 (*a*) $I_c = 2.89$ mA (*b*) fan out = 8 gates

Chapter 12

12-1 $V_{out} = -4.0$ volts

12-3 (*a*) $V_{out} = -5.75$ volts
(*b*) $V_3 = +5$ volts

12-5 (*a*) 0.1 volt (*b*) $V_{out} = -0.047$ V, or nearly half of the V_{out} due to the signal

12-7 (*a*) 4.0 = 0110 (*b*) error = 0.25 V or 6.25 percent of input

Chapter 13

13-1 (*a*) R_5 carries too much current (*b*) Q_z (*c*) Output shows high impedance to ground and high to V_{CC} (*d*) High-*Z* state (*e*) Q_7 and emitter of Q_4

13-3 1001; 0001 0101; 0010 0111; 0111 0111; 1001 0010 0111; 0001 0001 0001 0111 0011

13-5 53; 123; 7090 1000

13-7

7	8	9	19
111	001 000	001 001	010 011
↓	↓	↓	↓
7	10	11	23

$$\begin{array}{r} 30 \\ -16 \\ -8 \\ -4 \\ -2 \\ \hline =0 \end{array}$$

011 110

36

Chapter 17

17-1 (*a*) T (*b*) F (*c*) F
(*d*) F (*e*) T (*f*) F
(*g*) T (*h*) T (*i*) F
(*j*) T (*k*) F

17-3 140 Ω, 19.7 to 24.6 V

17-5 (*a*) 0.081 sec (*b*) 12.35 per sec

17-7 (*a*) 50 mA (*b*) 50, 30, 20 mA
(*c*) 30, 10, 20 mA

17-9 (*a*) 105 V (*b*) 2.5 kΩ

Chapter 18

18-1 (*a*) T (*b*) F (*c*) F
(*d*) F (*e*) T (*f*) T
(*g*) F (*h*) F (*i*) F
(*j*) T (*k*) T (*l*) F
(*m*) T (*n*) T (*o*) F
(*p*) T (*q*) T (*r*) F
(*s*) T (*t*) T (*u*) F
(*v*) T (*w*) T

18-3 B, 11.1%, 980 A; C, 14.3%, 1980 A; D, 18.2%, 3960 A

18-5 (*a*) 11.1%, not overloaded (*b*) 1400 A, 13.9% overloads *B*; use *C*

18-7 (*a*) 3000 A at 7.14%
(*b*) 1500 A at 21.4%
18-9 (*a*) or (*b*) 43.5%, 1700 A
(*c*) 18.2%, 3800 A;
36.4%, 2200 A
18-11 *B*, 26.7%, 440 A; *C*, 25.9%,
1050 A; *D*, 32.6%, 2100 A
18-13 (*a*) 43.1%, 720 A (*b*) 40.2%,
1800 A (*c*) 10
18-15 (*a*) 20%, 530 A (*b*) 33.3%,
360 A (*c*) 40%, 310 A
18-17 450 welds per minute
18-19 About 30% reduction

Chapter 19

19-1 (*a*) F (*b*) T (*c*) F (*d*) F
(*e*) F (*f*) T (*g*) F (*h*) F
(*i*) F (*j*) T

Chapter 20

20-1 (*a*) T (*b*) F (*c*) F (*d*) T
(*e*) F (*f*) F (*g*) F (*h*) F
(*i*) T (*j*) F (*k*) F (*l*) T
(*m*) T (*n*) T (*o*) T (*p*) F
(*q*) F (*r*) T
20-3 (*a*) High shield current, short
life (*b*) perhaps −250 V
20-5 (*a*) 29° (*b*) does not fire

Chapter 21

21-1 (*a*) T (*b*) F (*c*) T (*d*) F
(*e*) F (*f*) F (*g*) T (*h*) T
(*i*) F (*j*) F (*k*) T (*l*) T
(*m*) T

Chapter 22

22-1 (*a*) T (*b*) F (*c*) F
(*d*) T (*e*) T (*f*) F
(*g*) T (*h*) F (*i*) T
(*j*) F, T (*k*) T (*l*) T
(*m*) T (*n*) T (*o*) F
(*p*) F (*q*) T (*r*) T

22-3

(a)

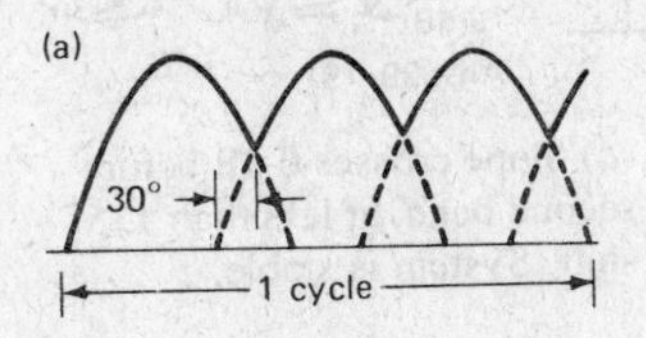

(b) $V_{dc} = 1.17V$

(c) $V_{dc} = \frac{1.17}{2}$ V

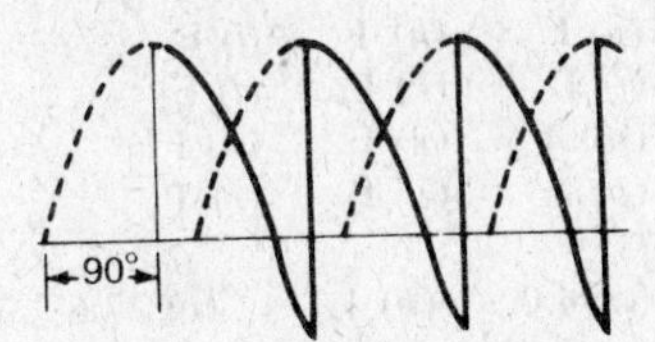

22-5 (*a*) 478 V, 23.9 kW (*b*) 952 V,
35.7 kW (*c*) 450 V, 22.5 kW
22-7 (*a*) 176 V (*b*) 424 V
(*c*) 60 to 173°
22-9 (*a*) 23.4 V, 36 A (*b*) 46.7 V,
36 A (*c*) 17.3 V/leg; 23.4 V,
72 A
22-11 (*a*) 510 V (*b*) 40 A
(*c*) 566 V (*d*) 12.75 Ω

Chapter 23

23-1 (*a*) T (*b*) F (*c*) T
(*d*) F (*e*) F (*f*) F
(*g*) T (*h*) F (*i*) F
(*j*) F (*k*) F (*l*) T
(*m*) F (*n*) T (*o*) T
(*p*) F
23-3 95 stations

Chapter 24

24-1 (*a*) T (*b*) T (*c*) T
(*d*) T (*e*) F (*f*) T
(*g*) F (*h*) T

Chapter 26

26-1 (*a*) F (*b*) T (*c*) T
(*d*) T (*e*) T (*f*) F
(*g*) F (*h*) T (*i*) F
(*j*) F (*k*) F (*l*) T
(*m*) F (*n*) T (*o*) F

Chapter 28

28-1 (*a*) F (*b*) F (*c*) T
(*d*) T (*e*) F (*f*) T
(*g*) T (*h*) F (*i*) T
(*j*) T (*k*) F (*l*) T
28-3 (*a*) 300 (*b*) 0.25 (*c*) 90 kΩ
(*d*) 38 V

Chapter 29

29-1 (*a*) T (*b*) F (*c*) T
(*d*) F (*e*) T (*f*) T
(*g*) F (*h*) T (*i*) F
(*j*) T (*k*) F (*l*) F
(*m*) T (*n*) F (*o*) F
(*p*) T (*q*) F (*r*) T
(*s*) F

29-3 (*a*) 4.0 (*b*) 1.7 (*c*) 27.6

29-5 (*a*) 3.17 (*b*) too much overshoot for most systems (*c*) 8

29-7 $K\beta = 3.5$

For $K\beta = 1$

ω	Vector length	Angle
0.5	1.94	73.2°
1.0	0.866	57.7°
2.0	0.347	33.7°
2.5	0.242	24.6°
3.0	0.177	17.0°

Ratio $B/R = 2$ when $K\beta = 3.5$

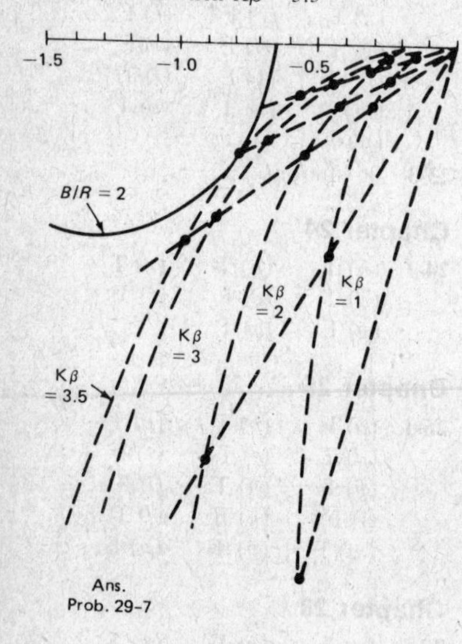

Ans. Prob. 29-7

29-9 (*a*) 2.25 at $\omega = 53$
(*b*) 10 rad/sec (*c*) 1.84 at $\omega = 45$; 10 rad/sec

29-11 (*a*) $\dfrac{j\omega 0.25}{1 + j\omega 0.25}$

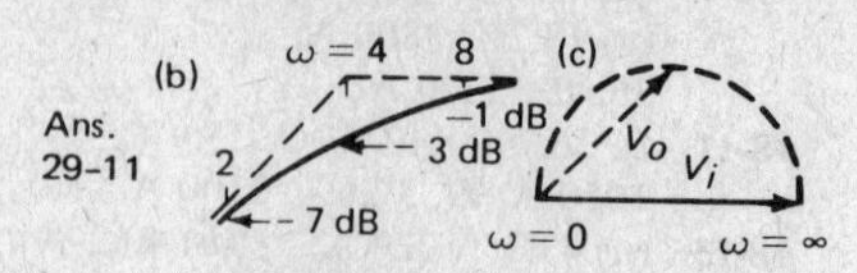

29-13 (*a*) $\dfrac{j\omega 0.67 + 1}{5(j\omega 0.133 + 1)}$

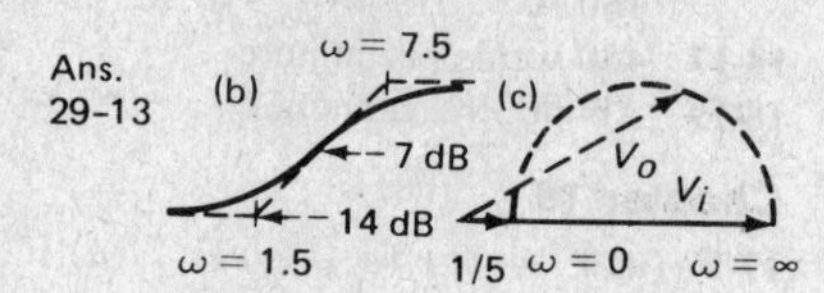

29-15 (*a*) $\dfrac{j\omega 0.025 + 1}{j\omega 0.2 + 1}$
(*d*) $R_1 = 0.25\ \text{M}\Omega$
$R_2 = 1.75\ \text{M}\Omega$

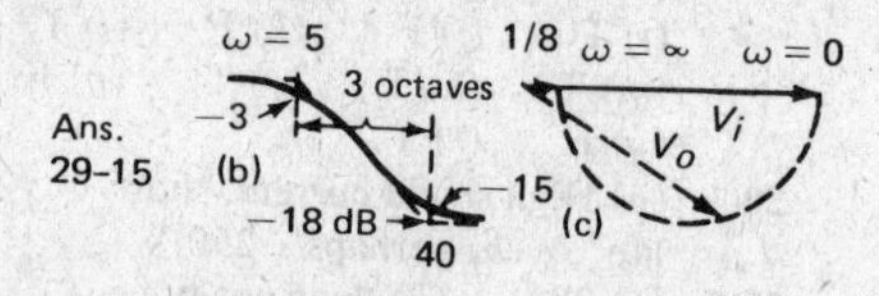

29-17 (*a*) $R_2 = 2R_1$
Example: $R_1 = 1\ \text{M}\Omega$
$C = 1\ \mu\text{F}$, $R_2 = 2\ \mu\Omega$

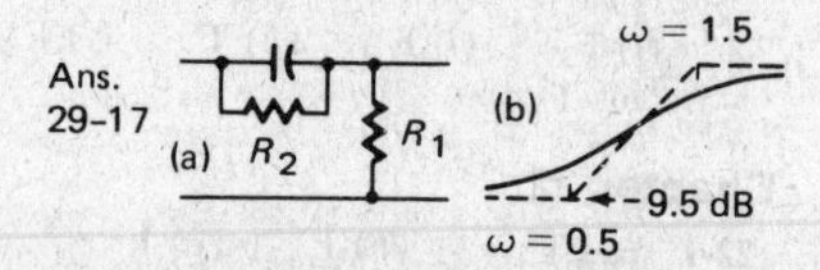

29-19 (*a*) $R_2 = 3R_1$
(*d*) no

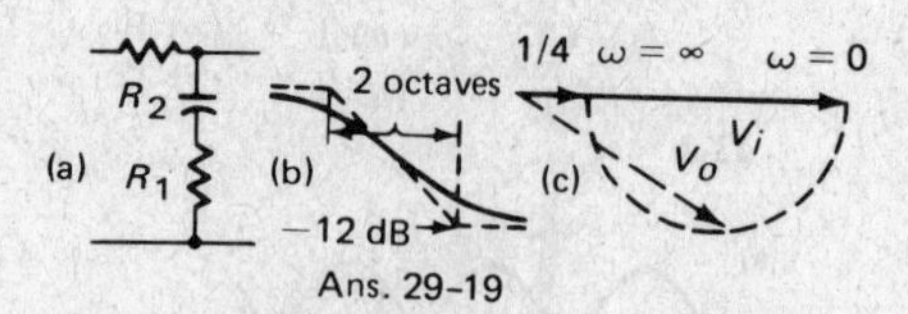

Ans. 29-19

29-21 (*a*) Slope crosses 0 dB before second bend, at less than 135° shift. System is stable.

(*b*) gain = 7.94; 8.94 times better

29-23 (*b*) Crossover 90 rad/sec
(*c*) stable

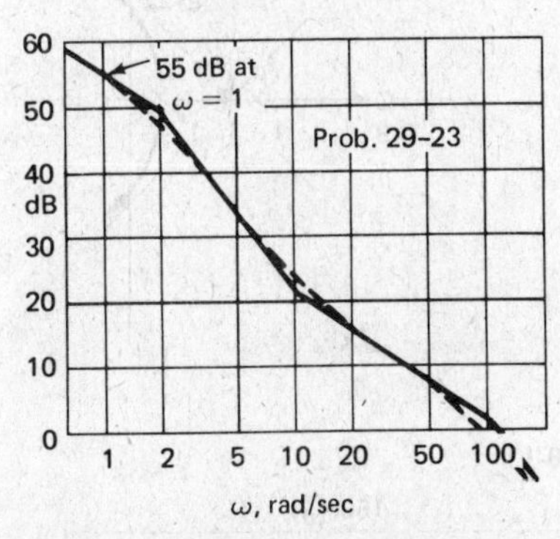

29-25 (*b*) Crossover 5.6 rad/sec
(*c*) stable

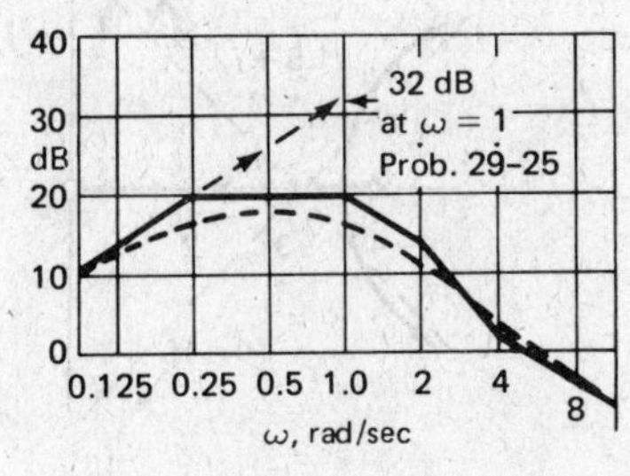

29-27 (*b*) Crossover 12 rad/sec
(*c*) stable
(*d*) Not present; for a symmetrical notch, a phase-lag corner is needed at $\omega = 8$ rad/sec.

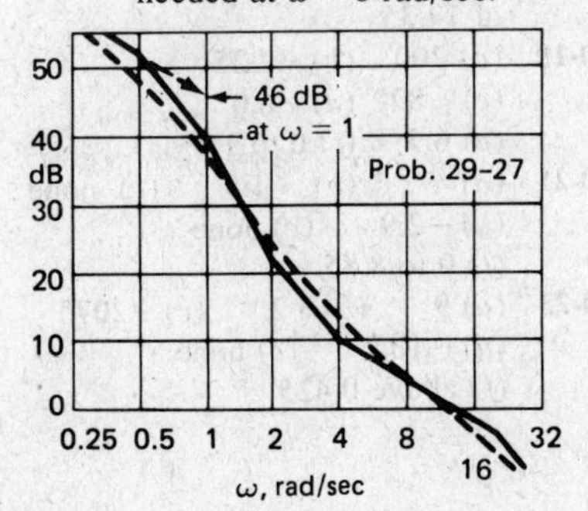

29-29 (*a*) $\dfrac{1000(j\omega 0.25 + 1)(j\omega 0.167 + 1)}{j\omega(j\omega 2 + 1)(j\omega + 1)(j\omega 0.02085 + 1)(j\omega 0.0125 + 1)}$

(*b*) Before correction, unstable; crossover 200°. After correction, conditionally stable. At 60 dB gain, stable (153°); unstable at gains between 10 and 38 dB.

Chapter 30

30-1

(*a*) T	(*b*) F	(*c*) T
(*d*) T	(*e*) F	(*f*) T
(*g*) T	(*h*) T	(*i*) T
(*j*) F	(*k*) T	(*l*) T
(*m*) F	(*n*) T	(*o*) T
(*p*) T		

30-3

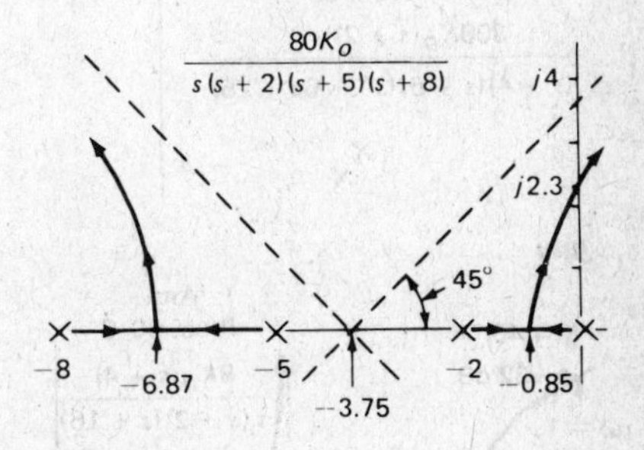

30-5

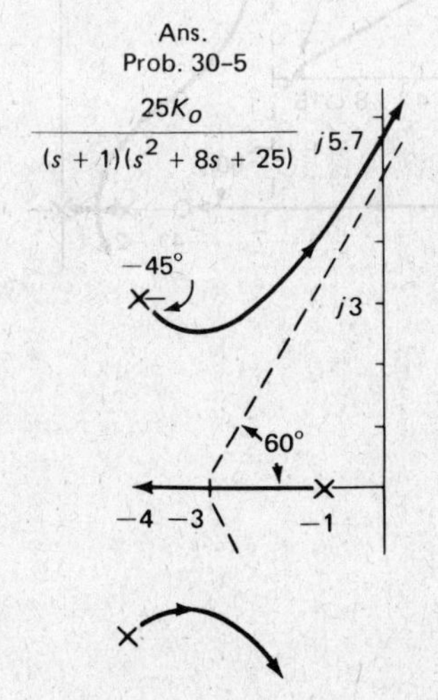

30-7

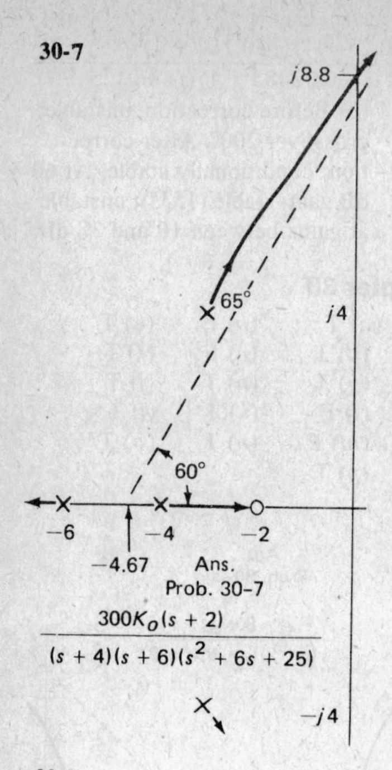

30-9

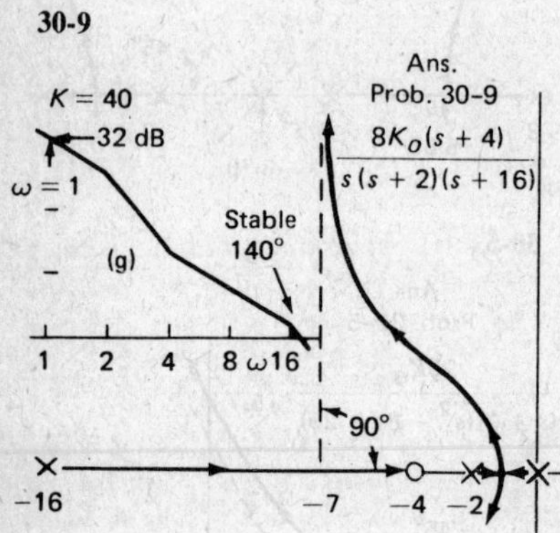

30-11

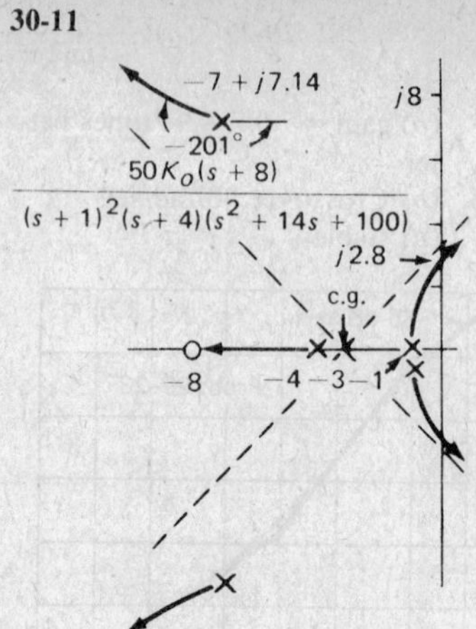

30-13

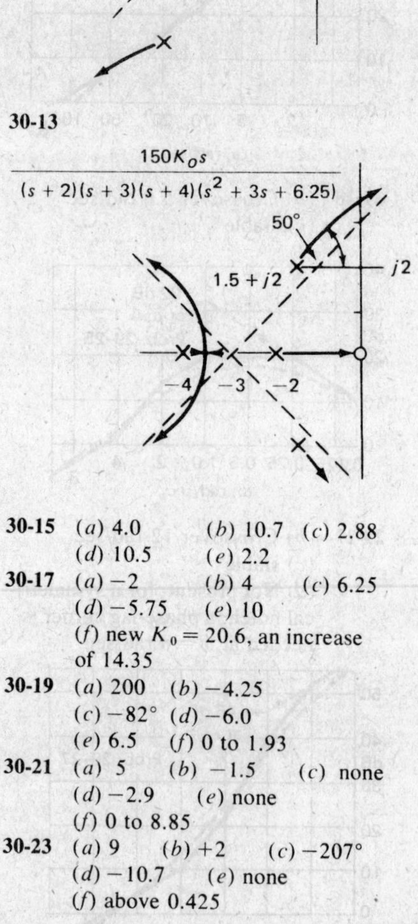

30-15 (*a*) 4.0 (*b*) 10.7 (*c*) 2.88 (*d*) 10.5 (*e*) 2.2

30-17 (*a*) −2 (*b*) 4 (*c*) 6.25 (*d*) −5.75 (*e*) 10 (*f*) new $K_0 = 20.6$, an increase of 14.35

30-19 (*a*) 200 (*b*) −4.25 (*c*) −82° (*d*) −6.0 (*e*) 6.5 (*f*) 0 to 1.93

30-21 (*a*) 5 (*b*) −1.5 (*c*) none (*d*) −2.9 (*e*) none (*f*) 0 to 8.85

30-23 (*a*) 9 (*b*) +2 (*c*) −207° (*d*) −10.7 (*e*) none (*f*) above 0.425

30-25 (*a*) 1.6 (*b*) −8 (*c*) −55°
(*d*) −4 (*e*) none
(*f*) 0 to 3.4

30-27 (*a*) 8.33 (*b*) −1.33
(*c*) −121° (*d*) −0.93 and −7.6
(*e*) 6.35 (*f*) 0 to 3.0

30-29 (*a*) 0.08 (*b*) +7.5 (*c*) none
(*d*) −11.9 and 0 (*e*) above 20
(*f*) above 127

Chapter 31

31-1 (*a*) T (*b*) F (*c*) T
(*d*) T (*e*) T (*f*) F
(*g*) T (*h*) T (*i*) T
(*j*) F (*k*) T

31-3 (*a*) 60 V (*b*) 54 V
(*c*) 45 V

31-5 (*a*) $X = 225$ V, $A = 10$ V, $B = 50$ V,
$C = 15$ V, $D = 150$ V
(*b*) $A = 6.11$ V, $B = 28.1$ V,
$C = 7.75$ V

Chapter 32

32-1 (*a*) T (*b*) F (*c*) F
(*d*) T (*e*) T (*f*) T
(*g*) F (*h*) F (*i*) F

INDEX

Absolute stability, 464, 494
Ac bridge signal, 401
Ac load line, 68, 71
Ac motor drive, 388
Ac power supply, 339, 340
Ac switch, SCRs as, 264
Ac to dc conversion, 23–40
Ac volts, measuring of, 29, 509
Ac wave, 5, 29
Acceptor atom, 82
Accuracy of follow-up, 438
Active device, 180
Active pull-up, 182, 217
Active region, 88
Adder, 170
Addressing, computer, 223
Adjustable speed ac drive, 388
Admittance or y parameters, 107
α (alpha) :
  of asymptotes, 498
  servo-divider ratio, 480
  in transistor, 52, 88
Alphanumeric code, 228
Aluminum, 42, 81, 286
AM (amplitude modulation) radio, 365–366
Ampere-turns, 404
Amperes, average and rms, 29, 30, 279
Amplidyne, 337, 531
Amplifier, 56, 73
  capacitor-coupled, 67, 399
  cathode-follower, 53
  class A, B, or C, 58
  coupled, 62, 66, 67
  differential, 65, 199, 208
  direct-coupled, 62
  equivalent circuit for, 92, 99
  load-line analysis, 49
  magnetic (*see* Magnetic amplifier)
  in oscillograph, 522
  parallel, 59
  push-pull, 59, 417
  saturable reactor, 403
  transformer-coupled, 67
  transistor, 56–74, 98
Amplifier gain, 98
Amplitude of movement, 457
Analog computer, 155
Analog-to-digital converter (ADC), 211
AND gate, 164
AND-OR-INVERT gate, 185
Angle, breakaway, 498
Angstrom (Å), 370
Angular velocity (ω), 459
Anode, 5, 131
Antihunt action, 465, 534
Antihunt networks, 465, 474–484
Antihunt transformer, 534–535
Antimony, 76, 80
Applied control, 436
Arc-back in vapor tube, 315
Arc-discharge tube, 261
Arc drop, 260
Argon gas in tube, 259, 262, 315
Armature-voltage control, 327
Arrangement of electrons, 77
Arsenic, 80
Asymptote, 498
Atom, 75–82
Atomic number, 75
Attenuation (of servo), 457, 470
Audio frequency (AF), 366
Automatic control, dc motor, 422–431
Automatic weld timer, 284
Avalanche-current breakdown, 44, 102, 150
Average current or voltage, 30, 134
Averaging time, 280, 283

B-H (magnetization) curve, 405
Back-to-back devices, 133, 264, 265, 273
Back voltage (cemf), 145, 326, 328, 422
Bailey GO/Line Recorder, 204
Balancing motor, 400
Balancing potentiometer, 397
Baldwin-Lima-Hamilton gage, 540
Band number, frequency, 365
Base, transistor, 44, 86
Base speed of motor, 327
Basic computer circuits, 163
Bats, flight of, 364
Battery-charging regulator, 336
BCD (binary-coded decimal) code, 226, 228
β (beta):
  in servo, 436
  in transistor, 46, 52, 90, 91

Bias, 43, 60, 61, 84
  effect of, 58
  self-, 61
Bias winding, 410, 411
Binary addition, 169
Binary code, 156, 226–228
Binary counting, 155, 162
Bipolar transistor, 78, 88, 107
Bistable circuit, 156
Blackbody radiation, 372
Blanking of oscilloscope trace, 523
Block diagram, 436, 443, 492, 519
Bode diagram, 470–483
  break in, 473
  summary of, 482
Bond within atom, 77, 78
Boron, use of, 42
Branches of root locus, 497
Breakaway angle from complex pole, 498
Breakaway point from real axis, 498
Breakdown (Zener) diode, 44, 101, 102, 264
Breakdown voltage, 44, 101
Bridge signal, ac, 401
Broadcast radio or TV, 365
Buffering, 225
Byte, 246

Calibration of locus, 495, 501
Capacitance, interelectrode, 101, 316, 383
Capacitor, 14
  commutating, 388
  ohms, 319
Capacitor-coupled amplifier, 67, 399
Carrier, majority or minority, 81, 82, 87, 124
Carrier frequency, 366
Carry in adder, 170
Cathode, 5, 9, 10
  mercury pool, 266
  SCR, 131
Cathode-ray oscillograph, 516–524
Cathode-ray tube, 516
Cell, load or fluid-pressure, 540
Center of gravity (cg) of asymptotes, 498
Centimeter waves, 363, 365
Central processing unit (CPU), 216, 241–249
Channel of FET, 105
Characteristic curves of transistor, 54, 55
Characteristic impedance (Z_o), 218
Charging time of capacitor, 16
Chip in IC, 179, 193–198
Chlorine, 76, 77
Chopper, 396
Class A, B, or C operation, 58
Classical servo method, 444
Clock as oscillator, 381
Clock pulse, 172, 309
Closed-loop systems, 432–438
Closed-loop versus open-loop action, 432, 439, 440
Closing of loop, 462, 492
Code:
  alphanumeric, 228
  BCD, 226, 228
  binary, 156, 226–228
  hexadecimal, 246
  octal binary, 226–227
Coherent light, 373
Coincidence, 300, 309
Cold-cathode tube, 261, 263
Collector, common, 52
Collector curves, 46, 52, 54, 55
Collector-to-base bias, 60, 61
Color, 369, 370
Color response of phototubes, 375
Color temperature, 372
Colpitts oscillator, 382
Combined *R* and *L* load, 143
Command signal, 434
Common-base circuit, 51, 87, 88
Common-collector circuit, 52
Common-emitter circuit, 44, 90
Commutating capacitor, 388
Commutation of SCR 131, 138
Commutator of motor, 325
Complementary MOS (CMOS), 189, 190
Complementary push-pull, 60
Complementary SCR, 146
Complementing flip-flop, 158
Complex plane, complex root or pole in, 491
Computer, analog or digital, 155
Computer arithmetic, 164, 202
Condensed-mercury temperature, 315
Condenser (*see* Capacitor)
Conditional stability, 482
Conductance, output (h_o), 93, 96
Conduction band, 79
Conductivity modulation, 123–124
Conjugate pair of roots, 491–494
Constant-current source, 66
Constant *M* circles, 464
Constant-voltage transformer, 535, 536
Contactor, ignitron, 272–274
Contacts, n-c or n-o,.114
Continuous-balance potentiometer, 397–401

Controlled rectifier, 130, 352
Conventional current, direction of, 6, 27
Converter:
  ac to dc, 379, 395, 396, 541
  analog to digital (ADC), 211
  digital to analog (DAC), 209
  parallel-to-serial, 220 – 221
  serial-to-parallel, 174 – 176
Cooking, electronic, 369
Copper-oxide rectifier, 27, 28
Core, 77, 403, 404
Corner frequency, 472
Corrective networks, 465, 474 – 484
Counter, binary, 155, 162
Counter emf of motor, 145, 326, 422
Coupled amplifiers, 62, 66, 67
Coupling, transformer, 67, 68, 71
CPU (central processing unit), 216, 241 – 249
Critical damping, 448, 483
Critical grid voltage, 314, 315
CRO (cathode-ray oscillograph), 516 – 524
Crossover angle or frequency, 480
Crystal-controlled oscillator, 384
Current, conventional direction of, 6, 27
Current amplification (β), 46, 52, 90, 91
Curves:
  ac, 5, 29, 30
  collector, 46, 52, 54, 55
  transistor, 54, 55
Cutoff, 50
Cycle, 4, 5, 362

Damping:
  critical, 448, 483
  viscous, 441, 490
Damping factor or ratio, zeta (ζ), 448
Darlington circuit, 63
Dc control of self-saturated reactor, 409
Dc generator, 332
Dc motor:
  control of, 328, 422 – 431
  parts of, 325 – 326
  speed control, 327, 328, 335
Dc versus ac load line, 68
Decade, 472, 474
Decade counter, 162
Decibel (dB), 470
Decimal system, 155
Deflecting plates, 517
Deionization time, 313
Delay timer, 115, 124, 257
Δ (delta), 89
Delta connection (Δ), 340
Demand current, 279
Depletion mode, 110
Depletion region, 43, 85, 102, 106
Developed torque, 441
Diac, 147
Dielectric heating, 368
Differential amplifier, 65, 199, 208
Differential equation, 444 – 452
Differential gear, 445 – 446
Differential selsyn, 536
Digital computer, 155
Digital-to-analog converter (DAC), 209
Dimensionless form, 451, 496
Dimming of lamps, 133, 147
Diode, 4, 41 – 44
  gas- or vapor-filled, 259
  germanium or silicon, 41 – 42
  point-contact, 42
  Schottky barrier (SBD), 184
  Shockley, 150
  tunnel, 102 – 104
  Zener, 44, 101, 102, 264
Direct-coupled amplifier, 62
Direction of conventional current, 6, 27
Discharge, capacitor, 15, 17
Disk rectifier, 27, 32
Dissipation, heat, 50
Distortion, 57
Disturbance, 436, 437
Donor atom, 80, 81
Doping of semiconductor, 77, 80, 81
Dot in tube circle, 316
Double-ended magnetic amplifier, 417
Drain, 106, 107
Drift effects, 64
DTL (diode transistor logic), 180, 181
Dummy load with welder, 275
DuMont oscillograph, 520 – 524
Duplex tube, 25
Duty, percent of ignitrons, 279 – 282
Dynamic MOS gate, 188
Dynamic response of servo, 444, 456
Dynamic shift register, 231, 232

ECL (emitter-coupled logic), 185
Edison effect, 9
Effective (rms) current, 29
Efficiency, rectifier, 31
Electromagnetic radiation, 360
Electron behavior, 3 – 12
Electron emission, 12
  kinds of, 267

Electron flow, 6, 27, 44
Electron gun, 517
Electron-hole pairs, 79, 80
Electron theory, 12, 75, 76
Electronic heating, 366
Electronic timer, 114, 124, 149
Electronic voltmeter, 505–516
Electronvolt (eV), 13, 80
Emission, kinds of, 267
Emitter, 7, 10
  common, 44–47, 90
Emitter-follower circuit, 52
Energy level, 79, 84–87, 91–92
Energy-level diagram, 79, 82–87, 104
Energy-storage devices, 455–458
Enhancement mode of FET, 110
Epitaxial layer, 179, 193
ϵ (epsilon, 2.718), 16
Equivalent circuit:
  of FET, 107
  of transistor, 92–94
Erasable PROM, 238
Error detector or corrector, 435
Error-rate control, 450, 467
Error voltage, 65
Esaki current, 104
Eta (η, standoff ratio), 123
Etching of IC, 194–196
Evans, W. R., 489
Eye response, human, 370

FALSE or zero, 164
Feedback, electrical, 412
Feedback factor (β), 436
Feedback oscillator, 458
Feedback winding, 412
Fermi level, 82–83
FET (field-effect transistor), 105–111
Field control of motor, 327
Field emission, 267
Filament, 9
Filter:
  electric, 33–36
  light, 375
  pi versus L, 34–36
Flashing light, 525–527
Flip-flop, 157, 171
  with NAND gates, 171
Fluid pressure cell, 540
Fluorescent lamp, 372
Flux, magnetic, 403, 404
Flywheel as inductance, 34
FM (frequency modulation), radio, 365–366
Follow-up of servo, 456, 457
Forbidden energy gap, 79
Forcing action in servo, 477
Forward current transfer ratio (h_f), 94, 96
Forward gain (K), 436
Four-layer diode, 150
Frequency, 362, 363
  corner, 472
  high, 359–377
    in solid state, 101
  for induction heating, 366, 367
  natural, 448
  of oscillator, 382
Frequency ratio by scope, 520
Frequency response, servomechanism, 438, 444, 455–488
Frequency spectrum, 360–362
Friction in servo, 441
Full adder, 171
Full-wave rectifier (*see* Rectifier)
Function:
  ramp or step input, 444, 450, 461
  transfer (*see* Transfer function)
  work, 13, 42, 83
Furnace regulator, 437

Gage, strain, 539–541
Gain:
  loop, 436
  of magnetic amplifier, 410
  of transistor, 88, 98–100
Gallium arsenide, 77
Gamma rays, 376
Gas, ionized, 259, 312, 360
Gaseous (vapor-filled) tube, 259–269
  thyratron (*see* Thyratron)
Gate:
  AND or OR, 164–166
  CMOS, 189, 190
  MOS, MOSFET, 110, 186–189
  NAND or NOR, 166–169, 171, 180–183
  of PUT, 304
  of SCR, 130, 131
Gate-pulse generator, 429
Gate winding, 404, 429
Gating half cycle, 414
Gear, differential, 445–446
Gearing, electric, 536
General Electric controls:
  CR7515CT105, 126
  ST100 inverter, 388–393
  3S7504ET550, 124
  3S7504ET560, 114

General Electric controls (*cont.*):
3S7505PS510, 119
3S7511RS570, 116
3S7511VS580, 117–119
3SRA71, 425–427
Logitrol 500, 254
Speed Variator, 427
General Radio Company:
Strobotac, 506, 525–529
Variac, 329, 330
Generator, 332
amplidyne, 337, 531
gate-pulse, 429
tachometer, 335, 438, 439, 451
Germanium, 75–81
Gigacycle (Gc), 362
Glow lamp or tube, 261–265
Graphical meaning:
of h parameters, 95
of y parameters, 108
Greek letter symbols:
α (alpha), 52, 88, 480, 482, 498
β (beta), 46, 52, 91, 436
Δ (delta), 89, 340
ϵ (epsilon), 16
η (eta), 123
ω (omega), 459
π (pi), 34
τ (tau), 459
θ (theta), 446
ζ (zeta), 448
Grid:
control, 11
shield, 316, 317
Grid construction, 315
Ground clip, 507
Gun, electron, 517
Gun-position control, 456

h parameters, 93-98
Half adder, 170
Half-wave dc motor drive, 423, 425–427
Half-wave rectifier (see Rectifier)
Hardware, 239
Hartley oscillator, 383
Heat, 366–369
in IC, 179, 193
in motor or tube, 280
of weld, 271
Heat control of welder, 317
Heat dissipation in transistor, 50
Heat ray, 371
Heat sink, 50
Heating, induction or dielectric, 367–369
Hertz or cycles per second, 359–361
Hewlett-Packard digital voltmeter, 506, 511–516
Hexadecimal code, 244
High-fidelity (hi-fi) equipment, 364
High frequencies, 101, 359–377
Hill, conduction or valence, 84–85
Hold time in welder, 284, 300
Holes in semiconductors, 78
Honeywell potentiometer, 397–399
HTL (high-threshold logic), 181
Hunting, 433, 534
Hybrid (h) parameters, 92–95
Hysteresis loop, 404

I_{CBO}, 87
I_{CEO}, 46
IC (integrated circuit), 178–199
Ignitor, 267
Ignitron, 266–288
Ignitron contactor, 272–274
Imaginary (j) axis or quantity, 491
Impedance matching, 53, 69
Impurities, controlled, 42, 80
Incrementing in register, 241
Induced-channel FET, 111
Inductance, 33
of anode transformer, 350
of steel core, 404
time delay of, 19
Induction heating, 367
Inductive circuit, 71, 72, 139–142, 412, 471
Inductive load:
ac load line for, 71, 72
SCRs with, 139–142
Infinity (∞), 460
Information conversion, 216–230
Information storage, 171
Infrared rays, 371
Input-output (I/O) equipment, 216–217
Input resistance (h_i or R_i), 93, 99
Instability:
of servo, 457
of transistor, 60
Instruments, electronic, 505–528
Insulated-gate FET, 110
Integrated circuit, 178–213
Intel 8080 microprocessor, 240
Interbase voltage, UJT, 123
Interelectrode capacitance, 101, 316, 383
Interface, 225
Internal feedback, 414
Interphase transformer, 354, 355

Intrinsic semiconductor, 78
Inverse-parallel connection, 133, 264, 265, 273
Inverse voltage (reverse voltage), 32
Inverted logic, 168
Inverter:
  logic symbol of, 170
  SCR, 384, 387–393
  vibrating contact, 541
Ionization level, 79
Ionization time, 313
Ionized gas, 259, 312, 360
Isolation diffusion, 194
Isolator, optical, 152

j (transfer function), 459
JEDEC number, 45
JK flip-flop, 173
jω (displacement transfer function), 469, 478, 490
Jones circuit, 138
Junction FET, 106
Junction rectifier (PN), 43

K (forward gain), 436
K (Kelvin), 372
k (kilohms), 362
kc (kilocycle), 362
kHz (kilohertz), 362

L filter, 36
L/*R* time constant, 456
Lag-lead network, 480
Lag network:
  limited, 476
  phase, 459, 470, 474–477
Lagging power factor, 275, 285
Laser, 373
Lead network, 465, 477
Leakage current, 43, 85, 131
LED (light-emiting diode), 376
Leg voltage, 26, 340
Level:
  energy, 79, 84–87, 91–92
  Fermi, 82–83
Level translator, 225
Light, 369
  flashing, 525–527
  modulated, 120
Light controls, 119
Light-dimming control, 133, 147

Limited phase lag, 476
Linear IC, 197
Lissajous figures, 520
Load cell gage, 540
Load line, 49, 68, 71
Load ratings of ignitron tubes, 278–283
Loci in real axis, 493, 497
Locus, root, 489
Log-magnitude plot, 470
Logarithmic scale, 278, 360, 470
Logic:
  CMOS, 189
  DTL, 180
  ECL, 185
  HTL, 181
  inverted, 168
  MOS, 186
  three-state, 219–220
  TTL, 182
Loop:
  closed or open, 432
  hysteresis, 404
Loop gain, 436
LSI (large-scale integration), 179

M circles, 464
Magnetic amplifier, 403–420
  with dc load, 411
  feedback, 412
  in motor control, 429
  push-pull, 417
  single-versus double-ended, 417
  speed of response of, 416
  for switching, 419, 420
  waveshape of, 414
Magnetic strain gage, 541
Magnetomotive force, 404
Majority carriers, 81, 82, 87, 124
Mask for IC, 194
Matching of impedance, 53, 69
Mathematics by op amp, 202, 204
Maximum power transfer, 69–71
Mc (megacycle), 362
Mechanical system, transfer function of, 468
Memory, 171, 231–237
Mercury-pool cathode, 266
Mercury-vapor pressure, 315
Metallic rectifiers, 27, 28, 33, 273
MHz (megahertz), 362
Microfarad, 15
Microprocessors, 239–249
Minority carrier, 81, 82, 124
Modulated-light relay, 122

Modulation (AM or FM), 365–366
Modulation, conductivity, 123–124
Monostable vibrator, 225
MOS gate, 186–189
MOSFET (metal oxide semiconductor field-effect transistor), 110, 186–188
Motor, dc (*see* Dc motor)
Motor control, 328, 422–431
Motor equations, 325–327, 441, 442
Multiplexer (MUX), 221
Multivibrator, 225, 385, 527

n-c or n-o contacts, 114
N-type material, 80
NAND gate, 166, 167, 171, 180–183
Nanometer, 370
Nanosecond, 362
Natural frequency (ω_n), 448
Natural logarithm, Lln, 16
Negative-control thyratron, 316
Negative feedback, 412–414
Negative logic, 168
Negative-resistance diode, 103
Neon lamp or tube, 260, 261
Network, corrective, 465, 474–484
Neutral of Y, 340
Noise margin, 181, 190, 191
Nonelectronic devices, 531–542
NOR gate, 168, 169
Normalized form in servo, 491
Normally closed contacts, 114
Notch network, 480, 481
NPN transistor, 44
Nucleus, 79
Number:
  atomic, 75
  binary or decimal, 155
  of locus branches, 497
Number display, 228, 515
Nyquist approach, 461

Octal binary code, 226–227
Octave, 364, 471
Off time, 284, 300
Ohms:
  L or *C*, 319, 458
  measuring of, 510
  per volt, 505
ω (omega), 459
One-way register control, 126
Open-circuit parameters, 95
Open loop, 432
Operating point *Q*, 48, 49, 57
Operation code (Op), 244
Operational amplifier, 199–202
OR circuit or gate, 165, 166
Order of magnitude, 156
Oscillator, 379–384
  Colpitts, 382
  crystal-controlled, 384
  Hartley, 383
  phase-shift, 458
  relaxation, 135, 385
  tuned-grid, 384
Oscillograph (oscilloscope), 24, 275, 516–524
Output conductance (h_o), 93, 96
Output resistance (R_o), 99, 100
Overshoot, 448, 457, 496
Overvoltage, prevention of, 44, 142, 263, 537, 538

P-channel FET, 109
P-type material, 42, 81
Pairs, electron-hole, 79, 80
Parallel, devices in, 59, 197
Parallel-to-serial converter, 220–221
Parameters, 46
  hybrid (*h*), 93–98
  open- or short-circuit, 94, 95
  y, 107–108
Passive device, 180
PC (printed circuit) board, 178
Peak-point current, 103
Peak reverse voltage (PRV), 32, 348, 351
Pedestal and ramp, 136
Percent duty of ignitrons, 279–282
Phanotron, 259
Phase control, 134, 135, 317
  with IC, 205
  by pedestal and ramp, 136
  of SCR, 134, 136
Phase lag, 457, 471, 475
  limited, 476
Phase-lag network, 459, 470, 474–477
Phase-lead network, 466, 477
Phase-shift heat control, 317
Phase-shift oscillator, 458
Phase shifter, selsyn, 536
Phase splitter, 183
Phasor diagram, 319, 459
Photodiode *PD*, 119, 120
Photoelectric register control, 125–128
Photoelectric relay:
  modulated-light, 122
  reflex, 119, 120

Photoresist, 194
Phototube, 375
Pi (π) filter, 34
Piano frequency range, 364
Picofarad (pF), 362
Piezoelectric effect, 384
Pinch-off voltage in FET, 109
Plane, s or complex, 491
Plastics, molding of, 369
Plate (anode) of tube, 6
PN junction, 42, 82
PNP transistor, 47
PNPN device, 130, 149, 150
Point-contact rectifier, 42
Polar plot (Nyquist), 461–468
Pole, 491
Polyphase rectifier, 339–355
Positioning servo, 456, 467, 478
Positive feedback, 412, 414, 420
Positive logic, 168
Potential barrier, 84
Potential energy of atom, 79
Potentiometer, Honeywell, 397–399
Power factor, 275, 276, 285
Power rectifier, 31
Power transfer, maximum, 69–71
Programmable PUT, 304
Programmable read-only memory (PROM), 236
PRV (peak reverse voltage), 32, 348, 351
Pull up, 182
Push-pull, complementary, 60
Push-pull operation:
  of ICs, 199
  of magnetic amplifiers, 417
  of transistors, 59
PUT ring counter, 304
PUT welder control, 305–308

Q, operating point, 48, 49, 57
Quadratic equation, 448, 484
  behavior of roots of, 491, 494
Quadrature circuit, 472

R and L load combined, 143
Radiation, electromagnetic, 360
Radio, 363, 365–366
Radium, 376
RAM (random-access memory), 232
Ramp and pedestal, 136
Ramp in voltmeter, 512
Ramp input, 450
Random-access memory (RAM), 232
Rate-of-change correction, 450, 467
Rating, diode or ignitron, 278, 349
Ratio of frequencies by CRO, 520
RC time constant, 14
RCA integrated circuit, 198
RCA VoltOhmyst, 506, 507
Reactive ohms, 459
Reactor, 34, 404
  saturable, 403
  self-saturated, 407–410
Read-only memory (ROM), 235
Real axis, 491
  breakaway (p_b) from, 499
  loci in, 493, 497
  loci leaving, 493, 499
Real root, 491
Recombination time, 138
Recorder, temperature, 204, 395–402
Rectified dc for welder, 286–290
Rectifier, 4, 23–37
  anode transformer for, 347
  average current of, 29, 30
  with back-emf load, 145
  biphase, 26
  bridge: diode, 26
    single-phase, four-diode, 25, 26
    three-phase, six-diode, 344
  controlled, 130, 352
  diode or disk, 27, 32
  diode ratings for, 349
  double-Y, 348, 355
  effective current of, 29
  efficiency of, 31
  four-diode, half-wave, 342
  full-wave bridge, 26, 330, 344
  gas-tube, 259
  germanium, 41
  half-wave: four-phase, 342
    single-phase, 25, 422
    six-phase, 342
    three-phase, 340, 341
  junction, 43
  load current of versus firing angle, 144
  metallic, 27, 28, 33, 273
  peak reverse voltage of, 32, 348, 351
  performance of, 346
  phanotron, 259
  phase-shifted, 143, 144, 329, 351
  point-contact, 42
  polyphase, 339-355
  with R and L load, 143
  ripple ractor of, 31, 346
  selenium, 28

Rectifier (*cont.*):
semiconductor, 41
silicon, 42
silicon controlled (SCR), 130–135
single-phase, 25
diametric, 26
full-wave bridge, 28
half-wave, 25
Reference field, 533
Reference input, 434, 436
Reference voltage, 334
Reflex photorelay, 119
Region, depletion, 43, 85, 102, 106
Register, 164, 171
Register control, 125–128
Regulator:
action of, 330
battery-charging, 336
oil-furnace, 437
speed, 335, 438
voltage (*see* Voltage regulator)
Regulator loop, 460
Regulator tube (VR), 262–265
Relaxation oscillator, 135, 385
Relay:
photo- (*see* Photoelectric relay)
resistance-sensitive, 116
time-delay, 114–115, 124, 149
voltage-sensitive, 117–119
Reliance Electric motor control, 422–425
Repeat weld, 310
Reset control, 415
Reset pulse, 161, 310
Resistance of ignitron tube, 280
Resistance load, SCRs with, 139
Resistance-sensitive relay, 116
Resistance welding, 271–290, 294–311
Resistance-wire strain gage, 539
Resonance, 381, 382
Response, speed of, for magnetic amplifier, 416
Reverse voltage, 32
Reverse voltage transfer ratio (h_r), 93, 97
Ring counter, 304, 308
Ripple factor, 31, 346
Rms (root-mean-square) voltage, 29
ROM (read-only memory), 235
Root-locus method, 489–501
Root-mean-square (rms) voltage, 29
Roots, 448–489
complex, 490
of quadratic equation, 491, 494,
RS flip-flop, 171
s for $j\omega$, 447, 490
s operator, 489
s plane, 489–491
Salt (NaCl), 77
Sample-and-hold, 213
Saturable reactor, 403
Saturation, 50, 403–408
Sawtooth oscillator, 385, 524
SBD (Schottky barrier diode) switching, 184
Schmitt trigger, 64
SCR [(solid-state controlled rectifier) (silicon controlled rectifier)], 130–135
SCRs back-to-back, 278
SCRs with inductive load, 139–142
SCS (silicon controlled switch), 150
Secondary emission, 267
Secondary utilization factor, 349
Selenium rectifier, 28
Self-balancing circuit, 395
Self-oscillation in servo, 457
Self-saturating reactor, 407–410
Selsyn, 536, 537
Semiconductor, 41, 42, 77
Semiconductor theory, 75–113
Sequence, 285, 288, 298
Sequence timer, 284, 285
Serial-to-parallel converter, 174–176
Servo, 433
types 0, 1, and 2, 467
Servo motor, 441, 467
Servomechanism, 432, 452
analysis by root locus, 489–501
frequency response (*see* Frequency response, servomechanism)
Settling time of servo, 448, 450
Shell of electrons, 75–78
Shield-grid thyratron, 316, 317
Shift-register memory, 174, 231
Shockley diode, 150
Short-circuit parameters, 94
Short-wave broadcasts, 365
Shunt dc motor, 325, 326
Silicon, 42, 77–80
Silicon controlled rectifier (SCR), 130–135
Sine wave, 29
Single-ended magnetic amplifier, 417
Sink, heat, 50
Skin effect, 367
Slope, unit, 472, 474
Slope control of welder, 286
Slowdown action of network, 476
Small motors, control of, 329
Small-signal characteristics, 98

Software, 239
Solar cell, 376
Solid-state controlled rectifier (SCR), 130–135
Solid-state device, 41
at high frequencies, 101
Solid-state lamp, 376
Solid-state relay, 152
Solid-state switching, 155–177
Solid-state voltage regulator, 323, 324
Solid-state welding control, 294–311
Sound, 360, 363
Source:
constant-current, 66
in FET, 106, 187
Space charge, 11, 260
Spectrum, frequency, 360–362
Speed:
of capacitor discharge, 15
control of, by SCR, 422–427
motor, 327–331, 335
of response of magnetic amplifier, 416
Speed equation of dc motor, 327
Speed regulator, 335, 438
Speed Variator, 427–428
Speedup action, 477
Spirule, 495
Split-field motor, 330
Squeeze time, 284, 300
Stability, 464, 494
absolute, 464, 494
conditional, 482
useful, 464
Stabilizer, voltage, 535
Stable root, 495
Stage, amplifier, 62
Standard, 334, 432
Standard I and V of transistor, 89
Standoff ratio (η), 123
Standstill accuracy, 436–438
Static control, 421
Statotrol GE motor control, 425–427
Status latch strobe, 247
Steady-state error, 447
Step-function input, 444, 450, 461
Stiffness of servo, 438
Stored energy in servo, 455, 457
Strain gage, 539–541
Stroboscope, Strobotac, 506, 525, 526
Substrate, 193
Summary of Bode plots, 482
SUS (silicon unilateral switch), 331
SUS oscillator, 390, 391
Sweep circuit, 518, 525
Swing compared to oscillator, 458, 490
Switching:
by magnetic amplifier, 419, 420
by SCR or tube, 264, 265
solid-state, 155–177
by transistor, 49
Symbols, logic gate, 167
SYNC signal, 245
Synchronizing by clock pulse, 172
Synchronizing of CRO, 524
Synchronous timing of weld, 284–286
Systems:
closed-loop, 432–438
speed-regulating servo, 438

Tachometer generator, 335, 438, 439, 451
Tank circuit, 381
τ (tau), 459
Television, 365
Temperature:
K, 372
of thyratron, 315
Temperature effects, 64
Temperature recorder, 204, 395–402
Temperature-sensitive thermistor, 42, 137
Ten, counter of, 162
Theory:
electron, 12, 75, 76
semiconductor, 75–113
Thermal runaway, 61
Thermionic emission, 12, 267
Thermistor, 42, 137
Thermocouple, 395
Three-phase power, 339, 340
Three-state logic, 219–220
Thyratron, 312–321
with R or L load, 139
Thyrector, Thyrite, 537, 538
Thyristor, 149, 150
Time constant:
L/R, 456
RC, 14
in servo (τ), 459
Time-delay action, 14–22
Time-delay relay, 114–115, 124, 149
Time-selector switch, 163
Timing in CPU, 246
Timing of light flashes, 527
Torque, developed, 441
Transducer, 435, 451, 539
Transfer, maximum power, 69–71
Transfer function, 459, 460, 467, 468, 471, 476, 478, 490, 496

Transformer:
antihunt, 534–535
constant-voltage, 535, 536
interphase, 354, 355
Scott-connected, 342
turns ratio of, 70
Y, Δ, 340
Transformer coupling, 67, 68, 71
Transient current, 285
Transient response, 444, 445, 489
Transistor, 8, 41–55, 86–99
bipolar, 78, 88, 107
field-effect, 105–111
h parameters of, 92–94
unijunction, 123, 134, 135, 385
Transistor amplifier, 56–74, 98
Triac, 146
with solenoid valve, 309
Triac time-delay relay, 149
Trigger, Schmitt, 64
TRUE = + V = 1, 164, 165
Truth table, 164, 165
TTL logic, 182
Tube control of dc motor, 328
Tubes:
gas-or vapor-filled [*see* Gaseous (vapor-filled) tube]
ignitron, 266
voltage-regulator (VR), 262–264
Tungsten cathode, 13
Tunnel diode, 102–104
Turnoff of SCR, 138
Turns ratio of transformer, 70
Types 0, 1, and 2 servo, 467

Ultrasonics, 364
Ultraviolet rays, 372
Unijunction transistor (UJT), 123, 134, 135, 385
Unipolar FET, 107
Unit slope, 472, 474
Usefully stable system, 464
Utilization factor of transformer, 349

Valence band, 79
Valence electrons, 77
Valence hill, 84–85
Valley-point current, 103
Vapor-filled tube [*see* Gaseous (vapor-filled) tube]
Variable-voltage dc drive, 326
Variac, 330
Varistor, 538
Vector, 319, 459
Vibrator, 541
Viscous damping, 441, 490
Visible frequency range, 370
Volatile memory, 235
Volt, electron (eV), 13, 80
Voltage:
comparing, 334
peak reverse (PRV), 32, 348, 351
rms, 29
Voltage change, *dv/dt*, 142
Voltage compensator, 322
Voltage regulator, 323, 324, 332, 333, 335, 336
Voltage-regulator tube (VR), 262–264
Voltage-sensitive relay, 117–119
Voltage stabilizer, 535
Voltmeter, electronic, 505–516
VoltOhmyst, RCA, 506, 507

Wafer, silicon, 193
Water-flow switch, 275
Wavelength, 363
Waveshape, 29, 30, 35, 276, 277, 414
Web-register control, 125–128
Weld heat, 271
Weld time or timer, 285
Welder load, 276
Welding:
with dc, 286–290
resistance (*see* Resistance welding)
with solid-state circuits, 294–311
Weltronic welding control, 294–311
White noise, 371
Winding, bias, 410, 411
Work function, 13, 42, 83
Writing into memory, 233

X-rays, 376

Y connection of transformers, 340
y parameters, 107–108

Zener (breakdown) diode, 44, 101, 102, 264
Zero:
for FALSE, 164
for OFF, 155
in root-locus plot, 491
Zero-voltage switching circuit, 151
Zeta (ζ), damping ratio, 448